Advances in Neutron Capture Therapy
Volume I, Medicine and Physics

The front cover shows the typical total physical absorbed dose contours in normal tissue that would be produced by the BMRR epithermal-neutron beam for a human glioma patient with a uniform brain-boron concentration of 15 ppm. The 100% dose contour corresponds to approximately 9.1 cGy/min per MW of BMRR power. Photo courtesy of Idaho National Engineering Laboratory and Brookhaven National Laboratory, USA.

The back cover shows an artist's impression of the Petten BNCT Facility showing reactor, beam tube and a patient on the therapy table in the beam Observation/Control Area. Graphic provided by courtesy of the Institute for Advanced Materials of the Joint Research Centre of the European Commission, Petten, The Netherlands.

Advances in Neutron Capture Therapy
Volume I, Medicine and Physics

Proceedings of the Seventh International Symposium on
Neutron Capture Therapy for Cancer,
Zürich, Switzerland, 4–7 September 1996

Editors:

Börje Larsson
John Crawford
Regin Weinreich

Institute for Medical Radiobiology of the University of Zürich
and the Paul Scherrer Institute
Switzerland

1997

ELSEVIER

Amsterdam – Lausanne – New York – Oxford – Shannon – Singapore – Tokyo

CZIFRUS, S., Institute of Nuclear Techniques, Technical University of Budapest, Müegyetem rkp.3-9, H-1521 Budapest, Hungary. Tel.: +36-1-4632552. Fax: +36-1-4631954. E-mail: czifrus@eikvms.bme.hu

DE STASIO, G., IPA-EPFL, CH-1015 Lausanne, Switzerland. Tel.: +41-21-6935479. Fax: +41-21-6934666. E-mail: pupa@eldpa.epfl.ch

DEEN, D.F., University of California, 505 Parnassus, P.O. Box 0520, San Francisco, CA 94143-0520, USA. Tel.: +1-415-4764590. Fax: +1-415-4769687. E-mail: ddeen@itsa.ucsf.edu

DIAZ, A.Z., Department of Radiation Oncology, University Medical Center, University of NY at Stony Brook, Stony Brook, NY 11794-7028, USA. Tel.: +1-516-3447123. Fax: +1-516-3447244. E-mail: azdiaz@radonc.som.sunysb.edu

DILWORTH Jr., G.F., Tennessee Center for Research and Development, 830 Corridor Park Boulevard, Suite 200, Knoxville, TN 37932, USA. Tel.: +1-423-9665430. Fax: +1-423-9667302. E-mail: georged@tcrd.com

ELOWITZ, E.H., Department of Neurosurgery, Beth Israel North Hospital, 170 East End Avenue, New York, NY 10128, USA. Tel.: +1-212-8709650. Fax: +1-212-8709396. E-mail: eric340@aol.com

ENOKIDO, Y., The Energy Research Center, Wakasa Bay, Toyo-chou 1-1, 914 Tsuruga-shi, Fukui-ken, Japan. Tel.: +81-770-242300. Fax: +81-770-242303. E-mail: enod@mitene.or.jp

FANKHAUSER, H., Department of Neurosurgery, Universitaire Vaudois, CHUV, Centre Hôpitalier, CH-1011 Lausanne, Switzerland. Tel: +41-21-3419393. Fax: +41-21-3419392. E-mail: heinz.fankhauser@dmed.unil.ch

FARNWORTH, C.R., Centronic Ltd., King Henry's Drive, New Addington, Croydon, Surrey CR9 0BG, UK. Tel.: +44-1689-842121. Fax: +44-1689-841822.

FEAKES, D.A., Chemistry Department, Southwest Texas State University, 601 University Drive, San Marcos, TX 78666, USA. Tel.: +1-512-2457609. Fax: +1-512-2452374. E-mail: df10@swt.edu

FEINENDEGEN, L.E., US Department of Energy, 19901 Germantown Road, Gaithersburg, MD 20874, USA. Tel.: +1-301-9031372. Fax: +1-301-9030567. E-mail: ludwig.Feinendegen@oer.doe.gov

FIKE, J., University of California at San Francisco, 505 Parnassus, U-378, San Francisco, CA 94143-0520, USA. Tel.: +1-415-4764453. Fax: +1-415-4769687. E-mail: jfike@itsa.ucsf.edu

FISCHER, C.-O., Hahn-Meitner-Institute, Glienicker-Strasse 100, Berlin D-14091, Germany. Tel.: +49-30-80622742. Fax: +49-30-80622082.

FLEGO, M., JRC Petten, Institute for Advanced Materials, Westerduinweg 3, NL-1755 ZG Petten, The Netherlands. Tel.: +31-224-565125. Fax: +31-224-562036. E-mail: mflego@jrc.nl

FUJIMORI, H., Biomed. NMR Forschungs GmbH, Am Max-Planck-Institut für biophysiklische Chemie, am Fassberg 11, D-37077 Göttingen, Germany. Tel.: +49-551-2011721. Fax: +49-551-2011307. E-mail: hfujimo@gwdg.de

FUKUDA, H., Department of Nuclear Medicine and Radiology, Tohoku University, IDAC, 4-1 Seiryo-machi Aoba-ku, Sendai 980-77, Japan. Tel.: +81-22-7178556. Fax: +81-22-7178560. E-mail: hiro@idac.tohoku.ac.jp

FUKUMORI, Y., Faculty of Pharmaceutical Science, Kobe Gakuin University, 518 Arise, Ikawadori-cho, Nishi-ku, Kobe 651-21, Japan. Tel.: +81-78-9741551. Fax: +81-78-9745689. E-mail: fukumori@ipc.kobegakuin.ac.jp

FÜLÖP, M., Institute of Preventative & Clinical Medicine, Limbová 14, SK-83101 Bratislava, Slovakia. Tel.: +42-7-373560. Fax: +42-7-373906. E -mail: fulop@upkm.sanet.sk

GABEL, B., Universität Bremen, Fachbereich Chemie, Postfach 330 440, D-28334 Bremen, Germany. Tel.: +49-421-2182200. Fax: +49-421-2182871. E-mail: gabel@chemie.uni-bremen.de

GABEL, D., Fachbereich Chemie, Universität Bremen, NW2, B2090, Leobener Strasse, Postfach 330 440, D-28334 Bremen, Germany. Tel.: +49-421-2182200. Fax: +49-421-2182871. E-mail: gabel@chemie.uni-bremen.de

GAHBAUER, R.A., A. James Cancer Hospital, Ohio State University, 300 W. 10th Avenue, Columbus, OH 43210, USA. Tel.: +1-614-2938413. Fax: +1-614-2934044. E-mail: rgahbaue@magnus.acs.ohio-state.edu

GAMBARINI, G., Dip. di Fisica dell Universita, Via Celoria 16, I-20133 Milano, Italy. Tel.: +39-2-2392243. Fax: +39-2-2392630. E-mail: gambarini@mvmidi.mi.infn.it

GAVIN, P.R., Department of Veterinary Clinical, Medicine and Surgery, Washington State University, McCoy Hall, Pullman, WA 99164-6610, USA. Tel.: +1-509-3350779. Fax: +1-509-3350880. E-mail: prg@vet11.vetmed.wsu.edu

GEDDA, L., Biomedical Radiation Sciences, Uppsala University, P.O. Box 535, S-751 21 Uppsala, Sweden. Tel.: +46-18-4713431. Fax: +46-18-4713432. E-mail: lars.gedda@bms.uu.se

GHANEOLHOSSEINI, H., Department of Organic Chemistry, Uppsala University, PO Box 531, S-751 21 Uppsala, Sweden. Tel.: +46-18-4713798. Fax: +46-18-504582. E-mail: hadi@kemi.uu.se

GILBERT, B., Laboratiore de Physique des Materiaux Electroniques, Institut de Physique Appliquee, EPF Lausanne, Attn: Prof G. Margaritondo, CH-1015 Lausanne, Switzerland. Tel.: +41-21-6934471. E-mail: giorgio.margaritondo@ipa.dp.epfl.ch

GOLDIN, L., Jefferson Physical Laboratory, Harvard University, Cambridge, MA 02138, USA. Tel.: +1-617-9645230. Fax: +1-617-4950416. E-mail: goldin@fas.harvard.edu

GOLDSTEIN, G., US Department of Energy, 10038 Maple Leaf Drive, Gaithersburg, MD 20879, USA. Tel.: +1-301-9035348. Fax: +1-301-9030567. E-mail: gerald.goldstein@mailgw.er.doe.gov

GOODMAN, J.H., Division of Neurological Surgery, University Medical Center, The Ohio State University, 473 West 12th Avenue, Columbus, OH 43210, USA. Tel.: +1-614-2938587. Fax: +1-614-2934281. E-mail: jogoodma@magnus.acs.ohio-state.edu

GRAFFMAN, S., Department of Oncology, Lund University Hospital, S-221 85 Lund, Sweden. Tel.: +46-46-177506. Fax: +46-46-137027. E-mail: sten.graffman@onk.lu.se

GREEN, S., Department of Medical Physics, Queen Elizabeth Hospital, Edgbaston, Birmingham, B15 2TH, UK. Tel.: +44-121-6272267. Fax: +44-121-6272386.

GRIEBENOW, M.L., Neutron Technology Corporation, 436 N 55 W, Idaho Falls, ID 83402, USA. Tel.: +1-208-5232043. Fax: +1-208-5237906.

HANSEN, H.-J., Institute for Organic Chemistry, University of Zurich, Winterthurerstr. 190, CH-8057Zurich, Switzerland. Tel.: +41-1-2574231. Fax: +41-1-3619895. E-mail: hjhansen@oci.unizh.ch

HARITZ, D., Department of Neurosurgery, Baltic Sea Hospital, D-24349 Damp, Germany. Tel.: +49-4352-806236. Fax: +49-4352-806234.

HARLING, O.K., Nuclear Reactor Laboratory, Massachusette Institute of Technology, NW12-204, 138 Albany Street, Cambridge, MA 02139, USA. Tel.: +1-617-2534201. Fax: +1-617-2537300. E-mail: oharling@mit.edu

HASELSBERGER, K., Department of Neurosurgery, Univesity of Graz, Auenbruggerplatz 29, A-8036 Graz, Austria. Tel.: +43-316-3852708. Fax: +43-316-3853368.

HAWTHORNE, M.F., Department of Chemistry and Biochemistry, UCLA, 405 Hilgard Avenue, Los Angeles, CA 90095-1569, USA. Tel.: +1-310-2063182. Fax: +1-310-8255490. E-mail: mfh@chem.ucla.edu

HAYAKAWA, Y., Institute of Basic Medical Science, University of Tsukaba, Tennoudai, Tsukuba, Ibaraki-ken 305, Japan. Tel.: +81-298-642571. Fax: +81-298-642575. E-mail: hayakawa@medaxp.kek.jp

HEINZEL, V., Forschungszentrum Karlsruhe, Inst. für Reaktorsicherheit, P.O. Box 3640, D-76021 Karlsruhe, Germany. Tel.: +49-7247-823761. Fax: +49-7247-823718. E-mail: heinzel@irs.fzk.de

HENSSEN, C., Institute of Organic Chemistry, Uppsala University, P.O. Box 531, S-751 21 Uppsala, Sweden. Tel.: +46-18-4713798. Fax: +46-18-508542. E-mail: cecileh@kemi.uu.se

HIDEGHÉTY, K., Klinik und Poliklinik für Strahlentherapie, Universitätsklinikum Essen, Hufelandstrasse 55, D-45122 Essen, Germany. Tel.: +49-201-7232052. Fax: +49-201-7235908. E-mail: w.sauerwein@uni-essen.de

HIGGS, C.E., Institute for Medical Radiobiology, Paul Scherrer Institute, OBUA/1, CH-5232 Villigen PSI, Switzerland. Tel.: +41-56-3102062. Fax: +41-56-3104412. E-mail: higgs@imr.psi.ch

HILDEBRAND, J., Hopital Erasme, Cliniques Université de Bruxelles, Route de Lennik 808, B-1070 Bruxelles, Belgium. Tel.: +32-2-5553346. Fax: +32-2-5553942.

HIRATSUKA, J., Department of Radiation Oncology, Kawasaki Medical School, 577 Matsushima, Kurashiki City, Okayama 701-01, Japan. Tel.: +81-86-4621111. Fax: +81-86-4621199.

HONDA, C., 5-17-12 Izumidai, Kita-ku, Kobe 651-11, Japan. Tel.: +81-78-5946885. Fax: +81-78-5946885.

HOPEWELL, J.W., Research Institute, The Churchill Hospital, University of Oxford, Oxford, OX3 7LJ, UK. Tel.: +44-1865-225825. Fax: +44-1865-225847. E-mail: resin@ermine.ox.ac.uk

HOWARD, W., M.I.T., 45 Carleton Street, #5F, Cambridge, MA 02139, USA. Tel.: +1-617-2588825. Fax: +1-617-2530760.

HUBBARD, T.R., Nuclear Reactor Facility, University of Virginia, Charlottesville, VA 22903-2442, USA. Tel.: +1-804-9825440. Fax: +1-804-9825473. E-mail: hubbard@virginia.edu

HUISKAMP, R., Radiobiology & Radioecology, Netherlands Energy Resources Foundation, P.O. Box 1, NL-1755 ZG Petten, The Netherlands. Tel.: +31-224-564069. Fax: +31-224-563491. E-mail: huiskamp@ecn.nl

HÅKANSSON, H., Elekta Instrument AB, PO Box 7593, S-103 93 Stockholm, Sweden. Tel.: +46-8-4025400. Fax: +46-8-4025500.

ICHIKAWA, H., Faculty of Pharmaceutical Sciences, Kobe Gakuin University, Arise, Ikawadani-cho, Nishi-ku, Kobe, Japan. Tel.: +81-78-9741551. Fax: +81-78-9745689. E-mail: ichikawa@pharm.kobegakuin.ac.jp

IMAHORI, Y., Department of Neurosurgery, Kyoto Prefecture University of Medicine, Kawaramachi-Hirokoji, Kamigyo 602, Kyoto, Japan. Tel.: +81-75-2515543. Fax: +81-75-2515544.

INAMOTO, Y., Department of Chemistry, Faculty of Science, Shinshu University, 3-1-1 Asahi, Matsumoto Nagano, Japan. Tel.: +81-263-354600. Fax: +81-263-372559. E-mail: 96sa302@ripms.shinshu-u.ac.jp

INGERSOLL, D.T., Oak Ridge National Laboratory, P.O. Box 2008, MS 6363, Oak Ridge, TN 37831-6363, USA. Tel.: +1-423-5746102. Fax: +1-423-5749619. E-mail: dti@ornl.gov

JAMES, N., CRC Institute for Cancer Studies, University of Birmingham, Birmingham B15 2TH, UK. Tel.: +44 121-4143803. Fax: +44-121-4143700. E-mail: n.d.james@bham.ac.uk

JANULIONIS, E., Lithuanaian Oncology Center, P.O. Box 1579, 2010 Vilnius, Lithuania. Tel.: +370-2-720284. Fax: +370-2-614130. E-mail: ernestas@ktl.mii.lt

JATUFF, F.E., INVAP S.E., F. P. Moreno 1089, (8400) Bariloche, Rio Negro, Argentina. Tel.: +54-944-22121. Fax: +54-944-21100.
E-mail: jatuff@invapqq.com.ar

JAUSSI, R., Paul Scherrer Institute, OFLD/O01, CH-5232 Villigen PSI, Switzerland. Tel.: +41-56-3102877. Fax: +41-56-3104417. E-mail: rolf.jaussi@imr.psi.ch

JOEL, D., Medical Department, Brookhaven National Laboratory, 30 Bell Avenue, Upton, NY 11973, USA. Tel.: +1-516-3443603. Fax: +1-516-3445311. E-mail: djoel@bnl.gov

JONO, K., Faculty of Pharmaceutical Science, Kobe Gakuin University, Arise 518, Ikawadani-cho, Nishi-ku, Kobe 651-21, Japan. Tel.: +81-78-9741551. Fax: +81-78-9745689. E-mail: ichikawa@ipc.kobegakuin.ac.jp

KABALKA, G., Biomedical Imaging Center, Department of Chemistry, University of Tennessee, Knoxville, TN 37996-1600, USA. Tel.: +1-615-9743260. Fax: +1-615-9742997. E-mail: kabalka@utk.edu

KAGEJI, T., Department of Chemistry, University of Bremen, P.O. Box 330440, D-28334 Bremen, Germany. Tel.: +49-421-2182200. Fax: +49-421-2182871. E-mail: kageji@chemie.uni-bremen.de

KAHL, S.B., School of Pharmacy, University of California San Francisco, S-926, 513 Parnassus Avenue, San Francisco, CA 94143-0446, USA.
Tel.: +1-415-4764684. Fax: +1-415-4760688. E-mail: sbkahl@itsa.ucsf.edu

KAITA, K., Department of Technical Physics, Helsinki University of Technology, FIN-02150 Espoo, Finland. Tel.: +358-9-4566340. Fax: +358-9-4566390. E-mail: karoliina.kaita@vtt.fi

KALLIO, M.E., Research Institute, Helsinki University Central Hospital, Tukholmank 8F, FIN-00290 Helsinki, Finland. Tel.: +358-9-4712139. Fax: +358-9-4715550. E-mail: merja.kallio@mei.hyks.hyks.mailnet.fi

KANDA, K., Research Reactor Institute, Kyoto University, Kumatori-cho, Sennun-gun, Osaka 590-04, Japan. Tel.: +81-724-532145. Fax: +81-724-530360. E-mail: kanda@kuca.rri.kyoto-u.ac.jp

KANE, R.R., Department of Chemistry, Baylor University, P.O. Box 97348, Waco, TX 96798-7348, USA. Tel.: +1-817-7553311. Fax: +1-817-7552043. E-mail: bob.kane@baylor.edu

KIRIHATA, M., Department of Applied Biochemistry, Osaka Prefecture University, 1-1 Gakuencho, Sakai, Osaka 593, Japan. Tel.: +81-722-521161. Fax: +81-722-520341. E-mail: kirihata@biochem.osakafu-u.ac.jp

KITAMURA, K., Department of Neurosurgery, A-nan Kyoei Hospital, Hanoura-cho, Naka-gun, Tokushima 779-11, Japan. Tel.: +81-884-443131. Fax: +81-884-444179. E-mail: hiroshi@clin.med.tokushima-u.ac.jp

KITAOKA, Y., Research Reactor Institute, Kyoto University, Noda, Kumatori-cho, Sennan-gun, Osaka 590-04, Japan. Tel.: +81-724-520901. Fax: +81-724-527364. E-mail: kitaoka@rri.kyoto-u.ac.jp

KLEIHUES, P., Department of Pathology, University of Zurich, Schmelzbergstrasse 12, CH-8091 Zurich, Switzerland. Tel.: +41-1-2552107. Fax: +41-1-2554440. E-mail: kleihues@iarc.fr

KLINKOWSTEIN, R.E., Newton Scientific Incorporated, 245 Bent Street, Cambridge, MA 02141, USA. Tel.: +1-617-3549469. Fax: +1-617-3549479. E-mail: rek@world.std.com

KNESPL, D., Institute for Medical Radiobiology, Paul Scherrer Institute, OBUA/1, CH-5232 Villigen PSI, Switzerland. Tel.: +41-56-3104002. Fax: +41-56-3104412. E-mail: knespl@imr.psi.ch

KOBAYASHI, M., Research Reactor Institute, Kyoto University, Noda, Kumatori-cho, Sennan-gun, Osaka 590-04, Japan. Tel.: +81-724-520901. Fax: +81-724-527364. E-mail: mitsue@rri.kyoto-u.ac.jp

KOBAYASHI, T., Research Reactor Institute, Kyoto University, Kumatori-cho, Sennan-gun, Osaka 590-04, Japan. Tel.: +81-724-520901. Fax: +81-724-535810. E-mail: kobato@rri.kyoto-u.ac.jp

KONIJNENBERG, M.W., Mallinckrodt Medical BV, Westerduinweg 3, P.O. Box 3, NL-1755 ZG Petten, The Netherlands. Tel.: +31-224-567191. Fax: +31-224-567045. E-mail: nlmktmk1@ibmmail.com

KONONOV, V.N., Institute of Physics and Power Engineering, 1 Bondarenko Square, 249020 Obninsk, Kaluga region, Russia. Tel.: +7-8439-98992. Fax: +7-095-2302326 or +7-095-8833112. E-mail: kononov@ippe.rssi.ru

KOSUNEN, A., Finnish Centre for Radiation and Nuclear Safety, P.O. Box 14, FIN- Helsinki, Finland. Tel.: +358-9-75988446. Fax: +358-9-75988450. E-mail: antti.kosunen@stuk.fi

KULVIK, M., Research Institute, Helsinki University Central Hospital, Tukholmank 8F, FIN-00290 Helsinki, Finland. Tel.: +358-9-4712139. Fax: +358-9-4715550. E-mail: martti.kulvik@mei.hyks.hyks.mailnet.fi

KUNZE, J.F., College of Engineering, Idaho State University, P.O. Box 8060, Pocatello, Idaho, USA. Tel.: +1-208-2362902. Fax: +1-208-2364538. E-mail: kunzejay@isu.edu

KUSUKI, T., Department of Neurosurgery, Kyoto Prefecture University of Medicine, Kawaramachi-Hirokoji, Kamigyo 602, Kyoto, Japan. Tel.: +81-75-2515543. Fax: +81-75-2515544.

KÄRKKÄINEN, M., Department of Clinical Veterinary Science, Faculty of Veterinary Medicine, University of Helsinki, P.O. Box 57 (Hämeentie 57), FIN-00014 Helsinki University, Finland. Tel.: +358-9-70849620. Fax: +358-9-70849670. E-mail: Marjatta.Karkkainen@helsinki.fi

KÜCK, K., Fachbereich Chemie, Universität Bremen, NW2, B2090, Leobener Strasse, Postfach 330 440, D-28334 Bremen, Germany. Tel.: +49-421-2182219. Fax: +49-421-2182871. E-mail: alberts@chemie.uni-bremen.de

LAHANN, T.R., College of Pharmacy, Idaho State University, Pocatello, ID 83209-8334, USA. Tel.: +1-208-2364456. Fax: +1-208-2364482. E-mail: lahann@elixir.isu.edu

LAISSUE, J.A., Institute of Pathology, University of Bern, Murtenstrasse 31, Postfach, CH-3010 Berne, Switzerland. Tel.: +41-31-6323221/22. Fax: +41-31-3820065. E-mail: laissue@unibe.ch

LANGEN, K., Fermilab, Neutron Therapy Facility, Batavia, IL 60510, USA. Tel.: +1-708-8403456. Fax: +1-708-8408766. E-mail: langen@ntf2.fnal.gov

LARAMORE, G.E., Department of Radiation Oncology, University of Washington Medical Center, P.O. Box 356043, Seattle, WA 98195-6043, USA. Tel.: +1-206-5484110. Fax: +1-206-5486218. E-mail: george@radonc.washington.edu

LARSSON, B., Institute for Medical Radiobiololgy, University of Zurich, August Forel-Strasse 7, CH-8029 Zurich, Switzerland. Tel.: +41-56-3102059. Fax: +41-56-3104412. E-mail: larsson@imr.unizh.ch

LAWACZECK, R., Institut für Diagnostikforschung, Spandauer Damm 130, D-14050 Berlin, Germany. Tel.: +49-30-4687863. Fax: +49-30-30352046.

LEE, B.C., Research Reactor Analysis Department, HANARO Center, Korea Atomic Energy Research Institute, P.O. Box 105 Yusung, Taejon, 305-600, Korea. Tel.: +82-42-8688489. Fax: +82-42-8688341. E-mail: bclee2@nanum.kaeri.re.kr

LEE, S.-H., Department of Neurosurgery, Laboratory of Cell Biology, Korea Cancer Center Hospital, Gongnueng-Dong, Nowon-Gu 215-4, Seoul 139-240, Korea. Tel.: +82-2-9701235. Fax: +82-2-9782005.
E-mail: kmalshjw@unitel.co.kr

LEENDERS, K.L., PET Programme, Paul Scherrer Institute, WMSA/B11, CH-5232 Villigen PSI, Switzerland. Tel.: +41-56-3103683. Fax: +41-56-3103132.
E-mail: leenders@psi.ch

LEMMEN, P., Institute for Organic Chemistry and Biochemistry, Technical University Munich, Lichtenbergstrasse 4, D-85747 Garching, Germany.
Tel.: +49-89-28913319. Fax: +49-89-28913329.
E-mail: plemmen@nucleus.org.chemie.tu-muenchen.de

LENNOX, A., Neutron Therapy Facility, Fermi National Accelerator Laboratory, P.O. Box 500, Mail Stop 301, Batavia, IL 60510, USA. Tel: +1-630-8404850.
Fax: +1-630-8408766. E-mail: alennox@fnal.gov

LEVIN, V., IAEA, Vienna, Alfred Wegenergasse 7, P.O. Box 100, A-1190 Vienna, Austria. Tel.: +43-1-2060-21654. Fax: +43-1-2060-7.
E-mail: levinv@ripo1.iaea.or.at

LIBERMAN, S.J., Com. Nac. de Energia Atomica, Ave del Liberador 8250, 1429 Buenos Aires, Argentina. Tel.: +54-1-7041349. Fax: +54-1-7041022.
E-mail: liberman@cnea.edu.ar

LIM, S.-M., Korea Cancer Center Hospital, 215-4 Kongnenng-Dong, Nowon, K-139-240 Seoul, Korea. Tel.: +82-2-9742501. Fax: +82-2-9782005.

LIU HSUEH, Y.-W., Department of Nuclear Engineering and Engineering Physics, National Tsing Hua University, Hsinchu 30043, Taiwan.
Tel.: +886-35-719103. Fax: +886-35-720724. E-mail: ywhliu@ne.nthu.edu.tw

LORUSSO, G.F., Lawrence Berkeley Laboratory, One Cyclotron Road, MS 2-400, Berkeley, CA 94720, USA. Tel.: +1-510-4866853. Fax: +1-510-4864550.
E-mail: glorusso@grace.lbl.gov

LORVIDHAYA, V., Division of Radiation Oncology, Faculty of Medicine, Chiangmai University, Chiangmai 50200, Thailand. Tel.: +66-53-221122 ext. 5456. Fax: +66-53-217144.

LUDEWIGT, B., Lawrence Berkeley National Laboratory, 1 Cyclotron Road, MS 71-259, Berkeley, CA 94720, USA. Tel.: +1-510-4867733. Fax: +1-510-4865788. E-mail: baludewigt@lbl.gov

LUTZ, S., Fachbereich Chemie, Universität Bremen, NW2, B2090, Leobener Strasse, Postfach 330 440, D-28334 Bremen, Germany. Tel.: +49-421-2182219. Fax: +49-421-2182871. E-mail: lutz@chemie.uni-bremen.de

LÜDEMANN, L., Institut für Werkstofforschung, GKSS Forschungszentrum, Max-Planck-Str, D-21502 Geesthacht, Germany. Tel.: +49-40-47176745. Fax: +49-40-47172846. E-mail: luedemann@ure.uni-hamburg.de

LÜTOLF, U.M., Klinik und Poliklinik für Radio-oncology, Universitätsspital, University of Zurich, Rämistr. 100, CH-8091 Zurich, Switzerland. Tel.: +41-1-2552930. Fax: +41-1-2554435. E-mail: uml@dmr.usz.ch

MAASS, I., University of Bremen, Leobenerstr., D-28359 Bremen, Germany. Tel.: +49-421-2182119. Fax: +49-421-2182871. E-mail: maass@chemie.uni-bremen.de

MAKÓ, E.K., Department of Radiology, Semmelweis University of Medicine, Üllói ut 78/a, 1082 Budapest, Hungary. Tel.: +36-1-2100307. Fax: +36-1-2100307. E-mail: mako@radi.sote.hu

MANZINI, A., Com. Nac. de Energia Atomica, Ave del Liberador 8250, 1429 Buenos Aires, Argentina. Tel.: +54-1-3798316. Fax: +54-1-3798322. E-mail: amanzini@cnea.edu.ar

MAREK, M., NRI Rez, CZ-25068 Rez, Czech Republic. Tel.: +42-2-66172368. Fax: +42-2-6857147. E-mail: mam@nri.cz

MAREŠ, V., Institute of Physiology, Academy of Sciences, Videnska 1083, CZ-14200 Prague, Czech Republic. Tel.: +42-2-4752572. E-mail: lisa@biomed.cas.cz

MARGELOS, H., Institute for Medical Radiobiology, University of Zurich, August Forel Str. 7, CH-8029 Zurich, Switzerland. Tel.: +41-1-3856511. Fax: +41-1-3856204. E-mail: margelos@imr.unizh.ch

MARKOVITS, C., Accelerator Division, Paul Scherrer Institute, WBGA/C14, CH-5232 Villigen PSI, Switzerland. Tel.: +41-56-3103405. Fax: +41-56-3103383. E-mail: christa.markovits@psi.ch

MARTIN, R.F., Peter MacCallum Cancer Institute, Locked Bag No. 1, A'Becket Street, Melbourne, Vic 3000, Australia. Tel.: +61-3-96561357. Fax: +61-3-96531411. E-mail: roger93@ariel.ucs.unimelb.edu.au

MASUNAGA, S., Radiation Oncololgy Research Laboratory, Research Reactor Institute, Kyoto University, Noda, Kumatori-cho, Sennan-gun, Osaka 590-04, Japan. Tel.: +81-724-512406. Fax: +81-724-512627. E-mail: rorl@rri.kyoto-u.ac.jp

MATSUMOTO, T., Atomic Energy Research Laboratory, Musashi Institute of Technology, 971 Ozenji, Asao-ku, Kawasaki-shi, Japan. Tel: +81-44-9666131. Fax: +81-44-9556071. E-mail: mtetsuo@atom.musashi-tech.ac.jp.

MATSUMURA, A., Department of Neurosurgery, Institute of Clinical Medicine, University of Tsukuba, 1-1-1 Tennodai, Tsukuba, Ibaraki 305, Japan. Tel.: +81-298-533220. Fax: +81-298-533214. E-mail: matsumur@md.tsukuba.ac.jp

MATSUOKA, R., Association for Nuclear Technology in Medicine, 7F, 5th Mori Building, 1-17-1 Toranomon, Minato-ku, Tokyo 105, Japan. Tel.: +81-3-35043961. Fax: +81-3-35041390. E-mail: reiko@post.co.jp

MAUEC, M., Reactor Physics Division, Joňef Òtefan Institute, Jamova 39, SLO-1000 Ljubljana, Slovenia, Tel.: +386-61-1885206. Fax: +386-61-374919. E-mail: marko.maucec@ijs.si

MAUGHAN, R.L., Gershenson Radiation Oncology Center, Harper Hospital and Wayne State University, 3990 John R., Detroit, MI 48201, USA. Tel.: +1-313-7452487. Fax: +1-313-7452314. E-mail: maughanr@kci.wayne.edu

MAUTE, A., School of Veterinary Medicine, University of Zurich, Winterthurstrasse 260, CH-8057 Zurich, Switzerland. Tel.: +41-1-6358485.

MERCANTI, D., CNR-Institute of Neurobiology, Vec Marx 15/43, I-00137 Rome, Italy. Tel.: +39-6-86894968.

MICHEL, C., University of Zurich, Institute for Medical Radiobiology, August Forel-Str. 7, CH-8029 Zurich, Switzerland. Tel.: +41-1-3856513. Fax: +41-56-3856204. E-mail: chmichel@imr.unizh.ch

MIJNHEER, B.J., Radiotherapy Department, The Netherlands Cancer Institute, Plesmanlaan 121, NL-1069 CX Amsterdam, The Netherlands. Tel.: +31-20-5122203. Fax: +31-20-6691101. E-mail: bmijn@nki.nl

MISHIMA, Y., Mishima Institute for Dermatological Research, 1-4-32 Sowa-cho, Nada-ku, Kobe 657, Japan. Tel.: +81-78-8426342. Fax: +81-78-8426340. E-mail: rxm02257@niftyserve.or.jp

MIURA, M., Medical Department, Brookhaven National Laboratory, Building 490, 30 Bell Avenue, P.O. Box 5000, Upton, NY 11973-5000, USA. Tel.: +1-516-3443618. Fax: +1-516-3445311. E-mail: miura@bnl.gov

MO, D., Pool Reactor for BNCT, Institute of Nuclear Energy Technology, Tsinghua University, Beijing 100084, China. Tel.: +86-10-2594842. Fax: +86-10-2564177. E-mail: ean@tsinghua.edu.cn

MOORE, D.E., Department of Pharmacy, University of Sydney, Sydney, NSW 2006, Australia. Tel.: +61-2-3512334. Fax: +61-2-3514391. E-mail: demoore@pharm.usyd.edu.au

MORRIS, G.M., Research Institute, Churchill Hospital, University of Oxford, Old Road, Headington, Oxford, OX3 7LJ, UK. Tel.: +44-1865-225850. Fax: +44-1865-225847. E-mail: gmorris@radius.jr2.ox.ac.uk

MORRIS, J.H., Department of Pure and Applied Chemistry, Strathclyde University, 295 Cathedral Street, Glasgow G1 1XL, Scotland, UK. Tel.: +44-1436-675610. Fax: +44-141-5520876. E-mail: cbas51@strath.ac.uk

MOSS, R.L., JRC Petten, HFR Division, Joint Research Centre of the EC, Westerduinweg 3, NL-1755 ZG Petten, The Netherlands. Tel: +31-224-565126. Fax: +31-224-561449. E-mail: moss@jrc.nl

MYRSETH, E., Neurosurgical Department, Haukeland Hospital, N-5021 Bergen, Norway. Tel.: +47-55-972948. Fax: +47-55-972949.

NAESLUND, C., Department of Organic Chemistry, Uppsala University, P.O. Box 531, S-751 21 Uppsala, Sweden. Tel.: +46-18-4713798. Fax: +46-18-508542. E-mail: lottan@kemi.uu.se.

NAKAGAWA, Y., Department of Neurosurgery, National Kagawa Children's Hospital, Zentsuji-cho, 2603, Zentsuji City, Kagawa 765, Japan. Tel.: +81-877-620885. Fax: +81-877-625384.

NAKAMURA, H., Department of Chemistry, School of Science, Tohoku University, Sendai 980-77, Japan. Tel.: +81-22-2176583. Fax: +81-22-2176784. E-mail: h.nakamura@yy2.chem.tohoku.ac.jp

NAKAO, H., Osaka Prefecture University, 1-1 Gakuencho, Sakai, Osaka 593, Japan. Tel.: +81-722-521161 ext. 2467. Fax: +81-722-520341. E-mail: nakao@region.envi.osakafu-u.ac.jp

NICHOLS, T., University of Tennessee, 5815 Westover Drive, Knoxvolle, TN 37919, USA. Tel.: +1-423-5843093. Fax: +1-423-5446509. E-mail: tnichol@utkux.utcc.utk.edu

NIEMKIEWICZ, J., Department of Radiation Oncology, Grant/Riverside Methodist Hospital, 3535 Olentangy River Road, Columbus, OH 43214, USA. Tel.: +1-614-5665714. Fax: +1-614-2652440. E-mail: john@melanoma.eng.ohio-state.edu

NIEVERGELT, C., Institute for Medical Radiobiology, University of Zurich, August Forel-Strasse 7, Postfach, CH-8029 Zurich, Switzerland. Tel.: +41-1-3856523. Fax: +41-1-3856204. E-mail: carmen@imr.unizh.ch

NIGG, D.W., Idaho National Engineering Laboratory, P.O. Box 1625, Mail Stop 3890, Idaho Falls, ID 83415-7113, USA. Tel.: +1-208-5267627. Fax: +1-208-5260528. E-mail: dwn@inel.gov

NISHIAKI, M., Osaka Prefecture University, 1-1 Gakuen-cho, Sakai, Osaka 593, Japan. Tel.: +81-722-521161 ext. 2467. Fax: +81-722-520341. E-mail: kecha@region.envi.osakafu-u.ac.jp

NOVAK DESPOT, D., Department of Biochemistry and Molecular Biology, Joñef Òtefan Institute, Jamova 39, SLO-1000 Ljubljana, Slovenia. Tel.: +386-61-1773215. Fax: +386-61-273594.

OHMORI, Y., Department of Neurosurgery, Kyoto Prefecture University of Medicine, Kawaramachi-Hirokoji, Kamigyo 602, Kyoto, Japan. Tel.: +81-75-2515543. Fax: +81-75-2515544.

OLSSON, P., Department of Biomedicine Radation Sciences, Uppsala University, P.O. Box 535, S-751 21 Uppsala, Sweden. Tel.: +46-18-4713829. Fax: +46-18-4713432. E-mail: par.olsson@bms.uu.se

ONO, K., Research Reactor Institute, Kyoto University, Kumatori-cho, Sennan-gun, Osaka 590-04, Japan. Tel.: +81-724-512475. Fax: +81-724-512627. E-mail: onokoji@rri.kyoto-u.ac.jp

ORLOVA, A., Department of Organic Chemistry, Uppsala University, P.O. Box 531, S-751 21 Uppsala, Sweden. Tel.: +46-18-4713796. Fax: +46-18-508542. E-mail: ssj@kemi.uu.se

OTERSEN, B., Fachbereich Chemie, Universität Bremen, Postfach 330 440, D-28334 Bremen, Germany. Tel.: +49-421-2182381. Fax: +49-421-2182871. E-mail: otersen@chemie.uni-bremen.de

OTT, K.O., School of Nuclear Engineering, Purdue University, Building 1290, West Lafayette, IN 47907-1290, USA. Tel.: +1-317-4945751. Fax: +1-317-4949570.

OZSAHIN, E.M., Universitaire Vaudois, CHUV, Centre Hospitalier, Service de Radio-Oncologie, 46, rue du Bugnon, CH-1011 Lausanne, Switzerland. Tel.: +41-21-3144604. Fax: +41-21-3144601. E-mail: ozsahin@hospvd.ch

PATEL, H., Research Institute, The Churchill Hospital, Headington, Oxford, OX 3 7LJ, UK. Tel.: +44-1703-796860. Fax: +44-1703-704236. E-mail: h.patel@soton.ac.uk

PATRASHAKORN, S., Office of Atomic Energy for Peace, Reactor Physics Group, Vibhavadi Rangsit Road, Chatuchak, Bangkok 10900, Thailand. Tel: +66-2-5620117. Fax: +66-2-5620118. E-mail: sunanp@mozart.inet.co.th

PELLETTIERI, L., Department of Neurosurgery, University Hospital, S-413 45 Göteborg, Sweden. Tel: +46-31-604490. Fax: +46-31-416719.

PERLEBERG, O., Fachbereich Chemie, Universität Bremen, NW2, B2090, Leobener Strasse, Postfach 330 440, D-28359 Bremen, Germany. Tel.: +49-421-2182119. Fax: +49-421-2182871. E-mail: perle@chemie.uni-bremen.de

PERO, R., Department of Cell and Molecular Biology, University of Lund, Wallenberg Laboratory, P.O. Box 7031, S-220 07 Lund, Sweden. Tel.: +46-46-2224480. Fax: +46-46-2224624. E-mail: ronald.pero@ wblab.lu.se

PEYMANN, T., Department of Chemistry and Biochemistry, UCLA, Hilgard Avenue, Los Angeles, CA 90034, USA. Tel.: +1-310-2069444. E-mail: tope@xenon.chem.ucla.edu

PHILIPPO, H., Netherlands Energy Research Foundation, P.O. Box 1, NL-1755 ZG Petten, The Netherlands. Tel.: +31-224-564280. Fax: +31-224-563491. E-mail: philippo@ecn.nl

PICHA, P., Section of Experimental Oncology, Research Division, National Cancer Institute Thailand, Rama VI Road, Rajthevee, Bangkok 10400, Thailand. Tel.: +66-2-2460061, ext. 1413. Fax: +66-2-2479428. E-mail: picha@health.moph.go.th

PIGNOL, J.-P., Centre Antoine Lacassagne, Cyclotron Biomedical, 227 Avenue de la Lauterne, F-06200 Nice, France. Tel.: +33-492-031061. Fax: +33-492-031570.

PINTO COELHO, P.R., Institute de Pesquisas Energéticas e Nucleares IPEN-CNEN/SP, Travessa R, 400, Cidade Universitária, Sao Paulo SP 05508-900, Brazil. Tel.: +55-11-8169396. Fax: +55-11-8169432. E-mail: prcoelho@net.i-pen.br

PISAREV, M.A., Com. Nac. de Energia Atomica, Ave del Liberador 8250, 1429 Buenos Aires, Argentina. Tel.: +54-1-3798249. Fax: +54-1-4800615. E-mail: pisarev@cnea.edu.ar

PIVOVAROV, V.A., Institute of Physics and Power Engineering, Bondarenko Square 1, 249020 Obninsk, Kaluga region, Russia. Tel.: +7-8439-98068. Fax: +7-095-2302326. E-mail: root@ippe.rssi.ru

PLOTNIKOV, S.V., Applied Linacs Laboratory, Institute of Theoretical and Experimental Physics (ITEP), B. Cheremushkinskaya 25, 117259 Moscow, Russia. Tel.: +7-095-1236584. Fax: +7-095-1236524. E-mail: plotnikov@vxitep.itep.ru

PREUSSE, D., Department of Chemistry, University of Bremen, Leobenerstrasse, D-28359 Bremen, Germany. Tel.: +49-421-2182119. Fax: +49-421-2182871. E-mail: preusse@chemie.uni-bremen.de

PROKES, K., Oncological Laboratory, Charles University, Unemocnice 2, CZ-12808 Prague 2, Czech Republic. Tel.: +42-2-294304. Fax: +42-2-298490.

PÖLLER, F., Institut für Med. Strahlenphysik, Universitätsklinikum Essen, Hufelandstrasse 55, D-45122 Essen, Germany. Tel.: +49-201-7232052. Fax: +49-201-7235965.

RAAIJMAKERS, C.P.J., Department of Radiotherapy, The Netherlands Cancer Institute, Plesmanlaan 121, NL-1066 CX Amsterdam, The Netherlands. Tel.: +31-20-5122173. Fax: +31-20-6691101. E-mail: nraay@nki.nl

RAITZIG, A., Universität Bremen, Leobener Strasse, D-28359 Bremen, Germany. Tel.: +49-421-2182375. Fax: +49-421-2182871.

RATAJ, J., Department 803, NRI Rez, CZ-25068 Rez, Czech Republic. Tel.: +42-2-66172465. Fax: +42-2-6857147. E-mail: rataj@nri.cz

REIST, H.-W., Institute for Medical Radiobiology, Paul Scherrer Institute, WMSA/B13, CH-5232 Villigen PSI, Switzerland. Tel.: +41-56-3103685. Fax: +41-56-3103132. E-mail: hans.reist@imr.psi.ch

REW, G., The University of Birmingham, Edgbaston Park Road, Birmingham B15 2TT, UK. Tel.: +44-121-4144689. Fax: +44-121-4144725. E-mail: gayle@aps3.ph.bham.ac.uk

RIVARD, M.J., Wayne State University, 3990 John Road, Detroit, MI 48201, USA. Tel.: +1-313-7452486. Fax: +1-313-7452314. E-mail: rivardm@kci.wayne.edu

ROBERTO, A., Division Toxicology, Department Pharmceutical Bioscience, Uppsala University, P.O. Box 594, S-751 24 Uppsala, Sweden. Tel.: +46-18-4714252. Fax: +46-18-4714253. E-mail: amilcar.roberto@tox.uu.se

ROELCKE, U., Paul Scherrer Institute, WMSA/B14, CH-5232 Villigen PSI, Switzerland. Tel.: +41-56-3104246. Fax: +41-56-3103132. E-mail: ulrich.roelcke@psi.ch

RONG, F.-G., College of Pharmacy, The Ohio State University, 500 West 12th Avenue, Columbus, OH 43210, USA. Tel.: +1-614-6883149. Fax: +1-614-2922435. E-mail: rong.1@osu.edu

ROSSI, S., CERN, CH-1211 Geneva, Switzerland. E-mail: sandro.rossi@cern.ch

ROTARU, J., The Ohio State University, 1645 Neil Avenue, 165 Hamilton Hall, Columbus, OH 43210, USA. Tel.: +1-614-2920693. Fax: +1-614-2927072. E-mail: jrotaru@magnus.acs.ohio-state.edu

RUF, S., University of Bremen, Leobenerstr, D-28359 Bremen, Germany. Tel.: +49-421-2182119. Fax: +49-421-2182871. E-mail: ruf@chemie.uni-bremen.de

RUKSAWIN, N., Section of Nuclear Medicine, Department of Radiology, Siriraj Hospital, Mahidol University, Prannok, Bangkok 10700, Thailand. Tel.: +66-2-4127165. Fax: +66-2-4121371. E-mail: sinrs@mucc.mahidol.ac.th

RYDIN, R.A., Mechanical Aero and Nuclear Engineering, University of Virginia, 626 Cabell Avenue, Charlottesville, VA 22901, USA. Tel.: +1-804-9825468. Fax: +1-804-9825473. E-mail: rar@watt.seas.virginia.edu

SADAYORI, N., Department of Chemistry, Graduate School of Science, Tohoku University, Aramaki, Aoba-ku, Sendai 980-77, Japan. Tel.: +81-22-2176583. Fax: +81-22-2639207. E-mail: sadayori@funorg.chem.tohoku.ac.jp

SAKURAI, Y., Department of Radiation Medical Physics, Research Reactor Institute, Kyoto University, Kumatori-cho, Sennan-gun, Osaka 590-04, Japan. Tel.: +81-724-520901 ext. 2604. Fax: +81-724-5303060. E-mail: ysakurai@kurri1.rri.kyoto-u.ac.jp

SALFORD, L.G., Department of Clinical Neuroscience, Department of Neurosurgery, Lund University Hospital, S-221 85 Lund, Sweden. Tel.: +46-46-172142. Fax: +46-46-189287. E-mail: leif.salford@neurokir.lu.se

SANO, T., Center for Advanced Biotechnology, Boston University, 36 Cummington Street, Boston, MA 02215, USA. Tel.: +1-617-3538505 or 8500. Fax: +1-617-3538506. E-mail: tsano@enga.bu.edu

SANTOS, D., Paul Scherrer Institute, CH-5232 Villigen PSI, Switzerland. Tel.: +41-56-310. Fax: +41-56-310. E-mail: ddossantos@access.ch

SAUERWEIN, W., Klinik und Poliklinik für Strahlentherapie, Universitätsklinikum Essen, Hufelandstrasse 55, D-45122 Essen, Germany. Tel.: +49-201-7232052. Fax: +49-201-7235908. E-mail: w.sauerwein@uni-essen.de

SAVOLAINEN, S., Department of Physics, University of Helsinki, P.O. Box 9, FIN-00014 Helsinki, Finland. Tel.: +358-9-4712595. Fax: +358-9-471. E-mail: ssavolainen@phcu.helsinki.fi

SCHAFFER, S., Fachbereich Chemie, Universität Bremen, Ruppertshainerstr 11, D-28334 Bremen, Germany. Tel.: +49-421-2182200. Fax: +49-421-2182871. E-mail: schaffer@chemie.uni-bremen.de

SCHUBIGER, P.A., Paul Scherrer Institute, ODRA/107, CH-5232 Villigen PSI, Switzerland. Tel.: +41-56-3102813. Fax: +41-56-3102849. E-mail: schubiger@psi.ch

SCHWEIZER, M.P., Department of Medicinal Chemistry, 308 Skaggs Hall, University of Utah, Salt Lake City, UT 84112, USA. Tel.: +1-801-5817599. Fax: +1-801-5817087. E-mail: marty@doug.med.utah.edu.

SCHWEIZER, P.M., University of Zurich, Institute for Medical Radiobiology, August Forel Str. 7, CH-8029 Zurich, Switzerland. Tel.: +41-1-3856518. Fax: +41-1-3856204. E-mail: pascal@imr.unizh.ch

SCHWINT, A.E., Departamento de Radiobiologia, Com. Nac. de Energia Atomica, Avenida del Libertador 8250, 1429 Buenos Aires, Argentina. Tel.: +54-1-7547149. Fax: +54-1-7547121. E-mail: schwint@cnea.edu.ar

SEPPÄLÄ, T., VTT Chemical Technology, P.O. Box 1404, FIN-02044 VTT, Finland. Tel.: +358-9-4566351. Fax: +358-9-4566390. E-mail: tiina.seppala@vtt.fi

SERŠA, G., Department of Tumor Biology, Institute of Oncology, Zaloška 2, SLO-1105 Ljubljana, Slovenia. Tel.: +386-61-323063 ext. 2933. Fax: +386-61-1314180. E-mail: gsersa@mail.onko-i.si

SHEFER, R.E., Newton Scientific Incorporated, 245 Bent Street, Cambridge, MA 02141, USA. Tel.: +1-617-3549469. Fax: +1-617-3549479. E-mail: res@world.std.com

SHELLY, K., Department of Chemistry and Biochemistry, UCLA, 405 Hilgard Avenue, Los Angeles, CA 90095-1569, USA. Tel.: +1-310-2069444. Fax: +1-310-8255490. E-mail: shelly@chem.ucla.edu

SHIBATA, Y., Department of Neurosurgery, University of Tsukuba, 1-1-1 Tennohdai, Tsukuba, Ibaraki 305, Japan. Tel.: +81-298-533220. Fax: +81-298-533214.

SIEFERT, A., Department of Radiation and Radio-Oncology, University Hospital Grosshadern, Marchioninistrasse 15, D-81377 Munich, Germany. Tel.: +49-89-70953770. Fax: +49-89-70953845. E-mail: siefert@radonc.med.uni-muenchen.de

SILVANDER, M., Department of Physical Chemistry, University of Uppsala, P.O. Box 532, S-751 21 Uppsala, Sweden. Tel.: +46-18-4713657. Fax: +46-18-508542. E-mail: mats.silvander@fki.uu.se

SIVAEV, I., A.N.Nesmeyanov Institute of Organo-Element Compounds, Vavilova Street 28, 117813 Moscow, Russia. E-mail: bre@ineos.ac.ru

SJÖBERG, S., Department of Organic Chemistry, University of Uppsala, P.O. Box 531, S-751 21 Uppsala, Sweden. Tel.: +46-18-4713796/98. Fax: +46-18-508542. E-mail: ssj@kemi.uu.se

ŠKRK, J., Office of the Director, Institute of Oncology, Zaloka 2, SLO-1000 Ljubljana, Slovenia. Tel.: +386-61-1314225. Fax: +386-61-1314180. E-mail: jskrk@mail.onko-i.si

SKÖLD, K., Neutron Research Laboratory, University of Uppsala, S-611 82 Nyköping, Sweden. Tel.: +46-155-221849. Fax: +46-155-263001. E-mail: kurt.skold@studsvik.uu.se

SLABBERT, J., National Accelerator Centre, ZA-Faure CP 7131, South Africa. Tel.: +27-21-8433820. Fax: +27-21-8433382. E-mail: natalie@nac.ac.za

SMITH, D.R., Baker Laboratory, Department of Chemistry, Cornell University, Ithaca, NY 14853-1301, USA. Tel.: +1-607-2553884. Fax: +1-607-2554137. E-mail: ds50@cornell.edu

SMITH, M.D., Department of Pharmacy, University of Sydney, Parramatta Road, Sydney NSW 2006, Australia. Tel.: +61-2-6922333. Fax: +61-2-5523760. E-mail: michaels@pharmacy.pharm.su.oz.au

SMORON, G.L., Fermilab, Neutron Therapy Facility, Mail Stop 301, P.O. Box 500, Batavia, IL 60510, USA. Tel.: +1-630-8403865. Fax: +1-630-8408766. E-mail: alennox@fnal.gov

SOLARES, G.R., Harvard / MIT, 85 Melrose Street, Arlington, MA 02174, USA. Tel.: +1-617-6670176. Fax: +1-617-9755233. E-mail: gsolares@mit.edu

SOLOWAY, A., College of Pharmacy, The Ohio State University, 500 West 12th Avenue, Columbus, OH 43210, USA. Tel: +1-614-2922509. Fax: +1-614-2922435. E-mail: soloway.1@osu.edu

SPANNE, P., European Synchrotron Radiation Facility, BP 220, F-38043 Grenoble CEDEX, France. Tel.: +33-476-882647. Fax: +33-476-882542. E-mail: spanne@esrf.fr

SPIELVOGEL, B., Boron Biologicals Incorporated, 620 Hutton St, Suite 104, Raleigh, NC 27606, USA. Tel.: +1-919-8322044. Fax: +1-919-8325980. E-mail: bbi@ipass.net

SPRYSHKOVA, R., Radioisotope Laboratory, Cancer Research Center, Russian Academy of Medical Sciences, Kashirskoye Shosse 24, 115478 Moscow, Russia. Tel.: +7-095-3241949 or 2704. Fax: +7-095-3241949. E-mail: helen@edito.msk.su

STECHER-RASMUSSEN, F., Netherlands Energy Research Foundation, ECN, P.O. Box 1, NL-1755 ZG Petten, The Netherlands. Tel.: +31-224-564537. Fax: +31-224-563490. E-mail: rasmussen@ecn.nl

STEEN, S., Universität Bremen, FB II / NW II, Leobenerstr, D-28359 Bremen, Germany. Tel.: +49-421-2182119. Fax: +49-421-2182871.
E-mail: steen@chemie.uni-bremen.de

STELZER, K.J., Department of Radiation Oncology, Medical Center, University of Washington, P.O. Box 356043, Seattle, WA 98195-6043, USA.
Tel.: +1-206-5484115. Fax: +1-206-5486218.
E-mail: keith@radonc.washington.edu

STEPANEK, J., Institute for Medical Radiobiology, Paul Scherrer Institute, OBUA/23, CH-5232 Villigen PSI, Switzerland. Tel.: +41-56-3102084.
Fax: +41-56-3104412. E-mail: jiri.stepanek@imr.psi.ch

SUNNERHEIM-SJÖBERG, K., Department of Organic Chemistry, University of Uppsala, P.O. Box 531, S-751 21 Uppsala, Sweden. Tel.: +46-18-4713755.
Fax: +46-18-508542. E-mail: kss@kemi.uu.se

SUZUKI, M., Research Reactor Institute, Kyoto University, Kumatori-chu, Sennan-gun, Osaka 590-04, Japan. Tel.: +81-724-520901.

SYCHEV, B., Moscow Radiotechnology Institute, RAS, Varshavskoe shosse 132, Moscow, Russia. Tel.: +7-095-3153122. Fax: +7-095-3141053.
E-mail: sychev@mankobv.msk.ru

TAKAGAKI, M., Radiation Oncology Research Laboratory, KURRI, Kumatori-cho, Sennan-gun, Osaka 590-04, Japan. Tel.: +81-724-520901 ext. 2300.
Fax: +81-724-528194. E-mail: rorl@rri.kyoto-u.ac.jp ormtakaga@ibm.net

TAMBUNCHONG, C., Department of Chemistry, Srinakharinwirot University, Sukumvit 23, Prakanong, Bangkok 10110, Thailand. Tel.: +66-2-2586402.
Fax: +66-2-2584006. E-mail: chinda-t@psm.swu.ac.th

TANG, J., Oak Ridge National Laboratory, Building 6011, P.O. Box 2008, Oak Ridge, TN 37831-6370, USA. Tel.: +1-423-5745266. Fax: +1-423-5763513.
E-mail: jst@ornl.gov

TATTAM, D., University of Birmingham, Edgbaston, Birmingham B15 2TT, UK. Tel.: +44-121-4144714. Fax: +44-121-4144725.
E-mail: tattamda@aps3.ph.bham.ac.uk

TEICHMANN, S., Paul Scherrer Institute, OBUA/2, CH-5232 Villigen PSI, Switzerland. Tel.: +41-56-3102966. Fax: +41-56-3104412.
E-mail: sabine.teichmann@imr.psi.ch

TIAN, B., Shenzhen OUR R & D Institute, DE Building, Xinsha Industrial Garden Pinghu, BNCT Project Manager, Longgang, Shenzhen, 518111, China. Tel.: +86-755-8857224. Fax: +86-755-8855430. E-mail: our@public.szptt.net.cn

TJARKS, W., Department of Organic Chemistry, Uppsala University, P.O. Box 531, S-751 21 Uppsala, Sweden. Tel.: +46-18-4713798. Fax: +46-18-508542. E-mail: wtjarks@kemi.uu.se

TURJANSKI, L., Hospital Argerich, Rep. de la India 3129, 1425 Buenos Aires, Argentina. Tel.: +54-1-4477045. Fax: +54-1-8011911.

TWILEGAR, R., Neutron Technology Corporation, 1205 N 11th, Boise, ID 83702, USA. Tel.: +1-208-3332336. Fax: +1-208-3361195. E-mail: twilorific@aol.com

UEDA, S., Department of Neurosurgery, Kyoto Prefecture University of Medicine, Kawaramachi Hirokoji, Kamigyo-ku, Kyoto 602, Japan. Tel.: +81-75-2515539. Fax: +81-75-2515544. E-mail: sueda@koto.kpu-m.ac.jp

VERBAKEL, W., Netherlands Energy Research Foundation, ECN, P.O. Box 1, NL-1755 ZG Petten, The Netherlands. Tel.: +31-224-564376. Fax: +31-224-56. E-mail: verbakel@cycl.phys.tue.nl

VILAITHONG, T., Physics Department, Faculty of Science, Chiangmai University, 239 Huay Kaew Street, Chiangmai 50200, Thailand. Tel.: +66-53-222774. Fax: +66-53-222776. E-mail: thiraph@chiangmai.ac.th

VROEGINDEWEIJ, C., Netherlands Energy Research Foundation, P.O. Box 1, NL-1755 ZG Petten, The Netherlands. Tel.: +31-224-564288. Fax: +31-224-563490. E-mail: corine@jrc.nl

VÄHÄTALO, J., Laboratory of Chemistry, Helsinki University, P.O. Box 55, FIN-00014 Helsinki University, Finland. Tel.: +358-9-4712139. Fax: +358-9-4715550. E-mail: jyrki.vahatalo@helsinki.fi

WAGNER, F.M., FRM-Reaktorstation Garching, Fachbereich Physik der Techn. Universität München, D-85747 Garching, Germany. Tel.: +49-89-28912156. Fax: +49-89-28912119. E-mail: fmwagner@physik.tu-muenchen.de

WANG, C., School of Mechanical Engineering, Georgia Institute of Technology, Atlanta, GA 30332-0225, USA. Tel.: +1-404-8943727. Fax: +1-404-8943733. E-mail: drwang@ckwang.gatech.edu

WANG, X., Department of Technical Physics, Peking University, Beijing 100871, China. Tel.: +86-10-2502704. Fax: +86-10-2501875.
E-mail: xyWang@ibmstone.pku.edu.cn

WATKINS, P., JRC Petten, Joint Research Centre, Institute for Advanced Materials, P.O. Box 2, NL-1755 ZG Petten, The Netherlands.
Tel.: +31-224-565120. Fax: +31-224-561449. E-mail: watkins@jrc.nl

WEINREICH, R., Institute for Medical Radiobiology, Paul Scherrer Institute, OBUA/23, CH-5232 Villigen PSI, Switzerland. Tel.: +41-56-3104070.
Fax: +41-56-3102309. E-mail: regin.weinreich@imr.psi.ch

WEISSFLOCH, L., Radiotherapy, MRI, Ismaningerstr 22, D-81675 Munich, Germany. Tel.: +49-89-41404305. Fax: +49-89-41404864.

WHEELER, F.J., Idaho National Engineering Laboratory, LITCO, P.O. Box 1625, Idaho Falls, ID 83415-3890, USA. Tel.: +1-208-5267641.
Fax: +1-208-5260528. E-mail: fjw@inel.gov

WHITTEMORE, W.L., General Atomics, P.O. Box 85608, 2365 Via Siena, La Jolla, CA 92037, USA. Tel.: +1-619-4578789. Fax: +1-619-4578786.

WIENER, E., College of Medicine, University of Illinois, at Urbana-Champaign, 1307 West Park Street, Urbana, IL 61801, USA. Tel.: +1-217-2447193.
Fax: +1-217-2441330. E-mail: e-wiener@uiuc.edu

WIERSEMA, R.J., Neutron Therapies Incorporated, 5340 Eastgate Mall, San Diego, CA 92121, USA. Tel.: +1-619-6788683. Fax: +1-619-6788615.
E-mail: wiersema@pacbell.net

WIERZBICKI, J., Wayne State University, 3990 John R, Detroit, MI 48201, USA. Tel.: +1-313-7452191. Fax: +1-313-7452314.

WITTIG, A., Institut für Med. Strahlenphysik, Universitätsklinikum Essen, Hufelandstrasse 55, D-45122 Essen, Germany. Tel.: +49-201-7232052.
Fax: +49-201-7235908.

WOLBERS, J.G., Department of Neurosurgery, Vrye University Hospital, P.O. Box 7057, NL-1007 MB Amsterdam, The Netherlands. Tel.: +31-20-4443714.
Fax: +31-20-4443784.

YAMAMOTO, T., Department of Neurosurgery, Institute of Clinical Medicine, University of Tsukuba, 1-1-1 Tennodai, Tsukuba City, Ibaraki 305, Japan. Tel.: +81-298-533220. Fax: +81-298-533214. E-mail: matsumur@md.tsukuba.ac.jp

YAMAMOTO, Y., Department of Chemistry, Graduate School of Science, Tohoku University, Sendai 980-77, Japan. Tel.: +81-22-2176581. Fax: +81-22-2176784. E-mail: yoshi@yamamoto1.chem.tohoku.ac.jp

YANAGIM, H., Department of Surgery, Institute of Medical Science, University of Tokyo, 4-6-1 Shiroganedai, Minato-ku, Tokyo-108, Japan. Tel.: +81-3-54495352. Fax: +81-3-54495439.

YANCH, J.C., Massachusetts Institute of Technology, Nuclear Engineering and Whitaker College of Health Science and Technology, 45 Carleton Street, Room E25-330, Cambridge, MA 02139, USA. Tel.: +1-617-2586999. Fax: +1-617-2530760. E-mail: jcy@imager.mit.edu

YANG, W., Department of Pathology, The Ohio State University, 165 Hamilton Hall, 1645 Neil Avenue, Columbus, OH 43210, USA. Tel.: +1-614-2920693. Fax: +1-614-2927072.

YLÄ-MELLA, H., Department of Physics, University of Helsinki, P.O. Box 9, FIN-00014 Helsinki University, Finland. Tel.: +358-9-4566357. Fax: +358-9-4566390. E-mail: hmym@tukki.jyu.fi

YOKOO, K., Research Reactor Utilization Division, Department of Research Reactor, Tokai Research Establishment, Japan Atomic Energy Research Institute, Tokai-mura, Naka-gun, Ibaraki 319-11, Japan. Tel.: +81-292-825593. Fax: +81-292-826763. E-mail: yokoo@jrr3fep2.tokai.jaeri.go.jp

YOSHINO, K., Department of Chemistry, Faculty of Science, Shinshu University, Asahi, Matsumoto 390, Japan. Tel.: +81-263-354600 ext. 4156. Fax: +81-263-335323. E-mail: kyoshino@ripms.shinshu-u.ac.jp

YUE, G., Department of Technical Physics, Peking University, Beijing 100871, China. Tel.: +86-10-62501874. Fax: +86-10-62501875. E-mail: gyue@ihipms.ihip.pku.edu.cn

ZAMENHOF, R., Deaconess Hospital / Harvard, 1 Deaconess Road, Boston, MA 02215, USA. Tel.: +1-617-7322003. Fax: +1-617-7322005. E-mail: zamenhof@mit.edu

ZSOLNAY, É.M., Institute of Nuclear Techniques, Technical University of Budapest, Müegyetem rkp. 3-9, H-1521 Budapest, Hungary. Tel.: +36-1-4632523. Fax: +36-1-4631954. E-mail: zsolnay@reak.bme.hu

Hiroshi Hatanaka Lecture:
Search for new tumor-seeking compounds in Japan, *Yoshinori Yamamoto*

Ralph G. Fairchild Awards for Young Scientists:

Teruyoshi Kageji, Bremen, Germany
Deborah dos Santos, Zurich, Switzerland
Michael D. Smith, Sydney, Australia
Pär Olsson, Uppsala, Sweden
Birte Otersen, Bremen, Germany

Country	Participants	Accompanying Persons
United States of America	82	23
Japan	40	5
Switzerland	34	5
Germany	29	2
Sweden	21	1
United Kingdom	12	2
The Netherlands	12	1
Finland	11	0
Argentina	8	0
Russia	7	2
Thailand	6	0
Czech Republic	5	0
China	4	2
Australia	4	2
Slovenia	4	1
Italy	4	0
Hungary	4	0
Korea	3	0
France	3	0
Austria	2	1
Taiwan	2	0
Lithuania	2	0
Belgium	2	0
South Africa	1	0
Slovakia	1	0
Poland	1	0
Norway	1	0
Israel	1	0
Canada	1	0
Brazil	1	0
Total: 30 countries	308	47

Total ISNCT membership (4 Sep 1996)	335
Total ISNCT members attending	185
New ISNCT members attending	84
Non-ISNCT members attending	123

Contents — Volume I

Theory

Existing facilities

Proposed facilities

xliv

Towards hospital-based NCT

Introductory lectures

©1997 Elsevier Science B.V. All rights reserved.
Advances in Neutron Capture Therapy.
Volume I, Medicine and Physics.
B. Larsson, J. Crawford and R. Weinreich, editors.

Biology in relation to treatment in malignant glioma

J. Hildebrand

Service de Neurologie, Hôpital Erasme, ULB, Brussels, Belgium

Over the last 25 years remarkable progress has been made in our understanding of the biology of cancer, including malignant glioma. Virtually every discovery has been exploited to design new therapeutic approaches. Unfortunately, in malignant glioma these attempts have largely failed so far.

Many believe that the lack of success may be related primarily to tumor heterogeneity. Different treatment modalities tested could well be active but not on all cells of a tumor. Consequently, the biological features we shall review may not apply to all cells forming a malignant glioma. Essentially our attempts to increase the efficacy of medical treatments of malignant glioma aimed to achieve:
1) higher drug concentrations in tumor cells;
2) overcoming drug resistance; and
3) making use of biological differences between normal and tumor cells.
Most systems using gene therapy also belong to the last category of therapeutic prospectives. In this review I have selected four biological features of malignant glioma which have been most extensively exploited to increase the therapeutic response.

Implication of the blood-brain barrier in the treatment of malignant glioma

The greater part of the CNS is surrounded by a barrier which prevents most of naturally occurring substances and drugs from penetrating the brain. The main morphological support of this blood-brain barrier (BBB) is the structure of brain capillaries consisting of a single layer of endothelial cells which are joined by tight junctions, and form a continuous cellular layer. Other characteristics of brain endothelium are the lack of fenestration, and a considerable reduction of plasmalemma vesicles which transport molecules by pinocytosis. Other structures such as basement membrane, extracellular matrix, astrocyte processes have a minor structural role, but are essential in maintaining the peculiar structure of CNS-endothelium [1].

The integrity of BBB may be explored by radionuclide scan, contrast-enhanced CT scan, MRI or, rubidium 82-PET scan. All these examinations demonstrate that BBB is largely destroyed in at least 95% of malignant glioma. However, the alteration of BBB in malignant glioma is partial and presents regional variations. In addition, malignant small foci which usually infiltrate the apparently normal brain are largely protected by BBB. To reach these cells most drugs will have to diffuse across the endothelium. This diffusion is related to: free drug concentration, time spent in the capillaries, capillary surface and blood flow, and, last but not least, drug lipid solubility and molecular size. Few anticancer agents cross (like the nitrosoureas do) the BBB readily, which explains the large number of attempts to overcome or circumvent this obstacle.

Intrathecal or local chemotherapy

Drugs exchange between the CSF and extracellular brain compartment through diffusion along concentration, hence the use of the intrathecal route. This form of therapy is limited by neurotoxicity to only a few agents: methotrexate, cytosine arabinoside and thio-TEPA, and by the short distance of drug diffusion across tumor tissue. Therefore intrathecal administration is primarily used in the treatment of leptomeningeal metastases.

Other techniques bring drugs directly in contact with brain tumors. They include drug injection into the tumor or tumor cavity either during operation or via implanted catheters or pumps. The modern version of this approach is the use of drug-impregnated biodegradable polymers [2].

Intra-arterial chemotherapy

The rationale of intracarotid drug administration is based on the assumption that it achieves higher drug concentrations in the tumor for a lower systemic toxicity. This treatment modality is restricted to drugs which are rapidly extracted from the blood, since the benefit is limited to the first passage. With drugs used so far (mainly BCNU and cisplatin given alone or in combination) the local toxicity, consisting mainly of blindness and encephalopathy, is high [3,4]. In our view, this method, which cannot be easily repeated, remains experimental.

Autologous bone marrow transplantation

In patients with malignant glioma, bone marrow hardly ever contains neoplastic cells. Therefore rescue with autologous graft taken before the administration of chemotherapy allows a substantial dose increase. This method has been shown to be feasible [5,6] but its therapeutic benefit remains uncertain.

Disruption of the blood-brain barrier

Intracarotid infusion of hypertonic solutions of mannitol 20 to 25% or glycerol 15% produces a reversible opening of the BBB in the perfused hemisphere lasting 1 to 2 h. Unfortunately the increase of BBB permeability is much greater in the normal cortex than in tumors, and it remains uncertain whether the therapeutic benefits outweigh toxicity.

More recently, products such as RMP-7 peptide, an analogue of bradykinin, have been shown to be able to increase BBB permeability (through a receptor-mediated mechanism), selectively in abnormal brain areas where BBB appears grossly normal, such as tumor-adjacent brain [7]. Clinical trials testing this agent in conjunction with chemotherapy are currently being carried out.

Polyamines

Their names: putrescine, spermidine, spermine or cadaverine indicate that for a long time they have been regarded as end products. Today these organic poly-cations are thought to play an important role in many cell reactions. Polyamines bind electrostatically a variety of negatively charged molecules, such as DNA, RNA or proteins. Putrescine, in particular, behaves as a growth factor during embryonic growth, and normal or malignant proliferation. Polyamines are ubiquitous; they are found in tissues and in biological liquids such as CSF [8]. In neuro-oncology, their use has been considered for various purposes:
1. Tumor grading, because polyamine concentrations are correlated with the degree of malignancy.
2. Follow-up, where their use has been best demonstrated in medulloblastomas by monitoring CSF concentrations [9].
3. Cancer treatment.

Putrescine derives from ornithine which is either present in the plasma or formed from arginine (urea cycle). This reaction is catalyzed by ornithine decarboxylase, a key enzyme (Fig. 1). Putrescine can be catabolized into spermidine and then spermine by a reaction catalyzed by spermidine and spermine acetyl transferase (Fig. 1). In turn, putrescine may derive from spermidine, a reaction catalyzed by a polyamine oxidase. Polyamines synthesized in one organ may be released and redistributed in the organism. Red blood cells, where the metabolism of spermine and spermidine is low, seem to play a role in this transport. The rationale for following polyamine levels in red cells of patients with malignant brain tumors [10] is based on this mechanism.

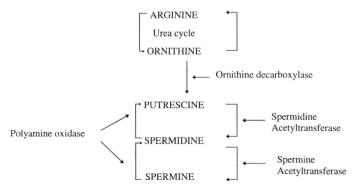

Fig. 1. Main metabolic pathways of polyamines.

The therapeutic approach based on polyamine metabolism aims to deplete tumor cells in putrescine. The first implementation of the understanding of polyamine metabolism was the administration of DFMO (difluoromethyl ornithine), a nontoxic, irreversible inhibitor of ornithine decarboxylase. Used alone the drug has no effect on tumor growth, presumably because putrescine may originate from spermidine by "retro-oxidation" or from an exogenous source. Thus DFMO should be combined with inhibitors of polyamine oxidase, such as N1-N4 bis allenylputrescine and putrescine analogues which will compete with the exogenous supply of the polyamine. Another interest of DFMO is the enhancement of BCNU cytotoxicity [11].

Growth factors and receptors

Growth factors and their receptors are involved in normal development. In cancer tissue, however, their expression may be excessive and untimely, and their structure sometimes abnormal. A number of studies have suggested that growth factors produced by tumor cells may play an important role in malignant transformation, and in apparently uncontrolled proliferation of neoplasia. Growth factors act, through corresponding receptors located on the cell membrane or inside the cell, in an autocrine fashion [13], stimulating cell division and motility (invasiveness) [14]. They may also change the environment by stimulating angiogenesis, which is absolutely essential for malignant growth, modifying the extracellular matrix, and normal glia. In malignant glioma the most extensively studied growth factors are the platelet-derived growth factor (PDGF), the epidermal growth factor (EGF), and their respective receptors [13–15]. PDGF is the product of c-sis gene located on chromosome 22. This 28–32 kD protein is a dimer. The AB form is produced by platelets, the AA or BB homodimers which may be produced by tumor cells also bind PDGF receptors [16]. PDGF appears as the mammalian-cell homologue of the transforming protein found in simian sarcoma virus (SSV). PDGF stimulates the proliferation of human glioma and presumably increases cell motility by inducing membrane budding containing actin [17]. Antibodies raised against PDGF decrease cell transformation by SSV.

Epidermal growth factor (EGF) is a small molecule of 6 kD. EGF coupled with ^{131}Iodine was capable of delivering, in a two-dimensional culture system, a dose of 250 cGy, of which 50% were specifically bound to EGF receptors [18]. Other radionuclides could be used for the same purpose, including ^{10}B. EGF receptor (EGFR) is a large 170-kD transmembrane protein coded by erb B located on chromosome 7. The density of EGFR has been estimated to about 2.10^5 receptors per cell. EGFR is also a ligand to transforming growth factor α. EGFR is amplified or/and mutated (most commonly truncation of extracellular domain) in approximately 40% of glioblastomas. This abnormality could represent a marker of primary glioblastoma. EGFR-antisense decreases cell growth but the effect of antibodies directed against EGFR, and the correlation with survival, are both uncertain. Berens et al. [19] have found that activation of EGFR stimulates cell motility more than proliferation.

The neoplastic activity of suramin, a drug used in the treatment of several neo-plasias including adrenocortical, prostatic and ovarian carcinomas is based, in part, on its ability to interfere with the binding of growth factors to their recep-tors. Suramin decreases neo-angiogenesis, and depresses tumor growth, but this activity does not seem to be mediated through PDGFR [20].

Drug resistance

Tumor resistance to chemotherapy may be present originally or acquired. In the case of malignant glioma, half of the patients will continue to progress when first treated with a single nitrosourea, thus showing an intrinsic (de novo) resistance. The other 50% will have some degree of initial response, either a stabilization (±30%) or an objective response (±20%); after which the tumor will progress despite treatment. This situation illustrates an acquired resistance. Drug resis-tance is a complex, probably multifactorial, situation. The clinically observed lack of response to chemotherapy may be related to pharmacodynamic or cellu-lar and molecular factors [21,22].

Pharmacodynamic factors

The role of BBB in the delivery of drugs to brain tumors has already been consid-ered. The fact that CNS offers a sanctuary to cells sensitive to hydrophilic drugs is best illustrated by the high rate of CNS relapses in acute leukemia before the generalization of prophylactic treatment.

Another important factor stressed by V. Levine is the large intercapillary dis-tance in brain tissue. Therefore drug concentration in areas equidistant from several capillaries may be insufficient even for agents which readily cross the BBB and have then to passively diffuse through brain parenchyma.

Cellular and molecular factors

The clinical observation that development of drug resistance may concern several agents functionally and structurally unrelated led to the identification of multi-drug resistance (MDR). MDR-1 gene is located on chromosome 17q21.1 and its product is P-glycoprotein (Pgp).

Pgp is believed to function as an ATP-energy dependent afflux pump, which lowers intracellular drug concentrations. MDR affects anthracyclines, vinca alka-loids, podophyllotoxins (VM-26 and VP-16), and taxus compounds (Taxol). But MDR does not affect, among others, nitrosoureas, procarbazine, and platinum derivatives (the most widely used agents in chemotherapy of malignant glioma). Therefore, MDR mechanism would not account for the resistance observed to these drugs in malignant gliomas where Pgp has been found to be expressed in only 5 to 25% of cases. Several agents are capable of reversing MDR, including

Ca^{2+} channel blockers, calmoduline, tamoxifen (used in treatment of brain glioma), or cyclosporine A. A therapeutic application of this inhibition was proposed by Takakura who reported a 60% rate of response to nimodipine followed by vincristine plus BNCU. Pgp is also found in vascular endothelial cells, especially in low-grade glioma [23]. These data suggest that Pgp may limit the efficacy of chemotherapy by affecting drug entry to the tumor at the BBB level.

A second mechanism of drug resistance which has been extensively studied in glioblastoma is the O_6 alkylguanine-DNA alkyl transferase (AGT). This enzyme repairs DNA cross-links formed by alkylating agents such as nitrosoureas or procarbazine. AGT is a "suicide" enzyme: it serves only once. Agents which deplete AGT increase the toxicity of nitrosoureas in originally resistant rat glioma cells [24]. A clinical application of this principle has prompted the use of procarbazine to deplete AGT, followed by BNCU administration. Unfortunately this combination is also more toxic.

Finally cell heterogeneity remains a major obstacle for the success of chemotherapy. Resistant recurrent tumor may well correspond to a selection of originally resistant clones. This selection has been elegantly demonstrated by J.R. Shapiro et al. who observed that glioblastoma initially sensitive to BCNU were largely polyploid, whereas recurrent resistant cells were predominantly nearly diploid [24].

References

1. Delattre J-Y, Posner JB. The blood-brain barrier: Morphology, physiology and its changes in cancer patients. In: Hildebrand J (ed) Neurological Adverse Reactions to Anticancer Drugs. Berlin: Springer-Verlag, 1990;3—24.
2. Brem H. Local therapy of brain tumors. Special issue of J Neuro Oncol 1995;26:89—158.
3. Stewart DJ, Grahovac Z, Benoit B et al. Intracarotid chemotherapy with combination of 1,3-bis (2-chloroethyl)-1-nitrosourea (BCNU), cis-diaminedichloroplatinum (cisplatin), and 4'-0-demethyl-1-0-(4,6-0-2-thertyliodeme-B-D-glucopyranosyl)epipodo-phyllotoxin (VM-26) in the treatment of primary and metastatic brain tumours. Neurosurgery 1984;15:828—833.
4. Mahaley MS, Whaley RA, Blue M, Bertsch L. Central neurotoxicity following intracarotid BCNU chemotherapy for malignant gliomas. J Neuro Oncol 1986;3:297—314.
5. Hildebrand J, Badjou R, Collard-Ronge A et al. Treatment of brain gliomas with high doses of CCNU and autologous marrow transplantation. Biomed 1980;32:71—75.
6. Phillips GL, Wolff SN, Fay JW et al. Intensive 1,3,-bis (2-chloroethyl)-1-nitrosourea (BCNU) monochemotherapy and autologous marrow transplantation for malignant glioma. J Clin Oncol 1986;4:639—645.
7. Cloughesy TF, Black KL. Pharmacological blood-brain barrier modification for selective drug delivery. J Neuro Oncol 1995;26:125—132.
8. Quemener V, Khan NA, Moulinoux JPh. Polyamines in cancer (Review). Cancer J 1990;3: 45—52.
9. Marton LJ, Edwards MS, Levin VA et al. CSF polyamines: a new and important means of monitoring patients with medulloblastoma. Cancer 1981;47:757—760.
10. Moulinoux JPh, Quemener V, Chatel M, Darcel F. Polyamines in human brain tumors: a correlation study between tumor, CSF, and red blood cell free polyamine levels. J Neuro Oncol 1984;4:174—180.
11. Levin VA, Prados MD, Yung WKA et al. Treatment of recurrent gliomas with effornithine. J Natl

Cancer Inst 1992;84:1432—1437.

12. Cavanaugh PF, Pavelic ZP, Porter CW. Enhancement of 1,3 bis (2-chloroethyl)-1-nitrosourea-induced cytotoxicity and DNA damage by difluoromethyl ornithine. Cancer Res 1984;44: 3856—3860.

13. Sporn MB, Roberts AB. Autocrine growth factors and cancer. Nature 1985;331:745—747.

14. Westermark B, Magnusson A, Heldin CH. Effect of epidermal growth factor on membrane motility and cell locomotor in cultures of human clonal glial cells. J Neurosci Res 1982;8: 491—507.

15. Karatsu J, Estes JE, Yokota S et al. Growth factors derived from a human malignant glioma cell like U-251MG. J Neuro Oncol 1989;7:225—236.

16. Escobedo JA, Navankasatussas S, Cousens LS et al. A common PDGF receptor activated by homodimeric A and B forms of PDGF. Science 1988;240:1532—1534.

17. Nakamura T, Takeshita I, Fukui M. Glioma-derived PDGF-related protein presents as 17 kD intracellularly and assembled form induces actin reorganization. J Neuro Oncol 1991;11: 215—224.

18. Capala J, Prahl M, Scott-Robson S et al. Effect of ^{131}I-EGF on cultured human glioma cells. J Neuro Oncol 1990;9:201—210.

19. Berens ME, Rief MO, Shapiro JR et al. Proliferation and motility responses of primary and recurrent glioma related to changes in epidermal growth factor expression. J Neuro Oncol 1996;27:11—22.

20. Westphal M, Ackermann E, Hoppe J, Herrmann HD. Receptors for platelet derived growth factor in human glioma cell lines and influence of suramin on cell proliferation. J Neuro Oncol 1991;11:207—213.

21. Lehnert M. Multidrug resistance in human cancer. J Neuro Oncol 1994;22:239—243.

22. Feun L, Savaraj N, Landy HJ. Drug resistance in brain tumors. J Neuro Oncol 1994;20: 165—176.

23. Henson JW, Cordon-Cardo C, Posner JB. P-glycoprotein expression in brain tumors. J Neuro Oncol 1992;14:37—43.

24. Hotta T, Saito Y, Mikami T et al. Interrelation between O^6-alkylguanine-DNA alkyltransferase activity and susceptibility to chloroethylnitrosoureas in several glioma cell lines. J Neuro Oncol 1993;17:1—8.

25. Shapiro JR, Ebrahim SAD, Mohamed AN et al. BCNU-sensitivity in parental cells clones from four freshly resected near-diploid human glioma: an astrocytoma, an anaplastic astrocytoma and two glioblastomas multiforme. J Neuro Oncol 1993;15:209—234.

© 1997 Elsevier Science B.V. All rights reserved.
Advances in Neutron Capture Therapy.
Volume I, Medicine and Physics.
B. Larsson, J. Crawford and R. Weinreich, editors.

Melanoma and nonmelanoma neutron capture therapy using gene therapy: overview

Yutaka Mishima

Mishima Institute for Dermatological Research, Kobe, Japan

Keywords: ^{10}B-BPA uptake within the subcellular compartments of melanoma cells, ^{10}B-BPA NCT for nonmelanoma cancers, ^{10}B-BPA affinity to melanoma, ^{10}B-BPA/melanin monomer complex, ^{10}B-BPA melanoma NCT, application of gene therapy to boron neutron capture therapy (BNCT), BNCT for lentigo malignant melanoma, evaluation of human melanoma patients with TNM classification, gBNCT, high affinity of ^{10}B-BPA to malignant melanoma, induction of melanogenesis in nonpigment cells by the transfection of genes, melanogenic gene-transfected nonmelanoma cancer cells, melanoma, nodular melanoma, nonmelanoma neutron capture therapy using gene therapy, therapeutic efficacy of ^{10}B-BPA NCT.

Introduction

Since 1972 we have developed melanoma boron neutron capture therapy (BNCT) (different from glioblastoma BNCT which utilizes the reduction of the blood-brain barrier at the site of the brain tumor) based on the specific affinity of ^{10}B-compounds toward the accentuated metabolic activity in target cancer cells. Malignant melanoma, a cancer of pigment cells, generally possesses accentuated melanogenesis and is thus a perfect prototype for such a new type of cancer BNCT. Since cancer-seeking ^{10}B compounds are used we can selectively eradicate even those target cells invading unobservable subclinical satellite metastasis by the ^{10}B(n,α)Li^7 reaction together with the primary lesion.

This plenary presentation includes the following three major aspects of our current work:

1) A concise up-to-date evaluation of our 18 BNCT-treated human melanoma patients as to therapeutic efficacy based on the Union Internationale Contre le Cancer (UICC) TNM classification.
2) Newly found mechanisms for specific affinity of ^{10}B-p-boronophenylalanine (^{10}B-BPA) to malignant melanoma: chemical complex formation of ^{10}B-BPA with melanin monomers, rich in melanoma cells.
3) Induction of the formation of melanin monomers and polymers in nonmelanoma cells by the transfection of melanogenic genes, leading to a broader application of ^{10}B-BPA NCT with the application of rapidly developing gene therapy.

Address for correspondence: Yutaka Mishima MD, PhD, Mishima Institute for Dermatological Research, 1-4-32 Sowa-cho, Nada-ku, Kobe 657, Japan.

¹⁰B-BPA melanoma NCT

Basic principles

Pigment cells undergo clinically and biologically recognizable progressive multi-step focal carcinogenesis. Generally parallel to this progressive cancerization is increased melanogenesis [1]. This can clearly be seen in most fully developed human melanoma lesions; in the early steps as peripheral light-brown maculae, in the next step as infiltrating brownish-black precancerous plaque and in the final stage, the deeply invading black melanoma nodule with ulceration at the center.

Incubation of melanoma sections with dopa reveals the greatly accentuated ability of melanoma to pick up large amounts of dopa and convert it to deep black dopa melanin. This conversion was until recently believed to be controlled by the single enzyme tyrosinase, as described by Raper-Mason [2].

However, we have now found that three major enzymes control melanogenesis (Fig. 1). In addition to tyrosinase, dopachrome tautomerase (TRP2: tyrosinase-related protein 2) and 5,6-dihydroxyindole-2-carboxylic acid, DHICA-oxidase (TRP1) also regulate the formation of melanin monomers, which are then the base for polymers. As discussed later, we now have transfectable genes for all of these three enzymes by which we have been successfully inducing melanogenesis in nonmelanoma cells.

Dopachrome tautomerase can form the key melanin monomer DHICA from dopachrome. Another melanin monomer, dihydroxyindole, DHI, is also produced from dopachrome and further to melanin polymer by tyrosinase. With these two monomers, ¹⁰B-BPA has been found to form chemical complexes within melanoma cells, thus exhibiting these monomers' affinity to melanoma.

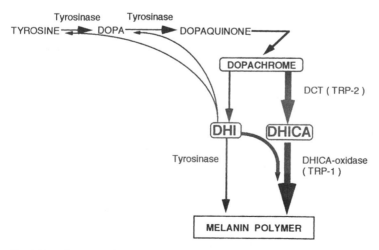

Fig. 1. Regulatory pathway to melanin polymer biosynthesis.

12

High affinity of ^{10}B-BPA to malignant melanoma

Meanwhile, we synthesized various derivatives of the melanin precursor, ^{10}B-labeled dopa analogues. First we synthesized ^{10}B-para-boronophenylalanine (^{10}B-BPA) of hydrochloric derivatives. At the First Symposium held at M.I.T. in 1983, we reported that ^{10}B-BPA can deliver ^{10}B selectively into melanomas sufficient for successful BNCT. Since then, Drs Yoshino and Kakihana of our team have synthesized the ^{10}B-BPA-fructose complex, which is more water soluble at neutral pH [3].

Parallel with this, together with Drs Honda, Hiratsuka, Wadabayashi and others, we extensively analyzed the selective uptake and retention of ^{10}B-BPA by melanoma [4]. The oral administration of ^{10}B-BPA•HCl also shows excellent selective uptake by melanoma as compared to normal skin. After multiple injections of ^{10}B-BPA•fructose complex, the absolute amount of ^{10}B concentration in melanoma further increased in a stepwise manner, keeping the desirable melanoma-to-skin as well as melanoma-to-blood ratios (Fig. 2) as compared to normal skin.

^{10}B-BPA also exhibits the highly selective uptake of this compound by melanoma compared to other organs and tissue such as liver and substantia nigra.

Selective uptake of ^{10}B-BPA by melanoma is generally parallel to its synthetic

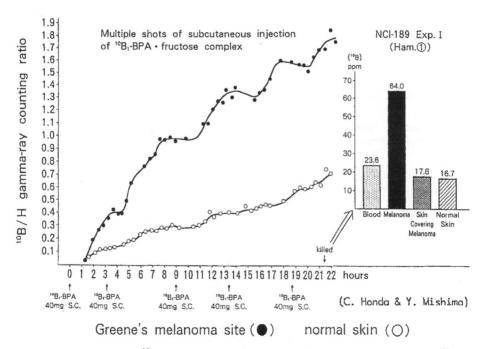

Fig. 2. In vivo dynamics of ^{10}B concentration following multiple subcutaneous injection of ^{10}B-BPA in Greene's melanoma-bearing hamsters.

activity of melanin monomer and polymer. Melanotic cells accumulate twice the boron as compared to amelanotic [5]. In 1987, Dr Coderre [6] also reported similar high uptake of ^{10}B in Harding Passey melanoma in comparison with various organs of mice, but not in adenocarcinoma.

After safety confirmation of ^{10}B-BPA with acute and subacute toxicity tests, we investigated the dynamics of ^{10}B in melanoma patients who underwent surgical treatment. Again, good selective differential uptake of ^{10}B in melanoma as compared to skin and blood can be seen [7].

Analysis of our accumulated data with Prof Fukuda and other colleagues seemed to indicate that ^{10}B in melanoma and ^{10}B in skin can be estimated in general by multiplying ^{10}B ppm value in blood by factors of 3.0 and 1.2, respectively. ^{10}B concentration in blood was continually measured and maintained by drip infusion in the range of 6.0 ppm or 6.0 mg/g [8].

Therapeutic efficacy of ^{10}B-BPA NCT

Concerning the effectiveness of our BNCT for melanoma, I will limit myself to two representative cases. Then, I will give a 1996 summary and analysis of the clinical results attained from our 18 cases based on the UICC TNM classification [9].

BNCT for lentigo malignant melanoma

The application of BNCT for the treatment of melanoma on the face required accumulated therapeutic experience and data. Lentigo malignant melanoma occurs most frequently on the sun-exposed facial region. Therapeutic procedure on a case of lentigo malignant melanoma, $T_3N_0M_0$, occurring on the face of a 64-year-old housewife is briefly described. The ^{10}B kinetics in blood and skin at the time of BNCT were measured and provided presumed ^{10}B concentration in the target lesion according to our formula [7]. The lesion was irradiated for 84 min at 5 MW. The clinical appearance of the widespread lesion is shown before (Fig. 3A) and after (Fig. 3B) treatment. Thermal neutrons were given at 0.8×10^{13} nvt with minimum exposure to other parts of the body (Fig. 3C). These figures clearly show not only the extent to which this patient was cured, but also her joy. It has been over 5 years and no recurrence has been observed.

Nodular melanoma

The worst form of human melanoma is nodular melanoma, two primary lesions $(T_4N_0M_0)$ of which we have successfully treated with complete disappearance without recurrence or metastasis (Table 1A). One of these was on the outer heel of an 85-year-old woman who could not undergo surgery due to heart disease. Marked regression of this melanoma was achieved 4.5 months after BNCT in which we irradiated the deeply invading tumor for 210 min at 5 MW with result-

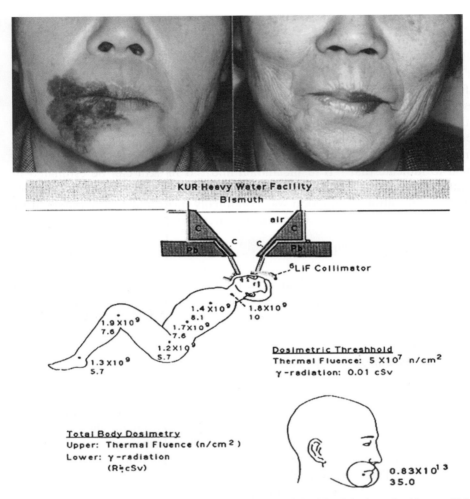

Fig. 3. **A:** Lentigo malignant melanoma occurring on the right side of the face of a 66-year-old female before treatment. **B:** Twenty months after single NCT leading to complete regression. **C:** Collimation and dosimetry of this NCT.

ing fluence of 1.2×10^{13} nvt following administration of 170 mg/kg BW ^{10}B-BPA•fructose complex. At 6.5 months after BNCT, we achieved complete regression of this melanoma. The remaining light bluish macule exhibited at this point was caused by phagocytized melanin tattooing. It has been 7.5 years since treatment and this patient has shown no recurrence to date.

Evaluation of our 18 human melanoma patients with TNM classification

An update and evaluation of our clinical cases treated by BPA•NCT can be seen

Table 1. Clinical results of human melanoma cases treated by our NCT method based on TNM classification as of January 1996.

A.

T_{3-4}, N_0, M_0	Age, sex (initial), region	Irradiation date	Treated Mm	Survival	Classification
I. ALM	80, M (N.O.) Right sole	4/7/88	cured	3 years, 20 months (death from old age)	$T_3\,N_0\,M_0$
	50, M (Y.W.) Right thumb	4/13/89 6/30/89	regressed eradicated	3 years, 7 months (brain cancer, unknown nature)	$T_4\,N_0\,M_0$
	79, M (F.M.) Left sole	10/23/89	cured	living > 6 years	$T_4\,N_0\,M_0$
	51, F (T.N.) Left sole	7/13/92	cured	living > 3.5 years	$T_3\,N_0\,M_0$
	70, M (T.I.) Left sole	7/13/93 11/2/93	regressed eradicated	living > 2.5 years	$T_3\,N_0\,M_0$
	58, F (H.A.) Right 5th finger	11/22/94	cured	living > 1 year	$T_3\,N_0\,M_0$
II. Nodular	85, F (N.N.) Left foot	6/30/88	cured	living > 7.5 years	$T_4\,N_0\,M_0$
	59, F (F.K.) Right sole	6/29/89	cured	2 years 2 months (ovarium cancer)	$T_4\,N_0\,M_0$
III. LMM	64, F (S.S.) Right face	6/10/91	cured	living > 4.5 years	$T_3\,N_0\,M_0$
	48, M (T.M.) Right face	9/14/93	cured	living > 2 years	$T_2\,N_0\,M_0$
	84, F (K.M.) Right cheek	12/12/94	cured	living > 1 year	$T_3\,N_0\,M_0$

B.

T_{3-4}, N_{1-2}, M_1	Age, sex (initial), region	Irradiation date	Treated Mm	Survival	Classification
I. ALM	66, M (T.Y.) Occiput	7/11/87	cured	10 months	$T_4\,N_2\,M_1$
	75, M (K.I.) Right heel, lymphnode	11/11/91	regressed	2 years, 2 months	$T_4\,N_2\,M_1$
II. Nodular	74, F (K.Ka.) Right leg	3/2/88	suppressed	1 year, 6 months	$T_4\,N_2\,M_1$
	61, M (K.Ko.) Scalp	10/5/89 2/13/90	suppressed suppressed	1 year, 3 months	$T_4\,N_2\,M_1$
	57, M (Y.A.) Left sole	11/19/90	regressed	1 year, 1 month	$T_4\,N_2\,M_1$
	67, F (T.Ot.) Right sole	6/7/94 9/13/94	regressed	1 year	$T_4\,N_2\,M_1$
	77, F (T.On.) Left sole	7/19/94	regressed	living > 1.5 years	$T_4\,N_2\,M_0$
II. LMM	—				

in Table 1. We started in July 1987, thus the longest case has been observed for 9 years. Clinical zonal analysis should be based on types of melanoma and degree of disease advancement. We have treated three major types of melanoma and they are evaluated here based on the UICC TNM classification for disease advancement [9]. The TNM classifies the degree of invasion of primary melanoma as well as lymph node and distant metastasis. The T number represents the level of invasion in tissue; T_3 invading down through the dermis and T_4 is the deepest invasion into fatty tissue. N number represents regional metastasis to lymph nodes while M number indicates distant metastasis to areas such as lung or brain.

Table 1 shows the clinical results for the 11 $T_{3-4}N_0M_0$ patients analyzed. From this summary, although the number of cases is still not great and the observation period is still rather short, it can so far be deduced that BNCT can produce a high rate of "cure" and "survival" in more than 90% of melanoma cases at this level of progression. However, BNCT for melanoma already advanced to $N_{1-2}M_1$ status shows much less efficacy, as expected (Table 1B). Overall survival rate, regardless of TNM stage, for cases observed 2 or more years is 78%.

Mechanisms of ^{10}B-BPA affinity to melanoma and its chemical complex formation with melanin monomers

We have recently found that in malignant melanoma ^{10}B-BPA forms chemical complexes with melanin monomers which are precursors of melanin polymers and are rich in these target cells. These findings show that the complex formation plays a critical role in the uptake and retention of ^{10}B-BPA in melanoma, and has provided us with a starting point for the development of gene-therapy-applied BNCT.

Dynamics of ^{10}B-BPA uptake within the subcellular compartments of melanoma cells

As previously reported [7], we are utilizing ^{10}B-BPA as ^{10}B-labeled dopa analogue though its detailed mechanism for specific affinity toward melanoma has not yet been fully elucidated.

Malignant melanoma principally shows high uptake of dopa, which is metabolized by tyrosinase and which is rich in melanoma cells. However, we soon found that in vitro, tyrosinase cannot utilize ^{10}B-BPA as its enzyme substrate in spite of its high affinity, uptake and retention in malignant melanoma in vivo. Therefore, we have been investigating the mechanisms of this compound's high affinity to malignant melanoma.

We have studied the possible chemical complex formation of ^{10}B-BPA with dopa and melanin monomers which are actively synthesized within melanoma cells.

In 1994, Yoshino of our group found that ^{10}B-BPA can form a chemical complex with dopa [10]. However, we thought that there should be some further mechanisms underlying BPA's affinity to melanoma associated with the highly occurring melanin monomers, DHICA and DHI, in melanoma cells. As previously shown, melanoma strongly picks up dopa and synthesizes dopa melanin. Under the electron microscope, we can see dopa melanin is accumulated within not only the melanin granules, called melanosomes and premelanosomes, but also the Golgi-associated endoplasmic reticulum called GERL and coated vesicles.

In pigment cells in general, melanogenic enzymes, including tyrosinase, are initially formed in the ribosome of endoplasmic reticulum and gradually transferred into the Golgi complex, where these enzymes receive their glycolyzation and become a mature form while passing through the tubular GERL. Then, these maturated enzymes bud off from the tip of GERL, forming small coated vesicles. These vesicles are well-known as a substance transporting system within the cells. Then, these coated vesicles are fused to the target organelle, melanin granule, called premelanosomes and melanosomes, thus transporting the enzyme tyrosinase into the premelanosome. Recently, however, we found that the melanin monomers called DHI and DHICA are already, by this time, highly formed within coated vesicles. Together with tyrosinase, these monomers are transported into the melanin granule [11]. We then investigated where injected ^{10}B-BPA is initially taken up in melanoma cells. We have isolated coated vesicles by the sucrose density gradient method. These coated vesicles within melanoma cells are now found to indeed be rich in melanin monomers [12].

Dr Shiono and I then pursued an assay of kinetics of ^{10}B-BPA hours after injection into melanoma-bearing hamsters [13]. ^{10}B-BPA is first highly concentrated and taken up in the coated vesicles and then, after 6 or 7 h gradually moved into premelanosomes and melanosomes (Fig. 4).

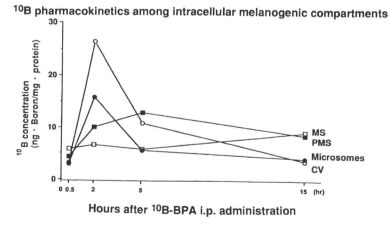

Fig. 4. ^{10}B-BPA found first to highly concentrate within the coated vesicles (CV) and later within premelanosomes (PMS) and melanosomes (MS) in malignant melanoma cells.

In vitro and in vivo evidence for ^{10}B-BPA/melanin monomer complex

The above findings advanced our theoretical prediction for BPA affinity to melanoma to a deeper working hypothesis. BPA must form a chemical complex with the melanin polymer precursors, melanin monomers (Fig. 1). Indeed, NMR after in vitro incubation of BPA with DHICA or DHI revealed how a sharp peak is formed (Fig. 5A). Detailed findings can also be found elsewhere in this volume [14].

Yoshino and I then proceeded to undertake in vivo studies. We injected 20 mg ^{10}B-BPA•HCl into melanoma-bearing hamsters and 2 h later melanoma was removed for NMR study. Similar to in vitro studies, we have indeed found that dihydroxy groups attached to benzene ring of dopa, DHICA and DHI do form a chemical complex with BPA in melanoma (Fig. 5B). Seventy-five percent of BPA was detected as chemical complex of BPA-DHI, BPA-DHICA and BPA-dopa, while only 25% of BPA was detected as free compound in melanoma cells. Presumed chemical structure of these BPA monomer complexes are shown in Fig. 5C. It has become clear that the increased affinity of ^{10}B-BPA toward malignant melanoma is due to the increased production of dopa and melanin monomers in these cells. We are now investigating other substances having a dihydroxy group attached to the benzene ring which can also form chemical complex with ^{10}B-BPA and provide a baseline affinity for melanoma and other cells.

Application of ^{10}B-BPA NCT for nonmelanoma cancers

Fortunately, now we have the genes to induce these melanin monomer synthesizing enzymes and tyrosinase within gene-transfected cells. These chemical findings and the availability of these genes led us to investigate the applicability of ^{10}B-BPA NCT for nonmelanoma cancers. We have, with H. Kondo of my institute, carried out transfection of genes to induce the formation of melanin monomers and polymer in fibroblasts and fibrosarcoma cells.

Induction of melanogenesis in nonpigment cells by the transfection of genes

L-929 mouse fibroblasts have been transfected with Prof Shibahara's tyrosinase cDNA and electroporation method, resulting in the induction of pigmented fibroblasts, named LHT2 cells. Figure 6 shows pellets of parental L-929 and induced pigmented transformant LHT2. Figure 7 is a light micrograph demonstrating parental nonpigmented cells on the left, and dopa-melanin producing transfected cells following dopa reaction on the right, indicating the presence of induced active tyrosinase. Electron microscopic examination of these dopa-positive transfected cells further show the induction of melanogenic activity even in tubular GERL and coated vesicles in addition to premelanosomes.

From our latest concept of melanogenesis, we know first, that by the action of tyrosinase on tyrosine and dopa, dopaquinone is formed followed by the non-

A

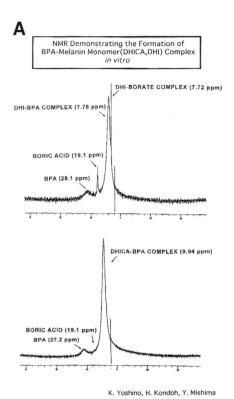

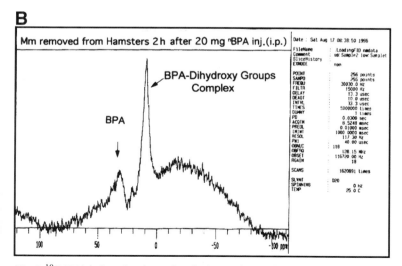

Fig. 5. ¹⁰B-BPA is found to form chemical complexes with melanin monomers in vitro (**A**) as well as in vivo (**B**) by NMR studies [14]. Presumed chemical structure of BPA/melanin monomer complexes are also shown (**C**, *next page*).

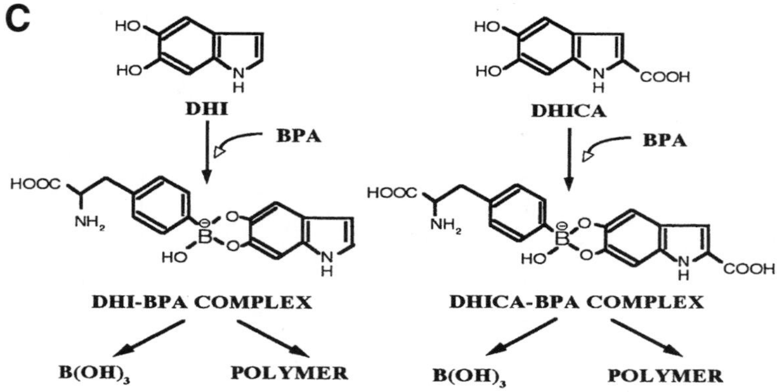

C

DHI

DHICA

BPA

BPA

DHI-BPA COMPLEX

DHICA-BPA COMPLEX

B(OH)₃   POLYMER

B(OH)₃   POLYMER

Fig. 5. **C.**

enzymic formation of dopachrome. To further proceed to form melanin mono-mer, DHICA, another enzyme, dopachrome tautomerase, DCT, is necessary. This enzyme is formed by the action of the TRP-2 gene (Fig. 1). By producing higher amounts of DHICA, we improve our chances of attracting a higher amount of ^{10}B-BPA into the BNCT target cells.

The induction of dopachrome tautamerase can produce DHICA synthesis in fibroblasts. We have found the kinetics of DHICA synthesis to be 31.4 pmol/h/mg protein. For our double transfection of tyrosinase and TRP-2 gene vectors, we first transfected a TRP-2 gene into a fibroblast and further transfected a tyro-sinase gene into the same cells. As a consequence, these double transfections into fibroblasts show significant increase in total melanin within these cells as compared to those with tyrosinase gene alone.

Conversion of amelanotic to melanotic melanoma by gene transfection

Melanogenic gene transfections may have another useful advantage. The conver-sion of amelanotic to melanotic melanoma cells by tyrosinase cDNA transfection

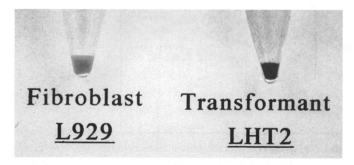

Fig. 6. Melanin polymer formation is induced in tyrosinase-transfected fibroblasts.

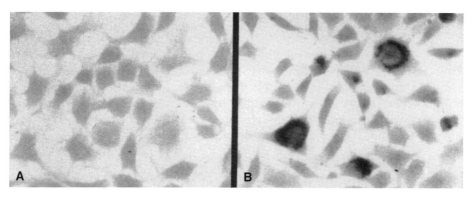

Fig. 7. Parental nonpigmented fibroblasts (**A**) acquire melanin synthesizing ability (**B**) after tyrosinase gene transfection. Light microscopic dopa reaction at × 175 magnification.

[5] enhances the killing effect of BPA NCT. After tyrosinase gene transfection, human amelanotic melanoma cells were converted to dark brown melanotic melanoma. Eumelanin as well as pheomelanin in amelanotic melanoma after transfection have been markedly increased.

Future direction of gBNCT

We are now investigating the application of gene therapy [15−17] to our BNCT to attack our next foe, nonmelanoma cancers. After in vitro radiobiological and therapeutic evaluations of ^{10}B-BPA NCT effectiveness on nonmelanoma cancer cells which have been transfected with tyrosinase and TRP-2 genes, we would like to proceed to explore the application of a modified current gene therapy in vivo using our ^{10}B-BPA NCT. We now refer to this as gBNCT.

Among current strategies employed in gene therapy for solid cancers, one modality utilizes the transfection of "suicide genes" into cancer cells. This gene induces, for example, cytosine diaminase which converts prodrug 5FC to active anticancer drug 5FU. Another strategy employs an immunological modality to transfect genes which induce cytokines such as IL-2, IL-4 and TNF into cancer cells. IL-2 which, for example, induces proliferation of T-lymphocytes, are used as a tumor vaccine.

Prodrug such as Tegafur, used in suicide gene chemotherapy, only become active 5FU after general conversion in the liver, thus producing unavoidable side effects in current chemotherapy. In contrast, suicide gene therapy utilizes cytosine diaminase-inducing genes which can give cancer cells instead of liver cells the ability to convert 5FC to 5FU, thus minimizing side effects.

In cancer gene therapy, specific delivery of genes into cancer only is crucial for success. One promising modality is to conjugate genes with antitumor antibodies. Another critical step is to induce gene expression specifically in the target cancer tissue. For this purpose, therapeutic genes can be ligated with cancer tissue-specific promoters.

First among noted critical factors for the success of cancer gene therapy is the fact that a certain number of neighboring nontransfected bystander cells are known to be also affected. Next, in vivo studies need a high level of efficiency of gene transfer among target cancer cells. The third point is the extent to which transferred genes persist after transfection, thus often using retroviral gene vectors which can be inserted and subsequently taken up in the chromosome and synchronized to the target cell division. Finally, gBNCT adds another dimension to the specificity of current cancer gene therapy, by three controllable factors which are noted below.

Figure 8 schematically illustrates our planned gBNCT. First, the melanogenic genes are inserted into the DNA of virus, which is used as a carrier vector. These vectors have molecules such as antibody or ligands that bind only to target cancer cells, thus making possible indirect gene transfer as opposed to direct injection into target cancer.

Second, such vectors are injected into the blood stream and they seek out and bind to tumor cells, unloading their genetic material (Fig. 8A).

The transfected vectors with melanogenic genes begin to express within the target cancer cell and produce melanin monomers, which attract administered ^{10}B-BPA by their ability to form a chemical complex. Then a thermal neutron beam is applied to the melanogenic gene-transfected nonmelanoma cancer cells, thus eradicating them selectively (Fig. 8B).

Figure 9 lists the unique features of our gBNCT. Different from current cancer gene therapy, in which we only have one steering handle such as dosage of pro-drug, so in gBNCT we have three major controllable handles, namely the dosage of ^{10}B-BPA, neutron flux and beam collimation. The strength of this modality lies first in the fact that you can measure the uptake of ^{10}B in target cancer by in situ prompt γ method [7] and/or ^{18}F-^{10}B-BPA positron emission tomography [18]. Then, you can determine optimal dosage of thermal and/or epithermal neutron and adjust collimation based on the extent of proliferating cancer.

One further strength of gBNCT is the difference in the cancer killing step. Current cancer gene therapy employs only available anticancer methodology such as chemotherapy and immunotherapy, whose general limitations are known. In contrast, our gBNCT employs ^{10}B-mediated specific and powerful killing effect with selective targeting by usage of melanin monomer-seeking ^{10}B-BPA and thermal neutrons which are themselves harmless. Induced α particles and ^{7}Li atoms, as heavy particles, kill cancer cells beyond DNA repairability concentrating within distances of 9 and 5 microns, respectively from activated boron atoms [7,19,20].

It was 1972 when the idea occurred to me that by using accentuated melano-genesis in malignant melanoma cells and ^{10}B(n, α)^{7}Li reaction, we could eradicate melanoma selectively. I have the same enthusiasm that I embraced almost a quarter of a century ago. My vision for gBNCT will hopefully add a new dimension to BNCT research to a wider spectrum of human cancer by the borderless 21st century. I here would like to express my appreciation to Prof B. Larsson,

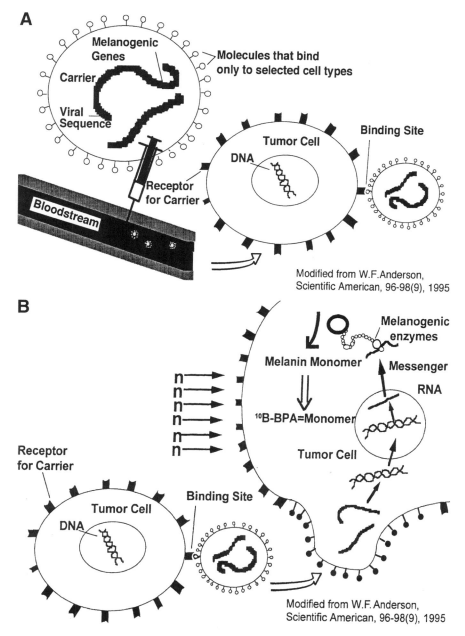

A

Melanogenic Genes

Molecules that bind only to selected cell types

Carrier

Viral Sequence

Binding Site

Tumor Cell

DNA

Bloodstream

Receptor for Carrier

Modified from W.F. Anderson,
Scientific American, 96-98(9), 1995

B

Melanogenic enzymes

Melanin Monomer

Messenger

RNA

$n \rightarrow$
$n \rightarrow$
$n \rightarrow$
$n \rightarrow$
$n \rightarrow$
$n \rightarrow$

^{10}B-BPA=Monomer

Tumor Cell

Receptor for Carrier

Binding Site

Tumor Cell

DNA

Modified from W.F. Anderson,
Scientific American, 96-98(9), 1995

Fig. 8. Schematic representation of our invisioned gBNCT with ^{10}B-BPA for nonmelanoma cancers.

President of ISNCT, for giving me the opportunity to deliver this Plenary Lecture and hope the young members of our society will synchronize their efforts at the global level to succeed in the greatest cultural venture to conquer human cancers.

24

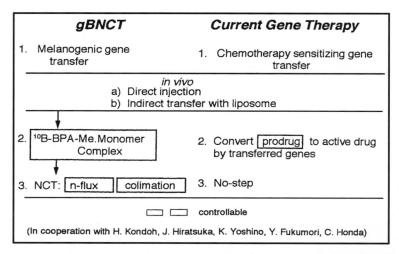

Fig. 9. Unique features of our gBNCT in comparison with current cancer gene therapy.

Acknowledgements

I would like to thank my many collaborators who have helped bring about the level of advancement that we have been able to achieve. Especially, I would like to name H. Fukuda and J. Hiratsuka (radiologists); K. Yoshino, H. Kakihana and T. Nakagawa (chemists); C. Honda, N. Wadabayashi, M. Shiono, and M. Ichihashi (dermatologists); H. Obara and J. Shirakawa (anesthesiologists); H. Karashima (health physicist); T. Kobayashi, T. Nozaki, O. Aizawa, T. Sato and K. Kanda (nuclear physicists). I also acknowledge the help of B. Jones in preparing this manuscript.

References

1. Mishima Y, Nakanishi T. Acral lentiginous melanoma and its precursor; Heterogenity of palmoplantar melanomas. Pathology 1985;17:258−265.
2. Mason HS. The chemistry of melanin. III. Mechanism of the oxidation of dihydroxyphenylalanine by tyrosinase. J Biol Chem 1948;172:83−92.
3. Yoshino K, Kakihana H, Mori Y, Torii N, Takehashi H, Mishima Y. Proposed mechanism of capture and release of p-boronophenylalanine in melanoma cells: Chemical behavior of p-boronophenylalanine-fructose complex in L-dopa solution. In: Soloway AH, Barth RF, Carpenter DE (eds) Neutron Capture Therapy. New York: Plenum Press, 1993;253−256.
4. Honda C, Shiono M, Wadabayashi N, Ichihashi M, Mishima Y, Kobayashi T, Kanda K, Hori Y, Yoshino K. Increased selective ^{10}B-uptake by malignant melanoma using systemic administration of ^{10}B$_1$-BPA-fructose complex. In: Allen BJ, Moore DE, Harrington BV (eds) Progress in Neutron Capture Therapy for Cancer. New York: Plenum Press, 1992;421−424.
5. Ando A, Mishima Y, Hanada S, Suemoto Y, Atobe J, Kurimoto M. Analyses of mixed melanogenesis in tyrosinase cDNA-transfected human amelanotic melanoma cells. J Invest Dermatol 1993;101:864−870.

6. Coderre JA, Bergland R, Chadha M, Chanana AD, Elowitz E, Joel DD, Liu HB, Slatkin DN, Wielopolski L. Boron neutron capture therapy of glioblastoma multiforme using the p-borono-phenylalanine-fructose complex and epithermal neutrons. In: Mishima Y (ed) Cancer Neutron Capture Therapy. New York: Plenum Press, 1996;553−561.
7. Mishima Y. Selective thermal neutron capture therapy of cancer cells using their specific metabolic activities — melanoma as prototype. In: Mishima Y (ed) Cancer Neutron Capture Therapy. New York: Plenum Press, 1996;1−26.
8. Fukuda H, Mishima Y, Hiratsuka J, Honda C, Wadabayashi N, Kobayashi T, Yoshino K, Karashima H, Takahashi J, Abe Y, Kanda K, Ichihashi M. BNCT of malignant melanoma — radiobiological analysis and data comparison with conventional radiotherapy. In: Mishima Y (ed) Cancer Neutron Capture Therapy. New York: Plenum Press, 1996;663−671.
9. Spiessl B, Beahrs OH, Harmanek P, Hutter RVP, Scheibe O, Sobin LH, Wagner G (eds) TNM Atlas — Illustrated Guide to the TNM/pTNM Classification of Malignant Tumours. New York: Springer-Verlag, 1990;163−172.
10. Yoshino K, Mori Y, Kakihana H, Takahashi H, Mishima Y, Ichihashi M. Chemical modeling with p-boronophenylalanine for boron accumulation to and release from melanoma. In: Mishima Y (ed) Cancer Neutron Capture Therapy. New York: Plenum Press, 1996;81−90.
11. Mishima Y. Molecular and biological control of melanogenesis through tyrosinase genes, and intrinsic and extrinsic regulatory factors. Pigment Cell Res 1994;7:376−387.
12. Hatta S, Mishima Y. Melanin monomers within coated vesicles and premelanosomes in melanin synthesizing cells. J Invest Dermatol 1988;91:181−184.
13. Shiono M, Shibata T, Ichihashi M, Mishima Y. The mechanism of the selective affinity of $^{10}B_1$-p-boronophenylalanine for malignant melanoma. Med J Kobe Univ 1992;53:35−41.
14. Yoshino K, Mishima Y, Kimura M, Hiratsuka J, Mori Y, Ito S, Kakihana H. Capture of p-boronophenylalanine in malignant melanoma cells by complex formation with melanin monomers, DOPA, DHI and DHICA. In: Larsson B, Crawford J, Weinreich R (eds) Advances in Neutron Capture Therapy. Volume 2, Chemistry and Biology. Amsterdam: Elsevier Science, 1997; 234−238 (these proceedings).
15. Zhu N, Liggitt D, Liu Y, Debs R. Systemic gene expression after intravenous DNA delivery in adult mice. Science 1993;261:209−211.
16. Mroz P, Moolten F. Retrovirally transducted *Escherichia coli* GPT genes combine selectablity with chemosensitivity capable of mediating tumor eradication. Hum Gene Ther 1993;4:589−595.
17. Vile R, Hart I. Use of tissue-specific expression of the herpes simplex virus thymidine kinase gene to inhibit growth of established murine melanomas following direct intratumoral murine melanomas following direct intratumoral injection of DNA. Cancer Res 1993;53:3860−3864.
18. Mishima Y, Imahori Y, Honda C, Hiratsuka J, Ueda S, Ido T. *In vivo* diagnosis of human malignant melanoma with positron emission tomography using specific melanoma-seeking ^{18}F-dopa analogue. J Neuro Oncol 1997;(In press).
19. Hiratsuka J, Kono M, Mishima Y. RBEs of thermal neutron capture therapy and $^{10}B(n,\alpha)^7Li$ reaction of melanoma-bearing hamsters. Pigment Cell Res 1989;2:352−355.
20. Mishima Y, Honda C, Ichihashi M, Obara H, Hiratsuka J, Fukuda H, Karashima H, Kobayashi T, Kanda K, Yoshino K. Treatment of malignant melanoma by single neutron capture treatment with melanoma-seeking ^{10}B-compound. Lancet 1989;II:388−389.

Neutron capture therapy 1996

Heinz Fankhauser

Department of Neurosurgery, Centre Hospitalier Universitaire Vaudois and Clinic Cecil, Lausanne, Switzerland

Introduction

What is probably most striking about boron neutron capture therapy (BNCT) is that it has been almost exactly 60 years since the first publication, but it has remained almost exclusively a research activity in the field of reactors, chemistry, pharmacology and biology. This is once more reflected in the content of this symposium. Out of a total of 268 abstracts, only 36 concern clinical work, which means work implying humans. Basic and preclinical BNCT research is certainly most interesting for ourselves and for healthy people, but the sick patient is not really interested in research; he seeks urgent available therapy. What is important for him is to know whether he can be accepted for treatment somewhere. I therefore collected information which may acutely interest the brain tumor patient, his family, and his physician, and I will summarize the clinical application of BNCT worldwide in 1996.

The discovery of a brain tumor is usually very bad news, as the doctor will have to tell his patient at some point, whatever treatment is applied. Nevertheless, the standard management for this condition will usually be prescribed, which is gross surgical resection, confirmation of the histological diagnosis and conventional radiation therapy. Some centers, especially in the USA would add chemotherapy. The prognosis, of course, remains very bad and is usually lethal. An exceptional patient or his family will not accept the terrible verdict. He will start to search across the world, to find out whether there is something special or new which offers a better chance to treat his cancer. Understandably, he seeks cure rather than just extension of life span. He will come across many new things and unavoidably he will learn about humans treated with BNCT since 1952. What will this brain tumor patient encounter if, in September 1996 he collects information on clinical BNCT and on his chances to be treated by this modality anywhere in the world? The best picture of what is at present on offer in BNCT is, of course, this Seventh International Symposium on Neutron Capture Therapy for Cancer. I had the abstracts available for a few weeks before the meeting.

Address for correspondence: Heinz Fankhauser MD, Croix-Rouges 2, CH-1007 Lausanne, Switzerland.

This allows me to summarize current clinical BNCT as reflected in the oral and poster sessions.

Treatment facilities in Japan

Our brain tumor patient will certainly learn about the pioneer Prof Hiroshi Hatanaka, to whom we owe the continuation of BNCT, and might try to call him. Sadly, he died in 1994, but his faithful secretary, Mrs Reiko Matsuoka, is still active in Tokyo, devoted to the promotion of nuclear medicine. She continues to take care of foreigners who go to be treated for BNCT in Japan. The situation in Japan is complex. There are four potential reactors, which may be or have recently been used for BNCT treatments. These reactors are the Kyoto University Reactor (KUR) of Kyoto University near Osaka, JRR-2 and JRR-4 at Tokai, North of Tokyo, and MuITR in the Tokyo area. The patient would be happy to learn that treatment is offered immediately, including to foreigners. He even has the choice among four medical teams; at the National Kagawa Children's Hospital, the University of Kyoto, Kyoto Prefectural University, or more recently Tsukuba University. Several hospitals near the reactors are cooperating in early patient care after BNCT. Some 108 patients had been treated by Prof Hatanaka at the MuIT reactor, which was stopped in 1989. Up to December 1995, most of the recent radiations took place at KUR. This reactor was then refurbished and significantly improved. It is no longer stopped between treatments. Besides thermal radiation, epithermal energy should also become available for BNCT treatment in the course of 1997. Reactor time is allocated to the medical teams in terms of days. For instance, the National Kagawa Children's Hospital team will have 6 reactor days per year; in 1 day they can treat up to three patients, i.e., 18 patients per year. Right now, JRR-2 is available for treatment with thermal neutrons. This reactor nevertheless will be stopped at the end of 1996. JRR-4 is also prepared for BNCT. This reactor should be available in 1998 for both thermal and epithermal neutrons. The MuITR should also be refurbished and used again for BNCT, perhaps by 1999 or 2000. In conclusion, Japan is presently able to accept patients, and by the turn of the century it should offer a choice of three reactors with thermal and epithermal neutrons.

Treatment facilities in the USA

Our brain tumor patient might first call the USA. He may have got some detailed information and the special telephone number of the Brookhaven BNCT office through the World-Wide Web on the Internet. He will learn that BNCT is presently offered at the BMRR at Brookhaven, in collaboration with two hospitals in the New York area. Between the end of 1994 and the beginning of 1996, 15 patients were treated. In 1996, five other patients received BNCT and four to eight more can be accepted before the end of the year. But our patient will be informed that only US citizens or permanent US residents are eligible.

Treatment facilities in Europe

If our patient would not like to travel to Japan and if he is not accepted for treatment in the USA, he may inquire about BNCT by the European Collaboration at the Petten Reactor in Holland. Most likely he will get in touch with the Department of Radiotherapy of the University of Essen, Germany, from where the future study is coordinated, or with any of the five neurosurgical departments through which the patients will have to go in order to be treated. At this moment, these are Bremen and Munich in Germany, Graz in Austria, Lausanne in Switzerland, and Nice in France. Our patient will be disappointed since he will learn that treatment in Petten has still not started. What is the reason? It is the complexity of the situation. During their treatment the patients will cross national borders and the medical responsibility will change. The nuclear facility in Petten is financed by several countries and it has not been used previously for medical purposes. The treatment room and medical installations are completed, and technically all components necessary to start treatment are ready. All local ethics committees have agreed with the proposed protocol. The responsible project leader is Prof Detlef Gabel in Bremen. Due to the reluctance of the Dutch radiotherapy community, a responsible clinical investigator has been appointed in Essen, in the person of Dr Wolfgang Sauerwein.

The remaining problems are mostly related to Dutch governmental agencies. Four ministries, as well as other services, boards and a national ethics committee are involved. Many questions are arising for the first time. The European Collaboration has to face situations where considerable perseverance, persuasion and even pressure are required. Our patient will therefore be informed that the start of treatment in Petten is imminent, but nobody can tell him how imminent. Anyway, with his disease he cannot wait and moreover he may not fulfil the very restrictive inclusion criteria of the proposed Petten trial.

Other treatment facilities

Are there other reactors or programs in the world which are likely to start clinical BNCT within 3 or 4 years? Although more than 10 reactor projects are represented at this symposium, in South America, Hungary, the Czech Republic, People's Republic of China, Slovenia, Sweden, Taiwan, Thailand and the USA, it appears today that the facility with the best chance of becoming available soon for patients is the Finnish reactor. This reactor offers epithermal neutrons and works at 250 kW. Even in the best case it would not be ready before the turn of the century.

Clinical BNCT research protocols

The patient's next question may be: would I be treated under a research protocol, with all its constraints of patient selection, extensive work-up, pages of informed consent, tough follow-up, etc., or would I be treated on a more routine basis, almost as if I were undergoing conventional radiotherapy? The answer is that Brookhaven and Petten apply very restrictive study designs, whereas to date Japan does not follow stringent research protocols.

Treatment in Japan

In Japan BNCT has a long tradition and this treatment has somehow entered the armaments of established therapy. Owing to the different reactors and medical teams operating in Japan, the situation there is more difficult to review, and the rules are not exactly the same in all places. Japan has been known to accept various types of patients, including tumors other than malignant gliomas, and cases treated previously with surgery, radiation therapy or chemotherapy. Patient selection is becoming more restrictive. Theoretically, only malignant glioma patients will now be accepted, but this rule is not absolute. Patients who have already had a full course of radiotherapy will no longer be accepted, since the risk of radiation necrosis is high. There are no age limits. Usually, tumors up to a diameter of 6 cm and a depth of 6 cm are considered for radiation, since at this time only thermal neutrons are available, but larger tumors can often be reduced to this dimension during the debulking operation which precedes BNCT.

If the patient wants to be treated in Japan, e.g., by the team of National Kagawa Children's Hospital, he is selected on the basis of history and imaging. A treatment strategy and dosimetry will then be worked out. This will be submitted to the medical committee which will quickly decide about the acceptability. There are several medical committees involved in Japan, either linked to the hospital of the medical team or to the reactor, and the procedure varies from one place to another, but no patient can be treated without clearance by an official medical committee. The patient will then be invited to come to the Kagawa Children's Hospital for further examination and a debulking operation. After recovery, usually some 10 days later, he will travel to the reactor, currently JRR-2. Since only thermal neutrons are available in Japan, every case will need reopening of the craniotomy site in the reactor. Depending upon the medical team, not BSH, but BPA is now used as a boron carrier. A silicon ball may be placed into the tumor resection cavity in order to spread out its margin. The procedure therefore closely resembles the one established by Prof Hatanaka, but admission criteria have become more restrictive, the administered boron dose is higher, and blood boron concentrations are increased from below 15 ppm to 30 or 40 ppm. The interval between boron administration and radiation has been shortened from 18 to 5 or 6 h. The radiation dose is higher. Dose planning is now used. Immediately after radiation, the head will be closed and the patient will be transferred to one of the nearby hospitals. After recovery, he will either return to the primary hospital or home. Follow-up is variable, but the minimum is a magnetic resonance imaging (MRI) examination every 3 months.

Treatment in the USA

In the USA, treatment started in September 1994 under a single-patient protocol and has since been continued under a phase I/II protocol. The outstanding feature of this protocol is the first ever use of an epithermal neutron beam. Its goal and challenge was to find a safe starting dose. Dose escalation was not included. BPA is evaluated as a boron carrier. This protocol was originally intended for 28 patients, but it has been replaced after 15 patients by a new protocol, adopted in 1996, and which is currently open. Early termination of the first protocol was justified by the observation that all patients got tumor recurrence and that in no case could radiation damage be demonstrated. Only supratentorial, unilateral glioblastomas can be included. They may be fresh cases, or cases which have already been operated on, under the condition that there is residual or recurrent tumor visible on MRI. The reason is that all these initial cases had to be operated or reoperated on in Beth Israel, in combination with a BPA biodistribution study. This, of course, needs at least some tumor tissue to be made available. Most recently, the protocol has again been amended; an individual BPA biodistribution study is no longer required and craniotomy will only be performed in patients not yet operated on. In no case can patients be accepted who have already undergone radiotherapy, chemotherapy, or immunotherapy. In the course of protocol changes, minimum age has been brought down from 50 to 18 years. The limitation to tumors with a maximum depth of 6 cm has also been abandoned, since the single radiation field has been replaced by two opposed fields and operation of the reactor at higher power. Practically, patient information has to be submitted to Brookhaven, where a Steering Committee will assess the eligibility. The patient will then be admitted to Beth Israel. BNCT will be scheduled within 2—4 weeks after craniotomy. Radiation will take 45—80 min. The important advance is, of course, that the head is not reopened, since epithermal neutrons are used. Follow-up includes regular clinical examination, brain scans and laboratory investigations. This can be done in Brookhaven, at Beth Israel, or in the home district of the patient by an appropriate board-certified specialist. This allows inclusion of patients from all over the USA, but not from abroad. Importantly, if a tumor recurs, the USA protocol does not exclude the possibility of further conventional radiotherapy.

Treatment protocol in Europe

The European protocol again is a phase I/II study. Its main goals are identical to the goals of the American study; it uses epithermal neutrons and BSH. It has two other distinctive features, since it is designed from the beginning as a dose escalation study, and since it will use four fractions of radiation. It is the most restrictive protocol as far as case selection is concerned. Not only patients with prior radiotherapy or chemotherapy, but also patients with prior craniotomy are excluded. Therefore, the European patients must harbor a probable glioblastoma on CT or MRI, but the histological diagnosis is not yet confirmed. Age must be 50 to 70 years. Only patients who can be followed permanently at one of the five primary neurosurgical centers are eligible.

If the preliminary inclusion criteria are fulfilled and if the beam is available within 4—6 weeks, the patient will undergo craniotomy for maximum debulking, combined with a BSH pharmacokinetic study, and confirmation of the histological diagnosis. If definite inclusion is confirmed, the patient will have to make his own way to Amsterdam to be admitted to the Hospital of the Free University. For BNCT he will be transported on 4 consecutive days to the Petten reactor after administration of four consecutive doses of BSH. Follow-up will be in the primary neurosurgical center and will include all potentially relevant aspects, such as endocrinology, ENT, ophthalmology and, of course, imaging. A significant difference between the USA and the European protocol is that the European protocol does not allow further radiotherapy in case of tumor recurrence.

Starting dose and escalation

A major issue in any such protocol is the determination of a safe starting dose which still offers the patient a chance to benefit from the treatment. Determination and description of dose are extremely important and complex aspects of BNCT will be treated abundantly in at least 40 presentations at this symposium. Agreement on all aspects has by no means been reached. A semiempirical approach to this problem is easier to understand and therefore has a critical place in the European protocol. The patient treatment facility in Petten has been tested with 40 healthy dogs with various blood levels of boron in BSH. After a period of observation these dogs showed either no abnormality, only MRI damage, or significant neurological symptoms. As expected with radiation, the dose-response curves are very close and steep. Even a minimal dose increase may lead to lethal neurological damage in a normal animal. The dose level proposed for the first Petten patients is just below the dose level where dogs developed MRI abnormalities after a single fraction. Furthermore, this dose will be given in four fractions, which may or may not add an additional safety margin. This concept is easily understandable. What is less obvious is whether the weighted dose units which are used to compare animal and human radiation effects are correct.

Dose escalation

The proposed dose escalation step in the European protocol is a 10% increase; this is also derived from the dog experiments. At the lowest proposed dose level no dog showed any abnormality. At dose levels 2 and 3, only MRI damage was observed and at dose level 4 neurological symptoms occurred when only one fraction was used. An important aspect of the quality of a protocol is that only a strict minimum of patients is included and that a sufficient observation time is allowed before conclusions are drawn. This is particularly true for radiation damage. In the Petten protocol, 10 patients are to be irradiated at the first dose level within 3 months. They will then be followed for at least 6 months. The data will be reviewed during the next month. Depending upon the result, the next 10 patients will be included at a higher dose level, the previous dose level will be repeated, or a dose de-escalation will be prescribed. This means that very few privileged cases will be eligible for this protocol, namely 40 patients from five neurosurgical centers during a 3½-year period.

Fractionation

Our patient may also ask about fractionation. Since in Japan the skull has to be opened, fractionation is impossible. In Brookhaven only one fraction is given, whereas in Petten four fractions are scheduled, which certainly makes things a lot more complicated, also for the patient. Logically, at least the low LET component of BNCT should benefit from fractionation as far as normal tissue tolerance is concerned. Also, fractionation is such a strongly established concept in classical radiotherapy that it seems reasonable to use it as long as there is no clear evidence against it. Many arguments will again be presented during this symposium. From recent animal experiments, it appears that if fractionation makes any difference, it is small. For the European Collaboration there are two main arguments in favor of fractionation. One is the observation that in a series of five normal dogs irradiated in the Petten beam with four fractions, there was no effect, whereas the same dose given in one fraction led to MRI damage in two out of five animals. This has to be taken into account, even if a similar observation was not made during dog experiments in the USA. Secondly, if radiation is given in a single fraction, it will be technically difficult to administer exactly the target dose. Dose deviations therefore may occur, and even if these are only in the order of 10–20%, this is critical owing to the steep dose-response curves. Furthermore, if the dose levels are not homogeneous it will be difficult to do a correct dose escalation study and to move from a phase I to a phase II protocol. With fractionation, it is theoretically possible to compensate for dose deviations. In practice, this issue is open, and it is fortunate that not all groups are exploring the same strategy.

BSH or BPA?

Two drugs are used for BNCT of brain tumors, BSH and BPA. Our patient might wonder why there is no consensus concerning the best one. During this symposium you will again hear arguments in favor of one over the other. The long clinical record, with a successful outcome as far as tumor control is concerned, and the absence of toxic problems in a large number of human administrations are stated as strong points in favor of BSH, even if BSH given in small animals has toxic effects which are not observed with BPA. On the other hand there is a question whether these toxic effects are really due to BSH or to impurities.

BPA will be presented as being more efficient than BSH in the control of experimental small animal tumors, but in patients this has not been demonstrated, and there is no realistic animal model for BNCT of a human brain tumor. This can be evaluated only in patients. It is therefore extremely important that both drugs are used in protocols. As during previous symposia, a large number of papers concerns existing or new boron compounds for BNCT. None of these is considered ready for clinical trials.

Ethics

For the first time, this topic will be specifically addressed. I do not know what will be said, but as far as I am concerned, I came to realize that ethics is not at all an established concept when it comes to precise questions of practical importance. The answer is highly dependent upon many things; the most important seems to be local tradition. It was obvious that in Europe no general ethical consensus could be found. Therefore it was decided that initial recruitment of patients would be limited to a few centers who can agree with the proposed protocol, which is already a compromise. The most basic ethical requirement is preservation of the study goal. The worst is to implement an overcautious approach to a point where the initial target can no longer be reached. This means that ethical considerations make the study unscientific. When looking at ethical standards established by ourselves or requested by ethics committees, it is obvious that most are not truly intended to protect the patient, but rather the researcher, the hospital, their insurance companies, and the ethics committee itself. Facing a disease with a desperate natural history, they may further lower the patient's already small chance to benefit from a new treatment. Informed consent may even put considerable additional stress upon him and his family. In a phase I/II BNCT study we certainly want to find out the toxic dose level and the organs at risk. Inevitably this may harm the patient at some point. We also want to demonstrate tumor control with the treatment. The difficult balance is then to obtain a maximum of information with a minimum number of patients, and still remain within ethical limits. If we diminish the risk of radiation damage by half, we may need twice as many patients to reach our study goal. An increased risk accepted in an individual study patient may result in an increased chance of benefit to the whole community of glioblastoma patients. What are the priorities of the study and what is more ethical? After all, why are we deciding what is ethical for our patient? Should he not have the possibility to participate in the decision, and perhaps even in the design of the ethical safeguard of the study protocol? Major ethical issues in the European Collaboration include discussion of the age group and performance status at recruitment of glioblastoma patients. BNCT will replace conventional radiotherapy, which has no clear benefit after the age of 50 years. This has therefore been chosen as the minimum age, whereas in the USA the age limit is now 18 years. In some places in Europe, elderly glio-

blastoma patients undergo only a biopsy, but no craniotomy, and often no radiotherapy. These centers suggested omitting a debulking operation from the protocol. On the other hand, in some places even reoperation is not exceptional when
a glioblastoma recurs after treatment. It was therefore proposed that reoperation
should be an integral part of the European study protocol, since this would allow
histological examination of tissues after BNCT. Some investigators feel that
autopsy should be mandatory and that consent should be requested from all
patients or families at recruitment. They feel it is unacceptable that any patient
should die after BNCT without histological confirmation of the cause of death
and without examination of the brain for radiation damage. In other places,
requesting autopsy as part of a protocol would be unethical and totally unacceptable.

Results

Results are the thing which we are looking for most, and our brain tumor patient
even more. The interim results from Japan and the USA will be presented at this
meeting. What could the patient be told if he were to be treated in Japan? If we
take, for instance, the glioblastoma cases radiated at KUR, the 2-year survival
with the older dose level is 7%; but with a higher dose used since June 1993 it is
40%. Three-year survival for all patients is 7%, but if only the limited superficial
cases are considered, it is 35%. In the USA, by February 1996, no clear effect of
BNCT could be demonstrated, since tumor recurrence was the rule and no
radiation damage was seen either.

Costs

It is not fashionable for doctors to discuss money, but the patient may need to
know about treatment costs. Expenses strictly limited to the execution of the protocol in the USA and Europe are funded, although extra costs may be generated
by travel, hotel, etc. In Japan, a foreigner would have to pay for the expenses of
BNCT, and this may amount to US$50,000, plus travel. This price is entirely jus-
tified, but still it is one more barrier between BNCT and patients in 1996.

Progress

Looking at the wealth of the abstracts, the organizers of this symposium can be
proud. There are tremendous numbers of new ideas and new solutions related to
BNCT, many of which we would not even have thought of in the past. On the
other hand, I am somehow disappointed. It seems to me that a few years ago,
when we had much less to offer, we were closer to introduction into clinical trials
and patient treatments. At the 1988 symposium in Bremen, for instance, it
seemed obvious to me that the European Collaboration should not engage in
archaic BSH, since much more selective drugs would be available very soon. In

1996, I am amazed that the discussion and controversy on clinically useful drugs is limited to BSH and BPA. I also remember the 1990 symposium in Sydney, when accelerator-based BNCT seemed likely to become available within months for clinical trials. Today, although we have many more accelerator solutions, predictions about their clinical testing are cautiously avoided. Why, in 1996, do we have a very much wider spectrum of solutions for BNCT, but these are farther away from introduction into clinical investigation than ever? You have seen how little we offer to the patient in 1996, despite the success which this meeting undoubtedly will have. Why is it so difficult to make the final step towards clinical investigation and application, since we all agree that glioblastoma urgently needs a solution? There are of course many reasons. One is certainly the extreme difficulty in proceeding from laboratory to clinical research. The regulations which govern clinical investigations have become so demanding that they are almost prohibitive for noncommercial research teams. It needs a tremendous amount of people, money and time, and the outcome of a clinical research project is totally uncertain, even if hundreds of thousands of working hours have already been spent.

After all, there is little public support for BNCT. It is true that glioblastoma is a personal disaster for the patient and his family, but on the whole it is a marginal disease in terms of public health worldwide, and it has nothing in common with other epidemics.

Even if found totally efficient, there is certainly no big money in successful BNCT for glioblastoma, and there will be no big honor for the researcher either, since too many people have already made invaluable contributions. On the other hand, the idea of BNCT has become somehow accepted by the international community, which is prepared to offer money for small-scale research. This is useful and makes BNCT laboratory research more and more popular, but there is insufficient incentive to go beyond that, and it does not necessarily help the patient. In order to allow BNCT to progress into the clinic, you need a very special type of person, who does not follow all the established rules, whose motivation may escape our understanding and who pushes things ahead even if logically one should admit that there is hardly a chance to comply with all regulations, to get the necessary funding, and to get all the many necessary peoples and teams move together. Such pioneers do, of course, exist. They may be doctors, such as Bill Sweet or Hiroshi Hatanaka; or they may even be a patient, as has happened in the USA. The European Collaboration hopes that its study will soon be under way and that Detlef Gabel's name can be added to those pioneers.

Acknowledgements

The author acknowledges financial support of the European BNCT study from the Neurosurgery 2001 Foundation, Lausanne, Switzerland.

Clinical experience

©1997 Elsevier Science B.V. All rights reserved.
Advances in Neutron Capture Therapy.
Volume I, Medicine and Physics.
B. Larsson, J. Crawford and R. Weinreich, editors.

Boron neutron capture therapy for malignant glioma at Kyoto University reactor

Koji Ono[1], Satoshi Ueda[2], Yoshifumi Oda[3], Yoshinobu Nakagawa[4], Shinich Miyatake[5], Masao Takagaki[1], Masami Osawa[6] and Toru Kobayashi[1]

[1]*Research Reactor Institute, Kyoto University, Osaka;* [2]*Department of Neurosurgery, Kyoto Prefecture University of Medicine, Kyoto;* [3]*Department of Neurosurgery, Kobe City Hospital, Kobe;* [4]*Department of Neurosurgery, Kagawa Children's Hospital, Kagawa;* [5]*Department of Neurosurgery, Kyoto University Hospital, Kyoto; and* [6]*Department of Anesthesiology, Kyoto University Hospital, Kyoto, Japan*

Keywords: ^{18}F-BPA, BPA, BSH, malignant glioma, PET.

Introduction

The treatment results of malignant astrocytomas by using ordinary low LET radiation such as X-rays are quite unsatisfactory. The standard 5-year survival rates are reported to be 20–35% even in the case of anaplastic astrocytoma, and in general the patients with glioblastoma could not survive over 5 years [1]. Two factors are considered to be responsible for these poor treatment outcomes. Firstly, the tumor cells have low intrinsic radiosensitivity, and secondly the tumors widely invade the normal brain. Therefore, large radiation doses have to be delivered to large fields for eradicating tumor cells completely. However, this would induce serious damage in the normal brain. In this regard, boron neutron capture therapy (BNCT) seems to be ideal. The α particle and ^{7}Li nucleus emitted by the ^{10}B(n,α)^{7}Li reaction have the characteristics of high LET radiation with large relative biological effectiveness and small, almost equal to unity, oxygen enhancement ratio. Therefore, they can destroy the radioresistant tumor cells. Another characteristic is their limited ranges of penetration. They do not exceed approximately one cell diameter (<10 µm). Therefore, if a boron compound accumulates in tumor cells selectively or at high enough concentration ratio between tumors and normal tissues, BNCT can cure the radioresistant and highly invasive tumors, such as malignant glioma. In Japan, BNCT has been applied to malignant glioma in more than 100 patients by Hatanaka and others [2]. The first patient of malignant glioma at Kyoto University reactor (KUR) was treated in 1974 by Hatanaka. Thereafter, BNCT was stopped, and we restarted BNCT for malignant glioma using KUR in 1990. We report the accumulated data here.

Address for correspondence: Koji Ono MD, Radiation Oncology Research Laboratory, Research Reactor Institute, Kyoto University, Noda, Kumatori-cho, Sennan-gun, Osaka 590-04, Japan. Tel.: +81-724-51-2475. Fax: +81-724-51-2627.

Methods and Materials

Patients and boron compounds

Patients enrolled in the trials are presented in Table 1. Forty-four patients consisted of 27 men and 17 women. Grade IV cases were predominant in number, 31 grade IV vs. 13 grade III. Fifteen grade IV tumors were located in the unilateral hemisphere and the deepest point of the tumor invasion did not exceed 4.0 cm from the brain surface (limited cases). Fourteen patients were recurrent tumor cases who received 18—60 Gy of radiation previously.

BSH was dissolved in saline and drip-infused in 1—2 h (5 g/body). BPA is very hard to be dissolved in saline, and BPA-fructose complex was prepared. In 1 h 12—15 g BPA/body was administered intravenously.

Operation and thermal neutron irradiation

The skull of the patient was reopened in front of the D_2O facility of KUR. The thermal neutron irradiation started 15—17 h after BSH administration according to the protocol recommended by Hatanaka until May 1993. However, since June 1993, the time interval between BSH administration and irradiation was shortened to 5—7 h. The thermal neutrons through the beam port (20 cm diameter) were collimated to the exposed tumor by shielding the normal brain with ^6LiF-containing thermoplastic board. At the typical treatment position, the thermal neutron flux and γ ray dose rate were $1-3 \times 10^9$ cm^{-2}s^{-1} and 0.1—0.15 cGy s^{-1} at 5 MW operation, respectively. Au wires were inserted into the lesions as deep as possible to measure neutron fluences. The fluence at the surface of the brain was also measured. TLD was used for γ ray dosimetry.

Estimation of boron concentration in tumors and radiation doses

BSH

According to our clinical study, ^{10}B-concentrations in the brain tumors did not exceed those in the blood. Therefore, the concentration was assumed to be equal to that in the blood for radiation dose calculation. The blood concentrations dur-

Table 1. Patients characteristics.

Sex:	men 27, women 17
Age:	mean 44.3 (4—73 years)
Histopathology:	grade III 13, grade IV 31
Tumor extension of grade IV cases:	advanced 16, limited 15
Previous radiotherapy:	+14 (18—60 Gy),
	−24
Boron compounds:	BSH (5 g/bogy) 36
	BPA (12—15 g/kg) 8

ing the neutron exposure were lower than 15 ppm until May 1993. It has increased to 30—40 ppm after June 1993 because the time interval between BSH injection and neutron irradiation was shortened.

BPA

The accumulation of BPA in tumors can be visualized easily on PET using ^{18}F-radio-labeled BPA (^{18}F-BPA), and the percentage of total injection doses in tumors and normal tissue regions can be calculated. The accumulation of ^{18}F-BPA in glioma increased with the grade of malignancy, and the ratio reached 3:5 in malignant astrocytoma (S. Ueda et al. 7th Int. Symp. NCT). In clinical BNCT, the blood was collected just before irradiation to measure ^{10}B-concentration, and the estimation by PET was confirmed by comparing the estimated value with the real ^{10}B concentration.

^{10}B concentrations in the blood or tissues were measured by prompt γ ray spectrometry using a thermal neutron guide tube. The doses in Gy delivered by ^{14}N(n,p)^{14}C and ^{10}B(n,α)^{7}Li reactions were calculated as follows: $3.483 \times 6.782 \times 10^{-14} \times$ fluence and ^{10}B-concentration (ppm) $\times 6.933 \times 10^{-14} \times$ fluence for nitrogen- and boron-neutron reactions, respectively [3]. In this calculation, nitrogen content (w/w) in the tissues was postulated as 3.483%. When we considered the BNCT effects on malignant gliomas, the effects of contaminated γ rays were neglected because the glioma cells were highly radioresistant and radiation doses were delivered at the reduced dose rates (2.5—3.0 Gy/h), and therefore significant effects on tumors were hardly to be expected. The estimated absorbed doses at the deepest point in the tumors were lower than 6 Gy (high LET radiation dose alone) before May 1993. On the other hand, these were usually increased to 10—16 Gy after June 1993.

Analysis of the survival rates of the patients

Survival time was defined as the term from the day of BNCT to the day of death or analysis. Survival data were analyzed by the Kaplan-Meier method, and the statistical significance was investigated by the generalized Wilcoxon test.

Results

Survival rates of all cases

Survival data of all cases are presented in Fig. 1. The survival rates decreased with time after BNCT, and the median survival time of 12 months and 3-year survival rates of 31% were achieved. The survival rate was stable after 2½ years.

Difference in survival rates; grade IV vs. grade III patients

The survival data were analyzed according to the grade of malignancy (Fig. 2).

42

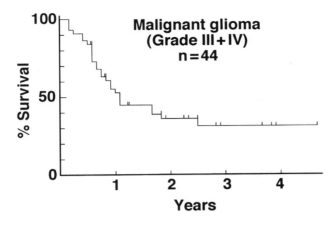

Fig. 1. Survival rates of all cases after BNCT.

The median survival time and 3-year survival rate of grade IV patients were 11 months and 22%, respectively. On the other hand, 3-year survival rate of grade III patients was 52%. This difference in the survival rate was significant ($p < 0.05$).

Difference in survival rates of grade IV patients; limited vs. advanced cases

The 3-year survival rate of the limited grade IV patients was 38% and 2-year survival rate of the advanced grade IV patients was 7% (Fig. 3). This difference was also significant ($p < 0.05$).

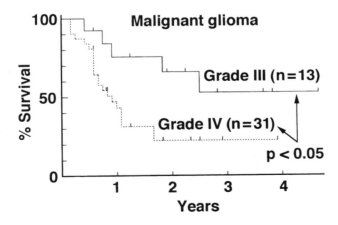

Fig. 2. Survival rates of grade III and grade IV glioma patients after BNCT.

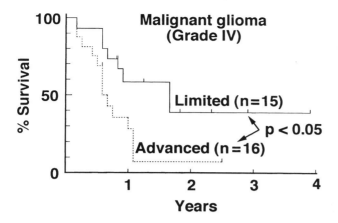

Fig. 3. Survival rates of the limited and advanced grade IV glioma patients after BNCT.

Difference in survival rates of grade IV patients according to the treatment era

The 3-year survival rate of the grade IV patients treated by larger radiation doses since June 1993 was 40%, significantly higher than the 7% achieved before May 1993 ($p < 0.05$) (Fig. 4).

Discussion

The survival data of all cases are worse than those reported by Hatanaka previously. He reported a 5-year survival rate of higher than 50% [4]. However, in

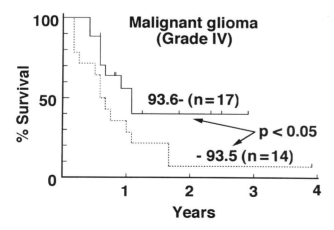

Fig. 4. Survival rates of grade IV glioma patients treated before and after June 1993 by BNCT.

the recent analysis by Nakagawa of the cases including Hatanaka's cases, 2-year survival rates were 12, 56 and 62% for grade IV, grade III and low-grade astrocytomas, respectively (Y. Nakagawa et al. 7th Int. Symp. for NCT, 1996). This finding is quite similar to our present analysis. The reason for the high survival rates in Hatanaka's report is the unclassified grouping of the patients.

In our study, the limited grade IV cases showed better survival than the advanced cases. In general, the limited cases have a good prognosis. However, this might be a reflection of the physical characteristics of thermal neutrons. The tissue penetration ability of thermal neutrons is poor, i.e., at 4 cm depth the neutron flux decreases to the 20—25% level of that at the surface. From these characteristics, it is reasonable that BNCT produced significantly better survival rates in the limited cases. Grade III tumors are less invasive than grade IV in general. Therefore, this difference could be partly explained by the poor penetration ability of thermal neutrons. Grade III and limited grade IV tumors might be a good indication of BNCT. However, the extended grade IV cases will also be an indication when more penetrating neutron beams, namely epithermal neutrons, become available.

Our clinical BNCT trial for malignant glioma was started according to the protocol that was recommended by Hatanaka. However, the survival after BNCT was much lower than that reported by him. Then, we re-evaluated the radiation doses which were given to the deepest points in the tumors by high LET particles in May 1993, and the doses were less than 6 Gy in almost all cases. This dose was considered to be insufficient for eradicating tumor cells. We determined the relationship between the tumor control probability (TCP) and the absorbed high LET radiation doses in Gy by using experimental mouse tumors and in vivo/in vitro colony assay [5]. In BPA-BNCT, TCP90 (90% tumor control probability) dose was around 11 Gy when it was assumed that 1 g of tumor contained 10^5 tumor cells with unlimited proliferation activity. On the other hand, 14 Gy was needed to achieve TCP90 in BSH-BNCT. According to this calculation, the radiation dose that should be delivered to the deepest point of tumors has increased since June 1993. As it is apparent in Fig. 4, the treatment outcome has significantly improved in comparison with those until May 1993. This suggests that the curative dose of grade IV glioma determined by experiments is reliable.

The usefulness of BPA was proved in our trial. BPA accumulated in malignant glioma at high concentration, and it was maintained long enough for BNCT. The concentration was estimated by PET. This point was an another advantage of BPA compared with BSH. However, there is an important point which we have to consider. BPA selectively delivered boron to areas of the tumor identified as actively dividing by uptake of treated thymidine [6], and could not accumulate in quiescent tumor cells [7]. Therefore, although the initial tumor responses following BPA-BNCT are satisfactory, the careful observation on the final tumor response is necessary.

References

1. Nelson DF, McDonald JF, Lapham LN, Qazi R, Rubin P. Central nervous system. In: Rubin P (ed) Clinical Oncology, a Multidisciplinary Approach for Physicians and Students, 7th edn. Philadelphia: Saunders Company, 1993;617–644.
2. Hatanaka H, Nakagawa Y. Clinical results of long-surviving brain tumor patients who underwent boron neutron capture therapy. Int J Radiat Oncol Biol Phys 1994;28(5):1061–1066.
3. Kobayashi T, Kanda K, Ujeno Y, Fukuda H, Ando K, Hiratsuka J, Mishima Y, Ichihashi M. Irradiation conditions based on absorbed dose estimation in boron neutron capture therapy for superficially located malignant melanoma. Radiat Biol Res Comm 1990;25:53–64.
4. Hatanaka H. Boron-neutron capture therapy for tumors. In: Karim ABM, Law ER Jr (eds) Glioma. Berlin, Heidelberg: Springer-Verlag, 1991;233–249.
5. Ono K, Masunaga S, Kinashi Y, Takagaki M, Kobayashi T, Imahori Y, Ueda S, Oda Y. The dose planning of BNCT for brain tumors. In: Mishima Y (ed) Cancer Neutron Capture Therapy. New York: Plenum Press, 1966;563–569.
6. Coderre JA, Glass JD, Fairchild RG, Roy U, Cohen S, Fand I. Selective targeting of boronophenylalanine to melanoma for neutron capture therapy. Cancer Res 1987;47:6377–6383.
7. Ono K, Masunaga S, Kinashi Y, Takagaki M, Akaboshi M, Kobayashi T, Akuta K. Radiobiological evidence suggesting heterogeneous microdistribution of boron compounds in tumors: its relation to quiescent cell population and tumor cure in neutron capture therapy. Int J Radiat Oncol Biol Phys 1996;34(5):1081–1086.

The University of Tsukuba BNCT research group: first clinical experiences at JAERI

Akira Matsumura[1], Yasushi Shibata[1], Tetsuya Yamamoto[3], Takashi Yamada[3], Hiroyuki Fujimori[1], Kei Nakai[1], Yoshinobu Nakagawa[4], Yoshinori Hayakawa[2], Masahiko Isshiki[5] and Tadao Nose[1]

[1] *Department of Neurosurgery, Proton Medical Center, University of Tsukuba, Tsukuba Science City, Ibaraki;* [2] *Proton Medical Center, University of Tsukuba, Tsukuba Science City, Ibaraki;* [3] *Department of Neurosurgery, Naka Central Hospital, Naka, Ibaraki;* [4] *Department of Neurosurgery, National Kagawa Children's Hospital, Zentsuuji, Kagawa; and* [5] *Japan Atomic Energy Research Institute, Tokai, Ibaraki, Japan*

Keywords: boron neutron capture therapy, BSH, clinical study, criteria, epithermal neutrons.

Introduction and background

The University of Tsukuba is the nearest School of Medicine to the Japan Atomic Energy Research Institute (JAERI) at Tokai, Ibaraki, which led us to create a project for clinical and basic study on boron neutron capture therapy (BNCT). This project was set up in 1992 in collaboration with Prof Hatanaka. Since then, the Tsukuba BNCT Clinical Research Group has been preparing for the launch of a BNCT clinical study at JAERI. Our clinical study for BNCT began in November 1995. However, before starting this BNCT project, many issues had to be solved.

First, we had to develop a collaborating Neurosurgical Department, for which Naka Central Hospital was chosen. This hospital is one of our teaching hospitals and is located in the vicinity of JAERI (15 min by car). Medical staff, operating nurses, medical equipment for operation and drugs were offered from this hospital. An ambulance car was also introduced for transportation of the patients. Initial operations, including craniotomy and tumor removal, are performed at the University of Tsukuba Hospital. Then, immediate pre- and post-BNCT care are given at Naka Central Hospital, and long-term follow-up is done at the University of Tsukuba.

Another important issue was obtaining the agreement from the ethics committee of the University Tsukuba Hospital for the BNCT clinical research. The ethics committee discussed the clinical safety, efficacy and other ethical issues of BNCT for 6 months before they finally decided to allow the BNCT trial.

Address for correspondence: Akira Matsumura MD, Department of Neurosurgery, Institute of Clinical Medicine, University of Tsukuba, 1-1-1 Tenodai, Tsukuba, Ibaraki 305, Japan. Tel.: +81-298-53-3220. Fax: +81-298-53-3214. E-mail: matsumur@md.tsukuba.ac.jp

Protocol

Patient criteria

Patients who fulfill the following criteria are considered for candidacy for BNCT:
1. Glioma patients with grade 3—4.
2. Less than 70 years of age.
3. Good general condition (KPS > 70).
4. No prior chemotherapy or radiation[1].
5. Tumor not deeper than 4 cm from the surface.
6. No serious systemic disease.

A recurrent patient is a patient who showed an initial response to the radiation therapy but then showed evidence of recurrence after a long-term follow-up. Such cases may include malignant transformation of glioma to glioblastoma. Therefore, patients who have just undergone conventional radiation therapy (up to 1 year) are excluded. In addition, patients who have received prior radiation therapy are excluded from the clinical evaluation group, since the condition is quite different from the initial cases.

Boron analysis

To study the uptake of boron, 1 g of $Na_2{}^{10}B_{12}H_{11}SH$ (BSH) is given (using 1 h drip infusion) 12 h before the first operation. Blood is taken up serially for boron concentration analysis. Specimens from various parts of the tumor are kept and analyzed for boron concentration.

The tumor-to-blood ratio data from the first tumor removal are used to calculate the tumor concentration for BNCT. The boron concentration of the tumor will be calculated from the previous tumor-to-boron ratio and the actual blood boron concentration at the time of BNCT, since the majority of the macroscopic tumor is to be removed during the first operation and the boron concentration of the tumor is assumed to be unreliable during the second operation.

Boron neutron capture therapy

For BNCT, 100 mg/kg BSH is given with 500 ml of saline for 1 h via intravenous drip infusion. The infusion is initiated 12 h before planned BNCT. The radiation dose is decided from the boron concentration of the tumor and the neutron fluence at the minimal target dose. This neutron flux will be obtained by withdrawing a gold wire 30 min after the start of radiation. The minimal target volume is defined as a 2 cm margin from the main tumor seen on T1-weighted Gd-DTPA-enhanced MRI. The surface neutron flux will also be monitored. The surface dose is limited to 5 physical Gy since a radiation injury above this dose is

---

[1] As a phase I study, patients with recurrent glioma with primary radiation therapy may be included.

expected. The minimum target dose is limited by the surface dose when using the thermal neutron beam although we usually try to get 15 Gy (physical dose).

Case description

Since November 1995, four patients (including two patients referred from Dr Nakagawa) were treated using our facilities.

Case 1. A 41-year-old female with recurrent grade 3 glioma 7 years after initial therapy. The patient underwent 60 Gy conventional irradiation and chemotherapy after her first operation. The patient was uneventful until 1996 when her neurological status deteriorated. A recurrent tumor was found on a T1-weighted Gd-DTPA enhanced image (Fig. 1) and as she had already received a full-dose radiation, BNCT was selected as an alternative therapy. The patient received BNCT on 23 November. A 10 g dose of BSH was given (100 mg/kg) 12 h before BNCT. The boron concentrations found in different parts of the tumor at pre-BNCT operation were 18 and 76 ppm and the blood boron concentration was 19 to 27 ppm during BNCT. The target tumor dose was 10 Gy (physical dose). On the follow-up MRI, the enhancement effect on the surface of the brain appeared 3 months after BNCT, while this patient was clinically doing well (Fig. 2). This patient died of severe enterocolitis after partial gastrectomy due to an incidental gastric cancer which became apparent 3 months after BNCT.

Case 2. A 1-year-old female with glioblastoma multiforme was treated on 13 December 1995. This patient also received 5 g BSH 48 h and 12 h before BNCT. The BNCT and postoperative course was uneventful. This patient had a

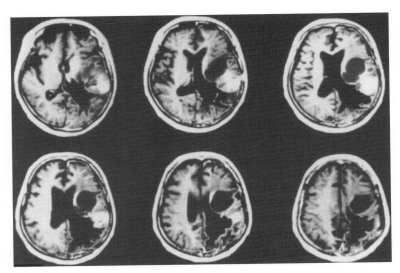

Fig. 1. T1-weighted enhanced MRI. A recurrent anaplastic astrocytoma in the left temporo-parietal region appears as a high-intensity enhanced lesion. There is also a cystic area frontal to the main tumor which also shows some enhancement of the cavity wall.

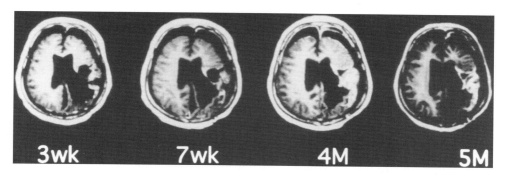

Fig. 2. Post BNCT serial T1 weighted enhanced MRI: There is defect after tumor removal and BNCT on the MRI (3 weeks post BNCT). After 4 months, an enhancement appeared on the surface of the irradiated brain and also on the surface of the cystic cavity. This phenomenon slightly decreased 5 months after BNCT. The patient showed no neurological deterioration during this period.

recurrent tumor 5 months later which is under treatment with another modality.

The other two patients (glioblastoma) tolerated the BNCT well and there is no recurrence in a short-term follow-up period of 2 and 4 months, respectively.

Discussion

To approach the clinical trial of BNCT, many issues including medical, socioeconomical, and ethical issues have to be solved. The implementation of collaborating hospitals, medical staff, and permission from the ethics committee were the main premedical and medical subjects.

As to the therapeutic planning, we used the tumor-to-blood ratio of the first operation, since at the time of BNCT (second operation) the boron concentration was thought not to be reliable due to the first surgical removal of the main tumor. Therefore, we multiplied the tumor-to-blood ratio by the mean of the measured pre- and post-BNCT blood boron concentrations, to estimate the tumor boron concentration during the BNCT. According to the data of Kageji et al. [1], the mean tumor-to-blood ratio was 1.30 ± 0.65, which is in good agreement with our limited experience. It is also known that the cellularity of the tumor correlates with the boron concentration [2], so that the variation of the boron concentration in BSH may also be explained by the difference in cellularity. It seems, therefore, to be justifiable to use the highest boron concentration, probably corresponding to highest tumor cellularity, for dose calculations in the planning of treatment.

However, more precise analysis of boron concentration in conjunction with cellularity should be performed with BSH.

As to the dosimetry, we are currently using gold wire in multiple directions and depths to calculate the neutron fluence. In the future, it is essential to introduce treatment-planning software in order to make a proper treatment evaluation feasible. The superimposition of boron distribution may be another step in improving the therapeutic accuracy, and for becoming able to compare the data of BNCT with other conventional radiation therapeutic modalities.

As to the patient selection, we made a criteria similar to other groups. Primarily, recurrent cases should not be included in the clinical evaluation since there may be a bias through the previous treatment. Nevertheless, we performed the first BNCT in recurrent cases to prove the safety of our therapeutic procedure. The question remains open whether such recurrent patients after conventional radiation therapy will also benefit from BNCT. In the advanced stage of the clinical trial, the BNCT protocol for recurrent gliomas after conventional radiation therapy may clarify this possibility. Thus, in the present stage, recurrent patients should be strictly excluded from BNCT unless there is no alternative therapy available.

In the near future, our group is planning to start clinical and basic research in the application of epithermal neutrons in collaboration with JAERI [3], which may prove the therapeutic effect of BNCT for malignant gliomas in deeper locations.

Acknowledgements

This project was supported in part by Grant-in-Aid from the Ministry of Education, Science and Culture of Japan (No. 7557091 to AM) and Tsukuba University Research Grant (to AM and TN). We appreciate Dr T. Minobe for his help in clinical settings.

References

1. Kageji T et al. Pharmacokinetics and boron uptake of BSH ($Na_2{}^{10}B_{12}H_{11}SH$) in patients with intracranial tumours. Programme and Abstracts. Seventh International Symposium on Neutron Capture Therapy. Zurich, 1996;87.
2. Joel DD et al. Biodistribution of p-boronophenylalanine: Uptake into glioblastoma multiforme correlates with tumor cellularity. Programme and Abstracts. Seventh International Symposium on Neutron Capture Therapy. Zurich, 1996;88.
3. Yamada T et al. A new medical irradiation facility at JRR-4. Programme and Abstracts. Seventh International Symposium on Neutron Capture Therapy. Zurich, 1996;132.

1997 Elsevier Science B.V.
Advances in Neutron Capture Therapy.
Volume I, Medicine and Physics.
B. Larsson, J. Crawford and R. Weinreich, editors.

Radiation doses to brain under BNCT protocols at Brookhaven National Laboratory

J. Capala[1], M. Chadha[2], J.A. Coderre[1], A.Z. Diaz[1,3], H.B. Liu[1], F.J. Wheeler[4], D.E. Wessol[4], L. Wielopolski[1] and A.D. Chanana[1]

[1]*Medical Department, Brookhaven National Laboratory, Upton, New York;* [2]*Department of Radiation Oncology, Beth Israel Medical Center, New York, New York;* [3]*Department of Radiation Oncology, State University of New York, Stony Brook, New York; and* [4]*Idaho National Engineering Laboratory, Idaho Falls, Idaho, USA*

Introduction

As of 31 August, 1996, 20 glioblastoma multiforme patients received boron neutron capture therapy (BNCT) under several treatment protocols at the Brookhaven Medical Research Reactor [1]. For treatment planning and dosimetry purposes, these protocols may be divided into four groups (Table 1). The first group comprises protocols employing an 8-cm collimator [2] with a prescribed peak normal brain dose of $\leqslant 10.5$ Gy-Eq to a volume of 1 cm^3 at the site of maximum thermal neutron flux (frequently confined to the tumor volume). For the second group, a peak normal brain dose of $\leqslant 12.6$ Gy-Eq was prescribed. The protocols of the third and fourth groups prescribed a peak normal brain dose of $\leqslant 12.6$ Gy-Eq (specified to be outside of the tumor volume), a 12-cm collimator [2], and allowed for single-field or double-field irradiation. We describe the treatment planning procedures and report the doses delivered to various structures of the brain in patients treated under these protocols.

Materials and Methods

The treatment planning process involves:
1. Obtaining a contrast-enhanced MRI scan (rarely CT scan) of the patient's head. Conventional positioning lasers and/or a mechanical isocentric device are used for establishing triangulation points on the patient's scalp. Scans are carried out with fiducial markers located over the triangulation points, which are then used for patient positioning [3].
2. Reconstruction of a three-dimensional model of the patient's head with defined anatomical structures (scalp, skull, brain, sinuses) and regions of interest (tumor = contrast enhanced volume, target = tumor + 2 cm margin) using a graphical environment provided by the BNCT-Rtpe treatment planning program [4].
3. Calculation of the neutron flux and secondary radiation distribution using a

Table 1. Summary of radiation doses delivered to the normal brain under different protocols.

	Group 1	Group 2	Group 3	Group 4
Protocols	Single use and #2	#3	#4a	#4b
Number of patients treated	11	4	1	4
Mode of irradiation (single/double field)	Single	Single	Single	Double
Collimator's diameter (cm)	8	8	12	12
Prescribed peak dose (Gy-Eq)	10.5	12.6	12.6	12.6
Estimated average dose (Gy-Eq)	2.2 ± 0.2 (1.9—2.6)	2.4 ± 0.2 (2.2—2.4)	3.3	4.7 ± 0.3 (4.4—5.0)
Maximum doses (Gy-Eq) to:				
basal ganglia	5.2 ± 1.3 (3.7—7.2)	3.2 ± 1.8 (1.2—5.6)	6.4	7.8 ± 0.9 (6.6—8.4[a])
thalamus	5.6 ± 1.1 (4.0—7.2)	4.2 ± 1.1 (3.0—5.6)	7.0	7.7 ± 0.9 (7.2—8.4[a])
optic chiasm	2.0 ± 1.4 (0.6—4.8)	2.1 ± 1.5 (1.0—4.3)	2.0	5.4 ± 0.5 (4.8—5.2)

[a]Doses > 7.5 Gy-Eq to normal brain sites included in the target volume. Protocol prescription for these sites is ⩽ 8.5 Gy-Eq.

three-dimensional Monte Carlo radiation transport program, rtt-MC [5].

4. Estimation of the absorbed dose distribution assuming a brain/blood boron concentration ratio of 1:1 and a tumor/blood boron concentration ratio of 3.5:1 [6]. The dose is expressed in Gray-equivalent [7]. The following biological effectiveness factors were employed: 1.0 for γ, 3.2 for high-LET beam components, and 1.3 and 3.8 for boron neutron capture products in the normal brain and tumor tissue, respectively [7,8].

5. Identification of the optimum treatment position, and calculation of the time of neutron irradiation required to deliver the prescribed peak normal brain doses of 10.5 Gy-Eq (group 1) or 12.6 Gy-Eq (groups 2, 3 and 4).

6. Posttreatment evaluation of the dose distribution using the actual irradiation time and the ^{10}B concentrations measured in the blood at the beginning, in the middle and at the end of the treatment.

Results

Table 1 summarizes the doses delivered to the normal brain of glioblastoma patients treated at BNL under different protocols. The following are the estimated volume-averaged BNCT doses for normal brain tissue: group 1 — 1.9 to 2.6 Gy-Eq; group 2 — 2.2 to 2.6 Gy-Eq; group 3 — 3.3 Gy-Eq; and group 4 — 4.4 to 5.0 Gy-Eq. Doses to certain sensitive sites of the brain (e.g., basal ganglia, thalamus and optic chiasm) outside of the target volume were kept ⩽ 7.5 Gy-Eq as per protocol prescription.

Isodose contours shown in the left panel of Fig. 1 illustrate the total dose distribution in a patient treated under a protocol from group 1 with a lateral exposure

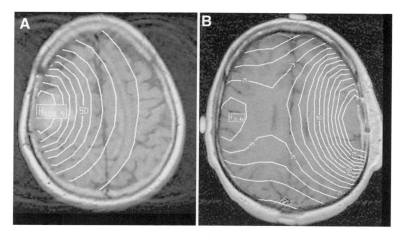

Fig. 1. Normal brain dose distribution in a representative glioblastoma patient treated under a protocol from group 1 (**A**: 100% = 10.4 Gy-Eq; isodose contours at 10% intervals) or group 4 (**B**: 100% = 12.0 Gy-Eq; isodose contours at 5% intervals).

resulting in a very large difference between distribution of the dose to the ipsilateral and contralateral normal structures of the brain. This patient received the following average doses: ipsilateral hemisphere 4.0 Gy-Eq (2.5 Gy-Eq high-LET, and 1.5 Gy-Eq low-LET); contralateral hemisphere 1.0 Gy-Eq (0.4 Gy-Eq high-LET, and 0.6 Gy-Eq low-LET dose). In the left panel of Fig. 2 are shown dose-volume histograms of total dose and its components in the brain of this patient. It is noteworthy that only a small fraction of the brain received doses over the prescribed volume-averaged brain dose of 7.5 Gy-Eq.

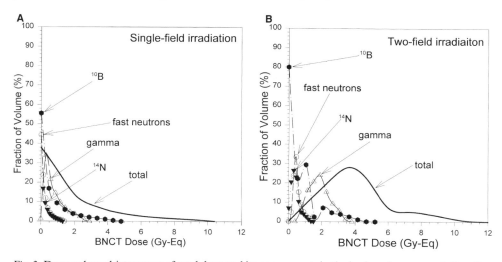

Fig. 2. Dose-volume histograms of total dose and its components in the brains of a representative glioblastoma patient treated under protocol from group 1 (**A**) or group 4 (**B**).

The dose distribution in the brain changes considerably for patients receiving double-field irradiations. The right panel of Fig. 1 illustrates the total dose distribution in a patient treated under Protocol #4b (group 4). For this patient, only 30% of the neutron irradiation was delivered from the contralateral side in order to spare healthy tissue of the contralateral hemisphere. The corresponding dose-volume histograms are shown in the right panel of Fig. 2. Again, although the average total brain dose increased significantly, only a relatively small fraction of the brain received doses greater than 7.5 Gy-Eq. The following volume-averaged doses were delivered to the hemispheres during this bilateral irradiation: ipsilateral hemisphere 7.0 Gy-Eq (4.8 Gy-Eq high-LET, and 2.2 Gy-Eq low-LET); and contralateral hemisphere 3.9 Gy-Eq (2.2 Gy-Eq high-LET, and 1.7 Gy-Eq low-LET dose).

Discussion

During BNCT, the brain is exposed to a complex mixture of radiations. Interactions between biological effects of components of this mixture of radiations on normal tissues are not fully understood. Therefore, it is extremely problematic to extrapolate the RBE or CBE of mixed field radiation obtained from animal experiments to predict safe doses to the normal human brain. As discussed by Coderre et al. [9] in this volume, because of the large differences in human vs. dog brain volumes and in the gradients in the BNCT dose distribution, dose volume histograms rather than peak doses offer more meaningful ways for comparison. Also, because the contributions of different dose components change with depth in the tissue, use of physical dose alone may be misleading. Expression of the total dose in weighted units such as Gy-Eq is a better alternative despite the intrinsic problems associated with the determination of compound-adjusted biological effectiveness of mixed-field BNCT radiations.

The BNCT doses to which our patients have been exposed are considerably lower than the doses that were shown to be safe in canine BNCT studies [9] and conventional radiotherapy in patients [10]. These observations suggest that further dose escalation to improve the outcome of BNCT may be possible.

Acknowledgements

This work was supported by the US Department of Energy contract #DE-AC02-76CH00016.

References

1. Chanana AD, Coderre JA, Joel DD, Slatkin DN. Protocols for BNCT of glioblastoma multiforme at Brookhaven: Practical considerations. In: Larsson B, Crawford J, Weinreich R (eds) Advances in Neutron Capture Therapy. Volume 2, Chemistry and Biology. Amsterdam: Elsevier Science, 1997;571–574 (these proceedings).

2. Liu B, Capala J, Joel DD, Brugger RM, Rorer DC. NCT facilities at the Brookhaven Medical Research Reactor. In: Larsson B, Crawford J, Weinreich R (eds) Advances in Neutron Capture Therapy. Volume 1, Medicine and Physics. Amsterdam: Elsevier Science, 1997;311—315 (these proceedings).

3. Wielopolski L, Capala J, Chadha M, Pendzick NE, Chanana AD. Considerations for patient positioning in static beams for BNCT. In: Larsson B, Crawford J, Weinreich R (eds) Advances in Neutron Capture Therapy. Volume 1, Medicine and Physics. Amsterdam: Elsevier Science, 1997;357—360 (these proceedings).

4. Nigg DW, Wheeler FJ, Wessol DE, Wemple CA, Babcock R, Capala J. Some recent developments in treatment planning software and methodology for BNCT. In: Larsson B, Crawford J, Weinreich R (eds) Advances in Neutron Capture Therapy. Volume 1, Medicine and Physics. Amsterdam: Elsevier Science, 1997;91—94 (these proceedings).

5. Nigg DW, Wheeler FJ, Wessol DE, Capala J, Chadha M. Computational dosimetry and treatment planning for boron neutron capture therapy. J Neuro-Oncol 1996;(In press).

6. Joel DD, Coderre JA, Nawrocky MM, Slatkin, ND, Chanana AD. Uptake of BPA into glioblastoma multiforme correlates with tumor cellularity. In: Larsson B, Crawford J, Weinreich R (eds) Advances in Neutron Capture Therapy. Volume 2, Chemistry and Biology. Amsterdam: Elsevier Science, 1997;225—228 (these proceedings).

7. Coderre JA, Makar MS, Micca PL, Nawrocky MM, Liu HB, Joel DD, Slatkin DN, Amols HI. Derivations of relative biological effectiveness for the high-LET radiations produced during boron neutron capture irradiations of the 9L rat gliosarcoma in vitro and in vivo. Int J Radiat Oncol Biol Phys 1993;27:1121—1129.

8. Morris GM, Coderre JA, Hopwell JW, Micca PL, Nawrocky MM, Liu HB, Bywaters A. Response of the central nervous system to boron neutron capture irradiation: evaluation using rat spinal cord model. Radiother Oncol 1994;32:249—255.

9. Coderre JA, Morris GM, Capala J, Micca PL, Fisher CD, Gavin PR, Blazek ER. Radiobiology in support of the BNCT clinical trial. In: Larsson B, Crawford J, Weinreich R (eds) Advances in Neutron Capture Therapy. Volume 2, Chemistry and Biology. Amsterdam: Elsevier Science, 1997;588—592 (these proceedings).

10. Shaw GS, Coffey RJ, Dinapoli RP. Neurotoxicity of radiosurgery. Sem Radiat Oncol 1995;5:235—245.

Advances in Neutron Capture Therapy.
Volume I, Medicine and Physics.
B. Larsson, J. Crawford and R. Weinreich, editors.

A phase I/II trial of BNCT for glioblastoma multiforme using intravenous boronophenylalanine-fructose complex and epithermal neutrons: early clinical results

E.H. Elowitz[1], M. Chadha[2], J. Iwai[3], J.A. Coderre[3], D.D. Joel[3], D.N. Slatkin[3] and A.D. Chanana[3]

Departments of [1]Neurosurgery and [2]Radiation Oncology, Beth Israel Medical Center, New York, New York; and [3]Medical Department, Brookhaven National Laboratory, Upton, New York, USA

Keywords: boron neutron capture therapy, boronophenylalanine, epithermal neutrons, glioblastoma multiforme.

Introduction

Boron neutron capture therapy (BNCT) is a binary treatment that allows for selective irradiation of cancer cells. Unlike conventional radiation therapy, the selectivity of BNCT depends less on the energy source than on the boron delivery agent. The interaction of the ^{10}B with slow neutrons (neutron capture) releases high-energy α particles (^4He) and lithium ions (^7Li), which have a path length of approximately 14 µm, about the diameter of one or two cells [1]. BNCT of glioblastoma multiforme (GBM) was initially performed at Brookhaven National Laboratory (BNL) in the early 1950s and continued at both BNL and the Massachusetts Institute of Technology until 1961. These trials were deemed unsuccessful and were discontinued, in large part because the boron compounds used showed little specificity for tumor. In Japan, Hatanaka et al. [2] have treated more than 150 patients with high-grade gliomas with BNCT using the sulfhydryl borane (BSH). The reports of long-term survival in selected patients with high-grade gliomas have served to maintain interest in BNCT.

Boronophenylalanine (BPA) is an amino acid analog that is blood brain barrier permeable. It was developed initially for use in BNCT of melanoma but has also been applied to malignant gliomas [3,4]. In the rat 9L gliosarcoma, BNCT irradiation, after BPA administration, has been effective in tumor control [4]. A biodistribution study performed in patients undergoing craniotomy for debulking of glioblastoma found no toxicity during or after 2-h intravenous BPA infusions [5]. Analysis of tumor samples indicated selective uptake into viable glioma cells with a boron tumor/blood ratio of at least 3.5:1. A phase I/II clinical trial of BNCT using intravenous p-boronophenylalanine-fructose (BPA-F) and epithermal neutrons was initiated to determine the safety and possible efficacy of BNCT for glioblastoma.

Material and Methods

Selection criteria for the study included patients with histologically confirmed GBM, tumor unilateral $\leqslant 6.0$ cm from the skin surface, age 18 years or older, Karnofsky Performance Status $\geqslant 70$, and no prior irradiation or chemotherapy. Patients were required to undergo craniotomy, and debulking of tumors with a concurrent biodistribution study of BPA-F boron concentrations in blood, brain, tumor and scalp samples. BNCT was performed at BNL using the Brookhaven Medical Research Reactor epithermal neutron beam at a minimum of 3 weeks following surgery. Treatment planning was performed with the software developed at the Idaho National Engineering Laboratory and is described in detail by Chadha et al. in these proceedings. A contrast-enhanced MRI scan was used to determine the tumor volume (area of contrast enhancement) and target volume (tumor volume plus a 2 cm surrounding margin). At BNL, patients received a dose of 250 mg/kg BPA-F in a 2-h intravenous infusion just prior to BNCT. Based on the measured blood boron values at the start and midpoint of BNCT, the irradiation time was adjusted to yield a normal brain endothelium dose of 10.5 Gy-Eq to the peak-dose volume. Following BNCT, the patients were observed in hospital for a minimum of 48 h.

Patients were followed with serial MRI or CT scans and physical examination. No specific kind of further therapy was prescribed for tumor progression in the protocol.

Results and Discussion

A total of 10 (seven females; three males; age 46–75 with median = 61) patients with GBM were treated on the described BNCT protocol with at least 1-year follow-up. All patients tolerated BNCT without complication and no new neurologic deficits were noted. Nine of the 10 patients underwent two craniotomies prior to BNCT. A time interval of 0.9–5.7 months (median = 2.9 months) was observed between the time of diagnosis and BNCT. The long delay in treatment seen for several patients was a result of those patients waiting for protocol changes.

Seizures were observed in three patients 2–7 days after BNCT; two had a history of prior seizures and one was not on anticonvulsants. It is therefore our recommendation that patients undergoing BNCT have therapeutic anticonvulsant levels.

Following BNCT, survival postdiagnosis was 3–16.8 months with a median time of 13.5 months (Table 1). Two of the 10 patients are still alive, although with recurrences. One patient died 3 months after diagnosis from disseminated leptomeningeal disease, an uncommon complication of glioblastoma. No relationship was seen between patient survival time and time to progression. (The patient with disseminated spinal disease expired prior to local disease progression.) Table 1 also describes the salvage therapy used once treatment failure was

Table 1. BNCT of glioblastoma: patient survival.

Postdiagnosis survival (months)	Time to progression (months)	Salvage therapy	Time from progression to endpoint (months)
3.0	—	—	Disseminated spinal disease
8.2	3.0	Debulking	1.4
9.5	6.0	BCNU	1.6
10.6	4.7	—	3.1
12.2	6.0	—	2.1
14.7	7.0	Debulking	4.0
15.0	6.0	Debulking	3.1
15.3	9.0	Chemo	3.3 alive
15.6	2.7	Radiosurgery Debulking	10.3 alive
16.8	3.5	Debulking Radiosurgery	10.9

diagnosed. The type of secondary therapy was determined by the patient's referring physician and was not mandated by the BNCT protocol. Half of the patients had further debulking surgery. Two of these five patients also underwent radiosurgery and were the longest survivors in this study. Table 1 illustrates that the main determinant of patient overall survival was the duration of time after tumor progression. This argues for more aggressive therapy in BNCT patients after treatment failure.

In this study, interval radiographic evaluations were performed to monitor possible tumor progression. The time to treatment failure was 2.7–9.0 months with a median of 6.0 months (Table 2). Although there was a tendency towards earlier recurrence times in deeper tumors, this was not statistically significant. Chadha et al. (this volume), describe a statistically significant correlation between higher median average tumor radiation dose and higher minimum target radiation dose in patients with longer times to failure.

Although this study was designed chiefly to help determine a safe starting dose for BNCT with BPA-F and epithermal neutrons, treatment outcomes as compared to conventional therapy for GBM were also analyzed. Curran et al. [6] performed a recursive partitioning analysis of 1,578 malignant glioma patients treated with radiation and chemotherapy. Six classes of patients were determined based on pathology, age and functional status. Evaluation of the BNCT patients indicates a similar survival to that expected from conventional therapy. For example, 7/10 BNCT patients would be graded as Curran Class V with an observed median survival of 12.2 months compared to 8.9 months in the Curran et al. analysis.

In summary, BNCT of glioblastoma using BPA-F and epithermal neutrons was found to be safe with a median survival time postdiagnosis of 13.5 months. Further trials of BNCT with higher radiation doses will be necessary to establish efficacy.

Table 2. BNCT of glioblastoma: tumor progression.

Time to progression (months)	Tumor depth from scalp (cm)	Tumor volume (cm³)	Minimum tumor dose (Gy-Eq)	Postdiagnosis survival (months)
2.7	5.5	23	19.8	15.6 alive
3.0	5.2	70	20.4	8.2
3.5	5.0	18	26.8	16.8
4.7	4.3	18	23.0	10.6
6.0	4.9	19	27.6	9.5
6.0	5.3	56	25.7	12.2
6.0	4.3	29	32.3	15.0
7.0	4.3	18	28.5	14.7
9.0	4.5	21	27.8	15.3 alive

Note: The patient who died early of spinal disease is not included.

References

1. Slatkin DN. A history of boron neutron capture therapy of brain tumors. Brain 1991;114: 1609–1629.
2. Hatanaka H, Nakagawa Y. Clinical results of long-surviving brain tumor patients who underwent boron neutron capture therapy. Int J Radiat Oncol Biol Phys 1994;28:1061–1066.
3. Mallesch JL, Moore DE, Allen BJ, McCarthy WH, Jones R, Stening WA. The pharmacokinetics of *p*-boronophenylalanine-fructose in human patients with glioma and metastatic melanoma. Int J Radiat Oncol Biol Phys 1994;28:1183–1188.
4. Coderre JA, Joel DD, Micca PL, Nawrocky MM, Slatkin DN. Control of intracerebral gliosarcoma in rats by boron neutron capture therapy with *p*-boronophenylalanine. Radiat Res 1992; 129:290–296.
5. Coderre JA, Elowitz EH, Chadha M, Bergland RM, Capala J, Chanana AD, Joel DD, Liu HB, Slatkin DN. Boron neutron capture therapy for glioblastoma multiforme using p-boronophenylalanine and epithermal neutrons; trial design and early clinical results. J Neuro Oncol (In press).
6. Curran WJ, Scott CB, Horton J, Nelson JS, Weinstein AS, Fischbach AJ, Chang CH, Rotman M, Asbell SO, Krisch RE, Nelson DF. Recursive partitioning analysis of prognostic factors in three Radiation Therapy Oncology Group malignant glioma trials. J Natl Canc Inst 1993;85: 704–710.

Advances in Neutron Capture Therapy.
Volume I, Medicine and Physics.
B. Larsson, J. Crawford and R. Weinreich, editors.

Clinical follow-up of patients with melanoma of the extremity treated in a phase I boron neutron capture therapy protocol

P.M. Busse[1,2], R. Zamenhof[1], H. Madoc-Jones[3], G. Solares[1], S. Kiger[4], K. Riley[4], C. Chuang[4], G. Rogers[5] and O. Harling[4]

[1]*Beth Israel Deaconess Medical Center, Boston, Massachusetts;* [2]*Joint Center for Radiation Therapy, Harvard Medical School, Boston, Massachusetts;* [3]*New England Medical Center, Boston, Massachusetts;* [4]*Massachusetts Institute of Technology, Cambridge, Massachusetts; and* [5]*Boston Medical Center, Boston, Massachusetts, USA*

Keywords: BNCT, BPA, Harvard, melanoma, MIT.

Introduction

The clinical use of boron neutron capture therapy (BNCT) is receiving renewed interest in the USA following the initial experiences with this modality 35 years ago. Active protocols are in place at the Brookhaven National Laboratory (BNL) and at Harvard/Massachusetts Institute of Technology (MIT) which are designed to evaluate the normal tissue tolerance following BNCT for glioblastoma (BNL and Harvard/MIT) as well as dermal tolerance following BNCT for melanoma (Harvard/MIT). Conceptually, melanoma is a very interesting and potentially favorable disease site for BNCT for a number of reasons. The first is the use of phenylalanine as a carrier molecule for boron as it is a precursor to melanin; second is the accessibility and superficiality of these tumors which lend themselves to biopsy and consequently objective measurement of response, availability for biopsy and a good distribution of dose. Data from Mishima using a thermal neutron beam indicate a high response rate for melanoma following BNCT [1]. This paper presents the initial results of a phase I trial designed to determine the skin tolerance to BNCT using an epithermal neutron beam in the setting of cutaneous melanoma of the extremity.

Materials and Methods

Between September 1994 and May 1996, four patients with biopsy-proven cutaneous melanoma of the extremity were treated to five separate sites as part of a phase I trial designed to study the normal tissue reaction following BNCT. Dose escalation was produced by an increase in the neutron fluence and a constant

---

Address for correspondence: Dr Paul M. Busse, Joint Center for Radiation Therapy, Harvard Medical School, 330 Brookline Avenue, Boston, MA 02215, USA. E-mail: Busse@JCRT.harvard.edu

administered dose of boron-10 which was delivered through *L*-boronophenyl-alanine-fructose (BPA). Initially, BPA was administered as a 400 mg/kg oral preparation (Centronic Ltd.); four patients received BPA in this fashion, the fifth received 250 mg/kg BPA-fructose via a 1-h intravenous administration. The neutron source was the MITR-II research reactor at MIT operating at 4.5 MW. The production and dosimetry of epithermal neutrons at this facility has been well-documented elsewhere [2].

All patients signed an informed consent and underwent a physical examination, routine blood work, EKG, and site-oriented CT scan for treatment planning purposes. The radiation dosimetry was determined through a custom-designed Monte Carlo based treatment planning program designed specifically for BNCT [3]. The treatment field measured 15 cm in diameter. Biopsies of tumor and normal tissue were obtained per protocol for determination of intracellular boron-10 concentration [4], blood concentrations of boron-10 were measured by prompt γ analysis or inductively coupled plasma-atomic emission spectroscopy (ICP-AES).

The study design was to escalate the total dose in five step-wise increments from 10 RBE-Gy to 20 RBE-Gy, three patients per dose level. The dose was prescribed as the normal tissue dose at D_{max}. Toxicity was scored according to the Lent Soma scale, and whenever possible an objective assessment was made of tumor response.

Results

The characteristics of the five patients are presented in Table 1. The median age was 65 years. All had recurrent melanoma at multiple sites within a lower extremity; all patients were free from known systemic disease. The boron-10 concentration in the blood, normal skin and melanoma as well as radiation dose at the D_{max} is shown in Table 2.

The pharmacokinetic profile of boron-10 in the blood following a 1-h intravenous administration is shown in Fig. 1. This produced a peak blood concentration of approximately 30–35 ppm followed by a characteristic biphasic pattern of elimination; the boron-10 concentration for the terminal, excretory phase was approximately 10 ppm. The isodose distribution of the treated extremity following i.v. BPA is shown in Fig. 2. Essentially the entire tumor-bearing tissue received

Table 1. Patient characteristics.

Initials	Age	Prim. site	Met. disease	Site treated	Tumor size
V.A.	65	R. foot	None	Sole R. foot	3 cm
G.H.	61	L. leg	None	L. leg	Mult. 2 cm
J.Y.	80	L. leg	None	Lower L. leg	Mult. 3 cm
P.D.	64	L. toe	Milt. cutaneous	R. med. thigh	2–4 mm
J.Y.	81	L. leg	None	Lower L. leg	Mult. 3.5 cm

Table 2. Boron-10 concentrations in blood, normal tissue and tumor.

Blood			Skin		Melanoma	
Initials	^{10}B ppm	RBE-cGy	^{10}B ppm	RBE-cGy	^{10}B ppm	RBE-cGy
V.A.	3.2	1001	3.7	1021	11.5	1317
G.H.	3.0	1001	3.5	1027	12.1	1512
J.Y.	4.5	1001	3.9	947	10.8	1389
P.D.	5.8	1250	N/A	N/A	N/A	N/A
J.Y.	11.5	1250	N/A	N/A	N/A	N/A

Note: N/A = not available. Blood concentrations measured through prompt γ analysis or ICP-AES. Tissue concentrations measured through high resolution autoradiography. RBE values used: ^{10}B, fast neutrons, thermal neutrons: 4; γ: 0.5.

a tumor-to-normal tissue RBE dose of at least 2:1.

The clinical endpoints of acute and chronic toxicity as well as tumor response to BNCT are shown in Table 3. No patient experienced toxicity. An interesting observation was the response of the melanotic nodules to BNCT. One patient was unevaluable as the nodules were removed during the biopsy for boron-10 analysis. One patient (JY) experienced a complete pathological response following BNCT; no tumor could be demonstrated in the biopsy specimen either by hematoxylin and eosin staining or by S-100 immunoperoxidase.

Discussion

This study provides additional follow-up with respect to the late normal tissue

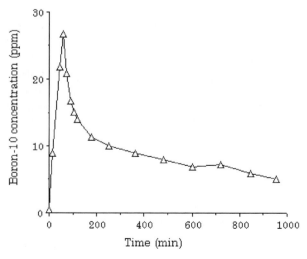

Fig. 1. Pharmacokinetic profile following i.v. BPA. Blood samples were obtained at the times indicated following a 1-h infusion of BPA-fructose 250 mg/kg.

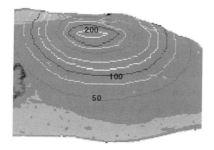

Fig. 2. Tumor isodose distribution following i.v. BPA. CT images were obtained through the lower extremity and the isodose distributions were generated with NCTPLAN. Isodose contour lines represent the percentage of the normal tissue D_{max}.

toxicity of the first cohort of patients treated with BNCT using oral BPA as the agent, and presents our initial data on the pharmacokinetic profile of boron-10 in the blood following intravenous administration. The absolute and relative concentrations of boron-10 in blood, normal tissue, and tumor were as predicted following oral BPA administration, and a higher concentration of boron-10 was consistently noted for melanoma which resulted in a therapeutic ratio of approximately 1.4:1. In order to achieve an even higher tumor concentration of boron-10 and to reduce the duration of neutron irradiation, the route of administration of BPA was changed after the first four subjects. BPA is now administered intravenously over 1 h at a concentration of 250 mg/kg in both glioblastoma and melanoma phase I protocols at Harvard/MIT. This produces a much more favorable intracellular boron concentration which translates into an increase in the therapeutic gain from 1.4:1 to 2:1.

To date, and perhaps most importantly, there has been no normal tissue reaction, either acute or chronic, associated with BNCT. The highest dose delivered has been 12.5 RBE-Gy.

Although technically not part of a phase I trial, the clinical response to BNCT was noted and it is gratifying that all evaluable patients experienced at least a partial response even at the lowest dose level. Three patients have experienced

Table 3. Normal tissue reactions and clinical response.

Initials	Follow-up	Skin reaction		Tumor response
		Acute	Chronic	
V.A.	11 months	None	Slight change in pigmentation	Partial
G.H.	17 months	None	None	Partial
J.Y.	19 months	Mild[a]	None	Complete (pathologic)
P.D.	10 months	None	None	Unable to evaluate[b]

[a]Tumor nodule became red and desquamated; [b]tumors removed with biopsy, no recurrence to date.

regrowth of disease within the irradiated volume. The single patient (JY) who achieved a complete response remains free of disease at this site.

Acknowledgements

This work was supported by a grant from the United States Department of Energy: DE-FG02-87ER-6060. Oral BPA was generously supplied by Centronic Ltd., Croydon, UK; Patient transport provided by American Medical Response, Boston, MA, USA.

References

1. Mishima Y. Selective thermal neutron capture therapy of cancer cells using their specific metabolic activities-melanoma as prototype. In: Mishima Y (ed) Cancer Neutron Capture Therapy. New York: Plenum Press, 1996:1–26.
2. Harling OK, Roberts KA, Moulin DJ, Rogus RD. Head phantoms for neutron capture therapy. Med Phys 1995;22:579–583.
3. Zamenhof R, Redmond E, Solares G et al. Monte Carlo-based treatment planning for boron neutron capture therapy using custom designed models automatically generated from CT data. Int J Radiat Oncol Biol Phys 1996;35:383–397.
4. Solares GR, Zamenhof RG. A new approach to the microdosimetry of neutron capture therapy. Proc Am Nucl Soc 1992;65:153–158.

Advances in Neutron Capture Therapy.
Volume I, Medicine and Physics.
B. Larsson, J. Crawford and R. Weinreich, editors.

What were important factors in patients treated by BNCT in Japan?

Yoshinobu Nakagawa[1], Pooh Kyonghon[1], Katsuji Kitamura[2], Teruyoshi Kageji[2] and Takashi Minobe[3]

[1]*Department of Neurosurgery, National Kagawa Children's Hospital, Zentsuji;* [2]*Department of Neurosurgery, Tokushima University, Tokushima; and* [3]*Japan Foundation for Emergency Medicine, Tokyo, Japan*

Introduction

Glioblastoma is a poorly differentiated glioma and is considered a carcinoma of the brain. It usually grows in the white matter of the cerebrum and rapidly invades the normal brain tissue in multiple directions before the time of diagnosis. Most of the patients with such an invasive glioma, not only glioblastoma but also anaplastic astrocytoma and low-grade astrocytoma, are beyond the point of curative surgical removal of the tumor because of the risk of damage to the surrounding normal brain tissue. Boron neutron capture therapy (BNCT) is an ideal treatment for such malignant brain tumors [1–5]. BNCT is based on the intracellular nuclear reaction that occurs between the ^{10}B nucleus and a thermal neutron. Upon capturing the thermal neutron, the boron nucleus disintegrates into highly energetic α particles (^{4}He) and recoiling lithium (^{7}Li) nuclei [6]. Because of the short pathways of these heavy particles and selective accumulation of ^{10}B in target tissues, the great potential advantage of BNCT is its cell level selective destruction of tumor tissue without significant damage to normal brain tissue. For a successful brain tumor treatment, it is essential to secure a sufficient radiation dose (enough α particles). This depends upon an adequate accumulation of boron in the tumor tissue and a satisfactory neutron fluence at the target area [7–9]. This paper reports the clinical results of the patients treated between 1968 and 1995. We also analyzed the radiation planning, dosimetry, and other basic data related to the prognostic factors in the clinical trial in Japan.

Material and Methods

Since August 1968, we have treated 152 patients with malignant brain tumors with the combination of BSH and thermal neutron beam of the reactors. BNCT

Address for correspondence: Yoshinobu Nakagawa, Department of Neurosurgery National Kagawa Children's Hospital, Zentsiji-cho 2603, Zentsuji City, Kagawa 765, Japan.

was performed a total of 167 times at five different reactors (HTR, JRR-3, MTII, KUR and JRR-2). Eligibility criteria included the presence of a histologically demonstrated malignant brain tumor, recurrent glioma (grade 2), deep-seated meningioma or huge AVM. Most of the tumors have been histologically classified according to the previous classification of WHO. In this series, all tumors were re-examined and reclassified according to the recent classification of WHO. It should be noted that 52% of the patients with glioma had glioblastoma multiforme. The definition "anaplastic astrocytoma" covered 40 patients, however the actual pathological diagnosis of the patients was: anaplastic astrocytoma, anaplastic oligodendroglioma and anaplastic ependymoma. Grade 3 astrocytoma is also included in this category. Seventeen patients had low-grade glioma (1 or 2) which includes oligoastrocytoma and ependymoma. A few patients were obscurely diagnosed as "grade 2 or 3". They were classified into the category of low-grade astrocytoma in this study. Most of the patients with low-grade astrocytoma had been treated by conventional radiotherapy or chemotherapy, with tumor recurrence having been demonstrated before BNCT. They were also classified as low-grade astrocytoma. Twenty-five patients out of 152 had other types of brain tumors (huge meningioma, PNET, metastatic brain tumors and huge AVM, etc.).

Results

Response rate

The tumor volume reduction rate after BNCT was studied in 84 patients having visible enhanced tumor on CT or MRI before BNCT. To evaluate the response to BNCT, we compared the contrast-enhanced CT or MRI studied before and after BNCT. The reduction rate was calculated by one or two slices of CT or MRI in which the largest part of the tumor was demonstrated before BNCT. The responses were classified into four groups. More than 50% reduction of the tumor areas on CT or MRI without an increase in secondary changes was recorded as a good response (GR). If there was less than 50%, but more than 25% reduction of the tumor area on CT or MRI without an increase in secondary changes, the patient was considered to have a partial response (PT). If there was less than 25% reduction of the tumor area on CT or MRI without an increase in secondary changes, the patient was considered to be in a stable condition (ST). The tumor was recorded as having progressed (RG) if there was more than a 25% increase in the tumor area accompanied by an increase in secondary change due to the tumor. When the tumor was scarcely visible on CT or MRI due to extensive surgical removal, the volume reduction was not evaluated (NE). However, if no new abnormally enhanced lesion was demonstrated on CT or MRI at 6 to 12 months after BNCT, these treatments were considered effective.

There were 37 GR and nine PR patients. In eight patients out of 13 patients in NE, no newly and abnormally enhanced lesion was demonstrated in the follow-up CT or MRI studied at one and at 6 months after BNCT. They were considered as effective. The overall response rate was 64%.

Survival rate

One out of 64 patients with glioblastoma, one out of 39 patients with anaplastic astrocytoma and three out of 16 patients with low-grade astrocytoma were excluded in this study.

Median survival time of glioblastoma was 640 days (39–8,138 days). Median survival time of patients with anaplastic astrocytoma was 1,811 days (17–6,641 days). Median survival time of the patients with low-grade astrocytoma was 1,668 days (256–2,638 days). Six patients (five glioblastoma and one anaplastic astrocytoma) died within 90 days after BNCT. Six patients lived more than 10 years (two glioblastoma patients and four anaplastic astrocytomas).

Prognostic factors

To investigate the prognostic factors which correlate to the result of BNCT, we divided the patients into two groups and analyzed the data: group 1 — the patients who lived less than 2 years; and group 2 — the patients who lived more than 2 years.

Histological factor

Thirty-seven out of 112 patients lived more than 2 years. There were seven patients with glioblastoma, 22 patients with anaplastic astrocytoma and eight patients with low-grade astrocytoma. 12% of glioblastoma, 56% of anaplastic astrocytoma and 62% of low-grade astrocytoma lived more than 2 years.

Previous treatment

Thirty-five patients (27 out of group 1 and eight out of group 2) had been treated by chemotherapy or conventional radiotherapy before BNCT. Median survival time of patients without previous treatment was 1,048 days, and 606 days in patients with previous treatment.

Median survival time of the patients with previous treatment in group 1 was 370 days and 348 in patients without previous treatment. Median survival time of patients without previous treatment in group 2 was 2,031 days, and 1,560 days in previously treated patients.

Age

The mean age of group 1 was 45.6 ± 14.1 years, and 37.6 ± 17.6 years in group 2. The difference is significant.

Radiation time

Mean radiation time was 255 ± 106 min in group 1, and 250 ± 90 min in group 2. The difference is not significant.

Target depth

This data factor does not mean the size of the tumor but the depth of the tumor from the brain surface in the center of the radiation field.

The target depth in group 1 was 5.8 ± 1.4 cm and 4.9 ± 1.6 cm in group 2. There was a statistically significant difference.

Neutron fluence

Neutron flux at the target point was measured by gold wires inserted in the tumor before irradiation in most of the cases. In cases where no suitable gold wires were inserted, the attenuation rate of the neutron beam was retrospectively calculated using a half-value layer of 1.6 cm. Maximum neutron fluence on the surface of the brain was 14.1 ± 8.5 (E + 12 n/cm^2) in group 1 and 15.9 ± 8.1 (E + 12 n/cm^2) in group 2. Neutron fluence at the target point was 4.8 ± 3.2 (E + 12 n/cm^2) in group 1 and 6.1 ± 3.5 (E + 12 n/cm^2) in group 2. There were no significant differences in maximum neutron fluence on the surface of the brain between the two groups; however, there were statistically significant differences in neutron fluence at the target point.

Boron concentration

Boron concentration was measured by chemical analysis (ICP-AES) or by using prompt γ-ray spectrometry. Boron concentration in the tumor was measured in 67 patients. Mean concentration of ^{10}B was 29.8 ± 17.3 ppm in group 1 and 21.7 ± 10.9 ppm in group 2.

Boron concentration in the blood was measured before and after the irradiation. The mean boron concentration of both data was 19.5 ± 14.5 ppm in group 1 and 15.4 ± 7.8 ppm in group 2.

There were no significant differences in boron concentrations in tumor or blood between the two groups.

Radiation dose

The radiation dose is provided by several components and not only the direct dose from the neutron beam but also γ rays, fast neutrons, etc. The dose was retrospectively calculated from boron neutron capture reactions ^{10}B(n,α) and ^{14}N(n,p)^{14}C, but excluding γ rays in this study. We did not use relative biological effectiveness (RBE) and the data was demonstrated as a physical absorbed dose

(Gy). One of the parameters for calculating the radiation dose is boron concentration. There are three possibilities: boron concentration in the tumor tissue, mean value in blood during the irradiation, and the mean value "26 ppm" which was reported by Hatanaka. We could not get enough specimens of brain tumor for boron analysis in some patients. The mean dose calculated using boron concentration in the tumor was 10.4 ± 8.1 Gy in group 1 and 11.3 ± 9.3 Gy in group 2. The dose calculated using mean values in blood was 7.3 ± 6.0 Gy in group 1 and 6.6 ± 4.0 Gy in group 2. The mean radiation dose calculated using 26 ppm of boron concentration was 9.3 ± 6.2 Gy in group 1 and 11.7 ± 6.8 Gy in group 2. There are significant differences between the two groups in the data calculated by boron concentration in the tumor or "26 ppm".

Conclusion

Survival rate in patients with glioblastoma treated by BNCT is less than that in the astrocytoma group (grade 2 and 3). To treat glioblastoma, higher radiation doses (more than 15 Gy of boron n,α reaction) may be necessary. We believe BNCT is one of the best forms of treatment for malignant brain tumors; however, to treat deep-seated brain tumors and recurrent tumors, BNCT needs further improvement such as a new boron compound and neutron beam.

Acknowledgements

This work has been continuously supported since 1969 up to 1992 by the Grants-In-Aid from the Ministry of Education, Culture and Science, and from 1992 through 1995 by Grants-In-Aid from the Ministry of Health and Welfare of Japan.

Boron-10 compounds have been supplied by the Shionogi Research Laboratories since 1967. This research was carried out as a research program of the Musashi Institute of Technology, Research Reactor Institute of Kyoto University and Japan Atomic Energy Research Institute (JRR-2).

References

1. Hatanaka H. Boron-neutron capture therapy for tumors. In: Karim ABM, Laws ER Jr (eds) Glioma. Berlin: Springer-Verlag, 1991;233–249.
2. Hatanaka H, Nakagawa Y. Clinical results of long-surviving brain tumor patients who underwent boron neutron capture therapy. Int J Radiat Oncol Biol Phys 1994;1061–1066.
3. Nakagawa Y et al. Boron neutron capture therapy for children with malignant brain tumor. Japan Atomic Energy Research Institute (ed) Proceedings of the 5th International Symposium on Advanced Nuclear Energy Research. 1993;907–914.
4. Nakagawa Y, Hatanaka Y. Recent study of boron neutron capture therapy for malignant brain tumors in Japan. In: Mishima Y (ed) Neutron Capture Therapy for Human Cancers. New York: Plenum Press, 1995;(In press).
5. Nakagawa Y, Hatanaka H. Boron neutron capture therapy: clinical brain tumor studies. J Neuro Oncol 1996;(In press).

6. Kobayashi K et al. Development of microanalysis system of 10-B in tissue for neutron capture therapy by prompt gamma-ray spectrometry. Ann Rep Res Reactor Inst Kyoto Univ 1981;14: 75−84.
7. Kageji T, Nakagawa Y, Hatanaka H. Pharmacokinetics and boron uptake of BSH ($Na_2B_{12}H_{11}SH$) in patients with intracranial tumors. J Neuro Oncol 1996;(In press).
8. Mukai K, Nakagawa Y, Matsumoto K. Prompt gamma ray spectrometry for in vivo measurement of boron-10 concentration in rabbit brain tissue. Neuro Med Chir (Tokyo) 1995;35(12): 855−860.
9. Nakagawa Y. Recent study of Boron neutron capture therapy for brain tumors. In: Wiersema RJ, Nigg DW (eds) Proceedings of the First International Workshop on Accelerator-Based Neutron Sources for Boron Neutron Capture Therapy. INEL report CONF-940976, Idaho Falls, 1994;11−23.

©1997 Elsevier Science B.V. All rights reserved.
Advances in Neutron Capture Therapy.
Volume I, Medicine and Physics.
B. Larsson, J. Crawford and R. Weinreich, editors.

Experience of boron neutron capture therapy in Japan

Keiji Kanda

Research Reactor Institute, Kyoto University, Kumatori-cho, Sennan-gun, Osaka, Japan

Keywords: boron neutron capture therapy, brain tumor, KUR, melanoma.

Introduction

Four research reactors are currently licensed for medical application in Japan. Throughout 1996, 215 clinical irradiations using these research reactors were performed for brain and skin tumors as indicated in Table 1. The number of chief medical doctors certified by the Government is 12 so far. Among them, eight doctors have already treated tumor patients using the Kyoto University Reactor (KUR). In the USA clinical trials have recently been restarted using epithermal neutrons at the Massachusetts Institute of Technology (MIT) and Brookhaven National Laboratory (BNL).

In this paper, the experience of clinical BNCT treatments which have been performed in Japan are reviewed from a physics standpoint, and current studies are also introduced.

History of physics studies for BNCT

The history of physics studies for BNCT can be described as follows:
1) To obtain intense thermal neutron sources — in Japan, only thermal neutrons from research reactors (KUR, JRR-2, MuITR) have been used.
2) To eliminate γ rays from neutron field — the bismuth scatterer concept was introduced to eliminate γ rays without reducing thermal neutron flux [1].
3) To collimate neutron beams — in Japan, various neutron shielding materials using LiF have been developed [2], by which the secondary γ rays are drastically reduced.
4) To measure or to calculate neutron flux distributions in the body in order to estimate $^{10}B(n,\alpha)$ ^7Li reactions in tumor and normal tissue — calculation codes using Monte Carlo method (MCNP) and discrete ordinate method (DOT) have been widely used, and phantom experiments are well-explained [3].

Recently in the USA, Europe and Australia, epithermal neutron fields have been intensively studied with a view to treating brain tumors, thus removing the need for surgical operation for irradiation [4,5]. In Japan most patients were treated by thermal neutrons, but for some exceptional patients we also upgraded the heavy water facility to realize an epithermal neutron field in the KUR [6].

72

Table 1. Number of BNCT irradiations in Japan (as of 9 August, 1996).

Reactor name	Institute	Brain	Melanoma	Total	Notice
HTR	Hitachi	13	0	13	until 1974
JRR-3	JAERI	1	0	1	until 1969
KUR	KURRI	47	14	61	since 1974
MITR	MuIT	99	9	108	until 1989
JRR-2	JAERI	32 (AVM5)	0	32	since 1990
Total		192	23	215	

KUR heavy water facility

The characteristics of the KUR heavy water facility shown in Fig. 1 are:
1) The only standard thermal neutron field in the world authorized by IAEA Advisory Group, with a pure Maxwellian distribution.
2) γ rays are of very low intensity.
3) Various neutron shielding materials such as tile, flexible sheet and textile, using LiF are available.
4) Irradiation equipment, such as an exposure pipe, an irradiation box with temperature and atmosphere control are used.

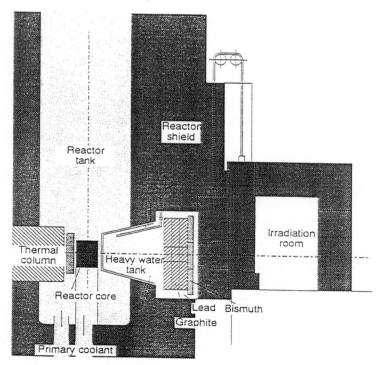

Fig. 1. KUR heavy water facility.

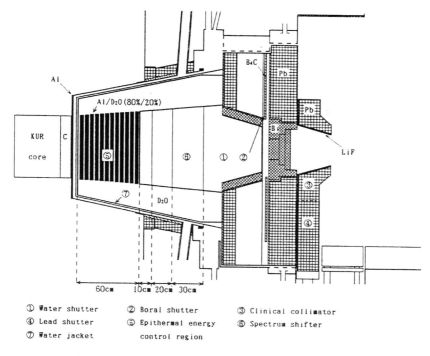

① Water shutter   ② Boral shutter   ③ Clinical collimator
④ Lead shutter   ⑤ Epithermal energy   ⑥ Spectrum shifter
⑦ Water jacket   control region

Fig. 2. Remodeling of the KUR heavy water facility.

5) An energy converter-fission plate of 25 cm in diameter, 90% enriched uranium of 1 kg, 3×10^{10} fission/s, is available for fast neutron experiments.
6) An irradiation room of 2.42×42.4 m is an integral part of the facility.
Recently, the budget of about US$6 million for remodeling the facility was approved, with which the facility has been significantly remodeled in order to utilize both thermal and epithermal neutrons, and to irradiate patients during continuous operation of the KUR as shown in Fig. 2.

Table 2. BSH and BPA.

	BSH	BPA
Name	Sodium mercaptoundeca-hydro-closo-dodecaborate	Para-boronophenyl-alanine
Chemical form	$Na_2B_{12}H_{11}SH$	p-$(HO)_2B$-C_6H_4-$CH_2CH(NH_2)COOH$
Concentration in tumor (ppm)	$3 \sim 20$	$15 \sim 40$
Concentration ratio of tumor to normal tissue	< 10	$2 \sim 4$
Concentration ratio of tumor to blood	~ 1	$3 \sim 5$
Applied tumor	glioblastoma	melanoma glioblastoma

Table 3. BNCT in KURRI since 1990 (as of 31 December, 1995).

Institute	Chief MD	Tumor	Number	B compound
Teikyo Univ.	H. Hatanaka	Brain tumor	7	BSH
Kagawa Children Hosp.	Y. Nakagawa	(mainly	15	BSH
Kyoto Univ.	Y. Oda	glioblastoma)	11	BSH or BPA
	M. Takagaki		4	
	S. Miyatake		3	
Kyoto Pref. Univ. of Med.	S. Ueda		6	BPA
Kobe Univ.	Y. Mishima	Melanoma	13	BPA
	M. Ichihashi			
Total			59	

Chemical compounds

Presently, two kinds of chemical compounds of boron are used for clinical trials; they are BSH and BPA as shown in Table 2. For glioblastoma patients, both BSH and BPA are used depending on their conditions.

Deep tumor treatment

So far, for deeper tumor treatment by thermal neutrons the following five techniques are applied:

Table 4. Record of cancer treatments using KUR since February 1990 (as of 31 December, 1995).

No.	Date	Age (years)	Sex	Nationality	Cancer[a]	Neutron influence	MD[b]
1	10/2/1990	64	M	Japanese	G	1.67×10^{13}	H.H.
2	10/2/1990	45	M	Japanese	G	1.97×10^{13}	H.H.
3	13/2/1990	61	M	Japanese	M	1.00×10^{13}	Y.M.
4 ~ 54 are skipped							
55	30/5/1995	31	M	Japanese	G	2.00×10^{13}	S.M.
56	11/6/1995	33	F	Japanese	G	2.00×10^{13}	S.M.
57	11/6/1995	54	F	Japanese	G	2.00×10^{13}	S.U.
58	11/10/1995	19	M	Japanese	G	1.80×10^{13}	M.T.
59	11/10/1995	51	M	Japanese	G	2.00×10^{13}	S.U.

[a]G: glioblastoma or astrocytoma, M: melanoma; [b]H.H.: H. Hatanaka (Teikyo University Hospital; G, seven patients); S.M.: S. Miyatake (Kyoto University; G, three patients); Y.N.: Y. Nakagawa (National Kagawa Children's Hospital; G, 15 patients); Y.O.: Y. Oda (Kyoto University; G ,11 patients); M.T.: M. Takagaki (Kyoto University; G, four patients); S.U.: S. Ueda (Kyoto Prefectural University of Medicine; G, six patients); M.I.: M. Ichihashi (Kobe University; M, three patients); Y.M.: Y. Mishima (Mishima Institute for Dermatological Research; M, 10 patients).

1) optimize the beam size [3];
2) adjust the forward directional components of neutron beam [3,7];
3) make a void in the human body [3,8];
4) replace natural body water (i.e., light water) partially with heavy water [3,9]; and
5) use epithermal or hyperthermal neutrons [4—6,10,11].

Experience of BNCT irradiation in the KUR

In 1974, we treated one patient at the KUR. Following that treatment all technology was transferred to Musashi Institute of Technology [12], where approximately 100 patients were treated. Due to problems at the Musashi reactor, the KUR has been utilized again for BNCT since 1990. Table 3 shows the record of the treatments and Table 4 shows the detailed data of some irradiations.

References

1. Kanda K, Kobayashi K, Okamoto S, Shibata T. Thermal neutron standard field with a Maxwellian distribution using the KUR heavy water facility. Nucl Instrum Methods 1978;148: 535—541.
2. Kanda K, Kobayashi T, Takeuchi M, Ouchi S. Development of Neutron Shielding Material Using LiF. Proceedings of the Sixth International Conference on Radiation Shielding. Tokyo, Japan: Japan Atomic Energy Research Institute (JAERI), May 1983;1258—1265.
3. Sakurai Y, Kobayashi T, Kanda K. A study on the improvement of thermal neutron dose distribution in tissue for neutron capture therapy. Annu Rep Res Reactor Inst Kyoto Univ 1992;25: 63—77.
4. Wheeler FJ, Parsons DK, Rushton BL, Nigg DW. Epi-thermal neutron beam design for neutron capture therapy at the Power Burst Facility and the Brookhaven Medical Research Reactor. Nucl Technol 1990;92:106—117.
5. Harling OK, Yanch JC, Choi JR, Solares GR, Rogus RD, Moulin DJ, Johnson LS, Olmez I, Wirdzek S, Bernard JA, Zamenhof RG, Nwanguma CI, Wazer DE, Saris S, Madoc-Jones H, Sledge CB, Shortkroff S. Boron neutron capture therapy and radiation synovectomy research at the Massachusetts Institute of Technology Research Reactor. Nucl Sci Eng 1992;110:330—348.
6. Sakurai Y, Kobayashi T, Kanda K, Fujita Y. Feasibility study on neutron energy spectrum shifter in the KUR Heavy Water Facility for Neutron Capture Therapy. Annu Rep Res Reactor Inst Kyoto Univ 1993;26:8—25.
7. Kobayashi T, Fujihara S, Kanda K. Effective thermal neutron collimation for neutron capture therapy using neutron scattering and absorption reactions. In: Allen BJ et al. (eds) Progress in Neutron Capture Therapy for Cancer. New York: Plenum Press, 1992;7—12.
8. Hatanaka H, Kamano S, Amano K, Hojo S, Sano K, Egawa S, Yasukochi H. Clinical experience of boron-neutron capture therapy for gliomas — a comparison with conventional chemo-immuno-radiotherapy. In: Hatanaka H (ed) Boron-Neutron Capture Therapy for Tumors. Niigata, Japan: Nishimura & Co, ISBN 4-89013-052-7, 1986;349—379.
9. Kobayashi T, Ono M, Kanda K. Measurement and analysis on neutron flux distributions in a heavy water phantom using the KUR neutron guide tube for BNCT. Strahlenther Onkol 1989;165:101—103.
10. Fairchild RG. Development and dosimetry of an "epithermal" neutron beam for possible use in neutron capture therapy. Phys Med Biol 1965;10:491—504.

11. Sakurai Y, Kobayashi T, Kanda K. A fundamental study on hyper-thermal neutrons for neutron capture therapy. Phys Med Biol 1994;39:2217—2227.
12. Aizawa O, Kanda K, Nozaki T, Matsumoto T. Remodeling and dosimetry on the neutron irradiation facility of the Musashi Institute of Technology Reactor for boron neutron capture therapy. Nucl Technol 1980;48:150—163.

©1997 Elsevier Science B.V. All rights reserved.
Advances in Neutron Capture Therapy.
Volume I, Medicine and Physics.
B. Larsson, J. Crawford and R. Weinreich, editors.

The clinical project at HFR Petten — a status report

Wolfgang Sauerwein

EORTC BNCT Study Group and the EU Shared Cost Action "Glioma BNCT", Universitäts-Strahlenklinik Essen, Germany

Introduction

Based on the work of the European Collaboration on Boron Neutron Capture Therapy, a phase I trial [1] has been prepared in order to initiate boron neutron capture therapy (BNCT) of glioblastoma at the high flux reactor (HFR) in Petten (The Netherlands), which is owned by the European Commission [2]. The knowledge of distribution and pharmacokinetics of the drug $Na_2B_{12}H_{11}SH$ (BSH) as well as its radiobiological effects in healthy brain tissue of dogs were the most important factors in planning the strategy for the trial [3—5]. A neutron beam of suitable characteristics for treatment of deep-seated tumors has been installed at the HFR [6]. It is one of three epithermal beams available worldwide for BNCT, and the only one with a high forward directionality of the neutrons [7]. The primary goal of the study is the investigation of possible adverse reactions to BNCT in order to establish the maximum tolerated dose in patients suffering from glioblastoma.

However, due to the multinational nature of the study, multiple administrative and legal obstacles had to be surmounted, causing considerable delay to the preparation phase.

Trial design

Cohorts of 10 patients with glioblastoma will undergo the following step-wise treatment for glioma with BNCT: surgical removal of the tumor accompanied by a BSH uptake study; radiotherapy with BNCT instead of conventional radiotherapy for the tumor; evaluation of the toxicity of the treatment (radiotoxicity as well as toxicity of the drug itself). In addition, survival and quality of life will be recorded. Patients will be selected for whom no benefit from conventional treatment can be expected, but who can be followed up for long enough to detect any adverse effects on brain tissue due to BNCT, or any unexpected benefit in survival. The selection criteria define a group of patients with a median survival of approximately 10 months after operation.

Eligibility criteria

— Aged between 50 and 70 years at inclusion;
— Karnovsky index $\geqslant 70$;
— tumor histology: glioblastoma, confirmed by reference pathology center;
— surgery: $> 70\%$ of the tumor removed, confirmed by postoperative magnetic resonance imaging (MRI);
— blood boron concentration $\geqslant 25$ ppm, 12 h after infusion of 100 mg/kg BSH;
— good recovery from surgery;
— beam available within 4 weeks after surgery; and
— informed consent.

Surgery with BSH uptake study

Approximately 18 h prior to operation, 100 mg/kg body weight BSH (enriched to $> 95\%$ ^{10}B) will be infused.

Standard craniotomy for gross total resection will be performed in order to:
1) confirm the diagnosis of glioblastoma by the reference pathology center;
2) debulk the tumor mass, offering the patient the benefit of a proven treatment; and
3) measure boron concentration in tumor, healthy tissues and in blood.

Radiation therapy

BNCT will be administered instead of conventional radiotherapy. The planning target volume includes the gross tumor volume plus 2 cm surrounding tissues. The treatment will be performed in four fractions on 4 consecutive days. BSH will be infused prior to each fraction. Reasons for fractionation are:
1) The delivered total dose can be adjusted more closely to the prescribed dose (unwanted over- and underdosage in one fraction, due to unanticipated variation of ^{10}B concentration during the treatment, can be corrected in the subsequent fractions).
2) There is a retargeting of BSH to tumor following repeated BSH administration.
3) Results of the dog experiments suggest a sparing of healthy tissue with fractionation.

For treatment planning, a program based on Monte Carlo calculations and using a computer code developed at INEL, Idaho, USA, by F.J. Wheeler will be used [8]. This program has been in use on patients for the Brookhaven trials since 1994.

The starting dose is set at 80% of the dose which in the healthy tissue tolerance study in dogs with a single fraction gave rise to a 50% incidence of neurological symptoms. This starting dose should be far enough away from the dose which causes serious adverse events. Nevertheless, the dose will be sufficiently close to a therapeutically effective dose to offer a potential benefit to the patient.

Administered amount of BSH and interval between administration and BNCT

For the first fraction, BSH will be administered at a concentration of 100 mg/kg body weight. Timing of the administration and amounts to be administered at the second, third, and fourth fractions will be such that an average concentration of 30 ppm ^{10}B in blood will be obtained for all fractions. The time of administration should be between 12 and 18 h prior to irradiation. This time schedule will allow the optimum dose ratio between tumor and healthy tissue.

Prescribing, recording and reporting BNCT

The definitions published in the ICRU reports as well as ASTM standards or other international accepted standards have to be taken into account. Nevertheless it has to be stressed that the ICRU recommendations for photon beam therapy [9] or clinical neutron dosimetry [10] cannot be applied directly and completely in BNCT. The absorbed dose as a macroscopic quantity is the basic parameter for prescribing, recording and reporting a radiotherapeutic procedure. Using this approach for our purposes, the microscopic dose distributions of short range high-LET particles (α, Li-nucleus and protons) are averaged over macroscopic volumes. The total dose distribution is provided by several dose components. In addition to the boron neutron capture absorbed dose, which depends on the concentration of ^{10}B, other dose components to be considered are the absorbed dose from recoil protons produced by the scattering of fast neutrons on hydrogen, the absorbed dose from protons emitted by ^{14}N(n,p)^{14}C, and the absorbed dose from incident γ radiation and photons generated in the ^{1}H(n,γ)^{2}H reaction. The total absorbed dose is the sum of all absorbed dose components of the complex beam. Reporting of the dose must always be done by describing the absorbed dose of each component.

Nevertheless, it may be helpful to add the different dose components to obtain one single "biologically weighted dose". The unit of this biologically weighted dose (D_{WU}) will be called "weighted dose unit" (WU) ("triple U"), which is the sum of the different dose components multiplied by their respective biological weighting factors [1]. D_{WU} allows the direct translation of the sum of the different dose components to photon doses. The factors which are used to describe biological effects of the different dose components have to be reported explicitly.

Radiation dose escalation

The dose is to be increased by 10% over that of the previous cohort, at the earliest 6 months after the treatment of the last patient of that cohort, if no treatment-related serious adverse events are seen. If during this period at least two of the already irradiated patients show serious adverse events clearly arising from the treatment tested, the trial is to be stopped.

Organizational structure and administrative obstacles

The University of Essen (Germany) irradiates patients sent from five different countries (Austria, France, Germany, Switzerland and The Netherlands) at the HFR Petten, which is owned by the European Commission and located in The Netherlands. During the period of treatment, patients are hospitalized at the Free University of Amsterdam. The monitoring of the trial is performed by the New Drug Development Office (NDDO) of the EORTC. The study is financed as a shared cost action by the European Commission, within the BIOMED II Program. The treatment in Petten is done in cooperation with ECN and JRC under the overall clinical responsibility of the Department of Radiotherapy of the University of Essen.

The practicalities of obtaining approval for such a complex multinational project were vastly underestimated. This was primarily due to the difficulties in identifying the appropriate authorities which had to be involved in the different countries. Even the ministries dealing with health policy could not answer our questions clearly. No European approach is available due to the fact that medical applications fall under national law and there is no harmonization on the European level. Some of the issues which had to be solved are mentioned briefly here:

— License to use the reactor as a facility for patient treatment.
— License to irradiate patients at a facility which is not part of a hospital.
— License for foreign physicians (EU and non-EU), who are staff members of a non-Dutch institution, to treat patients in The Netherlands.
— To enable a non-Dutch Medical Physicist to be responsible and liable for Medical Physics at HFR Petten.
— To identify the different liabilities towards patients for actions by persons coming from different institutions in different countries to cooperate in the treatment of one patient; furthermore, to describe the tasks of all participants, to create and to approve the appropriate agreements and contracts to define such structures.
— To reconcile the different points of view of different ethics committees in different countries.
— Establishment of the EORTC BNCT Study Group.
— Approval of the study protocol by different boards at different levels in multitude of institutions.
— Insurance for patients following different national procedures.
— Local approval concerning safety aspects at the reactor site.
— To build up the local infrastructure for patient care, including emergencies.
— Application of the appropriate rules for radioprotection of the patients and the staff, respecting both German and Dutch regulations.
— To handle a nonregistered drug to be used in different countries following the study protocol.
— To regulate the execution of the study protocol as well as the operation of the

facility by appropriate standard operating procedures respecting the rules of good clinical practice.
— Conclusion of contracts, subcontracts, association agreements, collaboration agreements, etc., with all involved parties as well as the European commission following the rules established for Shared Cost Actions.

In The Netherlands alone the following authorities had to be involved:
— Ministry of Health, Welfare and Sport (VWS);
— Ministry of Economic Affairs (EZ);
— Ministry of Social Affairs (SZW);
— Ministry of Environment (VROM);
— Ministry of Foreign Affairs (BZ);
— Health Inspectorate for North Holland; and
— Mayor's Office of the Community of Zijpe.

In the other countries as well as on European level, there were similar interactions which had to be done separately with no possibility of coordination. Now, 1 year after the official start of the project (not taking into account the many years of scientific preparation) all the problems seem to be solved and the first patient may be treated in summer 1997.

Acknowledgements

The project is supported by the BIOMED II program of the European Union (BMH4 CT960325). A special acknowledgment should be directed to D. Gabel for his tenacity and engagement which was the base for this success. Appreciation is also given to all the public servants throughout Europe who made their contributions to overcoming the various obstacles.

References

1. EORTC European Organization for Research and Treatment of Cancer, BNCT Study Group. Protocol 11 961 "Postoperative treatment of glioblastoma with BNCT at the Petten Irradiation Facility". Brussels: EORTC, 1997.
2. Gabel D, Sauerwein W. Approaching clinical trials of boron neutron capture therapy in Europe. In: Kogelnik HD (ed) Progress in Radio-Oncology V. Bologna: Monduzzi Editore, 1995; 315—319.
3. Haritz D, Gabel D, Huiskamp R. Clinical phase-I study of $Na_2B_{12}H_{11}SH$ (BSH) in patients with malignant glioma as precondition for boron neutron capture therapy. Int J Rad Oncol Biol Phys 1994;28:1175—1181.
4. Haselsberger K, Pendl G, Radner H. BNCT with Na2B12H11SH: boron biodistribution in patients with glioblastoma. In: Kogelnik HD (ed) Progress in Radio-Oncology V. Bologna: Monduzzi Editore, 1995;321—323.
5. Stragliotto G, Fankhauser H. Biodistribution of boron sulfhydryl (BSH) in patients with intracranial tumors. Neurosurgery 1995;36:185—293.
6. Moss RL, Stecher-Rasmussen F, Ravensberg K, Constantine G, Watkins P. Design, construction and installation of an epithermal neutron beam for BNCT at the high flux reactor in Petten. In: Allen BJ, Moore DE, Harrington BV (eds) Progress in Neutron Capture Therapy for Cancer. New York, London: Plenum Press, 1992;63—66.

7. Moss RL, Aizawa O, Beynon D, Brugger R, Constantine G, Harling O, Liu HB, Watkins P. The requirements and development of neutron beams for neutron capture therapy of brain cancer. J Neuro Oncol 1997;33:27—40.
8. Wheeler FJ. Radiation transport in tissue by Monte Carlo = Version X02. Idaho National Engineering Laboratory Report No. EEG-BNCT-11178; 1995.
9. ICRU report 50: Prescribing, recording and reporting photon beam therapy. ICRU, 1993.
10. ICRU report 45: Clinical neutron dosimetry part I: Determination of absorbed dose in a patient treated by external beams of fast neutrons. ICRU, 1989.

Therapy planning

1997 Elsevier Science B.V.
Advances in Neutron Capture Therapy.
Volume I, Medicine and Physics.
B. Larsson, J. Crawford and R. Weinreich, editors.

Optimization in neutron capture therapy planning

Floyd J. Wheeler

Idaho National Engineering Laboratory, Lockheed Martin Idaho Technologies Co., Idaho Falls, Idaho, USA

Introduction

Treatment planning dose calculations for epithermal-neutron capture therapy to date have relied on rigorous Monte Carlo (stochastic simulation) radiation transport calculations which require hours of computer time per field. Optimization consists of an intuition-aided trial and error approach which is adequate for single-field, fixed-aperture applications when sufficient time is available.

As degrees of freedom increase (number of fields, field size, aperture, etc.) it will not be possible to optimize each patient plan without faster and more automated procedures in treatment planning calculations. Without such tools, it will be very difficult to move from clinical trials, where large resources are available, to clinical application where planning must be done with little resources. The purpose of this study is to develop and implement a process addressing these needs.

Methodology

The Monte Carlo module of the Idaho National Engineering Laboratory (INEL) treatment planning software [1], rtt_MC [2], was modified to provide optimization capability.

Improvement in optimization requires:
1) a very rapid algorithm to compute (or closely approximate) three-dimensional dose patterns;
2) an organized method to evaluate available resources (aperture size, number of fields, etc.);
3) validation of results; and
4) proper presentation of plans for evaluation.

Approach

— Implemented capability into rtt_MC to parameterize all flux and dose components and generate dose table for any configuration.

Address for correspondence: Floyd J. Wheeler, Idaho National Engineering Laboratory, Lockheed Martin Idaho Technologies Co., P.O. Box 1625, Idaho Falls, ID 83415-3890, USA.

— Added option in rtt_MC to compute three-dimensional dose distribution using dose table from above step.
— Developed optimization algorithm based on three-dimensional integral of target dose which can optimize on:
    a) fractional cell survival;
    b) tumor control probability;
    c) minimum target dose; or
    d) microdosimetric event statistics.

A simple test of the algorithm

A simple model of a sphere (Fig. 1) was constructed. This model consisted of three concentric spherical material regions with radii 8.5, 9.0, and 10.0 cm. The inner region was assigned brain composition, next was skull and the outer region was skin. This sphere was made large to avoid adverse boundary effects. The Brookhaven epithermal neutron beam [3,4] with an 8-cm final aperture was used in the Monte Carlo simulations.

The rtt_MC Monte Carlo process was applied to determine flux and dose for the sphere. 24×10^6 particles were processed to determine all flux and dose components. In Fig. 2, the thermal flux at 3.5 cm depth is shown in isoflux format. An edit directive available in rtt_MC was also specified which caused the results to be automatically stored in a file to be used for the dose table calculations. This run required about 400 min on an HP 735 work station. Figure 3 shows results from the "quick" calculation option using dose tables generated in the rtt_MC run. Because of the symmetry of the sphere, there is no approximation in this calculation except for statistical error. The results using the "quick" calculation are actually better because the statistical error can be reduced by taking advantage of symmetry. This "quick" run required about 2 s on the HP 735, an improvement is speed of about a factor of 12,000.

Geometry used for Generation of Dose Tables

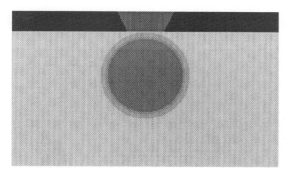

Fig. 1. Model of simple sphere used for validation of "quick" calculation.

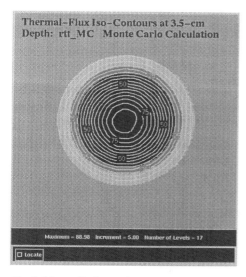

Fig. 2. Monte Carlo results for thermal neutron flux at 3.5 cm depth.

rtt_MC optimization process

Options were added to the rtt_MC Monte Carlo module to rapidly compute dose volume histograms using the dose tables. rtt_MC will compute these data for a grid over a specified range of ϕ and θ. Figure 4 shows the relationship of the two angles used to specify beam orientation.

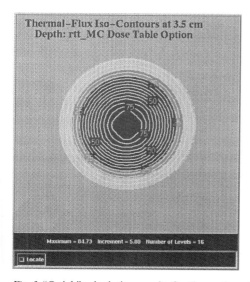

Fig. 3. "Quick" calculation results for thermal neutron flux at 3.5 cm depth.

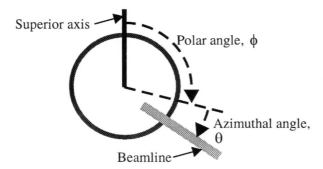

Fig. 4. Relationship of beam angles with an irradiated object.

Auxiliary software was written to analyze the rtt_MC-generated dose-volume data. As soon as the rtt_MC process begins, this software can read the partially completed output and perform ranking based on a desired criteria, such as fractional survival, tumor control probability (e.g., the Porter model [5]), minimum dose to tumor, or microdosimetric event statistics.

This ranking is based then, on a full, three-dimensional integration over the entire tumor (target) volume.

After the optimization process, a rigorous Monte Carlo (or other) calculation should be made to verify the results.

Application to a "fictitious" human model

For this exercise, optimization studies were performed on an image-based re-construction of a human volunteer with an artificial tumor and calculations of tumor control probabilities (TCP) based on the Porter model were performed. The Porter model is simply:

$$TCP = \int_V e^{-N \cdot FS} dV$$

where: N is the number of clonogenic cells before irradiation, FS is the surviving fraction, assuming uniform ^{10}B and clonogenic cell distribution.

MRI images of a volunteer were obtained and a simulated treatment volume with maximum depth 6 cm was modeled (Fig. 5) using the bnct_rtpe [6] treatment planning software. The rtt_MC optimization software was used in calculations of TCP to determine optimum beam orientations. Modeling was also performed for a simulated treatment volume with maximum depth of 8 cm.

First, a dose table for a standard human head model was generated with a sto-chastic calculation with rtt_MC. The generated dose table file was then used in the optimization study. For this trial study, a 12-cm beam aperture was used as well as the drug BPA-F (compound factor for healthy tissue was set to 1.3, and

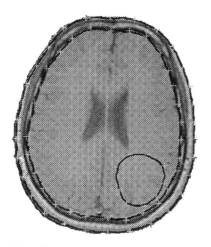

Fig. 5. One slice of model reconstruction showing "fictitious" tumor for human study.

for tumor was set to 3.8). The proton RBE was set to 3.2, the blood boron was set to 14.3 ppm and the tumor boron to blood boron concentration ratio was set to 3.5. The results shown in Fig. 6 required about 5 min computer time on an HP 735 UNIX work-station ($\sim$ 5 s per field). A study was also performed for the 8-cm depth case but predicted very low probability for efficacy with the single-field beam. The 8-cm depth requires two fields. Soon, the optimization software will be capable of treating two fields, a major increase in complexity.

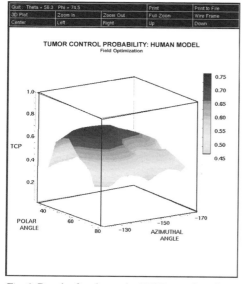

Fig. 6. Results for theoretical TCP as a function of beam angles.

Acknowledgements

This study was performed under the auspices of the US Department of Energy, Office of Energy Research, DOE Field Office, Idaho, Contract Number DE-AC07-76IDO1570.

References

1. Nigg DW, Wheeler FJ, Wessol DE, Wemple CE, Babcock RS. Some recent developments in treatment planning software and methodology for BNCT. In: Larsson B, Crawford J, Weinreich R (eds) Advances in Neutron Capture Therapy. Volume 1, Medicine and Physics: Amsterdam: Elsevier Science, 1997;91—94 (these proceedings).
2. Wheeler FJ. Radiation transport in tissue by Monte Carlo-Version X02.: EGG-BNCT-11178 January 1994.
3. Wheeler FJ, Parsons DK, Nigg DW, Wessol DE, Miller LG, Fairchild RG. Physics design for the Brookhaven Medical Research Reactor Epithermal Neutron Source. In: Harling OK, Bernard JA, Zamenhof RG (eds) Neutron Beam Design, Development, and Performance for Neutron Capture Therapy. New York: Plenum Press, 1990;83—95.
4. Liu HB, Brugger RB, Greenberg DD, Rorer DC, Hu JP, Hauptman HM. Enhancement of the epithermal neutron beam used for boron neutron capture therapy. Int J Radiat Oncol Biol Phys 1994;28:1149—1156.
5. Porter EH. The statistics of dose/cure relationships for irradiated tumors. Part II. Br J Radiol 1980;53:336—345.
6. Wessol DE, Babcock RS, Wheeler FJ, Harkin GJ. BNCT_rtpe: BNCT radiation treatment planning environment users' manual. Unpublished.

1997 Elsevier Science B.V.
Advances in Neutron Capture Therapy.
Volume I, Medicine and Physics.
B. Larsson, J. Crawford and R. Weinreich, editors.

Some recent developments in treatment planning software and methodology for BNCT

David W. Nigg[1], Floyd J. Wheeler[1], Daniel E. Wessol[1], Charles A. Wemple[1], Ray Babcock[2] and Jacek Capala[3]

[1]*Idaho National Engineering Laboratory, Idaho Falls, Idaho;* [2]*Montana State University, Bozeman, Montana; and* [3]*Brookhaven National Laboratory, Upton, New York, USA*

Over the past several years the Idaho National Engineering Laboratory (INEL) has led the development [1—3] of a unique, internationally recognized set of software modules (BNCT_rtpe) for computional dosimetry and treatment planning for Boron Neutron Capture Therapy (BNCT). The computational capability represented by this software is essential to the proper administration of all forms of radiotherapy for cancer. Such software addresses the need to perform pretreatment computation and optimization of the radiation dose distribution in the target volume. This permits the achievement of the optimum therapeutic ratio (tumor dose relative to critical normal tissue dose) for each individual patient via a systematic procedure for specifying the appropriate irradiation parameters to be employed for a given treatment. These parameters include angle of therapy beam incidence, beam aperture and shape, and beam intensity as a function of position across the beam front. The INEL software is used for treatment planning in the current series of human glioma trials [4] at Brookhaven National Laboratory (BNL) and has also been licensed for research and developmental purposes to several other BNCT research centers in the USA and in Europe.

Reconstruction of patient geometry from medical images in BNCT_rtpe is based on the calculation of free-form nonuniform rational B-spline (NURB) surfaces fitted to the various tissue compartments (or any desired subcompartments) of interest. With this method, one first outlines the regions of interest (e.g., skin, skull, brain, target volume, etc.) on each computer-displayed medical image plane. This may be done either manually or in some cases automatically via edge detection algorithms. Figure 1 shows an axial magnetic resonance image (MRI) scan of a glioma patient. In this case the normal anatomical regions as well as the tumor region and a 2-cm margin defining the target volume are outlined on the image planes. Several new features are available for medical image input, manipulation, and display. Additional MR and computed tomography (CT) image format translation capabilities are incorporated as needed in response to client requirements. New image colormap, contrast, and brightness tools have been developed along with a vertically and horizontally scrollable image container window.

Once the region outlines for all image slices are established, these representa-

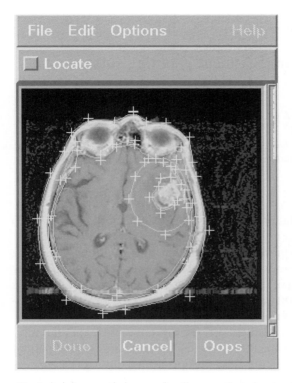

Fig. 1. Axial magnetic image of a glioma patient showing the outlines constructed by BNCT_rtpe for the various regions of interest, including the tumor and target regions.

tions are then mathematically combined to produce detailed equations describing the three-dimensional surfaces that enclose each volume of interest. The surface equations generated in the B-spline region reconstructions, in conjunction with appropriate region material descriptions, completely describe the problem and are subsequently used in a Monte Carlo radiation transport calculation performed by a specialized module incorporated into BNCT_rtpe. The ray-trace algorithm for the Monte Carlo calculation is based on searching nested hierarchies of bounding volumes enclosing the points of intersection of particles (neutrons or photons) with each reconstructed geometric NURBS surface describing a particular compartment of the patient anatomy. The spline surfaces can be combined with geometric primitive surfaces to further specify the calculational geometry, if needed. Any type of tomographic medical image data can be input to BNCT_rtpe. The radiation transport computational module within BNCT_rtpe will also accept paralleliped arrays constructed using the so-called "voxel reconstruction" technique [5], if desired.

Figure 2 illustrates some typical computed total physical dose contours registered on the original MR image of Fig. 1, which was used to construct the computational model. These results are based on the assumption that the patient is

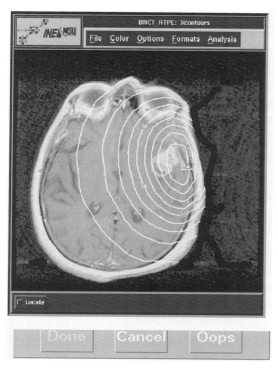

Fig. 2. Typical total physical absorbed dose contours in normal tissue that would be produced by the BMRR epithermal-neutron beam for a human glioma patient with a uniform brain-boron concentration of 15 ppm. The 100% dose contour corresponds to approximately 9.1 cGy/min per MW of BMRR power.

treated using the Brookhaven Medical Research Reactor (BMRR) epithermal-neutron beam as it was configured at the initiation of human studies in September, 1994. In the display the boron concentration is assumed to be 15 parts per million (ppm), uniformly distributed throughout the brain. The contours are thus representative of what would be seen by the normal tissue. The total dose includes the boron dose at 15 ppm as well as the contributions from the fast neutron component of the beam, the incident and capture photon components, the nitrogen component, as well as a fifth component that includes a few other small contributions from various other neutron interactions. The 100% contour corresponds to approximately 9.1 cGy/min/Mw of BMRR reactor power. Although BPA-f is typically present in the normal brain at about the same concentration as in the blood, this agent tends to concentrate in the malignant tissue at a level that is roughly 3–4 times the blood concentration for most patients. Thus the tumor dose includes all of the background components as well as a significantly higher boron dose corresponding to the higher tumor boron concentration. The tumor dose contours can also be displayed since the actual treatment plan is based on tumor dose, constrained by normal tissue tolerance, just as in photon therapy. Dose-volume histograms for each defined volume of interest can also be constructed as needed.

Efforts to include much faster, albeit approximate, dose computation methods in BNCT_rtpe are underway. An algorithm based on multidimensional parameter fitting from precomputed kernel functions (closely related to the so-called "pencil-beam" methods) has been incorporated and has proven to be quite effective for use in dose optimization studies prior to performing a Monte Carlo calculation for the final optimized plan for each patient. This capability should prove to be especially useful as clinical application of BNCT moves into the more complicated realm of multiport irradiations. In addition, an informal collaboration has been established with The Ohio State University to explore the utility of incorporating a computational option based on removal-diffusion theory [6]. Finally, it may be noted that the basic physics modules have been significantly upgraded to allow incident neutron energies up to about 100 MeV, with an explicit treatment of recoil proton transport, expanding the utility of this software into the field of fast neutron radiotherapy, with or without BNCT augmentation.

Acknowledgements

This study was performed under the auspices of the U.S. Department of Energy, Office of Energy Research, DOE Idaho Operations Office, under Contract Number DE-AC07-94ID13223, and under Brookhaven National Laboratory Contract Number DE-AC0Z-76CH00016.

References

1. Nigg DW. Methods for radiation dose distribution analysis and treatment planning in boron neutron capture therapy. Int J Radiat Oncol Biol Phys 1994;28:1121−1134.
2. Wheeler FJ, Nigg DW. Three-dimensional radiation dose distribution analysis for boron neutron capture therapy. Nucl Sci Eng 1992;110:16−31.
3. Wessol DE, Wheeler FJ. Methods for creating and using free-form geometries in Monte Carlo particle transport. Nucl Sci Eng 1993;113:314−323.
4. Coderre JA, Bergland R, Capala J, Chadha M, Chanana AJ, Elowitz E, Joel DD, Liu HB, Slatkin D. Boron Neutron Capture Therapy for Glioblastoma Multiforme using p-Boronophenylalanine and epithermal neutrons — Trial design and early clinical results. J Neuro-Oncol (In press).
5. Zamenhof R, Brenner J, Yanch J, Wazer D, Madoc-Jones H, Saris S, Harling O. Treatment planning for neutron capture therapy of glioblastoma multiforme using epithermal neutron beam from the MITR-II research reactor and Monte Carlo simulation. In: Allen BJ, Moore DE, Harrington BV (eds) Progress in Neutron Capture Therapy for Cancer. New York: Plenum Press, 1992;173−178.
6. Niemkiewicz J, Blue TE. Removal-diffusion theory for calculation of neutron distributions in BNCT. In: Barth R, Soloway A (eds) Advances in Neutron Capture Therapy. New York: Plenum Press, 1993;177−180.

1997 Elsevier Science B.V.
Advances in Neutron Capture Therapy.
Volume I, Medicine and Physics.
B. Larsson, J. Crawford and R. Weinreich, editors.

Comparison of TORT and MCNP dose calculations for BNCT treatment planning

Daniel T. Ingersoll[1], Charles O. Slater[1], Everett L. Redmond II[2] and Robert G. Zamenhof[3]

[1] *Oak Ridge National Laboratory, Oak Ridge, Tennessee;* [2] *Holtec International, Allston, Massachusetts; and* [3] *Beth Israel-Deaconess Medical Center, Harvard Medical School, Boston, Massachusetts, USA*

Keywords: deterministic, dose distributions, MCNP4A, Monte Carlo, NCTPLAN, nuclear data, TORT, treatment planning.

Introduction

Clinical trials to determine the efficacy of boron neutron capture therapy (BNCT) have been initiated in the USA at the Beth Israel-Deaconess Medical Center, Harvard Medical School (BIDMC) and the Massachusetts Institute of Technology (MIT) for the treatment of melanomas and glioblastomas and at Brookhaven National Laboratory (BNL) for the treatment of glioblastomas. An essential and time-consuming part of the preparation for treatments is the prediction of dose distributions in the patient so that appropriate beam orientations and exposure times can be decided. Medical physicists at BNL use the BNCT_RTPE treatment planning software [1] developed by the Idaho National Engineering Laboratory (INEL), while the BIDMC/MIT team uses their internally developed NCTPLAN software [2]. Both of these programs use Monte Carlo methods to simulate the transport of neutrons and γ rays from the external beam into the patient's anatomy and to calculate the resulting dose components. In the case of BNCT_RTPE, dose calculations are accomplished using the INEL-developed rtt_MC Monte Carlo module, which is specially tailored for BNCT applications. At BIIDMC/MIT, dose calculations are performed using the standard MCNP4A code [3] developed by Los Alamos National Laboratory. In both cases, the dose calculations are computationally intense and reductions in the running times would greatly expedite the treatment planning process.

The purpose of the present study was to assess the relative computational merit of using a deterministic code to calculate dose distributions for BNCT applications. In our study, the TORT discrete ordinates code [4] developed by Oak Ridge National Laboratory was used to replace the MCNP4A code in the dose analysis for a BIDMC/MIT human subject. The viability of TORT for this application

Address for correspondence: Daniel T. Ingersoll, Oak Ridge National Laboratory, P.O. Box 2008, Oak Ridge, TN 37830-6363, USA.

was demonstrated by INEL in earlier dosimetry studies using a dog head phantom [5]. However, the surface-based anatomical model produced by the image analysis portion of INEL's BNCT_RTPE code is not directly compatible with the orthogonal mesh requirements of TORT, hence TORT can not be easily incorporated into their treatment planning system. In contrast, the NCTPLAN program generates a voxel model of the subject's anatomy, which is ideally suited for solution using deterministic methods such as TORT. In a voxel-type model, the orthogonal geometry can be represented exactly and the fine spatial distribution of the dose is calculated directly.

Analysis model and parameters

The computational model used for this study represented the lower leg of a peripheral melanoma study subject treated by BNCT at BIDMC/MIT and is shown in Fig. 1. The model is based on computed tomography (CT) images in the region of a melanoma and was generated by the image processing portion of NCTPLAN [2]. The MCNP model contained 11,025 voxel cells, while the TORT model was expanded to 15,782 mesh cells to fully enclose the leg segment and the disk source. Figure 1 also shows the bounding box for the TORT model and the disk source at the exit of the MITR-II epithermal beam collimator. The segmentation portion of NCTPLAN reduced the high-resolution CT data into 1 cm^3 voxels and reduced the number of possible material compositions to 15 different combinations of tumor, muscle, bone, and air. These compositions corre-

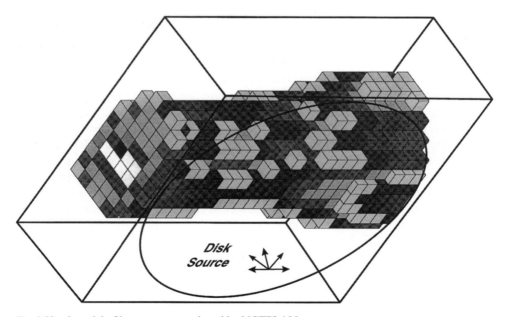

Fig. 1. Voxel model of leg segment produced by NCTPLAN.

spond to the different shades of gray in the model shown in Fig. 1.

Several parameters for both the MCNP and the TORT codes were varied in the study, including different nuclear data libraries and options, number of MCNP histories, and TORT input parameter such as mesh size, order of Legendre expansion of the anisotropic scattering, and the weighting parameter (θ) for the finite-difference model. For each of the cases, the MCNP and TORT results were compared for each of 2,247 preselected cells for boron kerma and muscle kerma responses, including kermas due to thermal neutrons, fast neutrons, and γ rays. Conclusions were made based on the frequency distributions of MCNP-to-TORT ratios for the 2,247 cells and by observing the number of cells for which the TORT results were within 1, 2, or 3 fsd (fractional standard deviation) of the mean MCNP values.

Analysis results

In terms of the MCNP variations, it was found that no significant difference was observed between using nuclear data from version V or version VI of the evaluated nuclear data file (ENDF). On the other hand, a substantial improvement was observed (compared to the reference TORT case) when the $S(\alpha,\beta)$ thermal scattering kernels were included in MCNP. A relatively significant change was observed when the number of particle histories was increased from 3 million to a statistically independent 10 million. Comparisons of the results from these two calculations are shown in Fig. 2 for the ^{10}B(n,α) dose and for total muscle dose.

In terms of the TORT variations, only slight differences (less than 7% max. change) were observed between using "off the shelf" multigroup cross-sections, specifically cross-sections from the BUGLE-93 library [6], and cross-sections which were specially weighted for this application. Also, reducing the mesh size to 0.5 cm resulted in relatively modest changes (less than 15% max. change) in

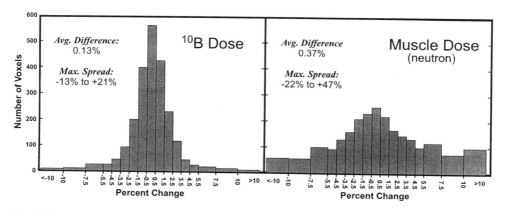

Fig. 2. Change in MCNP results when going from 3 million to 10 million particle histories.

the converged fluxes. Increasing the order of Legendre expansion of the cross-sections from P_3 to P_5 yielded no significant changes. The parameter which impacted the TORT results the most was the value of θ, a weighting factor internal to the flux solution model. Figure 3 shows the effect of changing the value of θ from 0.5 to 0.9 (θ must be in the range of 0 to 1). While the higher energy responses showed only modest impact, the thermal responses showed a significant bias due to different θ values.

The reference MCNP and TORT cases were selected to be those which yielded a ±5% agreement between the two methods for >95% of the comparison cells. For MCNP, this corresponded to using ENDF/B-VI nuclear data with the $S(\alpha,\beta)$ data and 10 million particle histories. The corresponding TORT calculation used flux-weighted 47-neutron/20-photon group cross-sections with P_3 Legendre expansion, an S_{12} angular quadrature, 1 cm mesh size, and a value of 0.9 for θ. These specifications yielded the desired agreement for all dose responses, including the ^{10}B dose and the muscle dose due to thermal neutrons, fast neutrons, and γ rays as shown in Fig. 4.

With respect to computational time, the reference MCNP calculation required 2,790 min on an IBM RISC/6000, Model 560 work station. In contrast, the reference TORT calculation required 188 min, nearly a factor of 15 times faster than MCNP. Increasing the Legendre order to P_5 increased TORT's running time only 17% to 220 min. Running times for MCNP were roughly proportional to the number of particle histories.

Conclusions

It is expected that with additional refinement and tailoring of the codes to this specific application, the performance of both MCNP and TORT can be improved further. It is clear from this study, however, that deterministic codes such as TORT offer the best and most natural choice for application to BNCT

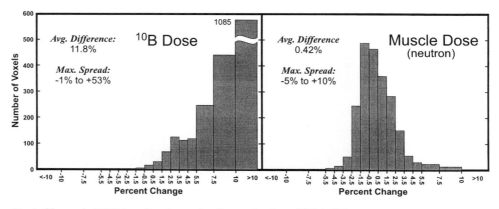

Fig. 3. Change in TORT results when going from a θ value of 0.5 to 0.9.

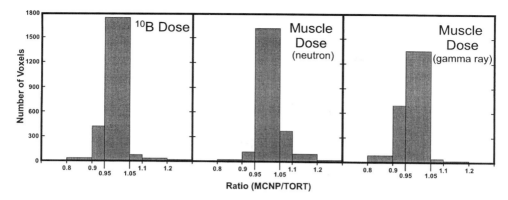

Fig. 4. Comparison between MCNP and TORT results for reference cases.

treatment planning for voxel-based anatomical models. For these cases, the voxel geometry can be modeled exactly and the deterministic method provides a direct solution of the dose components at every mesh cell. With proper selection of the numerical quadratures and flux model options, the deterministic method can yield fast and highly accurate solutions.

Acknowledgements

This work was performed in part with the support of DOE Grant DE-FG02-87ER6060.

References

1. Wessol DE, Babcock RS. BNCT_Rtpe: BNCT Radiation Treatment Planning Environment Users Manual. Unpublished.
2. Zamenhof RG, Redmond E II, Solares GR, Katz D, Kiger S, Harling O. Monte Carlo based treatment planning for boron neutron capture therapy using custom designed models automatically generated from CT data. Int J Rad Oncol Biol Phys 1996;32:383–397.
3. Briesmeister JF (ed). MCNP — A General Monte Carlo N-Particle Transport Code. Los Alamos National Laboratory report LA-12625-M, November 1993.
4. Rhoades WA. The TORT Three-Dimensional Discrete Ordinates Neutron/Photon Transport Code. Oak Ridge National Laboratory report ORNL/TM-13221, June 1996.
5. Nigg DW, Randolph PD, Wheeler FJ. Demonstration of three-dimensional deterministic radiation transport theory dose distribution analysis for boron neutron capture therapy. Med Phys 1991;18(1):43–53.
6. Ingersoll DT, White JE, Wright RQ, Hunter HT, Slater CO, Greene NM, Roussin RW, MacFarlane RE. Production and Testing of the VIITAMIN-B6 Fine-Group and the BUGLE-93 Broad-Group Neutron/Photon Cross-Section Libraries Derived from ENDF/B-VI Nuclear Data. Oak Ridge National Laboratory report ORNL-6795 (NUREG/CR-6214), January 1995.

MacNCTPLAN: an improved Macintosh-based treatment planning program for boron neutron capture therapy

R.G. Zamenhof[1], G.R. Solares[1], W.S. Kiger, III[2], E.L. Redmond II[2], P.M. Busse[1] and C.-S. Yam[2,3]

[1] Beth Israel-Deaconess Medical Center, Harvard Medical School, Boston, Massachusetts; [2] Nuclear Reactor Laboratory, Massachusetts Institute of Technology, Cambridge, Massachusetts; and [3] Entropic Systems, Inc., Woburn, Massachusetts, USA

Introduction

The physical and mathematical principles, architecture, operation, and application of the Monte Carlo based boron neutron capture therapy (BNCT) treatment planning code NCTPLAN have been described in previous reports [1—4]. The original version of the NCTPLAN code, written in FORTRAN on a VAX platform under the VMS operating system, has been used to plan irradiations for four subjects who completed a phase-I BNCT protocol for melanoma of the extremities [5]. With this history of experience in its use, a number of deficiencies were identified in the old NCTPLAN which would have required an extensive rewrite to rectify. In order to modernize the code platform, make the code more portable, and facilitate future modifications the code has been completely rewritten for the Power Macintosh platform using Pascal units nested within the widely available image processing code NIH Image (v. 1.59). To date, three glioblastoma multiforme (GBM) and one peripheral melanoma patients have been planned with MacNCTPLAN. This presentation will illustrate the operation of the MacNCTPLAN (v. 1.0) BNCT treatment planning code and discuss some of its features and limitations.

Methods and Materials

CT scans are acquired on the part of the patient's body to be irradiated both with (I+) and without (I−) iodinated contrast. The purpose of acquiring both I+ and I− image sets is that for the identification of the tumor and "target" regions an I+ image set is necessary, whereas to convert the CT values of the images into "materials" for the Monte Carlo transport calculations an I− image set is necessary. However, both sets of images have to be in perfect spatial registration with each other. The CT images are transferred from the CT scanner to a Power

Address for correspondence: Robert G. Zamenhof PhD, Department of Radiology, Beth Israel-Deaconess Medical Center West Campus, 1 Deaconess Road, Boston, MA 02215, USA.

Macintosh computer in 512×512 pixel uncompressed 16 bit format, and reformatted into $256 \times 256 \times 8$ bits. The I− set of images is then cleaned of extraneous materials that are deemed to be irrelevant to the radiation transport perspective (e.g., head-holder sponges, towels, barium paste markers, etc.) using thresholding and cropping operations. An outline of the body part in each CT image is automatically constructed using an adaptive thresholding algorithm which is later used to zero-out dose data outside the body to facilitate the generation of internal dose isocontours and to provide definitive entrance and exit points for the neutron beams. The tumor "target" region is then outlined utilizing the I+ CT images, defined as the enhancing tumor boundary plus 2 cm. The average differential boron concentrations for normal tissue and tumor that are assumed to exist during the neutron irradiation are then entered. Tumor-to-blood and tumor-to-normal tissue ^{10}B ratios of 3.5 are assumed during the planning calculations until the results of a retrospective analysis of actual tissue boron concentrations are available. The ^{10}B concentrations in blood are derived by prompt-γ activation analysis from the pharmacokinetic study that is done for each subject prior to neutron irradiation [5]. The intracellular ^{10}B concentrations in tissue are derived by high-resolution α-track autoradiography [6]. Selection of the beam entrance and exit points has been greatly improved by the ability to simultaneously view two orthogonal viewing planes through the CT image data which graphically depict the beam entrance and exit points as well as the exit surface of the neutron beam port. As the beam orientation is changed these viewing planes are graphically updated in real-time. The user can also view a plane normal to the beam direction to verify that the beam source plane does not intersect any portion of the patient's body. The user next loads in the I− set of images and selects a region-of-interest (ROI) in a representative CT image containing bone, soft tissue and air. MacNCTPLAN constructs a corresponding image intensity histogram from which appropriate thresholds to separate these tissues can be determined. Next, the user creates a "material" matrix that will be imputed to the MCNP code for the Monte Carlo dose calculation. The volume-weighted contributions of the four primary tissues are calculated for each of the 11,025 1 cm^3 cells in a $21 \times 21 \times 25$ cm box superimposed over the three-dimensional CT data. The mixtures of air, soft tissue, tumor and bone representing the cells of this box are rounded off to the nearest $\pm 10\%$ volume increment for each tissue and defined as one of 56 possible "materials" in the MCNP model. A detailed error analysis has indicated that this approximation has a very minor impact on the accuracy of the computed radiation doses [4]. MacNCTPLAN then writes the material matrix and associated beam orientation vectors to a file which is conditioned by an auxiliary FORTRAN program to conform to MCNP input format requirements. Output dose data from MCNP are imported back into MacNCTPLAN after conditioning by a second auxiliary FORTRAN program which removes from the MCNP output file any data that are not needed. Small linear correction factors ($< 1.0 \pm 15\%$) are applied to the individual dose components to force an agreement with measured doses. Comparison of measured and computed central axis dose components to both normal tissue and to tumor has demonstrated very close agreement [4]. In order to display RBE-dose isocontours, modified tumor and normal tissue boron concentrations, isodose normalization values, the desired anatomical planes, and RBE values for each radiation component and each individual tissue are specified. The RBE values used are: 3.2 for all neutrons in cranial tissues; 4.0 for all neutrons and ^{10}B in tissues in the extremities; 0.5 for gammas in all tissues; 3.8 for ^{10}B in brain tumor; and 1.35 for ^{10}B in normal brain. To compute smooth isodose contours, dose data for the 1 cm^3 cell matrix are interpolated onto a much finer (approximately 1 mm^3) matrix of approximately 9—12 million cells. Doses in cells outside the previously constructed boundary of the irradiated body part are set to zero to force closure of the isodose contours within the body. The user may then select arbitrarily oriented planes through the three-dimensional Monte Carlo model and display isodose contours superimposed on exactly corresponding reformatted CT image planes. For this stage of the procedure the I+ series of images is reloaded. By selecting a line through the three-dimensional model the user may also obtain a profile display of quantitative dose for any individual dose component or combination thereof. As a further aid to the interpretation of tissue doses, MacNCTPLAN permits the derivation of three-dimensional dose-volume histograms (DVHs) for arbitrary tumor or normal tissue volumes defined by manually drawn ROIs.

Results

To illustrate the use of MacNCTPLAN, the treatment planning results from an actual patient recently treated by BNCT in the Harvard/MIT protocol will be presented. Prior to CT scanning, small radio-opaque markers of barium paste were placed along the naso-occipital line. These markers permit a correlation between the CT scan images and the patient's exterior cranial anatomy, and also provide an objective confirmation of the spatial registration between the I+ and I— series of CT images. Figure 1 shows a three-dimensional rendering of the MacNCTPLAN generated model of the patient's head. Figure 2 shows the MacNCTPLAN display after neutron beam entrance and exit points for two almost coplanar unweighted parallel-opposed beams have been selected. The actual screen displays from MacNCTPLAN (Figs. 2—4) contain much additional numerical data which have been purposely erased due to the font size being too small. Figure 3 shows an isocontour plot of RBE-weighted doses for normal brain for a transverse plane approximately centered on the target region. Figure 4 shows an isocontour plot in the same plane for tumor, normalized to the maximum RBE-dose to normal brain equal to 100%.

Discussion and Conclusions

Revising the original NCTPLAN code has corrected many deficiencies, has

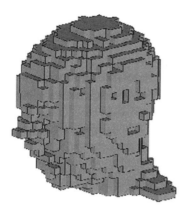

Fig. 1. Three-dimensional rendering of the cubical cell MCNP model generated by MacNCTPLAN from the patient's CT scans. Each cell is $1 \times 1 \times 1$ cm^3 in dimension and contains various mixtures, or materials, of normal brain, bone, air and ^{10}B.

improved code reliability, has provided a user-friendly interface that greatly facilitates the treatment planning process, and has provided code portability for the Macintosh platform. Cross-validation of the new MacNCTPLAN code against

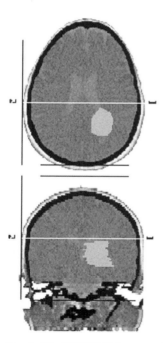

Fig. 2. MacNCTPLAN screen display showing the placement of two coplanar parallel-opposed beams with respect to the patient's anatomical landmarks. The tumor region is shown in light gray.

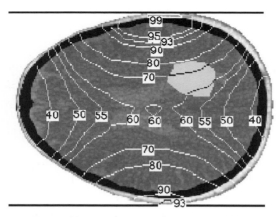

Fig. 3. RBE-isodose plot for normal brain generated by MacNCTPLAN. B-10 concentrations of 15 ppm for beam #1 and 10 ppm for beam #2 have been assumed. The selected anatomical plane is a transverse plane through the central axes of the coplanar parallel-opposed beams.

the older version and against experimental dosimetry provides confidence in its accuracy. MacNCTPLAN provides real-time graphical capability for the precise positioning of the mathematical model of the patient relative to the neutron beam and for the selection of arbitrary anatomical planes for isodose display. It provides visual validation of critical steps such as the selection of CT image intensity thresholds for the discrimination of different tissues. MacNCTPLAN also provides the capability for evaluating dose distributions in arbitrarily defined volumes through the utilization of dose-volume histogram analysis. MacNCT-PLAN is being used routinely in phase-I clinical trials of BNCT at Harvard/MIT.

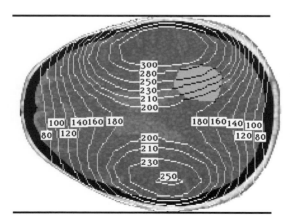

Fig. 4. RBE-isodose plot for tumor generated by MacNCTPLAN. ^{10}B concentrations of 52.5 ppm for beam #1 and 35 ppm for beam #2 have been assumed. The selected anatomical plane is a transverse plane through the central axes of the coplanar parallel-opposed beams.

Acknowledgements

US Department of Energy Grant No. DE-FGO2-87ER-6060, Beth Israel-Deaconess Medical Center's Department of Radiology, the Harvard Joint Center for Radiation Therapy, the MIT Department of Nuclear Engineering, and American Medical Response, Inc.

References

1. Zamenhof RG, Clement S, Lin K, Lui C, Ziegelmiller D, Harling OK. Monte Carlo treatment planning and high-resolution alpha-track autoradiography for neutron capture therapy. Strahlenther Onkol 1989;165:188—191.
2. Zamenhof RG, Clement SD, Harling OK, Brenner JF, Wazer DE, Madoc-Jones H, Yanch JC. Monte Carlo based dosimetry and treatment planning for neutron capture therapy. In: Harling OK, Bernard JA, Zamenhof RG (eds) Neutron Beam Design, Development, and Performance for Neutron Capture Therapy. New York: Plenum Press, 1990.
3. Zamenhof RG, Brenner J, Yanch JC, Wazer D, Madoc-Jones H, Saris S, Harling OK. Treatment planning for neutron capture therapy of glioblastoma multiforme using an epithermal neutron beam from the MITR-II research reactor and Monte Carlo simulation. In: Allen B, Moore D, Harrington B (eds) Progress in Neutron Capture Therapy for Cancer. New York: Plenum Press, 1992.
4. Zamenhof RG, Redmond E II, Solares G, Katz D, Riley K, Kiger S, Harling OK. Monte Carlo based treatment planning for boron neutron capture therapy using custom designed models automatically generated from CT data. Int J Radiat Oncol Biol Phys 1996;35:383—397.
5. Harling OK, Chabeus J-M, Lambert F, Yasuda G. A prompt-gamma neutron activation analysis facility using a diffracted thermal neutron beam. Nucl Instrum Meth Phys Res Section B 1993; 83:557—562.
6. Solares GR, Zamenhof RG, Novel ÒA. Approach to the microdosimetry of neutron capture therapy: Part I. High-resolution quantitative autoradiography applied to the microdosimetry of neutron capture therapy. Radiat Res 1995;144:50—58.
7. Harling OK, Roberts KA, Moulin DJ, Rogus RD. Head phantoms for neutron capture therapy. Med Phys 1995;22:579—583.

Advances in Neutron Capture Therapy.
Volume I, Medicine and Physics.
B. Larsson, J. Crawford and R. Weinreich, editors.

The use of a photon beam model for the treatment planning of boron neutron capture therapy

C.P.J. Raaijmakers, E.L. Nottelman and B.J. Mijnheer

Department of Radiotherapy, The Netherlands Cancer Institute (Antoni van Leeuwenhoek Huis), Amsterdam, The Netherlands

Keywords: epithermal neutron beam, treatment planning systems (TPSs), treatment planning.

Introduction

Treatment planning for boron neutron capture therapy (BNCT) requires a separate calculation of the thermal neutron fluence distribution, the γ ray dose distribution and the fast neutron distribution. These various dose components have radiation transport characteristics which are different from those of the γ rays used for conventional radiotherapy. This fact has led to the assumption that the relatively simple approximations done in conventional treatment planning are of limited use for the treatment planning of BNCT [1,2].

Monte-Carlo simulations have become the major tool for the treatment planning of BNCT. Treatment planning systems (TPSs) based on Monte-Carlo calculations are in principle capable of solving the complex radiation transport problems [1,2]. However, a major drawback of these systems is the excessive amount of calculation time needed to obtain sufficient statistics. Furthermore, reported clinical validations of these systems are scarce and restricted to comparisons between measurements and calculations along the central beam axis, while empirical correction factors are still needed to obtain a reasonable agreement between the two [2].

Dose calculation methods in conventional external beam radiotherapy are based on empirical beam data obtained under reference conditions, generally in large cubical water phantoms. For photon beams, calculations of relative dose distributions in an arbitrary geometry are generally based on interpolations of measured data which are corrected using semiempirical algorithms to account for differences between the reference conditions and the actual irradiation geometry. A simple method to account for the difference in contour shape between the patient and the reference phantom is the effective source-surface distance (SSD) method [3]. In this method the relative dose at a point in a homogeneous phantom is assumed to be equal to the relative dose in a large cubical phantom

Address for correspondence: Niels Raaijmakers, The Netherlands Cancer Institute (Antoni van Leeuwenhoek Huis), Plesmanlaan 121, 1066 CX Amsterdam, The Netherlands.

at the same off-axis distance and depth, when this phantom is positioned at the "effective" SSD. The "effective" SSD is defined as the distance between the phantom boundary and a virtual source along a line connecting the point to the virtual source. The depth is defined as the distance between the point and the phantom boundary along this line. The inverse square law is used to correct for the difference between the "effective" SSD and the reference SSD. It is the purpose of this work to investigate the applicability of this relatively simple contour correction method for the treatment planning of BNCT.

Materials and Methods

In order to compare the TPS calculations with measurements in a clinically relevant situation, an anthropomorphic human head phantom allowing for insertion of various detectors at predefined positions, was constructed. The capture therapy (CT) contours of a standard anthropomorphic human head phantom used in radiotherapy, were introduced into a computer-controlled milling machine which milled every contour automatically out of a 5-mm thick polymethylmethacrylate (PMMA) slab. Subsequently, holes for detector positioning were drilled in every slice and the slices were fixed together to form a head phantom. The most superficial measurement position at the central axis in the plane of irradiation was located at a depth of 2.7 cm (Fig. 1). This position, where the maximum thermal neutron fluence rate is expected, will be used as the dose normalization point in this work.

The head phantom was irradiated with the clinical BNCT beam at the High Flux Reactor in Petten, The Netherlands [4]. Use was made of an 8-cm diameter circular beam aperture. The phantom was positioned at a reference distance of 30 cm from the beam exit. The thermal neutron fluence in the phantom was determined using activation foils and a diode detector. Paired ionization chambers were used for the determination of the γ-ray dose and the fast neutron dose [5].

Beam data obtained in a 30-cm^3 water phantom [6] were introduced into a commercial TPS (Plato RTS 1.1.5, Nucletron International Ltd., The Netherlands). The data consisted of a percentage depth dose (PDD) curve along the central axis (PDD) and three or four beam profiles at various depths for each dose component. The data was stored by the TPS using PDD values and off-axis ratios. For the calculations of dose and fluence values in the phantom, the measured data were interpolated and corrected for the phantom contour using the effective SSD method. Since the influence of phantom-to-beam-exit distance on the absolute fluence and dose values could be modeled using a virtual source at a distance of 3.0 m from the beam exit [6], this position has been chosen as the virtual source position.

Absolute dose and fluence values at the normalization point were compared with those at the same depth in a 15-cm^3 PMMA phantom irradiated under the same conditions.

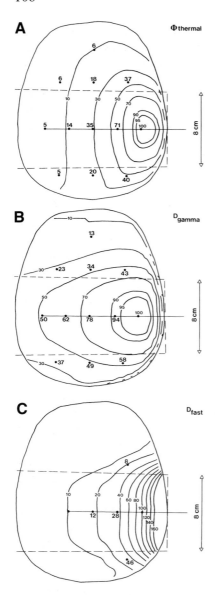

Fig. 1. Thermal neutron isofluence lines (**A**), γ-ray isodose lines (**B**) and fast neutron isodose lines (**C**) in a human head phantom calculated using a conventional TPS, compared with measurement (dots) in the phantom for a circular 8-cm diameter field.

Results

The measured absolute thermal neutron fluence values at the normalization point in the head phantom agreed within the measurement uncertainty (1 standard deviation (SD) (2%)) with the fluence at the same depth in the cuboid phantom. The agreement between the measured and calculated relative thermal neutron distribution was generally within 5%. Differences of up to 10% were, however, observed along the central beam axis (Fig. 1).

The measured γ-ray dose rate at the normalization point in the head phantom was approximately 5% lower than the dose at the same depth in the cuboid phantom. The calculated relative γ-ray dose at the central axis was in good agreement with the measurements. An asymmetry was detected in the measured relative γ-ray dose at off-axis positions which was not seen in the calculations. The relative γ-ray dose 5 cm above the central axis was approximately 15% lower than the dose at the same distance below the central beam axis (Fig. 1).

The absolute fast neutron dose at the normalization point was not significantly different from that in the cuboid phantom. On the central beam axis reasonable agreement was obtained between measurements and calculations. The deviations between measurements and calculations at depths larger than 5 cm can be attributed to the limited accuracy of the measurements at these depths. A similar asymmetry as observed for the γ-ray component was seen for this component (Fig. 1).

Discussion and Conclusions

The absolute dose and fluence values in the anthropomorphic human head phantom at the normalization point agreed well with those at the same depth in a simple cuboid phantom of approximately the same dimensions. This fact indicates that measurements in simple phantom geometries may well be used for patient dose calculation purposes. Although a reasonable agreement between measurements and calculations was also obtained for the relative thermal neutron distribution, clear limitations of the countercorrection method were observed. These limitations are best illustrated by the underestimation by the TPS of the thermal neutron fluence at a depth of approximately 6 cm on the central axis (Fig. 1). At this position a value of 71% was measured while a value of approximately 60% was obtained under reference conditions [7]. The increased penetration of thermal neutrons in the head phantom is probably caused by the curved shape of the phantom and is not predicted by the TPS which assumes that the percentage depth fluence on the central beam axis is independent of the shape of the phantom. Furthermore, when the contour correction is applied, the isofluence curves lose their circular shape present under reference conditions [6]. This is physically unlikely considering the large scattering properties of the thermal neutrons. Algorithms which take these scattering properties better into account, such as pencil beam algorithms, will be further investigated to improve the accuracy of the calculations.

For the γ-ray dose distribution, good agreement between measurements and calculations were obtained on the central beam axis. Asymmetry at off-axis positions was detected equivalent to a shift of the beam of about 1 cm. This value is much larger than the positioning accuracy, which is estimated to be approximately 2 mm (1 SD). It will be further investigated whether this asymmetry is due to positioning errors or to asymmetry in the beam. Also, for the γ-ray component the effective SSD method is physically not completely correct since the induced γ rays are generated in the phantom and do not originate from a distant virtual point source. However, since the reference conditions are rather similar to the actual geometry, the corrections are relatively small and a reasonable estimation of the γ ray dose distribution is obtained.

For the fast neutrons, scattering effects are of minor importance. Consequently, the effective SSD method should, in principle, be appropriate for this dose component. Due to the observed asymmetry in the dose distribution, definite conclusions about the applicability of the method, however, cannot be drawn.

In general, the preliminary results indicate that even when using relatively simple methods, which are from a physical point of view of limited applicability, reasonable agreement between measurements and calculations can already be obtained. This is due to the fact that the semiempirical calculations consist merely of corrections of dose values obtained under reference conditions which are not too dissimilar to the actual treatment conditions. We expect that the use of other conventional dose calculation methods, such as pencil beam algorithms, will further improve the accuracy of the calculations resulting in a semiempirical TPS capable of accurately calculating the various dose components at all relevant positions in a patient irradiated with an epithermal neutron beam.

Acknowledgements

The authors would like to thank K. Ravensberg for operating the beam and his skilful technical and experimental assistance and W. Voorbraak and A. Paardekoper for the activation foil measurements. This work was financially supported by a grant from The Netherlands Cancer Foundation (NKB Grant NKI 94-778).

References

1. Nigg DW. Methods for radiation dose distribution analysis and treatment planning in boron neutron capture therapy. Int J Radiat Oncol Biol Phys 1994;28:1121–1134.
2. Zamenhof R, Redmond E, Solares R, Katz D, Riley K, Kiger S, Harling O. Monte Carlo based treatment planning for boron neutron capture therapy using custom designed models automatically generated from CT data. Int J Radiat Oncol Biol Phys 1996;35:383–397.
3. Khan FM. The Physics of Radiation Therapy, 2nd edn. Baltimore: Williams and Wilkins, 1994.
4. Moss R, Casado J, Ravensberg K, Stecher-Rasmussen F, Watkins P. The completed boron neutron capture therapy facility at the HFR Petten. In: Larsson B, Crawford J, Weinreich R (eds) Advances in Neutron Capture Therapy, Volume 1, Medicine and Physics. Amsterdam: Elsevier Science, 1997; 331–335 (these proceedings).
5. Raaijmakers CPJ, Watkins PRD, Nottelman EL, Verhagen HW, Jansen JTM, Zoetelief J, Mijnheer BJ. The neutron sensitivity of dosimeters applied to boron neutron capture therapy. Med Phys 1996;23:1581–1589.
6. Raaijmakers CPJ, Konijnenberg MW, Mijnheer BJ. Clinical dosimetry of an epithermal neutron

beam for neutron capture therapy; Dose distributions under reference conditions. Int J Radiat Oncol Biol Phys (In press).

7.   Raaijmakers CPJ, Nottelman EL, Mijnheer BJ. Depth dose curves of an epithermal neutron beam for BNCT. In: Larsson B, Crawford J, Weinreich R (eds) Advances in Neutron Capture Therapy, Volume 1, Medicine and Physics. Amsterdam: Elsevier Science, 1997;153–158 (these proceedings).

Advances in Neutron Capture Therapy.
Volume I, Medicine and Physics.
B. Larsson, J. Crawford and R. Weinreich, editors.

Use of the BNCT_Rtpe/rtt_MC treatment planning system for BNCT irradiations of human patients at Petten

P. Watkins[1], C. Vroegindeweij[1], K. Aaldijk[2], F.J. Wheeler[3] and D.E. Wessol[3]

[1] *Commission of the European Communities, Joint Research Center, Petten, The Netherlands;* [2] *Energie Centrum Nederland, Petten, The Netherlands; and* [3] *Idaho National Engineering and Environment Laboratory, Idaho Falls, Idaho, USA*

Introduction

For the proposed patient irradiations at the Petten boron neutron capture therapy (BNCT) facility the chosen method for treatment planning is to use the three-dimensional system BNCT_Rtpe/rtt_MC, being developed at Idaho National Engineering and Environment Laboratory (INEL) [1]. This system uses medical image data (CT or MRI) to construct a three-dimensional model of a patient's head. The head is represented by means of B-spline approximations to the physical geometry. Within this geometry the dose distributions are evaluated via a three-dimensional particle transport calculation. This is performed using a Monte Carlo simulation of both the neutrons and photons. For BNCT a three-dimensional model of the particle transport and a detailed representation of the neutron scattering are essential to predict the dose distributions accurately. Use of lower dimensional and simplistic approximations for the complex geometry of the head and particle transport introduces uncertainties that are difficult to quantify. Most conventional treatment planning software cannot meet these needs.

The INEL system has been installed on several SUN workstations at Petten and validated against measurements in a number of standard phantoms. More recently it has been used successfully for a series of test cases, using representative image data from European medical centers. This exercise has led to the development of new, or modifications to existing, subsidiary codes that are used to present the results from rtt_MC in ways that have been requested for the European project. The use and examples of the results from the system as employed at Petten are described in this paper.

Image transfer and conversion

To use the BNCT_Rtpe/rtt_MC system the image data must be obtained in QSH format [2]. This poses a number of problems:
1. Medical image data (CT) are provided by six different centers within Europe which use imaging machines from different manufacturers that produce data

in different image formats. These may not always be ACR-NEMA.

2. Image data are passed to Petten via the Internet or on magnetic media. The security and anonymity of patient data presented problems, particularly as the national regulations in the countries of the participating centers vary. In some cases the secure storage of the data at Petten was emphasised, whilst other centers were concerned with data encryption during the transfer process. Both difficulties have been overcome with encryption software and better security of the Petten computers.

3. To obtain consistent data from the various centers the types of data required have been defined in a Standard Operating Procedure (SOP) to include: number and spacing of images, field of view, location of markers, image format, etc.

Conversion software is being developed at Petten to transform the image data into the QSH format required for BNCT_Rtpe. At present the software will process ACR-NEMA data completely and some related formats, extracting as many data from the image headers as possible. For other formats, QSH files can be produced but complete processing of the header data is not possible, as this requires additional user input. Conversion options are also being added to BNCT_Rtpe but the number of formats that can be treated is limited at present. The variety and complexity of the available image formats make the image transfer and conversion a difficult and time-consuming aspect of the treatment planning.

Use of BNCT_Rtpe

The code BNCT_Rtpe provides a Graphical User Interface (GUI) to generate the B-spline surfaces for a number of "bodies" identified on the image data. First, the image slices for the complete head are loaded and then the major anatomical features (brain, skull, eyes, etc.) are outlined by hand on each image in turn. The target volume, as identified by the medical staff, is entered in the same manner. Points within any "organs at risk" are identified for inclusion in the edits of the dose calculation. From the set of bodies a three-dimensional B-spline model of the head is automatically reconstructed for use in the particle transport calculations (Fig. 1).

Material compositions for the bodies defined above are selected from a library and these compositions together with the geometrical B-spline data are entered into an interface file that is used as input in the particle transport calculation. Certain manipulations of the image data are possible within BNCT_Rtpe to highlight important features. Additional processing capabilities are under development.

Further developments of BNCT_Rtpe will allow a more flexible input of the image data, control of the rtt_MC calculation, and better manipulation of the results. In the future it is expected that BNCT_Rtpe will become a complete treatment planning environment.

114

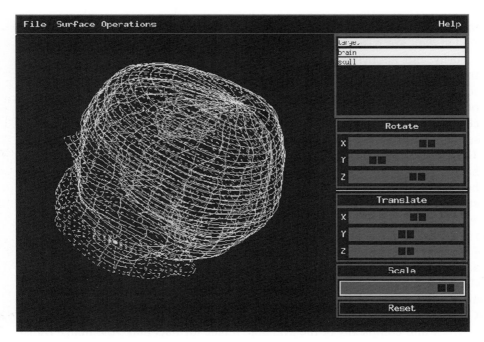

File   Surface Operations   Help

Large.
brain
skull

Rotate
X
Y
Z

Translate
X
Y
Z

Scale

Reset

Fig. 1. Geometrical reconstruction of a head in BNCT_Rtpe.

rtt_MC

The code rtt_MC performs the particle transport calculation using a Monte Carlo method to generate the dose distributions for all beam components over a pre-defined scoring mesh which is superimposed on the three-dimensional spline geometry.

The Monte Carlo simulation of the neutron and photon transport is used for a number of energy groups. Coupled neutron/photon calculations are performed which take 4—5 h for reasonable statistics on a SUN workstation (Sparcstation 10). The geometry is defined within the code in two ways. First the "source" is defined in terms of unions and intersections of simple geometrical shapes to specify the aperture, beam and irradiation surrounds. This includes the definition of the particle source plane, usually a disc with specified neutron and photon spectra, angular distributions and intensities. There may be several such source geometry files corresponding to different apertures or other beam parameters but they change little between patients. The patient geometry changes regularly and these data are provided on a second file, the interface file from BNCT_Rtpe.

Options are available to automatically place the head in the beam; typically this is used to find the orientation of the head so that the beam passes through the minimum amount of healthy tissue. Extensive edit capabilities generate data for processing later into contour plots, dose-volume histograms and depth-dose curves using a number of subsidiary codes. Multiple fields can be used by combining several rtt_MC calculations.

Presentation of results

At present the dose rate data are transferred by hand from rtt_MC to a spreadsheet for a number of predefined positions, e.g., prescription point, hot spots, eyes, etc. The spreadsheet calculates the irradiation time and the doses for all beam components given a prescribed physical dose at the prescription point. RBE and other factors may be included at this stage to give weighted unit (WU) doses (Fig. 2).

The same spreadsheet also records the positions of the entrance and exit positions of the beam center line on the patient mask together with the positions of two markers fixed on the mask and visible on the CT image. These data are processed in the spreadsheet to produce series of patient, mask and table movements to accurately position the patient in the beam.

Other data from the rtt_MC output files are extracted automatically by a set of auxiliary computer codes and processed to generate the following graphical displays:

Patient	Essen_test01	Weighting factors:			Power	45.000	MW
Date	08/08/96	W_n		3.9	Boron conc	30.000	ppm
Plan	plan01/rtt4/Essen2a_04.out	W_N		3.9	FACT$_{beam}$	1.00	(Reference beam factor)
Collimator	8 cm	W_g		1	D_B @ DGIP	0.065	Gy/min
		CF		0.37/0.81	Irr. time	122.21	min (based on D_B=8 Gy in DGIP)
Planner	P. Watkins				H density	6.3150E-02	atoms/barn-cm
					N density	7.9110E-04	atoms/barn-cm
					B density	6.0143E-08	atoms/barn-cm

	CF	D_n (Gy)	D_N (Gy)	D_g (Gy)	D_B (Gy)	D_T (Gy)	D_{WU} (WU)
Maximum dose (protocol)		1.00	0.50	5.00	8.00		13.81
MAD (DGIP)	0.37	0.45	0.45	4.20	8.00	13.10	10.67
Prescription point	0.37	0.42	0.44	4.34	7.85	13.06	7.71
Organs at risk							
skin							
- centre beam (s1)	0.81	1.34	0.11	2.73	1.89	6.06	9.90
- edge beam (s2)	0.81	0.44	0.06	1.32	0.00	1.82	3.28
- edge beam (s3)	0.81	0.56	0.03	1.26	0.00	1.86	3.59
- other side (s4)	0.81	0.00	0.00	0.61	0.00	0.61	0.62
Left eye (e1)	0.81	0.04	0.04	0.95	0.73	1.76	1.87
Right eye (e2)	0.81	0.03	0.03	0.91	0.46	1.43	1.11
Left ear (e3)	0.81	0.03	0.02	0.89	0.43	1.38	1.46
Right ear (e4)	0.81	0.02	0.02	1.13	0.34	1.52	1.30
Optic chiasm (c)	0.81	0.03	0.04	1.77	0.79	2.64	2.08
Pituitary gland (g1)	0.81	0.02	0.03	1.54	0.52	2.12	2.17
Left salivary gland (g2)	0.81	0.00	0.00	0.00	0.00	0.00	0.00
Right salivary gland (g3)	0.81	0.00	0.00	0.00	0.00	0.00	0.00
Hot spots		0.00	0.00	0.00	0.00	0.00	0.00

Fig. 2. Summary spreadsheet for the dose evaluation.

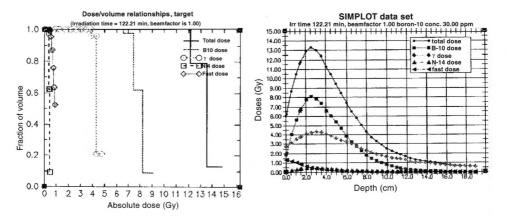

Figs. 3 (left) and 4 (right). Results from the "histo" and "simplot" postprocessors.

1. Dose-volume histograms — Dose-volume data generated in rtt_MC are extracted automatically by the "histo" code, processed and presented as a histogram display (Fig. 3).
2. Depth-dose plots — Dose rate data produced by rtt_MC along user defined lines are extracted automatically by the "simplot" code, processed and presented as one dimensional graphical displays (Fig. 4).
3. Contour plots of relative dose-rates may be provided for predefined planes through the target volume using the "xcontours" code and subsidiary files generated by rtt_MC.

Conclusions and Remarks

The BNCT_Rtpe/rtt_MC treatment planning system has been successfully installed at Petten and its use demonstrated for a European situation.

Image data from a number of medical centers have been transferred to Petten. Conversion of the data to "QSH" format is possible and is under development. Use of the Internet for image transfer is the preferred option and has been demonstrated for virtually all centers. The security implications have been addressed and encryption of the data is available if required.

Single- and multiple-field treatment plans have been performed successfully. Software tools to generate data from the calculations of rtt_MC have been developed (or adapted) to satisfy local requirements. Positioning of patients in the beam, utilizing the data from the original CT images, is being incorporated into the treatment planning process. SOPs for image transfer and treatment planning have been defined to provide consistency and quality assurance.

References

1. Wessol DE, Babcock RS, Wheeler FJ, Harkin GJ, Voss LL, Frandsen MW. BNCT_Rtpe: BNCT Radiation Treatment. Planning Environment User's Manual, Version 2.2, Idaho National Engineering and Environment Laboratory. Unpublished.
2. Maguire GQ Jr, Noz ME. QSH: A minimal but highly portable image display and handling toolkit. Comp Meth Prog Biomed 1988;27:229–240

118

Can epithermal boron neutron capture therapy treat primary and metastatic liver cancer?

B.J. Allen[1], S.A. Wallace[2] and M.G. Carolan[3]

[1]St George Cancer Care Centre, Kogarah, New South Wales; [2]Austin Hospital, Heidelberg, Victoria; and [3]Illawarra Cancer Care Centre, Wollongong, New South Wales, Australia

Introduction

Primary liver cancer in Australia has an incidence and mortality rate between 330–400 p.a. [1], suggesting misclassification of the cause of death but also indicating the incurable nature of the disease. The liver is also an important site for blood-borne metatases form colorectal cancer, melanoma, cervical, gastric, breast and other cancers. For example, some 64% of melanomas metastasise to the liver [2]. Life expectancy is only a few months if widespread hepatic metastases are present.

Primary and metastatic liver cancers are inevitably fatal. The extremely poor response rate for nonresectable hepatocellular carcinoma to systemic chemotherapy has prompted innovative treatment techniques such as transcatheter hepatic arterial chemoembolization (TACE), ^{131}I-lipiodol, adriamycin-lipoidal, ^{131}I-antiferratin, ^{90}Y microspheres, cryotherapy, hyperthermia, alcohol injection; some substantial remissions are observed. Survival rates for radical and palliative resection are 72% (1 year), 35% (3 years), 22% (1 year) and 0% (3 years), respectively, but for TACE survival increases to 98 and 78% for radical resection, and 68 and 22% for palliative resection [3]. Hepatic arterial infusion of FUDR gives partial responses and median survivals of 12–24 months [4]. Combined irradiation (21 Gy in three fractions) and doxorubicin and 5–FU, followed by ^{131}I-antiferratin or further full-dose chemotherapy give 15% partial response and only 6 months median survival. ^{131}I-antiferratin therapy of hepatoma gave 41% partial and 7% complete remission with median survival of 5 months for AFP+ and 10 months for AFP patients [5].

Irradiation of hepatic metastases has little effect on longevity, but symptoms are commonly relieved. Dose ranges from 20 Gy in 10 fractions to 30 Gy in 15 fractions with a boost to solitary metastases. Patients with colon carcinoma metastases and a Karnofsky score of 80 or more have a median survival of only 6 months [6].

Address for correspondence: B.J. Allen, St George Cancer Care Centre, Gray St, Kogarah 2217, NSW, Australia.

Thus metastatic cancer in the liver is responsible for a large fraction of deaths from a wide range of cancers. There is no current, palliative technique that can purge the liver of cancer cells.

Earlier murine studies of a melanoma liver xenograft showed a tumour-to-liver uptake ratio of around 4 for BPA.f [7]. If similar ratios could be achieved in human patients then boron neutron capture therapy could be indicated if the physics requirements can be satisfied. Bilateral epithermal neutron beams give a relatively uniform dose distribution for the brain. However, the liver is a much larger organ and it is uncertain whether a superposition of epithermal neutron beams could achieve a useful dose distribution over the entire liver. We have studied this problem using Monte Carlo methods in a trunk phantom to calculate neutron fluence and absorbed dose across the liver.

Method

The epithermal neutron beam used in this calculation is that produced by the JRC reactor at Petten in The Netherlands. This beam has been designed and constructed as part of the European Collaboration on boron neutron capture therapy (BNCT) [8]. We calculated dose depth distributions for boron neutron capture, fast neutrons and induced gammas using the Monte Carlo program MCNP. Results have been validated by dosimetry experiments in a human size, tissue-equivalent trunk phantom [9].

Dose rates are calculated for two orthogonal beams, viz the anterior and side beams. ^{10}B concentrations of 30 ppm in cancer cells and a tumour to tissue boron ratio of 4 are assumed. The potential success of epithermal BNCT depends on the therapeutic ratio that can be achieved throughout the liver, where the therapeutic ratio (TR) = tumour dose/tissue dose. Calculations are made at the skin, anterior and posterior liver.

Results

The isodose rate curves are shown in Fig. 1A−C for gamma, fast neutron and boron absorbed doses, using the Petten epithermal neutron beam as the incident beam. The general features of these data are:

Boron — The 100% dose value is 6.7 Gy/h, posterior liver is bound by the 50% isodose, anterior liver is bound by the 100% isodose.

Fast neutron — The 100% dose value is 1.2 Gy/h, the anterior liver receives 100%, skin receives 110%.

Gamma — The 100% dose value is 2.5 Gy/h, the anterior liver receives 120%.

Total absorbed doses are calculated at the skin (A), anterior liver (B) and posterior liver (C). The TR can then be obtained at each position, and for the worst case TR, i.e., tumour at (C) and normal liver at (B). Results are given in Table 1 for the skin, anterior liver and posterior liver. The total dose rates vary from 5.8

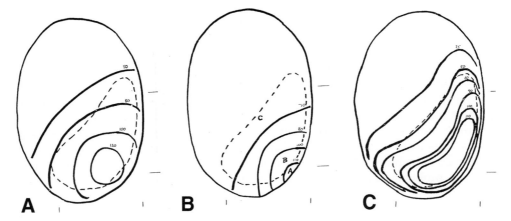

Fig. 1. Isodose rate contours for induced γ rays (100 = 2.5 Gy/h) (**A**), fast neutrons (100 = 1.2 Gy/h) (**B**), and boron (100 = 6.7 Gy/h) (**C**). Therapeutic ratios are calculated at the skin (**A**), anterior liver (**B**), and posterior liver (**C**).

Gy/h for the skin, 11.6 Gy/h for a tumour at the anterior (ANT) liver, and 5.4 Gy/h for a tumour at the posterior (POST) liver. Using the RBE values adopted at BNL [10,11] the RBE dose rates to anterior and posterior liver tumours are 35 and 14.5 Gy Eq/h, respectively.

While quite useful absorbed dose therapeutic ratios are found at each position (TR = 1.8 and 2.7 for absorbed and RBE dose), the worst case gives TR = 1.0 and 1.3. If cancer cells and hepatocytes have similar radiosensitivities to high LET radiation, then the former can only be controlled by sacrificing anterior liver. Thus, the Petten epithermal beam would require less than 1 h to deliver 30 Gy to a lesion in the anterior liver and 2 h for the posterior liver.

Table 1. Radiation dose rates (Gy/h and Gy Eq/h) and therapeutic ratios (TR).

Region	Fast neutron	γ	Tumour boron	Tissue boron	Tumour	Tissue	TR
RBE	3.2[a]	1.0	3.8[a]	2.5[b]			
skin (A) Gy	1.3	3.0	6.0	1.5	10.3	5.8	1.8
Gy Eq/h	4.2	3.0	22.8	3.8	30.0	11	2.7
Liver(B)Gy	1.2	3.0	7.4	1.8	11.6	6.0	1.9
Gy Eq/h	3.8	3.0	28.1	4.5	34.9	11.3	3.1
Liver(C)Gy	0.7	2.0	2.7	0.7	6.1	3.5	1.7
Gy Eq/h	2.2	2.0	10.3	1.8	14.5	6.0	2.4
Gy					6.0(B)	6.1(C)	1.0
Gy Eq/h					11.3	14.5	1.3

[a]Coderre et al. (1993) for in vitro and in vivo rat glioma; [b]Fukuda et al. (1994) for human skin.

Conclusion

Therapeutic ratios have been calculated for orthogonal irradiations of the liver with an existing epithermal neutron beam, using achievable values of 30 ppm ^{10}B in cancer cells and a tumour/tissue ratio of 4. Therapeutic ratios for absorbed dose and RBE dose of about 1.8 and 2.7, respectively, are found which are indicative of epithermal BNCT. However, the worst case TRs for a posterior liver tumour of 1.0 and 1.3, respectively, suggests that treatment would be marginal for the conditions adopted in this paper.

References

1. Jelf P, Coates M, Giles G et al. Cancer in Australia 1989–1990, Australian Institute of Health and Welfare 1996.
2. Stutte H, Muller PH, d'Hoedt B, Stroebel W. Ultrasonic diagnosis of melanoma metastases in liver, gall bladder and spleen. J Ultrasound Med 1989;8(10):541–547.
3. Li JQ, Zhang YQ, Zhang WZ, Yuan YF, Li GH. Randomized study of chemoembolisation as an adjuvant therapy for primary liver carcinoma after hepatectomy. J Cancer Res Clin Oncol 1995;1121(6):364–366.
4. Kemeny N, Seiter K. Colorectal carcinoma. In: Calabresi P, Schein PS (eds) Medical Oncology, 2nd edn. New York: McGraw-Hill, 1993;765–769.
5. Order SE. Radioimmunoglobulins in cancer therapy. In: Perez CA, Brady LW (eds) Principles and Practices of Radiation Oncology. Philadelphia: J.B. Lippincott Co., 1992;447–454.
6. Stevens KR. The liver and bilary system. In: Moss RL (ed) Radiation Oncology, 7th edn. St Louis: Mosby, 1994;452–461.
7. Mallesch J, Chiaraviglio D, Allen BJ, Moore DE. An intrapancreatic and hepatic nude mouse model for BNCT. In: Soloway AH, Barth RF, Carpenter DE et al. (eds) Advances in NCT. New York: Plenum Press, 1993;547–550.
8. Gabel D, Moss RL. Boron Neutron Capture Therapy, Towards Clinical Trials. New York: Plenum Press, 1992.
9. Wallace SA. Treatment planning for boron neutron capture therapy for cancer, PhD Thesis, University of Wollongong 1996.
10. Coderre JA, Makar MS, Micca PL et al. Derivations of RBE for the high LET radiations produced during boron neutron capture irradiations of the 9L rat gliosarcoma in vitro and in vivo. Int J Radiat Oncol Biol Phys 1993; 27:1121–1129.
11. Fukuda H, Hiratsuka J, Honda C et al. BNCT of malignant melanoma using BPA with special reference to evaluation of skin dose and damage to skin. Radiat Res 1994;138: 435–442.

A γ-ray telescope for on-line reconstruction of low boron concentrations in a human head during BNCT

Wilko Verbakel[1,2] and Finn Stecher-Rasmussen[1]

[1] Netherlands Energy Research Foundation ECN, Petten; and [2] Eindhoven University of Technology, Eindhoven, The Netherlands

Patient dosimetry by prompt γ-ray spectroscopy

In vivo dose monitoring for boron neutron capture therapy (BNCT) requires determination of the time-dependent boron concentration in the tumour and in the healthy tissue of a patient during irradiation. To date, this determination is performed by combining pre- and post-BNCT measurements of the boron concentration in blood with pharmacokinetics information from the patient [1,2]. However, since the $^{10}B(n,\alpha)$ reaction also leads to a release of a γ ray of 478 keV, these γ rays can serve as a measure of the boron concentration in a patient's head during therapy [3]. Position-dependent measurements with several detectors enable the determination of the ^{10}B concentration in both the healthy tissue and the tumour.

Boron determination by a two-detector configuration

In this study a two-detector γ-ray telescope system has been designed at the therapy facility of the HFR in Petten. One detector measures the boron neutron capture reaction rate of a large volume of the head without tumour (healthy tissue), the second detector measures the boron neutron capture reaction rate of a small volume of the head containing the tumour. From the measured reaction rates, the average boron concentrations in these volumes are calculated.

Detection of the small Doppler-broadened boron peak requires the effective shielding of this high background radiation field of γ rays and neutrons around the patient. Because of this high radiation field in the therapy room, the two detectors view the head through holes in the 20-cm thick steel roof. Figure 1 shows a cross-section of this therapy room with one detector. As neutron capture in hydrogen generates a 2.2-MeV γ ray, the γ-ray spectrum from the telescope also gives information about the thermal neutron distribution.

Reconstruction of the two boron concentrations out of two measurements

Address for correspondence: Wilko Verbakel, Netherlands Energy Research Foundation ECN, P.O. Box 1, NL-1755 ZG Petten, The Netherlands.

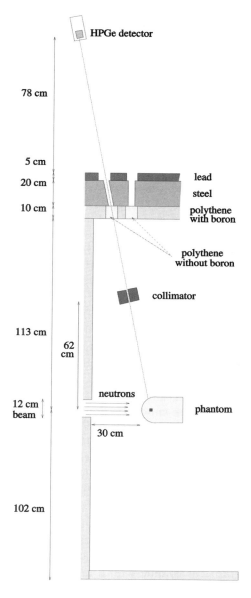

Fig. 1. Vertical cross-section of the therapy room at HFR, including the HPGe detector for the position-dependent prompt γ ray measurements.

requires the information from CT scans about the geometry of the head, the position and the geometry of the tumour. In the first instance a massive well-known shaped tumour is assumed. This will not be the case if the tumour of the patient has been debulked. There are two methods for this reconstruction:

1. Simulation of the boron detection rate in the detector, using a modification of the (Monte Carlo based) treatment planning program with the addition of a γ-ray transport module.
2. Simple geometric reconstruction by hand, from both the contents of the boron and hydrogen peaks. The ratio of these peaks (^{10}B/H) will eliminate a great part of the influence of the thermal neutron distribution.

The healthy tissue detector

In this study a head phantom is exposed to epithermal neutrons from the therapy facility of the HFR. The phantom, which consists of a perspex cylinder at one side combined with a hemisphere, is filled with water and 5 ppm ^{10}B, representing the healthy tissue. The tumour is represented by a small cylinder (volume 8.0 cm^3) which is filled with water with 62 ppm ^{10}B. One high purity germanium detector is used for a measurement of the γ rays emitted by a cylindrical volume of the phantom, not containing the tumour. The ^{10}B/H ratio is used to calculate the boron concentration in the healthy tissue. A homogeneous distribution of both boron and hydrogen is assumed.

Figure 2 shows integral measurements of almost the whole phantom (radius 7.5 cm) without the tumour. It leads to a very high count rate of 50,000 counts/s. No boron γ rays produced in the shielding of the therapy room were detected. One measurement for only 111 s yielded a boron peak of 9,500 counts (±2.8%) and a ^{10}B/H-ratio of 0.089.

The tumour detector and reconstruction of the boron concentrations

The second detector performs position-dependent measurements. For that purpose, a tungsten collimator is placed between the patient and the ceiling. Its optimum diameter and distance to the detector are analytically calculated and verified by Monte Carlo calculations (MCNP4A). In order to reduce the energy of the Compton-scattered contaminant γ rays from the neutron beam that reach the detector, they do not appear at the same energy as the boron peak, the detector views the phantom at an angle of 11°, compared to the vertical. This also enables us to perform the measurements with both detectors simultaneously. The ultimate detector configuration views a cylindrical volume with a radius of 1.75 cm which is aligned to the centre of the tumour. The presence of the tumour increases the ^{10}B/H-ratio to 0.22, see Fig. 3. To obtain an accuracy of 3% in the boron peak, a measuring time of 2 min is required. An MCNP model of the entire geometry enabled the prediction of the boron and hydrogen count rates. These correspond within 10% to the measured count rates.

Since the integral measurement provided the ^{10}B concentration in the healthy tissue, the ^{10}B concentration in the tumour can easily be extracted. The measured ^{10}B/H-ratio is equal to:

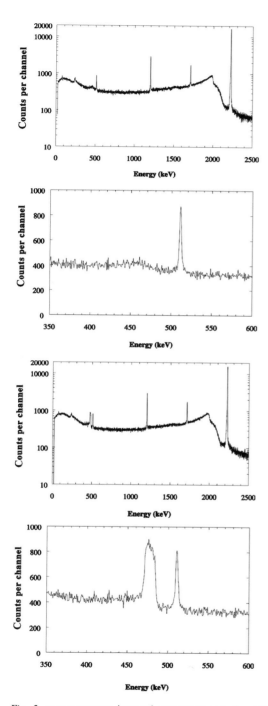

Fig. 2. γ-ray spectra integral measurements for 111 s of the phantom without boron and with 5 ppm ^{10}B.

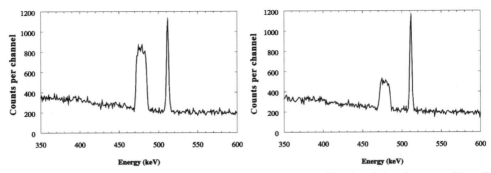

Fig. 3. γ-ray spectrum of the position-dependent measurement of 2 min of the phantom with and without tumour.

$$\frac{\Phi^B_{ht}[B_{ht}] + \Phi^B_{tum}[B_{tum}]}{\Phi^H}$$

adjusted for the difference in attenuation through the polythene ceiling, and the detector efficiency. $[B_{ht}]$ and $[B_{tum}]$ are the boron concentrations of healthy tissue (ht) and tumour (tum). The Φ's are the γ-ray productions of 1 ppm boron in ht, 1 ppm boron in tum and hydrogen in water, adjusted for their attenuation in the phantom (depending on their position of creation) and the detector geometric efficiency.

Our reconstruction of $^{10}B_{ht}$ = 5.2 ppm and $^{10}B_{tum}$ = 70 ppm, tallies very well with the actual concentrations of 5.0 ppm and 62 ppm, respectively. For real patients the reconstruction has to allow for the presence of bone, which contains no boron but has a higher attenuation.

Conclusions

Measurements with a two-detector system at the therapy facility of the HFR in Petten give adequate information for determination of the boron concentrations in healthy tissue and tumour. In fact, with patients, the tumour region of a glio-blastoma is not well-defined. Therefore only a boron concentration averaged over a specific volume can be reconstructed. For reconstruction, information of CT/MRI-scans about the shape and the geometry of the tumour, and the geometry of the head has to be used. Since each determination requires only 2 min, the change of the concentrations can be followed in time. In addition to boron and hydrogen γ rays, nitrogen γ rays can be measured as well, yielding information about the dose of the $^{14}N(n,p)^{14}C$ reaction. In a future stage, the time-dependent information about the nitrogen neutron capture rate together with the boron concentrations and the hydrogen neutron capture reaction rate are necessary for in vivo dosimetry of the patient.

References

1. Stragliotto G, Schüpbach D, Gavin PR, Fankhauser H. Update on biodistribution of boro-captate sodium (BSH) in patients with intracranial tumors. In: Soloway AH, Barth RF, Carpenter DE (eds) Advances in Neutron Capture Therapy. New York and London: Plenum Press, 1993;719–726.
2. Haritz D, Gabel D, Klein H, Huiskamp R. Results of continued clinical investigations of BSH in patients with malignant glioma. In: Soloway AH, Barth RF, Carpenter DE (eds) Advances in Neutron Capture Therapy. New York and London: Plenum Press, 1993;719–726.
3. Verbakel WFAR. A gamma-ray telescope for on-line measurements of low boron concentrations in a head-phantom for BNCT. ECN-report ECN–I–95–051 1995.

A neutron capture radiography facility at PSI

S. Teichmann, J.F. Crawford and B. Larsson

Institute for Medical Radiobiology of the University of Zurich and the Paul Scherrer Institute, Villigen, Switzerland

Introduction

At the Paul Scherrer Institute (PSI), the spallation neutron source SINQ [1] is scheduled to come into service in early 1997. We plan to establish a facility for neutron capture radiography (NCR) which will provide cold-neutron irradiations at one of the SINQ neutron guides and, to some extent, analysis of the detector foils. It will be open to external users, probably at some minimal cost depending on the services.

Irradiation facility

Figure 1 shows the neutron guide hall of the SINQ experimental area at PSI, in November 1995. The prospective site of the irradiation chamber for NCR is indicated at the end of guide RNR13. This guide is coated with supermirrors and has a curved length of 20 m, with a radius of curvature of 2,408 m, followed by a straight section of about 20 m (to even out intensity fluctuations across the guide). The dimensions are 30 mm wide × 120 mm high. Figure 2 shows a calculated neutron spectrum at the end of a supermirror guide [2]. The expected neutron flux is of the order of 10^9 n/cm^2 s, with essentially no contamination of neutrons above ~ 0.4 eV, ensuring a minimal background due to recoil protons. The irradiation chamber has to shield the primary neutron beam, scattered neutrons and secondary photons. It will consist of a lead box with 100-mm thick walls and with inner dimensions of approximately 1 m × 0.6 m × 0.95 m (width × depth × height), coated inside with a few millimeters of boron-plastic which contains at least 30% boron. The beam shutter at the guide exit and a γ monitor inside the chamber will be coupled to the opening mechanism of the door, to ensure radiation safety when the beam is on, or when the dose rate inside the chamber is above a certain limit due to activated materials. As an on-line neutron monitor, we plan to use a fission chamber.

At first, samples will be irradiated in a fixed position. Samples exceeding the width of the guide aperture will be mounted at an angle to the beam. The

Address for correspondence: Börje Larsson, Institute for Medical Radiobiology, University of Zurich and the Paul Scherrer Institute, CH-5232 Villigen PSI, Switzerland.

Fig. 1. Neutron guide hall in the SINQ experimental area; the circle indicates the prospective irradiation site.

expected intensity fluctuations across the guide exit are of the order of 15% [3]. In the next stage, it is foreseen to install a scanning table, so that large samples (up to 300 mm × 300 mm) could be scanned across the guide aperture. At the same time, intensity fluctuations would be averaged out. The scanning speed should be determined by the neutron monitor output, to ensure homogenous irradiation of the complete sample. An automatic sample change from a magazine on top of the irradiation chamber is also planned. It will be possible to mount several samples behind each other. Since this affects the neutron flux on each sample, it may be necessary to have standards on each one.

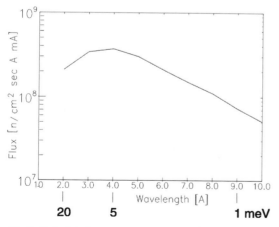

Fig. 2. Calculated neutron spectrum at the end of a supermirror guide [2].

Developments towards subcellular resolution

As an NCR facility we would also, at least in part, be responsible for the procedures following irradiation, i.e., etching of the detector foils and the subsequent analysis of their track-density distribution. Apart from quantitative analysis on the macroscopic scale, our goal is to be able to offer microscopic information on a subcellular scale. Here, we have made progress in two important aspects: three-dimensional (3-D) track analysis (see [4]) and specimen-detector correlation.

3-D track analysis

Using a confocal laser scanning microscope (CLSM), 3-D track viewing becomes possible and allows us, in principle, to extract the incident angle of the particle. Two important points must be considered for this [5]: 1) the tracks have to be fluorescently dyed; and 2) they must be viewed directly with an oil immersion lens such that the oil fills the tracks, to avoid refractive index mismatches. An easy dyeing method for CR-39 consists of treating the detector in a 1% solution of Nile Blue A at 55°C for 10 min, rinsing it with distilled water and then placing it for 1 min in 8% acetic acid solution [6]. Higher temperatures ($\sim 70°$C) were seen to produce better results, and omission of the last step did not seem to influence the outcome. The fluorescent tracks were observed using the 488-nm laser of the CLSM, a 510-nm dichroic mirror and a 515-nm emission filter. They remain fluorescent for at least 1 week.

Figure 3 shows fluorescently dyed tracks of 1.5 MeV α particles at the surface of a CR-39 detector (etched for 1 h with 6.25 n NaOH at 70°C) and a cross-sectional view of the tracks, obtained with a CLSM.

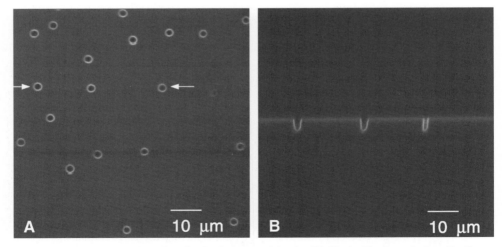

Fig. 3. Fluorescently dyed tracks of 1.5 MeV α particles in CR-39. **A**: Horizontal view. **B**: Cross-sectional view ($\rightarrow$).

Specimen-detector correlation

One possibility to correlate individual tracks in the detector foil with cells or morphological structures in the original specimen is to use specially marked detector foils. By using previously irradiated and etched detector foils, these markers could themselves consist of etched particle tracks. These marker tracks have to be distinguishable from the tracks later produced by the capture reactions; they should be distributed at an appropriate density that is low enough not to obscure the tracks of interest and high enough to allow image correlation, and they should be perpendicular to the foil so that their centres do not shift during etching.

We have made some tests with an etched CR-39 detector foil that had been irradiated with high-energy (~ 150 GeV) Pb ions and was supplied by Professor Heinrich from the University of Siegen, Germany [7]. The Pb tracks are perpendicular and penetrate the ~ 200-μm thick detector; size and density of these tracks can be adjusted according to need. Figure 4(A,B) shows the detector after irradiation with 1.5 MeV α particles (from an ^{241}Am source) and 1 h etching under the conditions mentioned above. The small α tracks can be clearly distinguished from the larger Pb tracks.

To observe cell nuclei under the microscope, they need to be stained. A thin (~ 2 μm) section of embedded mouse brain was brought onto a piece of the Pb-track detector and a standard Hematoxylin-Eosin (HE) staining procedure was applied. Unless the section was fixed with a glycerin-protein mixture, it did not stick to the detector surface, probably because of fluids penetrating through the Pb tracks from below. Figure 4(C) shows an image of the stained cell nuclei and a Pb track.

These tests show the feasibility of the method from a practical point of view. The techniques and the necessary software for the correlation have not yet been established. However, another group at our institute is working on a similar problem [8], and we expect to be able to adapt their methods to our needs.

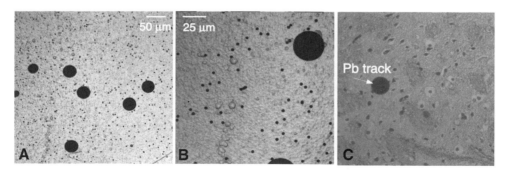

Fig. 4. **A** and **B**: CR-39 with tracks from high-energy Pb ions (large tracks) after irradiation with 1.5 MeV α particles and etching (small tracks). **C**: Pb-track detector with an embedded mouse brain section and HE-stained, to make the cell nuclei visible.

132

Acknowledgements

We would like to thank Mr K. Kohlik at the Paul Scherrer Institute for his enthusiastic support and help in the planning of the irradiation chamber, and Mrs V. Gut from the Institute of Medical Radiobiology in Zurich for her preparations of mouse brain sections and their staining.

References

1. Bauer G. The spallation neutron source SINQ. Published by the Paul Scherrer Institute, CH-5232 Villigen-PSI, Switzerland, 1994.
2. Atchison F, Böni P. Intensities at the SINQ Guide System. Internal PSI report project SINQ No. 816/AF30-404.-, 1994.
3. Copley JRD, Mildner DFR. Simulation and analysis of the transmission properties of curved-straight neutron guide systems. Nucl Sci Eng 1992;110:1—9.
4. Teichmann S et al. New developments in the use of solid state nuclear track detectors. Proceedings of the 6th International Symposium on NCT, 31 Oct. — 4 Nov. 1994, Kobe, Japan. Plenum Press (In press).
5. Teichmann S, Larsson B, Tuor S. 3-D Track analysis using a confocal laser scanning microscope. Radiat Protect Dosimet 1996;66:375—378.
6. Ostle AG, Holt JG. Nile Blue A as a fluorescent stain for poly-β-hydroxybutyrate. Appl Environ Microbiol 1982;44:238—241.
7. Heinrich W Prof., University of Siegen, Physics Department, Adolf-Reichwein Str. D-57076 Siegen, Germany.
8. Tuor S, Reist HW, Doria P. Track reconstruction to investigate cell damage by single particles. PSI Life Sci Newslet 1993;92—93.

1997 Elsevier Science B.V.
Advances in Neutron Capture Therapy.
Volume I, Medicine and Physics.
B. Larsson, J. Crawford and R. Weinreich, editors.

A treatment planning comparison of BPA- or BSH-based BNCT of malignant gliomas

J. Capala, J.A. Coderre and A.D. Chanana

Medical Department, Brookhaven National Laboratory, Upton, New York, USA

Introduction

Accurate delivery of the prescribed dose during clinical boron neutron capture therapy (BNCT) requires knowledge (or reasonably valid assumptions) about the boron concentrations in tumor and normal tissues. For conversion of physical dose (Gy) into photon-equivalent dose (Gy-Eq), relative biological effectiveness (RBE) and/or compound-adjusted biological effectiveness (CBE) factors are required for each tissue. The BNCT treatment planning software requires input of the following values: the boron concentration in blood and tumor, RBEs in brain, tumor and skin for the high-LET beam components, the CBE factors for brain, tumor, and skin, and the RBE for the γ component.

In addition to the ongoing clinical BNCT program in Japan using BSH and the planned trial in Europe with BSH, there is interest among several BNCT groups in the USA in BSH-based BNCT. There is some uncertainty in the BNCT community and literature about the parameters to be considered for BSH regarding tumor/blood ^{10}B concentration ratio (range: 0.5:1 to 2.2:1) [1,2], CBE factor in brain (range: 0.37 to 0.5) [3,4], and CBE factor in tumor (range: 1.2 to 2.3) [5,6]. In the present work, we applied different combinations of these parameters and used BNCT treatment planning software with actual patient geometry for a direct comparison of a BPA-based plan to the plan that would be obtained for patient treatment with BMRR epithermal neutron beam using BSH.

Materials and Methods

Treatment plans for BSH using different combinations of the input parameters (Table 1) were prepared and compared to the BPA plan used for a representative glioblastoma patient treated at Brookhaven National Laboratory. Treatment planning procedures and parameters used for estimation of radiation doses delivered during BPA-based BNCT are described in this volume by Capala et al. [7]. All treatment plans used a single-field exposure and were run with a prescribed limit

---

Address for correspondence: Jacek Capala, Medical Department, Brookhaven National Laboratory, Building 490, Upton, NY 11973, USA.

Table 1. Summary of results obtained from treatment plans using BPA or BSH.

Compound	BSH									BPA
^{10}B in the blood (ppm)	12.7	20	20	30	30	20	20	30	30	12.7
^{10}B in the tumor (ppm)	26.5	20	20	30	30	40	40	60	60	44
CBE in the brain	0.5	0.5	0.37	0.5	0.37	0.5	0.37	0.5	0.37	1.3
CBE in the tumor	2.3	1.2	2.3	1.2	2.3	1.2	2.3	1.2	2.3	3.8
γ RBE	1	1	1	1	1	1	1	1	1	1
Beam high-LET RBE	3.2	3.2	3.2	3.2	3.2	3.2	3.2	3.2	3.2	3.2
Time or irradiation at 3 MW reactor power (min)	51	45	49	39	44	45	49	39	44	38
Peak brain dose	12.6	12.6	12.6	12.6	12.6	12.6	12.6	12.6	12.6	12.6
Average brain dose	4.2	4.1	4.2	4.0	4.1	4.1	4.2	4.0	4.1	4.0
of which:										
boron	0.7	1.0	0.8	1.3	1.1	1.0	0.8	1.3	1.1	1.3
γ	2.2	2.0	2.1	1.7	1.9	2.0	2.1	1.7	1.9	1.7
N-14	0.6	0.5	0.6	0.5	0.5	0.5	0.6	0.5	0.5	0.4
fast n	0.7	0.7	0.7	0.6	0.6	0.7	0.7	0.6	0.6	0.6
Peak tumor dose	35.8	17.9	28.5	19.5	27.1	47.5	31.4	29.3	59.3	60.1
Average tumor dose	32.6	16.4	26.0	17.8	31.4	24.6	43.0	28.5	53.4	54.6
of which:										
boron	23.3	8.2	17.0	10.7	22.7	16.4	34.0	21.3	45.5	47.7
γ	5.0	4.4	4.7	3.8	4.2	4.4	4.7	3.8	4.2	4.9
N-14	2.0	1.8	2.0	1.6	1.8	1.8	2.0	1.5	1.8	1.5
fast n	2.3	2.0	2.2	1.8	2.0	2.0	2.2	1.8	2.0	1.7
Minimum tumor dose	23.8	12.5	17.8	13.3	22.3	18.1	30.9	20.6	37.9	38.1
Treatment plan #	1	2	3	4	5	6	7	8	9	10

of 12.6 Gy-Eq as the maximum dose to a 1 cm^3 volume of normal brain outside of the tumor volume (contrast enhanced volume on MRI scan) delivered in a single fraction.

Results and Discussion

Results of these simulations are listed in Table 1. Average doses to the whole brain volume were approximately 4 Gy-Eq and were similar with BPA and BSH. The BPA-based treatment delivered a minimum of 38.1 Gy-Eq to the deepest portion of the tumor. The doses to the tumor volume were considerably lower with BSH in all cases except those involving the most favorable set of assumptions. A typical dose volume histogram obtained from BPA-based treatment plan is shown in Fig. 1 along with examples of dose-volume histograms that resulted from different sets of assumptions regarding ^{10}B concentration in the blood and ^{10}B tumor-to-blood ratio for BSH-based treatment plans (Fig. 1). Only the most optimistic BSH-based treatment plan, which assumed CBE values of 0.37 and 2.3 for the brain and the tumor, respectively, [10]B concentration in the blood of 30 ppm and [10]B tumor-to-blood ratio of 2:1, produced dose-volume histograms comparable to those obtained using BPA as a boron delivery agent.

In this work we have, for BSH, used CBE factors and [10]B concentrations that, to the best of our knowledge, span the range of published values from both animal experiments and clinical studies. Published reports of BSH biodistribution in animal tumor models have generally shown that the boron concentration in the tumor is only about 50% of that in the blood, i.e., a tumor-to-blood ratio of 0.5:1. A recent report from Japan [1] described BSH biodistribution data from

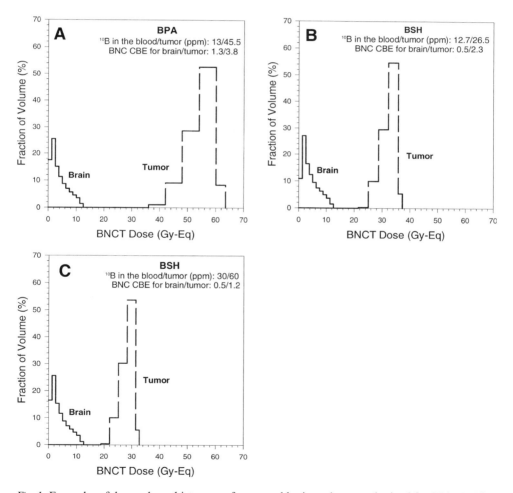

Fig. 1. Examples of dose volume histograms for normal brain and tumor obtained for BPA. **A:** Plan #10) or BSH using a range of possible blood/tumor [10]B concentrations and CBE values. **B:** Plan #1. **C:** Plan #8. **D** *(next page)*: Plan #9. **E** *(next page)*: Plan #6. **F**(*next page*): Plan #7.

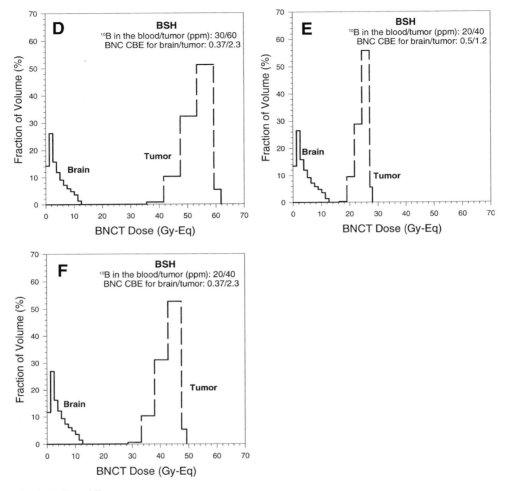

Fig. 1. **D**, **E** and **F**.

39 patients. The [10]B concentrations reported for tumor and blood were 26.5 ± 3.4 and 12.7 ± 0.8 mg [10]B/g, respectively, for a tumor-to-blood ratio of 2.1:1. The tumor-to-blood concentration ratios used for the simulations in this report were varied from 1:1 to 2:1. Treatment plans 1—9 (Table 1), represent various combinations of the input parameters for BSH. Plan 1 uses the values reported by Hatanaka [1]. Plans 2—9 use tumor-to-blood ratios of 1:1 (plans 2—5) and 2:1 (plans 6—9) at two different blood boron concentrations, 20 and 30 ppm, respectively. In addition, at each blood boron concentration, two sets of CBE factors were used as a way of exploring the effect of uncertainty in these parameters. The plans using 0.5 as the CBE factor for brain and 1.2 as the CBE factor for tumor are considered a "worst case", whereas the combination 0.37 as the CBE factor for brain and 2.3 as the CBE factor for tumor is considered a "best case"

scenario for BSH-based BNCT. Our results showed that if BSH were used in the current BNL protocol (BMRR epithermal neutron beam, single fraction), only very optimistic assumptions regarding CBE factors, and ^{10}B distribution would produce the radiation doses comparable to those obtained using BPA. However, computer simulations are only as good as their input assumptions. It is possible that new approaches to BSH-mediated boron delivery, as reported by Barth et al. [8] or Haselsberger et al. [9] in this volume may improve the ^{10}B distribution. It is also possible that a favorable microdistribution of BSH-delivered ^{10}B in human tumor cells, as reported by Otersen et al. [10], may increase the effectiveness of the treatment. The influence of fractionation and neutron beam characteristics (other than at BMRR) on the doses delivered to tumor and normal tissues during BSH-based BNCT remains to be explored.

Acknowledgements

This work was supported by the US Department of Energy under contract # DE-AC02-76CH00016.

References

1. Hatanaka H, Nakagawa Y. Clinical results of long-surviving brain tumor patients who underwent boron neutron capture therapy. Int J Radiat Oncol Biol Phys 1994;28:1061–1066.
2. Kraft SL, Gavin PR, Leathers CW, Dehaan CE, Bauer WF, Miller DL, Dorn RV, Griebenow ML. Biodistribution of boron in dogs with spontaneous intracranial tumors following borocaptate sodium administration. Cancer Res 1994;54:1259–1263.
3. Morris GM, Coderre JA, Hopewell JW, Micca PL, Nawrocky MM, Liu HB, Bywaters A. Response of the central nervous system to boron neutron capture irradiation: Evaluation using rat spinal cord model. Radiother Oncol 1994;32:249–255.
4. Huiskamp R, Gavin PR, Coderre JA, Phillip KHI, Wheeler FJ. Brain tolerance in dogs to boron neutron capture therapy with borocaptate sodium (BSH) or boronophenylalanine (BPA). In: Mishima Y (ed) Cancer Neutron Capture Therapy. New York: Plenum Press, 1996;(In press).
5. Coderre JA, Morris GM, Micca PL, Nawrocky MM, Fisher CD, Bywaters A, Hopewell JW. The therapeutic ratio in boron neutron capture therapy: Assessment using the rat 9L gliosarcoma and spinal cord models. In: Mishima Y (ed) Cancer Neutron Capture Therapy. New York: Plenum Press, 1996;6:757–762.
6. Aizawa O. Evaluation of neutron irradiation field for boron neutron capture therapy by using absorbed dose in a phantom. Int J Radiat Oncol Biol Phys 1994;28:1061–1066.
7. Capala J, Chadha M, Coderre JA, Diaz AZ, Liu HB, Wheeler FJ, Wessol DE, Wielopolski L, Chanana AD. Radiation doses to brain under BNCT protocols at Brookhaven National Laboratory. In: Larsson B, Crawford J, Weinreich R (eds) Advances in Neutron Capture Therapy. Volume 1, Medicine and Physics. Amsterdam: Elsevier Science, 1997;51–55 (these proceedings).
8. Barth RF, Yang W, Soloway AH, Goodman, JH. Alternative approaches for the delivery of boron-containing agents to brain tumors. In: Larsson B, Crawford J, Weinreich R (eds) Advances in Neutron Capture Therapy. Volume 2, Chemistry and Biology. Amsterdam: Elsevier Science, 1997;216–224 (these proceedings).
9. Haselsberger K, Rander H, Pendl G. Systemic hyaluronidase: a promising adjuvant for BNCT of glioblastoma with $Na_2B_{12}H_{11}SH$ (BSH). In: Larsson B, Crawford J, Weinreich R (eds) Advances

in Neutron Capture Therapy. Volume 2, Chemistry and Biology. Amsterdam: Elsevier Science, 1997;202—204 (these proceedings).

10. Otersen B, Sierralta W, Haritz D, Grochulla F, Bergmann M, Gabel D. Cellular uptake mechanism of BSH in tumor tissue of glioma patients. In: Larsson B, Crawford J, Weinreich R (eds) Advances in Neutron Capture Therapy. Volume 2, Chemistry and Biology. Amsterdam: Elsevier Science, 1997;169—174 (these proceedings).

Dosimetry

Advances in Neutron Capture Therapy.
Volume I, Medicine and Physics.
B. Larsson, J. Crawford and R. Weinreich, editors.

141

Dosimetry for BNCT in theory and practice

P. Watkins[1], R.L. Moss[1], F. Stecher-Rasmussen[2] and W. Voorbraak[2]

[1]*Commission of the European Communities, Joint Research Centre, Petten; and* [2]*Energie Centrum Nederland, Petten, The Netherlands*

Introduction

Dosimetry may be defined as the measurement of physical parameters that are related to some form of irradiation procedure. However, the multidisciplinary nature of BNCT has resulted in the word "dosimetry" assuming widely different meanings. Thus for a clinician, patient dosimetry is likely to concentrate upon dose evaluation, whilst for the physicist the emphasis is upon activation rates of foils to estimate particle fluxes. To confuse the issue further the various disciplines tend to use different detectors generating varying definitions of dose, flux, etc.

This diversity of "dosimetry" measurements within the relatively small BNCT community represents a barrier that prevents the most efficient use of limited data. There is a need to introduce standards for BNCT dosimetry for all disciplines to help in the intercomparison of different BNCT facilities and resolve uncertainties.

This paper seeks to quantify some of the available dosimetric methods currently in use by reference to the Petten experience, to highlight some problems and identify those dosimetry items that have been found to be useful in practice for a BNCT facility.

Categories of BNCT dosimetry

The possible application of dosimetry in BNCT may be divided into five main areas:
1. Source — monitor the neutron source prior to any filtering of the beam.
2. Beam — characterise free beam spectra, adjust calculated data and confirm the consistency of the neutron and photon components of the beam.
3. Phantom — beam characterisation at depth in tissue-like material. Validate treatment planning methods and estimate radiation doses.
4. On-line — continuous monitoring of the beam during patient irradiation and standard operation. Links to beam operation, safety systems and irradiation parameters.
5. Patient — measurements of delivered dose or a related parameter.

Address for correspondence: Dr P. Watkins, Institute of Advanced Materials, European Commission, P.O. Box 2, 1755 ZG Petten, The Netherlands.

Source dosimetry

Foreseeable BNCT facilities invariably consist of a neutron source and a filter configuration to modify the emergent neutron and photon spectra. It is important to monitor the condition of these two independently to quickly identify and isolate any faults. Thus a continuous measurement of the unfiltered source is needed. This is especially true when the filter contains liquids which may become contaminated or undergo phase changes in the case of accidents. In practice the required dosimetry measurement can be very simple. Typically an ionisation chamber placed in a strategic position to monitor the unfiltered neutron source on a continuous basis would be sufficient. Such measurements can also be introduced into any on-line monitoring system for the control of the system.

The need for such source monitoring was demonstrated at Petten when the beam intensity dropped by 40% between reactor cycles. No source monitoring was being performed and it was impossible to isolate the problem to the reactor core or to a failure of one of the filter components. The reactor could not simply be shut down because of the effects on other projects. It was only after a considerable effort that the fault was identified as humidity in the argon filter. A simple source monitor would have immediately localised the problem to the filter assembly.

Beam dosimetry

Free beam measurements remain a vital part of BNCT dosimetry to characterise the beam, demonstrate the beam consistency, and to provide data for validation of theoretical models. Frequently activation foil measurements are used for this purpose. Their simplicity also allows the foil activations to be calculated directly in computer simulations, thereby providing a valuable validation of the calculational methods and avoiding the additional complication of the definition of dose conversion functions. However, activation foils provide only an integral measurement over the neutron energy spectrum and do this incompletely. For BNCT the energy range 1 keV to 0.5 MeV is extremely important but no foils are responsive in this range.

Consequently it is necessary to turn to other techniques. Proton recoil counters have been used successfully at Petten to characterise the neutron spectrum above about 30 keV. These have the advantage of generating a spectrum directly. However, the existing gas-filled proton recoil detectors have to be used in neutron beams of low intensity, which restricts their applicability. Solid proton recoil devices have been tested in recent years at full source strength but need further development before being used as recognised tools. Various other techniques have been used at Petten and reported from different centres, including: BF_3 counters to estimate the beam profiles, and spectrum modification methods (Bonner Spheres) to extract spectral information from integral measurements. One promising technique is the use of semiconductor detectors, generally for thermal neutron measurements. All of these methods have been used at Petten.

Extensive numbers of activation foil measurements have been performed at most existing BNCT beams as part of the beam characterisation. However, the angular spread of the beam is usually inferred from calculations. Measurements of this important parameter are rarely reported and this appears to be an important omission.

For the photon component the usual choice is to use GM chambers or TLDs. Expertise in TLD measurement is widespread but not universal, especially when applied to the BNCT situation. In particular the sensitivity of the TLDs to thermal neutrons is important, particularly for lithium-based devices. It is often necessary to calibrate the TLDs individually, a capability that not all centres can achieve. However, for the free beam the thermal neutron component is usually very low and relatively simple TLD measurements are possible.

The establishment of a simple, standard set of free beam measurements that are performed at regular intervals should be considered essential for any BNCT facility. In the case of Petten a set of activation foils responsive to both thermal and fast neutron components together with TLD measurements has been used regularly over the last few years. The results from such measurements have provided the basis for a database that clearly demonstrates the consistency of the beam and which has been successfully correlated with calculations. It has proved invaluable on a number of occasions to have such data available.

Wherever possible it is important to develop computer models of the measurements. Apart from validating the theoretical methods, the calculations can identify experimental problems. This has been the case at Petten where models of paired ionisation measurements demonstrated that the addition of ^7Li enriched caps to remove thermal neutrons significantly perturbed the experiment. However, to achieve consistent results it is also necessary that standard computer codes and cross-section libraries be used.

Phantom dosimetry

Phantom measurements remain the definitive means of quantifying the neutron and photon components of the BNCT beams. The same type of detectors that are used for free beam dosimetry can be employed; thus activation foils, BF_3 counters, paired ionisation chambers etc. have all been reported in the literature. Given that these measurements are performed in materials that approximate to the composition of human tissue, the measurement of doses becomes a meaningful concept. To achieve this the paired ionisation chamber technique is used extensively with some adjustments for the BNCT situation [1]. However, it is important to clearly distinguish exactly which dose is being measured.

Measurement of the photon doses within phantoms using TLDs has proved to be very difficult at Petten. The greatly enhanced thermal neutron fluxes within the moderating material mean that correction factors for thermal neutron sensitivity are essential. To date it has not been possible to determine reliable correction factors for the Petten TLD measurements.

For all phantom dosimetry it is vital to have a well-defined set of phantoms of known dimensions and compositions. These should include simple solid geometrical shapes (typically cubes of lucite/PMMA) and water or TEL-filled lucite/plastic boxes. Such phantoms can easily be modelled accurately in treatment planning systems to simplify the validation process. Finally, anthropomorphic phantoms should be available to simulate the real patient geometry. Ideally such phantoms should be standardised within the BNCT community but regretfully this has yet to become reality.

It is generally accepted that immediately prior to any patient irradiation a "reference" measurement is made to accept the beam for clinical purposes and to identify any small variations in beam intensity. Usually this takes the form of a measurement in a well-defined phantom. In the case of Petten, paired ionisation chambers are used at predefined depths in a 15-cm^3 PMMA phantom.

On-line dosimetry

On-line dosimetry is required to continually monitor the beam usually by means of GM or ionisation chambers placed in the periphery of the beam. These generate a continuous response that is linked to the facility operational systems, thereby allowing the automatic shutdown in the case of beam faults or reactor scrams. Moreover, the responses from the on-line monitors may also be included in the definition of the monitor units used in delimiting the patient irradiation.

At Petten the on-line monitors consist of a number of GM and ionisation chambers installed around the final aperture of the beam. These are carefully located to provide a rapid indication of voiding in the argon chamber, which is of particular concern. To control the operation of the beam for patient irradiation several sets of correction factors are generated to account for variations in intensity. These include a reference phantom measurement using activation foils and semiconductor detectors that then calibrate the on-line detector response as monitor units. In this manner the response of the on-line detectors is used to automatically control the duration of the patient irradiation, closing the shutter after a predetermined number of monitor units have been delivered.

Patient dosimetry

The intention is to have a means of recording the actual dose delivered during a patient irradiation using methods independent of the on-line monitoring discussed above. The method must be relatively noninvasive for the patient and should not cause any significant perturbation of the irradiation conditions. Consequently, to date the only method that has been seriously considered is that of attaching activation foils and TLDs to the patient's head. However, the variation of irradiation conditions due to different patient geometry and the need to extrapolate from surface foil activations to dose at depth severely limit the usefulness of these measurements. In many cases these measurements have been omitted from the dosimetry programme.

However, considerable work is in progress on this topic using γ telescopes or holographic techniques to record the photon emission from the ^{10}B capture reaction. By suitable real-time processing these can be used to generate spatial boron distributions and boron doses.

Standards in BNCT dosimetry

For BNCT phantom dosimetry conventional radiotherapy standards are usually used, although with some modifications for the different modality. However, this is the exception rather than the rule. In most other areas of dosimetry there are very few "standards" with different centres employing their own techniques, often unused elsewhere. Thus, even straightforward activation foil measurements differ; Petten uses one set of nuclides and dilute foils while Brookhaven has a different set of solid foils.

The problem continues with no "standard" phantoms, defined in terms of geometry and composition, used between the various BNCT centres. At Petten a 15-cm^3 solid phantom of PMMA has been chosen for a reference case because of its geometrical simplicity. However, this is not used at other centres.

In addition to defining in detail the "standard" measurements it is also important to define consistent usage of the measured quantities, in particular doses. This becomes crucial when the "standard" dosimetry measurements are used to validate the calculational tools. Thus, is the dose measured by paired ionisation chambers in a PMMA phantom a tissue dose or the PMMA dose? Such discrepancies can introduce significant differences into any comparison of measured dose distributions to calculated ones. An associated problem is the need to define standard computer codes, cross-section data and flux-to-dose conversion factors that are accepted by all BNCT centres.

These differences make comparisons of dosimetry results between different measurements and between BNCT facilities very difficult. There is a clear need to introduce "standard" measurements, phantoms and definition of doses, fluxes into BNCT dosimetry. This would lead to more consistent comparisons of different BNCT facilities together with the possibility of better exploiting the different results from the various dosimetric measurements. An attempt is currently being made in Europe to initiate just such a project with funding from the European Commission [2].

Conclusions

The experience of BNCT dosimetry at Petten over a number of years has highlighted a number of points. The need for source, free beam and phantom dosimetry is clear and measurements should always be complemented by calculations wherever possible. The lack of standards for all aspects of BNCT dosimetry remains a significant obstacle that should be overcome. In the absence of accepted standards the establishment of local reference measurements that are well-defined, easily reproducible and performed regularly is essential. All the different measurements and calculations need to be correlated with each other but this is a time-consuming task that has to be carefully planned to be effective.

References

1. Raaijmakers CPJ et al. The neutron sensitivity of dosimeters applied to boron neutron capture therapy. Med Phys 1996;23(9).
2. Stecher-Rasmussen F et al. A Code of Practice for the Dosimetry of BNCT in Europe. Seventh International Symposium on Neutron Capture Therapy for Cancer, Zurich, September 1996.

On-line dosimetry for boron neutron capture therapy at the MIT Research Reactor

G. Solares[1], D. Katz[2], O. Harling[2] and R. Zamenhof[1]

[1]*New England Deaconess Hospital, Boston, Massachusetts; and* [2]*The Massachusetts Institute of Technology, Cambridge, Massachusetts, USA*

Introduction

An epithermal neutron beam has been constructed at the Massachusetts Institute of Technology (MIT) Research Reactor (MITR-II) for use in neutron capture therapy (NCT) or, since ^{10}B is often used as the capture agent, boron neutron capture therapy (BNCT) research and clinical trials [1]. This medical room was constructed as an integral part of the MITR and with the express purpose of providing a research and therapy facility for NCT. The purpose of the beam monitors and associated readout systems is to assure that the specified patient dose is delivered to the patient within acceptable dose tolerances of the target dose. Our approach to meeting the desired dose tolerances has included the development of a beam monitoring system which monitors and provides on-line display of the fluence of epithermal and thermal neutrons and which monitors the beam characteristics, e.g., energy distribution and spatial distribution, and indicates if these are stable during the irradiation. The beam monitoring system also indicates any changes in beam characteristics from those which existed when the beam was fully dosimetrically characterized and calibrated. The beam monitoring system, including radiation detectors, the readout and display system, and the performance of the entire beam monitor system are discussed in this paper. This paper does not deal with the systems required for patient positioning and immobilization, which are also important in assuring that the patient receives the desired dose distribution. Further details concerning the beam monitor system are found in [2].

On-line beam monitoring system

Detectors and detector positioning

The epithermal neutron beam at MITR-II has a maximum diameter of 30 cm and the final beam size incident upon the patient is determined by a beam delimiter, typically 10−20 cm in diameter, consisting of a few inches of lithiated paraffin. Fission counters, covered with $^6Li_2CO_3$ to reduce their thermal neutron sensitivity, are used to monitor the epithermal neutron flux. Unshielded fission counters or ^{3}He-filled ion chambers operating in the current mode are used to monitor the residual thermal neutron component of the beam. A high-pressure argon gas filled ion chamber, operating in the current mode is used to monitor γ rays. All of these beam monitoring detectors are small, less than ~ 1.6 cm over-all diameter including shielding when used, and a few centimeters in sensitive length. They are small enough so that when placed at the edge of the beam, they have a negligible effect on the beam. By choosing detectors primarily sensitive to epithermal neutrons, others sensitive to thermal neutrons or to γ rays, it is pos-sible to monitor the intensity, energy, and spatial distribution of the neutron beam.

The outputs of the beam monitors are sufficiently high, e.g., $\sim 10^3 - 10^4$ counts/s from the fission counters, nano-amperes for the current mode detectors, ^{3}He and Ar, to permit accurate intensity determination ($\pm 1\%$) within several sec-onds. Since irradiation times of $10-50$ min are required for an irradiation, the monitor signal strengths are more than adequate to permit an accurate delivery of a planned fluence. The fluence of neutrons, especially epithermal neutrons, is directly related to dose through in-phantom dosimetric measurements and our treatment.

Signal processing and display

Figure 1 shows the routing and processing of beam monitor signals on a block diagram. The fission chambers have their signals fed to a counter data acquisition board in a Macintosh Quadra 950 computer. Detectors operating in the current mode, the ^{3}He-filled ion chamber and the Ar-filled ion chamber, have their cur-rent signals converted to proportional frequency signals which are then routed to the counter board of the Macintosh.

The computer, using a versatile data acquisition and processing program called LabView 2 [3], is used to display on a large color monitor the detector count rates, integral counts, dose calibration factors, target counts, percentage of target counts, and irradiation time. A typical screen display is shown in Fig. 2. Detector output is shown in digital as well as analog form, color coded to each separate detector. The analog display in relative count rates on the lower left-hand side of Fig. 1 is designed for ease in rapidly diagnosing any significant changes or trends in the energy, spatial distribution, and intensity of the beam. The bar graph on the lower right-hand side of the screen with an analog display showing the per-cent of target detector counts is particularly useful in determining when the target dose is approached. Above the latter bar graph target counts, integrated counts and percentage target are also shown in digital form. An average of the epither-mal detector outputs is also calculated by the computer and this is displayed in analog form as percentage of target dose near the upper right-hand part of monitor. An audible signal is provided when the target dose, based on epithermal neutron counts, is reached. The information on the monitor is typically updated

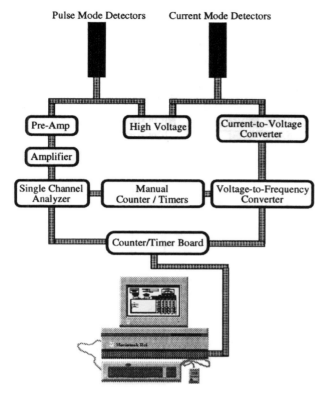

Pulse Mode Detectors   Current Mode Detectors

Pre-Amp   High Voltage   Current-to-Voltage Converter

Amplifier

Single Channel Analyzer   Manual Counter / Timers   Voltage-to-Frequency Converter

Counter/Timer Board

Fig. 1. Block diagram of beam monitor signal routing and processing.

every 5 s, although this can be set to any desired interval. A second display (Fig. 3) provides real time calculation of the equivalent dose and target count for each of the detectors. The calculation is based on previously characterized dose rates measured with the ion chambers in phantom, calibration parameters obtained from MacNCTPLAN [4], and the real time Boron-10 concentration measured in blood by either prompt γ activation analysis or ICP-AES. The center monitor display also shows the patient identification, i.e., name and hospital ID number and the dose calibration factors, i.e., epi counts per RBE-cGy. A magnetic disk record is made of the information displayed by the computer. Each patient has a separate floppy disk record of his/her irradiation therapy. A start/pause reset and status check control panel is in the upper left-hand part of the monitor display.

A separate monitor (not shown) provides additional information on the beam and the irradiation. There are "switches" which can be used to turn off an epithermal neutron beam monitor, e.g., if a monitor becomes erratic. Also, the reactor power planned for a specific fraction and the actual beam monitor count rates are displayed along with the expected, or reference, power and count rates. The

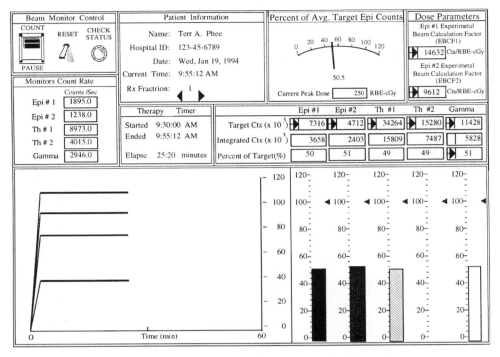

Fig. 2. A typical screen display of beam monitor count rates, integral counts, corresponding doses, target counts and doses, and irradiation time. These are displayed and color coded in digital and analog modes. Additional information such as patient identification is also displayed on the monitor.

ratios of all beam monitor count rates, including the statistical error on the ratios are also displayed. The latter information provides numerical indicators for beam symmetry, relative beam energy, and relative γ-ray intensity.

Before each irradiation, all beam monitors are tested by performing a calibration check point which is compared to the previous complete beam characterization. The failure rate of the monitoring system is estimated to be small, after several dry-run calibrations and 31 actual subject irradiations the system has functioned flawlessly. If one or more system components were to fail, a complete set of spare calibrated electronics is readily available in site.

Independent on-line dose monitoring

Signals from the on-line beam monitors (see Fig. 1) are also recorded on scalers, which can be read manually. This helps assure that any failures of the computer-based system will not result in a loss of the most important data. In addition to the beam monitors placed at the edge of the medical beam and the associated read-out systems, several reactor power monitors are used as an independent monitoring system for a BNCT irradiation. There is a well-known correlation

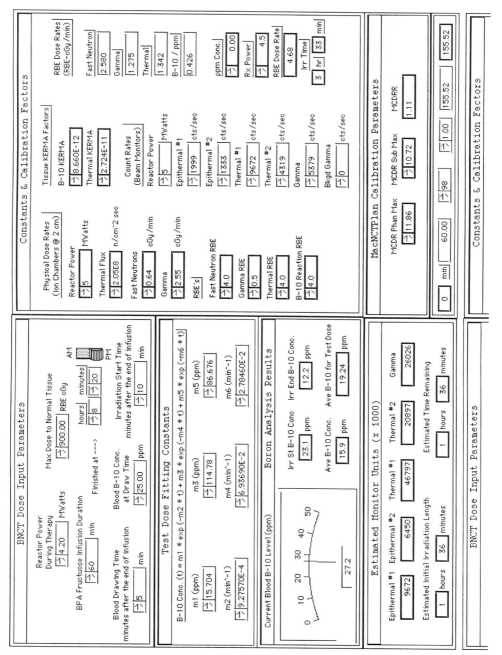

Fig. 3. A second display provides real time calculation of the equivalent dose and target counts for each of the detectors. The calculation is based on previously characterized dose rates measured with the ion chambers in phantom, calibration parameters obtained from MacNCTPLAN, and the real time ^{10}B concentration measured in blood by either prompt γ activation analysis or ICP-AES.

between reactor MW-min and epithermal neutron fluence. Therefore, during human trials or therapy the reactor operating staff also use MW-min to track an irradiation.

Conclusions

A beam monitoring system for neutron capture therapy irradiations of patients has been designed and constructed for use with the epithermal medical beam at the MIT Research Reactor. The detectors chosen and constructed for this application are pulse counting fission chambers, ^{3}He-filled and Ar-filled ion chambers operating in the current mode. A computer-generated display of γ and neutron flux and fluences is provided in digital and color coded analog form. A computer-generated display of γ and neutron flux and fluences is provided on several easy-to-read displays. The ratios of the outputs of the five detectors which are spaced around the beam aperture are continuously monitored by the computer and compared with reference values. These displays assure that significant changes in beam intensity, symmetry, or gross energy composition can be rapidly diagnosed. The computer display also facilitates the delivery of the prescribed fluence or dose. Independent hard-wired scalers operate in parallel to the computer-based system to assure redundancy for the most important data.

Acknowledgements

The assistance of Kent Riley and Reactor Operations is appreciated. The US Department of Energy, Contracts No. DE-FG02-87ER-60600 and No. DE-FG02-90ER12971, supported this research and the developments reported here.

References

1. Harling OK et al. Preparations for clinical trials at the MIT Reactor and the New England Medical Center. In: Soloway AH, Barth RF, Carpenter DE (eds) Advances in Neutron Capture Therapy. Columbus, OH: Plenum Press, 1993.
2. Harling OK, Moulin D, Chabeuf J-M, Solares GR. On-line beam monitoring for boron neutron capture therapy at the MIT Research Reactor. Nucl Ins Meth Phys Res 1995;B101:464—472.
3. LabView 2, National Instruments Corporation, Austin, Texas.
4. Zamenhof RG et al. MacNCTPLAN: an improved Macintosh-based treatment planning program for boron neutron capture therapy. In: Larsson B, Crawford J, Weinreich R (eds) Advances in Neutron Capture Therapy. Volume 1, Medicine and Physics. Amsterdam: Elsevier Science, 1997;100—105 (these proceedings).

©1997 Elsevier Science B.V. All rights reserved.
Advances in Neutron Capture Therapy.
Volume I, Medicine and Physics.
B. Larsson, J. Crawford and R. Weinreich, editors.

Depth dose curves of an epithermal neutron beam for BNCT

C.P.J. Raaijmakers, E.L. Nottelman and B.J. Mijnheer

Department of Radiotherapy, The Netherlands Cancer Institute (Antoni van Leeuwenhoek Huis), Amsterdam, The Netherlands

Keywords: depth dose curves, epithermal neutron beams, field size, reference conditions.

Introduction

Various epithermal neutron beams are currently available for boron neutron capture therapy. Clinical characterization of these beams is generally performed by determining along the central beam axis in a reference phantom the thermal neutron fluence rate, the fast neutron dose rate and the γ-ray dose rate. The influence of various physical parameters (e.g., field size, source-skin distance, angle of incidence, phantom shape, phantom size and phantom composition) on the dose distribution in a reference phantom is, however, also needed for clinical purposes. In general these parameters are investigated theoretically using Monte Carlo and deterministic techniques [1,2]. Experimental data supporting the relation between in-phantom dose distributions and the various beam parameters for clinical epithermal neutron beams are, however, scarce. In previous work the influence of beam aperture size on the beam profiles has been empirically determined [3]. The aim of this investigation was to experimentally determine the depth fluence and depth dose curves for the various components under reference conditions and to determine the influence of the field size on these curves.

Materials and Methods

The measurements were performed in the clinical epithermal BNCT facility at the high flux reactor (HFR) in Petten, The Netherlands [4]. The field size can be varied by changing a 19-cm long cylindrical beam aperture. The cavities of the three available apertures have a conical shape with entrance diameters of 9.0, 13.4 and 16.5 cm and with exit diameters of 8.0, 12.0 and 15.0 cm, respectively. They will be referred to by their exit diameter. The apertures consist of a sandwich of 5 cm lithiated polyethylene, 9 cm lead and 5 cm lithiated polyethylene.

Use has been made of a 30 cm^3 phantom made of 5-mm thick polymethylmethacrylate (PMMA) walls, filled with distilled water. In the phantom, scans

---

Address for correspondence: Niels Raaijmakers, The Netherlands Cancer Institute (Antoni van Leeuwenhoek Huis), Plesmanlaan 121, 1066 CX Amsterdam, The Netherlands.

and point measurements can be performed using a remotely controlled scanning device. Due to the size of the detectors and the thickness of the phantom wall, a complete determination of all dose components is not possible at depths smaller than 1.8 cm. The phantom was positioned with its central axis coinciding with the beam axis, a reference distance of 30 cm from the beam exit. The phantom was positioned on an aluminum irradiation table.

The absolute thermal neutron fluence rate was determined using AuAl (5 wt.% Au) and MnNi (88 wt.% Mn) activation foils with diameters of 9 or 20 mm. The relative thermal neutron fluence rate has been determined using a home-made PN diode detector. This detector consists of a silicon α detector on which a ^{6}Li containing converter plate is mounted, which "converts" the thermal neutrons into ^{4}He and ^{3}H particles through the ^{6}Li(n,α) reaction. The heavily charged particles are detected by the diode. For the determination of the γ-ray dose rate and the fast neutron dose rate, use was made of paired ionization chambers with a sensitive volume of 0.5 cm^3 and a wall thickness of 1 mm. A magnesium ionization chamber flushed with argon gas (Mg(Ar) chamber) was used as a "neutron insensitive" detector to determine the γ-ray dose rate. An ionization chamber made of tissue-equivalent plastic, flushed with a methane based tissue-equivalent gas (TE(TE) chamber), was used to determine the total dose. From the difference between the total dose and the γ-ray dose, the fast neutron dose was derived. A detailed description of the characteristics of the detectors and of the derivation of the fluence and dose values from the detector readings have been reported elsewhere [5,6]. All irradiations were performed using the epithermal neutron beam facility of the HFR operated at a thermal power of 45 MW. The thermal power of the reactor varied about 2% at maximum during all measurements.

Results

Depth fluence and depth dose curves were determined in the phantom for the three aperture sizes. The thermal neutron fluence rate on the central beam axis at a reference depth of 2 cm increases by approximately 50% when the field size increases from 8 to 15 cm. Simultaneously, the γ-ray dose rate and the fast neutron dose rate increase by approximately 65 and 5%, respectively (Fig. 1).

The position of the maximum thermal neutron fluence is shifted deeper inside the phantom for increasing field size and is located at 2.2 cm depth for the 8-cm field and at 2.5 cm depth for the 12-cm and 15-cm field (Fig. 1A). Also a somewhat deeper penetration of thermal neutrons at larger depth was observed for increasing field size. At 5 cm depth the percentage thermal neutron fluence amounts to 66, 73 and 74% for the 8-cm, 12-cm and 15-cm field, respectively. No significant difference was observed between the γ-ray percentage depth dose (PDD) curves for the 12-cm and 15-cm field. Compared to these field sizes, an approximately 5% higher relative γ-ray dose rate at a depth of 15 cm was observed for the 8-cm field. No significant effect of field size was observed for the fast neutron depth dose curves (Fig. 1C).

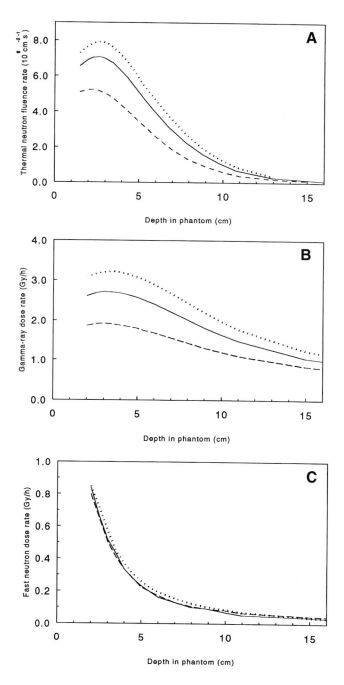

Fig. 1. Thermal neutron fluence rate (**A**), γ-ray dose rate (**B**) and fast neutron dose rate (**C**) as a function of depth along the central beam axis of an 8-cm (dashed line), 12-cm (solid line) and 15-cm (dotted line) diameter circular field in a 30 cm³ water phantom.

Discussion and Conclusions

The phantom measurements indicate various possible advantages of the use of the 12-cm and the 15-cm aperture sizes compared to the 8-cm field size. The increased absolute thermal neutron fluence rate observed with increasing field size results in shorter irradiation times which is of practical importance considering the relatively long irradiation times currently required for BNCT. Furthermore, the relative contribution of fast neutrons to the total dose decreases with approximately 30%. Due to the relatively high relative biological effectiveness of the fast neutrons this will result in a considerably lower healthy tissue dose at the position of the thermal maximum for a prescribed thermal neutron fluence. Finally the depth of the maximum thermal neutron fluence and the penetration of thermal neutrons at depth is somewhat increased with increasing field size. These effects probably will compensate for the increased relative γ-ray dose rate (10%) seen for increasing aperture size.

The large influence of field size on the absolute thermal neutron fluence rate on the central beam axis demonstrates the fundamental difference between the physics of an epithermal neutron beam and that of external photon radiotherapy beams, where the influence of field size on the central beam axis depth dose curves is much smaller. Due to elastic scattering with hydrogen nuclei, the epithermal neutrons entering the phantom rapidly loose their energy and forward directed orientation. After having reached thermal energy, the neutrons follow diffusion laws and can travel in random directions over distances of several centimetres. Due to these processes, epithermal neutrons entering the phantom at relatively large distances from the central axis still have a large contribution to the thermal neutron fluence on the central beam axis. For the 15-cm field, the thermal neutron fluence rate on the central beam axis was approximately 10% higher than for the 12-cm field, indicating that the low-energy neutrons can travel over distances of more than 6 cm in the lateral direction and that lateral scattering equilibrium might not be obtained even for the 15-cm field. Further increasing the field size might reveal interesting physical data on the scattering properties of the neutrons. The 15-cm field is, however, the largest field size available and is comparable to the size of the human head. Since brain irradiations are the first goal of the Petten BNCT project further increase of the field size is of limited practical use. The slight shift in depth of the position of the maximum fluence and the somewhat increased penetration at depth of thermal neutrons for increasing field size are other examples of the impact of the scattering processes on the resulting fluence curves.

The thermal neutron distribution can be considered as the source for capture γ-ray production. Consequently, parameters influencing the thermal neutron fluence also influence the γ-ray dose distribution. The absolute γ-ray dose along the central beam axis is more sensitive to changes in field size than the thermal neutron fluence at this position. This may be due to the deeper penetration in water of 2.2 MeV γ rays compared to thermal neutrons. Consequently, the increase in the thermal neutron fluence at large distance from the central axis affect the γ-ray component more than the thermal neutron component on the central axis. The somewhat higher relative γ-ray dose rate at depth for the 8-cm field compared to the 12-cm and 15-cm field can be explained from the lower absolute thermal neutron fluence rate and consequently lower capture γ-ray production for this field size. The incident γ-ray dose amounts to about 0.9 Gy/ h and is field size independent [5]. From the data shown in Fig. 1B, it can be deduced that for the 8-cm field the relative contribution of the incident γ-ray dose to the total γ-ray dose amounts to approximately 50% while for the 12-cm and 15-cm field this value amounts to approximately 30%. Due to the high energy of the incident γ rays (4–7 MeV) [5] this results in the observed deeper penetration at depth of the total γ-ray PDD for the 8-cm field. Further decreasing the field size would increase the relative contribution of the incident γ-ray dose to the total γ-ray dose in such a way that comparing the γ-ray depth dose curves for small and large field sizes might reveal interesting information on the separate depth dose curves of the incident and induced γ-ray component in the phantom.

Due to the relatively low scattering cross-section of the neutrons in the energy range between 10 keV and 10 MeV, which contribute mainly to the fast neutron dose, scattering processes have a low impact on the dose distribution for this component. Therefore, changes in field size only have a minor influence on the absolute value of the fast neutron dose.

A treatment planning system is under development to use the results of these measurements to calculate in a semiempirical way, the various dose components at all clinically relevant points in patients irradiated with the epithermal neutron beam [7].

Acknowledgements

The authors would like to thank K. Ravensberg for operating the beam and his skilful technical and experimental assistance and W. Voorbraak and A. Paardekoper for the activation foil measurements. This work was financially supported by a grant of the Netherlands Cancer Foundation (NKB Grant NKI 94-778).

References

1. Konijnenberg MW, Dewit LGH, Mijnheer BJ, Raaijmakers CPJ, Watkins, PRD. Dose homogeneity in boron neutron capture therapy using an epithermal neutron beam. Radiat Res 1995; 142:327–339.
2. Yanch JC, Harling OK. Dosimetric effects of beam size and collimation of epithermal neutrons for boron neutron capture therapy. Radiat Res 1993;135:131–145.
3. Raaijmakers CPJ, Konijnenberg MW, Mijnheer BJ. Beam profiles of an epithermal neutron beam. In: Mishima Y (ed) Cancer Neutron Capture Therapy. New York: Plenum Press, 1996; 451–456.
4. Moss R, Casado J, Ravensberg K, Stecher-Rasmussen F, Watkins P. The completed boron neu-

tron capture therapy facility at the HFR Petten. In: Larsson B, Crawford J, Weinreich R (eds) Advances in Neutron Capture Therapy. Volume 1, Medicine and Physics. Amsterdam: Elsevier Science, 1997;331—335 (these proceedings).

5. Raaijmakers CPJ, Watkins PRD, Nottelman EL, Verhagen HW, Mijnheer BJ. The neutron sensitivity of dosimeters applied for boron neutron capture therapy. Med Phys 1996;23:1581—1589.

6. Raaijmakers CPJ, Konijnenberg MW, Verhagen H, Mijnheer BJ. Determination of dose components in phantoms irradiated with an epithermal neutron beam for boron neutron capture therapy. Med Phys 1995;22:321—329.

7. Raaijmakers CPJ, Nottelman EL, Mijnheer BJ. The use of a photon beam model for the treatment planning of boron neutron capture therapy. In: Larsson B, Crawford J, Weinreich R (eds) Advances in Neutron Capture Therapy. Volume 1, Medicine and Physics. Amsterdam: Elsevier Science, 1997;106—111 (these proceedings).

©1997 Elsevier Science B.V. All rights reserved.
Advances in Neutron Capture Therapy.
Volume I, Medicine and Physics.
B. Larsson, J. Crawford and R. Weinreich, editors.

An intercomparison of dosimetry techniques used in BNCT and BNCEFNT

Chandrasekhar Kota[1], Mark Yudelev[1], Richard L. Maughan[1], Arlene Lennox[2,3], Katja Langen[2,4], Ruedi Risler[5], Lucian Wielopolski[6] and Rainer Schmidt[7]

[1]Gershenson Radiation Oncology Center, Karmanos Cancer Institute, Harper Hospital and Wayne State University, Detroit, Michigan; [2]Fermi National Accelerator Laboratory, Batavia, Illinois; [3]Saint Joseph Hospital, Elgin, Illinois; [4]Department of Medical Physics, University of Wisconsin-Madison, Madison, Wisconsin; [5]Department of Radiation Oncology, University of Washington Medical Center, Seattle, Washington; [6]Medical Department, Brookhaven National Laboratory, Upton, New York, USA; and [7]UKE Strahlentherapie Radiologie, Hamburg, Germany

Introduction

The boron neutron capture reaction can be used in two distinct modalities which have potential clinical applications. The first is boron neutron capture therapy (BNCT) which involves the use of thermal or epithermal neutron beams to irradiate shallow tumors (gliomas, melanomas) preferentially loaded with ^{10}B. The second is boron neutron capture enhanced fast neutron therapy (BNCEFNT) in which ^{10}B is used to obtain a preferential tumor boost in order to increase the therapeutic gain for the treatment. In both of these modalities it is necessary to know the absorbed dose in a reference phantom from the different dose components such as γ rays, neutrons of a range of energies and the boron neutron capture reaction products (boron dose). The boron dose is difficult to measure and different systems are in use by various researchers. In the present work, we report on the intercomparison of some of these dosimetry systems in a reference d(48.5) + Be fast neutron beam.

Dosimetry systems

Four different dosimetry systems in use at different institutions were compared:
1) Dual counter microdosimetric technique: this system is based on the use of two identical tissue equivalent (TE) proportional counters, one of which has boron uniformly distributed in its TE plastic wall [1]. It is assumed that such a counter wall simulates a tissue volume in which boron is uniformly distributed. Secondary charged particles are generated in the wall by neutron and γ

Address for correspondence: Chandrasekhar Kota, Gershenson Radiation Oncology Center, Harper Hospital and Wayne State University, 3990 John R., Detroit, MI 48201, USA.

interactions and deposit their energy in the sensitive gas volume of the counter. This volume is filled to a low pressure with a TE gas which is fairly well matched to the wall in atomic composition; the pressure is such that the effective pathlength of the charged particles in this volume is equivalent to micrometer pathlengths in unit density tissue. This simulated micrometer volume is chosen to approximate a Bragg — Gray cavity such that the dose measured in the gas volume is representative of the dose in A-150 TE plastic. The counter with the TE wall (TE counter) measures the spectrum of secondary charged particles depositing dose in TE plastic. In contrast, the counter with ^{10}B in its wall, (^{10}B counter) measures the additional spectrum of the dose due to the boron neutron capture reaction. Absorbed dose spectra are measured with each counter at each point of interest and are normalized to a reference value. The TE counter spectrum is subtracted from the ^{10}B counter spectrum to obtain the spectrum and dose due to the ^{10}B reaction.

This method gives a direct measure of the absorbed dose in TE plastic tissue due to the ^{10}B reaction. A more detailed description of this technique can be found elsewhere [1,2]. Two different sets of paired proportional counters were used in this study. The first, from the fast neutron therapy facility at Harper Hospital in Detroit, had 50 ppm of ^{10}B incorporated in the A-150 TE plastic. This boron-loaded TE plastic was manufactured by adding boron nitride (BN) particles with a stated mean particle size of 10 μm to the A-150 TE plastic. The second set, from the fast neutron therapy facility at Fermi Lab in Batavia, IL, had 200 ppm of ^{10}B in the A-150 TE plastic which was manufactured by adding BN particles of ∼1 μm average size to the A-150 TE plastic. Both samples of boronated A-150 TE plastic were supplied by Exradin Inc. of Lisle, IL, and both sets of proportional counters were manufactured by Far West Technologies of Goleta, CA.

2) Sodium activation in glass beads: this technique is in use at the University of Washington fast neutron therapy facility. It is based on the assumption that the cross section for the (n,γ) activation of ^{23}Na parallels the ^{10}B cross-section across most of the neutron energy range of interest. In this technique, spherical glass beads 5 mm in diameter are used. The ^{23}Na content in these beads is estimated to be 9.65%, based on inductively coupled plasma (ICP) analysis and reactor activation analysis. The γ rays emitted by ^{24}Na are measured using a high purity Ge detector which is calibrated with a ^{60}Co test source under identical geometry. The measured activity is used to calculate the number of boron atoms that would have interacted in that neutron field. The dose is calculated from the number of interacting boron atoms per unit mass and the kinetic energy of 2.34 MeV deposited by the lithium ion and the α particle produced in the interaction.

3) Boronated Fricke system: This system is used as a supplementary method for measuring the ^{10}B dose in the epithermal neutron beam at Brookhaven National Laboratory. In this method, 94.6% ^{10}B enriched boric acid is added to standard Fricke solution. Two identical samples, with and without boron in

the Fricke solution are irradiated at each point of interest. The difference in the absorbance (ΔA) of the irradiated and unirradiated samples is measured at a wavelength of 304 nm. The boron dose is given by:

$$D_{boron} = (\Delta A_{boron} - \Delta A_{no\ boron})/\epsilon\rho\ l\ G_{boron}$$

where ϵ is the molar linear absorption coefficient, ρ is the density of the solution, l is the pathlength for light and G_{boron} is the radiation chemical yield for α particles and lithium ions. Since the liquid in which the boronated and nonboronated Fricke solution is suspended is tissue equivalent, this method is expected to directly measure the boron dose.

4) Boron-coated magnesium ion chamber: This technique employs a 0.32 cm^3 magnesium-walled ion chamber internally coated with 0.7 mg/cm^2 of boron (92% isotopic abundance of ^{10}B) [3]. The chamber was manufactured by Wellhofer Dosimetry (Germany) as a modified IC-30 chamber. During measurements, the chamber is flushed with Argon gas. The chamber was calibrated in various low energy neutron fields at the Physikalisch-Technische Bundesanstalt (PTB) in Germany. The response of the chamber was found to be weakly dependent on the mean neutron energy of the calibration fields [3]. Therefore, with this method, a variation in the low-energy neutron spectrum in the phantom can result in errors in interpreting the ion chamber response. In these neutron fields, the response of this chamber was found to be greater than that of an identical chamber without any boron coating by a factor > 100; therefore, the calibrated response of this chamber was directly used to estimate the boron dose, without any corrections for contributions from the fast neutron dose. For the present measurements, a calibration factor of $R(4\pi, 37\ meV) = 1.02 \times 10^{-7}$ nC. cm^2 neutron^{-1} was used. The neutron fluence was converted to the boron dose using a dose conversion factor of 4.3×10^{-12} Gy. cm^2 neutron^{-1} for 50 μg/g of ^{10}B which was adapted from the work of Konijnenberg et al. [4].

Experimental setup

The fast neutron therapy facility at Harper Hospital is based on a d(48.5) + Be fast neutron beam produced by a superconducting cyclotron and collimated by a multirod collimator [5]. This neutron beam is isocentric, with a source to axis distance (SAD) of 182.9 cm. The fast neutron dose rate at the isocenter, at a depth of ~ 1cm in a water phantom (D_{max}) in a 10×10 cm^2 field is 48 cGy/min for 15 μA of beam current. At this point, the ^{10}B dose rate for 50 μg/g of ^{10}B as measured by the dual counter microdosimetric technique, is about 1.5 cGy/min. All measurements were made in a lucite walled water phantom $30 \times 30 \times 30$ cm^3 in dimension, placed at a source-to-surface distance (SSD) of 183 cm. The boron dose was measured as a function of depth along the central axis of a 15×15 cm^2 field defined at the SSD. For measurements made with the boronated Fricke system, the phantom was placed at an SSD of 143.5 cm and the field size at this distance was 19.6 cm^2. An inverse square correction was applied to convert these dose rates to an SSD of 183 cm. This was justified by the validity of such a procedure commonly used for correcting the fast neutron dose rates and the assumption that the thermal neutron fluence is produced by fast neutron interactions in water. In spite of these corrections, these results cannot be directly compared to others due to the difference in the field size. In this paper, it is assumed that the larger field size results in a systematic increase of the boron dose rate at all depths; therefore, the boronated Fricke results are assumed to provide an upper bound to the expected ^{10}B dose rates. Measurements with the boron-coated ion chamber, boronated Fricke system and the sodium activation were performed at high beam currents (~ 10 µA) and were normalized to the monitor chamber used in daily patient treatments. The proportional counter measurements were performed at low beam currents (< 0.1 µA) and were normalized to an external reference ion chamber reading which was cross-referenced to the monitor system at higher beam currents. The response of each set of detectors was analyzed by the respective participating collaborators according to their standard procedures. The ^{10}B dose rates reported by each collaborator are presented and discussed below.

Results and Discussions

Figure 1 shows the dose rates (cGy/monitor unit) for 50 µg/g of ^{10}B as a function of depth in the water phantom as measured by the different dosimetry systems. Smooth curves were fitted to the data points using power law functions. A wide variation in the dose rates measured by the different systems is observed at each

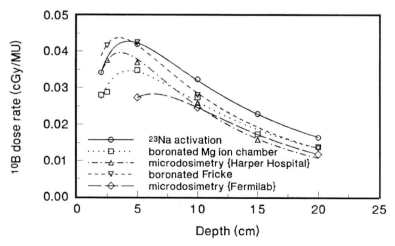

Fig. 1. Absolute ^{10}B dose rates (cGy/monitor unit) as a function of depth, measured by the different dosimetry systems.

depth. This could be due to a combination of systematic and random errors associated with the dosimetry systems. The data from the ^{23}Na activation system has a random uncertainty of ±2% due to counting statistics and a ±10% systematic uncertainty related to the sodium content in the glass beads. The dual counter microdosimetric system from Harper Hospital and Fermilab have an overall uncertainty of about ±20%. The boron-coated Mg ion chamber system has an uncertainty of ±10% due to the calibration procedure. The boronated Fricke system has uncertainty of ±10% arising from calibration and readout procedures. These uncertainties have not been included in Fig. 1 to retain clarity. From this figure, it can be seen that the variation in the dose rates measured by the different systems is significant, and ranges from ∼ 20 to ∼ 45% depending on the depth. To eliminate the contribution of systematic errors to these variations, each depth dose curve was arbitrarily normalized so that the depth dose at 10 cm is 100%.

Figure 2 shows the normalized data from the different systems. In this plot, three different sets of curves can be identified; the first set corresponding to the boronated Fricke system and the microdosimetric dual counter system from Harper Hospital; the second set corresponding to the boron-coated Mg ion chamber and the ^{23}Na activation system; the third set corresponding to the microdosimetric dual counter system from Fermilab. Within the first two sets, the maximum difference in the relative depth dose between the curves is ∼ 5%. If the assumption that the boron dose rate in the larger field (in which the Fricke measurements were made) is systematically higher is true, then these results suggest that the boron dose rates measured using the microdosimetric method and the Fricke method agree rather well at all depths. Similarly, the dose rates measured by the boron-coated Mg ion chamber and the ^{23}Na activation system agree with each other at all depths. The cause for the discrepancy of the Fermilab

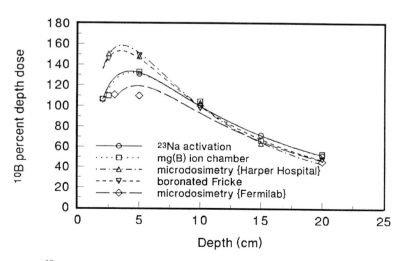

Fig. 2. ^{10}B percent depth dose curves with the dose at 10 cm depth measured by each system normalized to a value of 100%.

microdosimetric system results from others is unknown and is being investigated.

The microdosimetric method and the Fricke method provide a direct measure of the boron dose, while the boron-coated Mg ion chamber and the ^{23}Na activation system calculate the boron dose from the measured thermal fluence. The agreement within each set indicates a consistency in the methods, while the discrepancy between the first two sets could be indicative of uncertainties specific to either of the two sets of methods. More studies are being planned to investigate the effect of the neutron energy spectrum on these discrepancies.

Conclusions

Five different dosimetry systems used by different institutions for measuring ^{10}B dose in BNCT and BNCEFNT were compared in a d(48.5) + Be fast neutron beam with a maximum ^{10}B dose rate of about 1.5 cGy/min. Measurements were made at various depths in a water phantom. Three of these systems gave a direct measure of the ^{10}B dose; of these, two were based on the dual counter microdosimetric technique, the other was based on the boronated Fricke technique. The remaining two systems measured the thermal neutron fluence from which the ^{10}B dose was calculated. A variation of 20—45% is observed in the ^{10}B dose rates reported by the different methods at different depths. When normalized to a value of 100% at 10 cm depth to eliminate systematic errors between the different methods, an interesting trend is observed in the data. The methods giving a direct measure of the dose are grouped together separately from the methods measuring the fluence. These results indicate that further intercomparison studies are necessary to quantify the differences between these systems more thoroughly.

Acknowledgements

We would like to thank Dr A.T. Porter for his encouragement and support for this work.

References

1. Kota C, Maughan RL. A dosimetry system for boron neutron capture therapy based on the dual counter microdosimetric technique. Bull Cancer/Radiother 1995;83(Suppl 1):173s—175s.
2. Kota C. Microdosimetric considerations in the use of the boron neutron capture reaction in radiation therapy. Ph.D. Thesis, 1996. Detroit, USA: Wayne State University, 1996.
3. Ludemann L, Matzen T, Matzke M, Schmidt R, Scobel W. Determination of the thermal neutron flux in a fast neutron beam by use of a boron-coated ionization chamber. Med Phys 1995;22(11):1743—1747.
4. Konijnenberg MW, Dewit LGH, Mijnheer BJ, Raijmakers CPJ, Watkins PRD. Dose homogeneity in boron neutron capture therapy using an epithermal neutron beam. Rad Res 1995;142: 327—339.
5. Maughan RL, Yudelev M. Physical characteristics of a clinical d(48.5) + Be neutron therapy beam produced by a superconducting cyclotron. Med Phys 1995;22(9):1459—1465.

A review of the dosimetry measurements for the Petten healthy tissue tolerance study

P. Watkins[1], R.L. Moss[1], F. Stecher-Rasmussen[2], W. Voorbraak[2], A. Paardekooper[2] and H. Verhagen[2]

[1]Commission of the European Communities, Joint Research Centre; and [2]Energie Centrum Nederland, Petten, The Netherlands

Introduction

Following the construction of the boron neutron capture therapy (BNCT) facility at Petten in the HB11 beam of the high flux reactor (HFR) a healthy tissue tolerance study (HTTS) was undertaken. The HTTS involved the irradiation of 47 beagle dogs between April 1992 and June 1993 with various levels of the boron containing drug borocaptate sodium (BSH). For each beagle irradiation a number of activation foils and TLDs were attached to the dogs, to give data as to the neutron and photon fluxes. Free-beam measurements, foil activations and TLDs, were also made during the HTTS. Many additional measurements were performed using a variety of phantoms.

This paper summarises the measured dosimetry data from the HTTS with particular emphasis on beam consistency. The results presented here give only limited information as to the radiation doses actually received for two reasons. Firstly, the foils and TLDs were located on the surface of the heads and the correlation between dose at depth and surface foil activation is unknown. Secondly the foils are not sensitive to all of the neutron energy spectrum so that the fast neutron dose could not be determined.

Beagle irradiations — foil and TLD description

For each dog irradiation activation foils and TLD packs were attached to the head by adhesive tape at various positions. At the beam centre a three-foil pack was used, consisting of AuAl (1wt% Au in Al, 12 mm diameter, 0.2 mm thick), Cu (100wt%, 12 mm diameter, 0.1 mm thick) and MnNi (88wt% Mn in Ni, 12 mm diameter, 0.1 mm thick) foils. At four other positions, i.e., by the right eye, in the tubus, at the rear of the skull and by the thyroid glandula, a single AuAl foil (1wt% Au in Al, 12 mm diameter, 0.2 mm thick) was placed. The TLDs were of enriched ^{7}Li, type 700 from Harshaw and three were placed at each position, i.e., at the beam centre, in the tubus, by the thyroid glandula, between the shoulders and on the abdomen. In all cases the TLDs were contained in small polyethylene bags. After irradiation the foil activations and TLD values were measured and recorded on standard forms.

Foil activation from beagle irradiations

The results of all the foil activations from the dog irradiations at the beam centre position are given in Table 1. The activation rates given here are saturated values derived from the measured raw data by standard methods [1]. These data include all of the fractionated dog irradiations but exclude the first two dogs because of the particular beam conditions (unstable argon system) under which they were irradiated. Results from measurements on these two animals are reported elsewhere [2]. Table 2 contains summary data from all of the HTTS foil activation measurements.

The variations in time of the foil activations are shown in Fig. 1, with these data normalised to unity for the first dog irradiation, i.e., dog 491 on 3 April 1992. It appears from these data that there are small increases in the Mn and Cu activations with time but this trend is not seen for the Au foil. However, these data consist of "clusters" of results corresponding to short periods of time during which a number of irradiations were performed. The variation of results within a cluster is large and is a significant fraction of the overall variation. It is therefore difficult to conclude that there is a trend in the results. The correlation coefficients for the foil activations, Cu/Mn and Au/Mn ratios with time have also been evaluated. These are 0.58 for Mn, 0.49 for Cu, 0.17 for Au, -0.06 for Cu/Mn ratio and -0.10 for Au/Mn ratio. These are close to zero indicating no time dependence of the results except for the Mn and Cu foils which increase slightly in time although the dependence is not strong.

The measurements from early December 1992 were analysed in detail since they were made over a 4-day period within one reactor cycle so changes in the beam due to core loading and control rod motions are absent. Moreover these data apply to three dogs repeated 4 times as part of a fractionated study thereby minimising any dog-to-dog variation. For these data the minimum to maximum variations were; -9 to $+5\%$ for the Mn foil, -9 to $+7\%$ for the Cu foil and -4 to $+3\%$ for the Au foil. These are up to 75% of the variation of the complete set of data, suggesting that the variation is not due to changes in the beam characteristics but results from positioning and other sources of error.

The Cu/Mn and Au/Mn activation ratios provide a check on the variability of the foil activations and the neutron spectrum. The Mn foil activation is due to thermal neutron absorption, the Au activation is "epithermal" (strictly untrue since most of the response comes from absorption of neutrons of energies below 10 eV) and the Cu activation intermediate in energy between the Mn and Au. Both ratios decrease slightly in time so that the spectrum becomes more thermal. However, the effect is insignificant as indicated by the small correlation coefficients of -0.06 and -0.10 for the Cu/Mn and Au/Mn, respectively.

In summary, there is no evidence from the measured activation data of any

Table 1. Summary of Beagle dog foil activations — centre beam position.

Dog	Date	Mass Dog (kg)	Activation (Bq/atom)[a]		
			MnNi	Cu	AuAl
491	04/03/92	11.00	1.99	6.54	8.20
643	04/04/92	14.00	2.27	7.46	8.76
627	04/04/92	12.00	2.24	7.11	8.64
778	04/04/92	10.00	2.14	6.84	8.44
760	04/05/92	11.00	2.14	6.88	8.42
803	04/05/92	11.00	2.24	7.41	8.60
614	04/05/92	10.00	2.30	7.56	8.70
535	04/06/92	11.00	1.99	6.45	8.20
180	04/06/92	10.50	2.33	7.40	8.83
641	05/19/92	13.50	2.27	7.24	8.65
194	05/19/92	09.50	2.24	7.24	8.45
641	05/20/92	13.50	2.13	6.85	8.45
194	05/20/92	09.50			
641	05/21/92	13.50	2.09	6.82	8.24
194	05/21/92	09.50	2.08	6.74	8.17
641	05/22/92	13.50	2.13	7.01	8.12
194	05/22/92	09.50	2.02	6.59	8.10
480	05/25/92	15.00	2.24	7.35	8.46
644	05/25/92	12.50	2.31	7.64	8.65
845	10/27/92	11.50	2.36	7.60	8.72
494	10/27/92	12.00	2.22	7.16	8.33
517	10/29/92	09.50	2.36	7.61	8.67
516	10/29/92	11.00	2.39	7.65	8.65
790	11/03/92	10.50	2.21	7.33	8.47
518	11/03/92	10.00	2.11	6.87	8.25
573	11/04/92	12.50	2.22	7.19	8.20
763	11/04/92	12.00	2.34	7.50	8.40
746	12/01/92	10.00	2.38	7.75	8.71
804	12/01/92	09.50	2.32	7.56	8.59
647	12/01/92	13.00	2.23	7.27	8.31
746	12/02/92	10.00	2.36	7.47	8.72
804	12/02/92	09.50	2.31	7.48	8.52
647	12/02/92	13.00	2.12	6.85	8.13
746	12/02/92	10.00	2.36	7.47	8.72
804	12/02/92	09.50	2.31	7.48	8.52
647	12/02/92	13.00	2.12	6.85	8.13
746	12/03/92	10.00	2.32	7.34	8.46
804	12/03/92	09.50	2.10	6.72	8.23
647	12/03/92	13.00	2.20	7.02	8.28
746	12/04/92	10.00	2.31	7.44	8.51
804	12/04/92	09.50	2.06	6.56	8.12
647	12/04/92	13.00	2.20	7.28	8.57
661	01/05/93	10.80	2.20	7.10	8.16
667	01/05/93	11.00	2.31	7.37	8.41
638	01/07/93	10.00	2.32	7.49	8.47
765	01/07/93	11.50	2.25	7.21	8.20
561	01/19/93	13.00	2.44	7.76	8.70
813	01/19/93	13.00	2.49	7.93	8.70
665	01/21/93	12.50	2.42	7.79	8.66
832	01/21/93	14.00	2.44	7.81	8.59
659	02/16/93	11.50	2.35	7.55	8.65
660	02/16/93	12.00	2.33	7.29	8.49
817	02/18/93	10.00	2.37	7.58	8.65
764	02/18/93	11.80	2.32	7.51	8.69
637	02/25/93	11.50	2.26	7.30	8.51
773	02/26/93	11.50			
467	05/11/93	09.00	2.56	8.02	9.00
812	05/11/93	12.00	2.52	7.81	8.85
820	05/13/93	10.00	2.47	7.86	8.78
626	05/13/93	11.50	2.39	7.71	8.80
1059	06/08/93	12.00	2.27	7.21	8.47
1283	06/08/93	13.50	2.27	7.28	8.42
118	06/17/93	13.00	2.30	7.35	8.44
Mean		11.37	2.27	7.30	8.49
Std Dev		01.51	0.13	0.37	0.22

[a] Apply normalisation factors of 10^{-15} for MnNi, 10^{-16} for Cu and 10^{-14} for AuAl

Table 2. Summary data from all HTTS activation foil measurements.

Foil No.	Position	Foil composition	Standard error(%)	Variation from mean value	
				Min (%)	Max (%)
1	Centre of beam	AuAl	3	− 5	6
		Cu	5	− 12	10
		MnNi	6	− 12	13
2	Right eye	AuAl	50	− 58	188
3	Tubus	AuAl	50	− 69	149
4	Rear of skull	AuAl	55	− 69	229
5	Thyroid	AuAl	47	− 71	194

significant change in the neutron beam over the period of the HTTS. The data do suggest a slight softening of the neutron spectrum as the study progressed. For the activation foils located at off-centre positions much larger variations were observed. These foils provide no useful information as to the beam consistency. Apart from a crude indication as to thermal flux levels these data could only provide additional information if detailed comparisons were made with calculations of each individual dog, a task not being considered at present.

It was thought that the foil activations were dependent on the dog mass and would be time-dependent since the dogs aged during the study and became larger. However, there is no evidence that the dogs' weights increased during the HTTS (correlation coefficient is 0.01). The foil activations may depend on the size of the dogs' heads since this will alter the backscatter of neutrons to the foils but the experimental data suggest that this effect is insignificant.

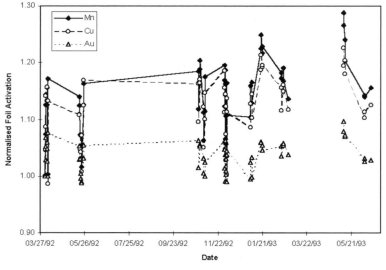

FFig. 1. Normalised foil activations from HTTS — centre beam position.

Table 3. Summary of HTTS TLD measurements.

TLD No.	Position	Standard error (%)	Variation relative to mean value	
			Min (%)	Max (%)
1	Centre of beam	10.5	−19	19
2	Tubus	48.3	−58	199
3	Thyroid	62.7	−94	278
4	Between shoulders	20.7	−38	39
5	Abdomen	32.2	−20	200

TLD results from beagle irradiations

The TLD results show a similar behaviour to that of the activation foils (Table 3). The centre-beam position providing reasonably consistent values whilst the results from the other positions have a very large statistical variation. The TLD results were quoted as Gy h^{-1} values as evaluated by the measuring team. However, these should not be considered as being true dose rates. In particular no corrections have been applied for thermal neutron sensitivity although it is known that a significant correction is needed. The large variability in the TLD results combined with the problems of interpreting the physical meaning of the data means that these are of little use, except as a check on the consistency of the beam.

Free beam dosimetry results

Measurements were also performed during the HTTS using a standard set of activation foils irradiated free in air. The foil set used a number of activation foils, some covered in cadmium, to cover as much as possible of the neutron energy range but there remains a highly significant part of the spectrum (approximately 10—500 keV) over which the foils are insensitive. These free beam foil activation measurements are very valuable since they are simple and were defined at the

Table 4. Normalised free-beam activation foil data for the HTTS.

Foil	Mn	Al	Cu	AuAl	AuAl	InAl	WAl	^{238}U	LaAl	Sc	I(n,n')Ni	Al	Cu/Mn	Au/Mn
Cd cover	Yes	Yes	Yes	Bare	Yes	Yes	Yes	Yes	Yes	Yes	Yes	Yes		
03/04/92	1.00	1.00	1.00	1.00	1.00	1.00	1.00	1.00	1.00	1.00	1.00	1.00	1.00	1.00
21/05/92	0.92	0.94	0.95	0.95	0.94	0.94	0.95	0.95	0.95	0.87	0.93	0.88	1.02	1.04
09/07/92	0.96	0.95	0.96	0.95	0.94	0.95	0.95	0.96	0.97		0.94	1.03	0.98	0.99
26/10/92	0.95	0.94	0.94	0.95	0.98	0.95	0.94	0.94	0.94	0.93	1.03	0.95	0.98	0.99
10/06/93	0.83	0.95	0.96	0.95	0.99	0.95	0.94	0.95	0.97	0.99	0.92	0.93	1.01	1.02

inception of the BNCT project, predating the HTTS study, and so provide an archive of beam consistency data. The time dependence of the measured activations is given in Table 4, which shows very little change over the period of the HTTS, with an initial 5% drop in all data and thereafter remaining remarkably constant. These data support the view that the beam changed very little ($< 5\%$) over the whole of the HTTS.

Conclusions

The results from the three-foil pack at the beam centre indicate very consistent beam conditions for the duration of the HTTS. There is a spread of values in the data but most of this is also seen over short intervals of time. This suggests that the variability is mainly due to positioning of the dogs and not to changes of the beam itself. Results for positions away from the beam axis show a larger variability, due to dog positioning differences, and hence these latter data provide little qualitative information.

The TLD results are of little use since the raw data were not corrected for thermal neutron sensitivity and the variability of the TLD results is large, especially away from the beam centre. This is a significant effect but no reliable method of establishing the correction factors has been provided. The free beam foil measurements also support the view that the beam remains constant, the measured data being within 5% of the average values except for isolated cases.

References

1. Baard JH, Nolthenius HJ. Program Description of Villa, ECN report FYS/RASA—89/05 1989.
2. Voorbraak WP, Freudenreich WE, Stecher-Rasmussen F, Verhagen H; Neutron Metrology in the HFR, Neutron and Gamma Metrology in Two Beagles and One Cylindrical Phantom, ECN-C–91-075 1991.

©1997 Elsevier Science B.V. All rights reserved.
Advances in Neutron Capture Therapy.
Volume I, Medicine and Physics.
B. Larsson, J. Crawford and R. Weinreich, editors.

Microdosimetric studies at the Harvard/MIT phase I clinical trial of boron neutron capture therapy

G.R. Solares[1], W.S. Kiger, III[2] and R.G. Zamenhof[1]

[1] *Beth Israel Deaconess Medical Center, Boston, Massachusetts; and* [2] *The Massachusetts Institute of Technology, Cambridge, Massachusetts, USA*

Introduction

Recently, we proposed a novel approach to the microdosimetry of neutron capture therapy that was developed using high-resolution quantitative auto-radiography (HRQAR) and two-dimensional Monte Carlo simulation [1]. The approach used consists of using actual histological and ^{10}B microdistribution data obtained from human subjects undergoing a phase I clinical trial of boron neutron capture therapy (BNCT) in the Harvard/MIT program. To assess the microdosimetric effects of the various boron distributions in tissue, without assumptions regarding geometric modeling of the tissues or boron distributions, we used a combination of Monte Carlo analysis, analytical calculations and image-processing techniques. Several parameters of importance to the micro-dosimetry of NCT are considered, including relative energy deposition, number of nuclear hits, average linear energy transfer (LET) in the nucleus, etc. These are used to estimate "compound factors" which can be used to evaluate various potential implications for NCT.

Materials and Methods

Histology and boron distribution

A unique form of high-resolution quantitative α track autoradiography has been developed in our laboratory [1]. This technique, which has a spatial resolution of only $1-2$ microns, allows simultaneous observation of tissue histology and α and ^{7}Li tracks. Contrary to other commonly used materials, the lexan detector used in this technique does not register proton tracks produced in the ^{14}N(n,p)^{14}C reaction.

Microdosimetry model

There are a number of approaches that have previously been taken by other investigators [2−7] as well as ourselves to study the microdosimetry of the ^{10}B neutron capture reaction, principally with the intention of deriving so-called "compound factors" for various boron compounds and predicting fundamental radiobiological parameters. In every case these approaches have involved simple mathematical modeling of the relevant microanatomical sites (e.g., capillaries, tumor cells, etc.) combined with either deterministic or stochastic (Monte Carlo) approaches to compute the resulting microdosimetric parameters. The limitations of most of these approaches have been:

1. The results are valid only for the specific sizes and shapes of the cells and structures modeled, which can involve only relatively simple mathematical representations.
2. The ^{10}B distributions in- and outside the cells have also been modeled with rather simple mathematical functions [2–7].

In the past such simple microdosimetric models have proved extremely useful for increasing our understanding of BNCT microdosimetry and have occasionally correlated well with observed experimental data.

We have developed a unique approach to BNCT microdosimetry which largely sidesteps both of the above limitations. Firstly, the actual ^{10}B microdistribution is derived with the HRQAR technique. Secondly, the principle of surrogate two-dimensional modeling is invoked to obtain, effectively, full three-dimensional Monte Carlo calculations for the tissues of interest based on the actual anatomy.

The principle of the two-dimensional surrogate approach is that a single plane passing through the tissue (i.e., a histological section) which contains the cross-sections of many randomly oriented cells is equivalent to sampling a single effective cell with a large number of randomly oriented planes. A single HRQAR autoradiogram of tissue containing tumor cells, for instance, provides not only the true ^{10}B distribution within that plane, but also the random sections of cells intersected by this plane. The surrogate approach to microdosimetry is realized in a two-dimensional Monte Carlo simulation in which the ^{10}B microdistribution measured in the autoradiogram constitutes the spatial distribution of the ^{10}B reaction source, and the two-dimensional cell anatomy of the autoradiogram (containing about 200 individual cell cross-sections) comprises the model in which charged particle transport is simulated and various microdosimetric parameters are tallied. Thus, in our approach to BNCT microdosimetry, unlike the usual approach in which a single cell or a single cell in a matrix of its nearest neighbors is modeled, microdosimetric parameters are tallied over many cells to obtain microdosimetric data for a single effective cell, which, in an average sense, is representative of all cells in the tissue. The equivalence of the surrogate two-dimensional charged particle transport simulation to a full three-dimensional microdosimetric calculation has been verified in a geometrically simple system [8,9]. The approximately one-dimensional character of the charged particle transport resulting from ^{10}B capture reactions allows this two-dimensional simulation to be viewed as a full three-dimensional calculation for a block of tissue in which the source spatial distribution and particle trajectories are sampled from a single plane. Since this plane intersects many randomly oriented cells, the cell morphology is well-sampled. In this work, we have used tissues, sectioned at a thickness of 4μm, from subjects admitted into the phase I clinical trial at the Harvard/ MIT BNCT program.

This more realistic approach to the microdosimetry of BNCT has at least two potential applications:

1. When correlated to the results of experimental cellular or in vivo survival studies it may lead to a clearer understanding of the fundamental radiobiology of the ^{10}B reaction.
2. When applied to cell culture samples or in vivo biopsy specimens taken from animals to which experimental boron compounds have been administered it may prove to be a useful predictor of the efficacy of new boron compounds, specifically with respect to their compound or localization factors.

The microdosimetric approach that is used for the two-dimensional Monte Carlo calculations employs the continuous slowing down approximation for charged particle transport in tissue. Using Monte Carlo methods and analytical calculations, particles are generated isotopically over many randomly selected angles, from points in the imaged cell microanatomy corresponding to the measured ^{10}B microdistribution. The energy deposition of each particle along its path and in each anatomical region of interest (i.e., nucleus, cytoplasm, extracellular space, etc.) is calculated using its linear energy transfer (LET) function as generated by the computer program TRIM [10]. Various microdosimetric parameters are calculated and compared to results using a computer-generated uniform boron distribution with the same average ^{10}B concentration as the actual one. In this way microdosimetric parameters are calculated which depend on the spatial distribution of ^{10}B captures as well as on the size and morphology of each microanatomical region. Typically, $10^4 - 10^5$ capture events are sampled per simulation.

Results and Discussion

Table 1 shows results for uniform and actual boron distributions in human normal brain tissue, normal skin and skin melanoma for subjects admitted to the

Table 1. Six different microdosimetric parameters or "compound factors" that were calculated using actual or uniform ^{10}B microdistributions for each of the three tissues analyzed: normal brain, normal skin, and skin melanoma. Monte Carlo statistical uncertainties for these results are less than 1.6%.

Tissue	Normal brain		Normal skin		Melanoma	
^{10}B Microdistribution	Actual	Uniform	Actual	Uniform	Actual	Uniform
Mean absorbed energy %	8.4	6.2	16.2	16.1	22.0	25.1
^{10}B origins	9.7	6.3	13.6	16.2	17.4	25.4
Mean LET (keV/μm)	31.2	23.0	69.3	74.9	86.2	100.3
Dose weighted LET (keV/μm)	42.7	31.0	89.3	96.2	119.6	138.8
Mean track length (μm)	0.5	0.4	0.9	0.9	1.3	1.4
% of nuclear hits	14.8	11.4	34.5	36.7	44.3	48.7

phase I BNCT melanoma or glioblastoma multiforme protocol at the Harvard/ MIT program. After admission to the Clinical Study Unit, a study subject was orally given a test dose of BPA; 4—7 h after BPA administration, either a stereo-tactic needle brain biopsy or a punch biopsy of the melanoma nodules and surrounding normal skin was taken. These tissues were frozen and subsequently analyzed by the methods described above.

Table 1 summarizes six different microdosimetric parameters that were calcu-lated for each of the three tissues analyzed: normal brain, normal skin and skin melanoma. The parameters calculated are as follows: the "mean absorbed energy" represents the average percentage of the total energy deposited in the nucleus; the "^{10}B origins" is the percentage of particles originating inside the nucleus; the "mean LET" is taken inside the nucleus of each of the two particles and averaged over all events (including misses); the "dose weighted LET" is the LET weighted by dose delivered to each segment along each particle track (by weighting the segments that have a higher LET, this factor relates to the biologi-cal effectiveness of a compound in depositing dose in the nucleus); "mean track length" is the average length traveled by an α particle or ^{7}Li ion inside the nucleus; and "% of nuclear hits" is the percentage of particles that actually hit the nucleus.

The mean absorbed energy shows no significant change when comparing actual and uniform distributions for the same tissue when using BPA. This indi-cates that the spatial distribution of BPA is relatively homogenous. However, when comparing to other tissues the mean absorbed energy is higher in the tumor (melanoma) than in normal skin and normal brain.

Table 2 shows the ratios of the various parameters when comparing two differ-ent tissues and distributions. The most noticeable result in this case occurs with the mean absorbed energy ratio of melanoma vs. normal brain, which is 2.63. This value is very close to the experimentally obtained value of 3 calculated from data reported by Coderre et al. at Brookhaven National Laboratory [11,12]. It is interesting to notice also that the mean absorbed energy ratio for melanoma vs. skin is only 1.35, which seems to correspond to recently measured

Table 2. The ratios of the six microdosimetric parameters when comparing two different tissues or ac-tual and uniform ^{10}B microdistributions. Monte Carlo statistical uncertainties for these results are less than 1.6%.

Ratios	Melanoma: Brain	Melanoma: Skin	Skin (uniform): Skin (actual)	Melanoma (uniform): Melanoma (actual)
Mean absorbed energy %	2.63	1.35	0.99	1.14
^{10}B origins	1.79	1.28	1.19	1.46
Mean LET	2.76	1.24	1.08	1.16
Dose weighted LET	2.80	1.34	1.08	1.16
Mean track length	2.73	1.38	0.99	1.12
% of nuclear hits	2.32	1.28	1.07	1.10

values by Coderre [12]. These results might help to explain the differences in the observed compound-RBE found experimentally in rats using glioma tumor cells and normal rat spinal cord. It is also worth noting that the differences among most of the parameters are not significant when comparing the results for the uniform and actual distributions in the same tissue.

All Monte Carlo statistical uncertainties for these results are below 1.6%.

The compound factors give only an indication of how effective a compound is at the microscopic level. The ultimate effectiveness of a potential boron compound for BNCT will depend on several other factors not considered in this analysis. In particular, the ability of a compound to selectively concentrate in tumor and the resulting concentration in normal tissues and blood is of major importance. If capillaries are to be considered as the limiting factor, their geometry is also very important, in the case of BSH, in assessing the performance of different potential compounds for BNCT.

Acknowledgements

The U.S. Department of Energy, under contracts No. DE−FG02−87ER−60600 and DE−FG02−90ER12971, supported this research and the developments reported here.

References

1. Solares GR, Zamenhof RG. A novel approach to the microdosimetry of neutron capture therapy, part I: high-resolution quantitative autoradiography applied to microdosimetry in neutron capture therapy. Radiat Res 1995;144:50−58.
2. Davis MA, Little JB, Ayyangar KM, Reddy AR. Relative biological effectiveness of the $^{10}B(n,\alpha)^7Li$ reaction in HeLa cells. Radiat Res 1970;43:534−553.
3. Rydin RA, Deutsh OL, Murray BW. The effect of geometry on capillary wall dose for boron neutron capture therapy. Phys Med Biol 1976;21:134−138.
4. Kobayashi T, Kanda K. Analytical calculation of boron-10 dosage in cell nucleus for boron neutron capture therapy. Radiat Res 1982;91:77−94.
5. Gabel D, Foster S, Fairchild RG. The Monte Carlo simulation of the biological effect of the $^{10}B(n,\alpha)^7Li$ reaction in cells and tissues and its implication for boron neutron capture therapy. Radiat Res 1987;111:14−25.
6. Wheeler FJ, Griebenow ML, Wessol DE, Nigg DW, Anderl RA. A stochastic model for high-LET response for boron neutron capture therapy (BNCT). In: Fairchild RG, Bond VP, Woodhead AD (eds) Clinical Aspects of Neutron Capture Therapy. New York: Plenum Press, 1989 165−178.
7. Verrijk R, Huiskamp R, Begg AC, Wheeler FJ, Watkins PRD. A comprehensive PC-based computer model for microdosimetry of BNCT. Int J Radiat Biol 1994;65:241−253.
8. Yam CS. Microdosimetric Studies for Neutron Capture Therapy and Techniques for Capture Element Selection. Ph.D. Thesis, Massachusetts Institute of Technology 1995.
9. Yam CS, Solares GR, Zamenhof RG. Verification of the two-dimensional approach for NCT microdosimetry. Trans Am Nucl Soc 1994;71:142.
10. Ziegler J. TRIM91, The Transport of Ions in Matter. IBM Res., Yorktown, NY 1991.
11. Coderre JA, Makar MS, Micca PL, Nawrocky MM, Liu HB, Joel DD, Slatkin DN, Amols HI. Derivation of relative biological effectiveness for the high-LET radiations produced during Bor-

on Neutron Capture irradiations of the GL Rat Gliosarcoma in vitro and in vivo. Int J Radiat Oncol Biol Phys 1993;27:1121—1129.

12. Coderre JA et al. Unpublished data.

1997 Elsevier Science B.V.
Advances in Neutron Capture Therapy.
Volume I, Medicine and Physics.
B. Larsson, J. Crawford and R. Weinreich, editors.

Microdosimetry of boron neutron capture irradiation in vitro based on particle track structure

Fred Pöller[1], Andrea Wittig[2] and Wolfgang Sauerwein[2]

[1]Institute for Medical Radiation Physics and [2]Department of Radiation Oncology, University of Essen, Essen, Germany

Keywords: cell survival, microdosimetry, Monte Carlo simulation.

Introduction

The Monte Carlo technique that is used performs quantitative microdosimetric calculations of cell survival after boron neutron capture (BNC) irradiations in vitro. The biophysical model of these calculations is based on the track structure of the released α particles and ^{7}Li ions and the X-ray sensitivity of the irradiated cells. The biological effect of these charged particles can be determined if the lethal effect of local doses deposited in very small fractional volumes of the cell nucleus is known. This can be deduced from experimental data of cell survival after X-ray irradiation assuming Poisson statistics for lethal events. The radial dose distribution inside the track of the released particles, the cell survival after X-ray irradiation, the geometry of the tumor cells, the subcellular ^{10}B concentration and the thermal neutron fluence are used as input in a PC-based computer program. Validations of computer calculations will be presented using previously published experimental data and measured cell survival data obtained after BNC irradiations with d(14)+Be-neutrons at the cyclotron facility in Essen. A good correlation was found after comparing experimental and calculated cell survival data.

Material and Methods

Human melanoma cells (MeWo), originally isolated by Dr Fogh's group in the Sloan Kettering Institute of Cancer Research, New York, were used throughout. Cells from exponentially growing culture were seeded into small culture flasks (250,000 cells, 25 cm^2 area, 5 ml minimum essential medium (MEM) containing 20% FCS). The cells were incubated for 24 h with borocaptate sodium (BSH) (enriched with 95% ^{10}B). Mean boron levels in the intracellular space (cytoplasm) and in the cell medium were measured using inductively coupled plasma optical emission spectroscopy (ICP-OES) [1].

Address for correspondence: Dr Fred Pöller, Institute for Medical Radiation Physics, University of Essen, Hufelandstr. 55, D-45122 Essen, Germany.

The in vitro irradiations of cultured MeWo cell populations, the colony-forming assay and the uptake of boron compounds have been described previously [2,3]. The cells were irradiated with d(14)+Be-neutrons (mean energy 5.8 MeV) in a polyethylene phantom (25 × 25 × 25 cm^3) at a depth of 6.5 cm (field size: 20 cm × 20 cm/125 cm) at room temperature. The total dose rate and the percentage photon contamination at this depth were 0.2 Gy/min and 11%, respectively. The thermal neutron fluence for a total dose of 1 Gy at the same depth was 3.4·10^{10} cm^{-2}. The measurements of thermal neutron fluence rates using gold activation have been described elsewhere [4].

Monte Carlo calculations on a microcomputer were carried out for quantitative determination of cell survival. The computer code TNC6.FOR of Charlton [5] was adapted and further developed for the calculation of cell inactivation after BNC-irradiations using a calculation model developed by Scholz and Kraft [6]. This model is an alternative approach of the parametric track structure model of Katz and co-workers [7]. The radial dose distribution inside the particle track is assumed to decrease with a $1/r^2$ law and with increasing radial distance.

Energy deposition of the α and ^{7}Li particles in water-equivalent modelled cells were calculated using reported data of stopping power generated with PC-TRIM (Transport of Ions in Matter), a microcomputer version of TRIM-92 [8]. The ^{10}B atoms are homogeneously distributed in different amounts of intra- and intercellular space, and the ^{10}B concentration is constant with time. Heterogeneity of boron uptake between cells was not taken into consideration. The movement of the heavy particles is isotropic and their path is a straight line in random direction, 180° from each other. The dose deposition in the cell nucleus was calculated cell by cell. The MeWo cell populations were modelled as a surface-attached monolayer with a closed packed structure. This cell monolayer consists of equal-sized cells and cell nuclei with an elliptical shape [3]. Cross-fire effects of six neighbouring cells was included in the calculations using a constant distance between the cells.

For each particle track in the cell nucleus the biological effect as the cell survival S_{nc} due to boron neutron capture was calculated using the particle track structure and the measured X-ray survival. Each track corresponds to a mean LET averaged over the particle track inside the cell nucleus. The track through the cell nucleus is divided into very small cylindrical segments [6]. For each segment the expected probability of cell inactivation by a given local dose is extracted from the known measured X-ray survival curve. Thus the inactivation probability of the cell is calculated by numerical integration over the whole track distribution in the cell nucleus. A uniformly distributed radiosensitivity throughout the whole cell nucleus has been assumed.

A minimum number of ^{10}B neutron capture reactions needs to be generated in the Monte Carlo simulation for an acceptable accuracy of the calculations of the survival S_{nc}. Typically, 200,000–500,000 neutron capture reactions were generated by choosing random locations for 5% statistical uncertainty. The total cell survival S_t after BNC irradiation of the cells in a neutron beam can be calculated by the expression: $S_t = S_{fn} \times S_{nc}$. using the measured cell survival S_{fn} after neutron irradiation without boron. The survival S_{fn} can be described by an exponential dose-effect curve using the linear-quadratic model. This survival depends on the normal radiation effects of the neutrons and accompanying γ radiation in the mixed irradiation field [3].

Results and Discussion

A preliminary validation of the computer calculations has been performed by the comparison of measured and calculated cell survival after BNC irradiations of the ambient or washed MeWo monolayer populations shown in Fig. 1.

For the Monte Carlo simulation of the washed cells an exclusively cytoplasmic location for boron was assumed. A mean boron level of 103 ppm ^{10}B in the cytoplasm was measured using ICP-OES.

The simulation of another experiment for validation has been performed using published measured survival data of V79 Chinese hamster cells from Gabel et al. [9]. The comparison between measured and calculated survival data for V79 cells is shown in Fig. 2.

The cells were irradiated in suspension at the thermal neutron fission beam of the Brookhaven Medical Research Reactor (BMRR). Calculations were performed assuming a homogeneous distribution of boric acid. The V79 cells were treated as isolated spherical cells with a radius of 6.5 μm containing a centrally located nucleus of 3.8 μm radius [10].

Calculations are in good agreement with the measured cell survival. This result supports the hypothesis that radial dose distribution inside the particle tracks and the X-ray dose effect curve are the main factors determining relative biological efficiency (RBE) of high LET irradiation [6].

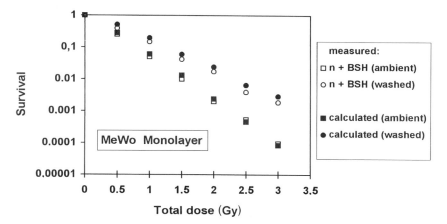

Fig. 1. Comparison between measured and calculated survival data for MeWo monolayer cells after BNC-irradiation with fast d(14)+Be-neutrons.

180

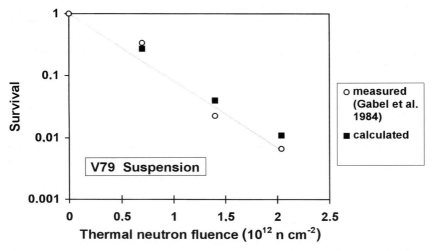

Fig. 2. Comparison between measured and calculated survival data for V79 cells after BNC-irradiation in suspension with the BMRR thermal neutron beam. The dashed line was fitted by eye.

Generally, the agreement between the measured and calculated survival values is strongly influenced by the exact knowledge of the real cell geometry and the subcellular boron distribution. The size of the cell nucleus and the radiosensitivity throughout the whole cell nucleus depend on the cell cycle stage. The results shown in Figs. 1 and 2 were obtained in a first approximation using a unique geometry for all cells and mean boron levels. These restrictions will be avoided in future developments of the model taking into account the real microdistribution of ^{10}B and the whole cell size distribution of asynchronous cell populations.

Acknowledgements

This work was supported by the Deutsche Forschungsgemeinschaft, Germany.

References

1. Pollmann D, Broekhard JA, Leis F, Tschöpel P, Tölg G. Determination of boron in biological tissues by inductively coupled plasma optical emission spectroscopy (ICP-OES). Fresenius J Anal Chem 1993;117:1–5.
2. Sauerwein W, Ziegler W, Szypniewski H, Streffer C. Boron neutron capture therapy (BNCT) using fast neutrons: effects in two tumor cell lines. Strahlenther Onkol 1990;166:26–29.
3. Pöller F, Sauerwein W. Monte Carlo simulation of the biological effects of boron neutron capture irradiation with d(14)+Be-neutrons in vitro. Radiat Res 1995;142:98–106.
4. Pöller F, Sauerwein W, Rassow J. Monte Carlo calculation of dose enhancement by neutron capture of ^{10}B in fast neutron therapy. Phys Med Biol 1993;38:397–410.
5. Charlton DE. Energy deposition in small ellipsoidal volumes by high-LET particles: application to thermal neutron dosimetry. Int J Radiat Biol 1991;59:827–842.

6. Scholz M, Kraft G. A parameter-free track structure model for heavy ion action cross section. In: Chadwick KH, Moschini G, Varma MN (eds) Biophysical Modelling of Radiation Effects. Brussels: Adam Hilger, 1992;185–192.

7. Katz R, Ackerson B, Homayoonfar M, Sharma SC. Inactivation of cells by heavy ion bombardment. Radiat Protect Dos 1971;47:402–425.

8. Ziegler JF, Niersack JP, Littmark U. The Stopping and Range of Ions in Solids. New York: Pergamon Press, 1970.

9. Gabel D, Fairchild RG, Larsson B, Börner HG. The relative biological effectiveness in V79 Chinese hamster cells of the neutron capture reactions in boron and nitrogen. Radiat Res 1984;98:307–316.

10. Gabel D, Foster S, Fairchild RG. The Monte Carlo simulation of the biological effect of the reaction $^{10}B(n,\alpha)^7Li$ in cells and tissue and its implication for boron neutron capture therapy. Radiat Res 1987;111:14–25.

182

Advances in Neutron Capture Therapy.
Volume I, Medicine and Physics.
B. Larsson, J. Crawford and R. Weinreich, editors.

The twin ionisation chamber technique in quality control of a mixed epithermal neutron and γ beam for NCT

A. Kosunen[1], H. Ylä-Mella[2] and S. Savolainen[2]

[1] *Finnish Centre for Radiation and Nuclear Safety (STUK), Radiation Metrology Laboratory, Helsinki;*
and [2] Department of Physics, Helsinki University, Helsinki, Finland

Introduction

Ionisation chambers are widely used in radiotherapy for dose measurements because of their reliability and well-known dosimetric features. For mixed field dosimetry of γ and fast neutrons a twin ionisation chamber technique has been commonly accepted, and international recommendations for dosimetry are presented by ICRU, ECNEU and AAPM [1−3]. In NCT, where neutrons are mostly in the epithermal range, the application of ionisation chambers is rare [4−6]. The existing dosimetry guideline cannot be adopted directly for NCT dosimetry because of lack of the physical data in the epithermal/thermal energy range.

In this work two pairs of gas flow ionisation chambers were tested under laboratory conditions in a mixed epithermal neutron/γ-field designed for BNCT [7]. The usefulness of ionisation chambers for quality control (QC) of beam monitor detectors and for dose determinations in a tissue-equivalent phantom was studied.

Materials and Methods

Technical data of the ionisation chambers used are presented in Table 1. Ionisation chambers were used with Keithley 6517 and NE Farmer 2570 electrometers. Tissue-equivalent (TE) gas was a mixture of N_2 (3.2 vol%), CO_2 (32.4 vol%) and CH_4 (64.4 vol%) gases. For Mg-ionisation chambers, extra pure Ar gas (99.9999%) was used. TE and Ar gas flows were controlled and regulated by gas pressure meters and rotameters. Gas flow inside the ionisation chambers was 5.0−10.0 ml/min and pressure increase 0.3−1.0 kPa.

The ionisation chambers were tested at laboratory conditions in a ^{60}Co γ beam at the Secondary Standard Dosimetry Laboratory (SSDL) of STUK and in a mixed epithermal neutron/γ beam at the TRIGA reactor in VTT, Otaniemi, Finland. The performance tests include determinations of the effects of the gas flow stability and the chamber signal affecting parameters, i.e., polarity of the collect-

Address for correspondence: Antti Kosunen, Finnish Centre for Radiation and Nuclear Safety (STUK), Radiation Metrology Laboratory, P.O. Box 14, FIN-00881 Helsinki, Finland.
E-mail:antti.kosunen@stuk.fi

Table 1. Technical data of the ionisation chambers.

Ionisation chamber	Wall material and thickness	Volume	Shape	Gas
Exradin, T2[a] Sno 442	A 150 plastic, 1 mm + A150 build-up cap, 4 mm	0.53 cm^3	Cylinder	Tissue equivalent
Exradin, M2[a] Sno 183	Mg, 1mm + Mg build-up cap, 2 mm	0.53 cm^3	Cylinder	Argon
Far West, IC-17[b] Sno 754-RTW	A 150 plastic, 5 mm	1 cm^3	Sphere	Tissue equivalent
Far West, IC-17M[b] Sno 755-RMW	Mg, 3 mm	2 cm^3	Sphere	Argon

[a]Manufactured by Exradin Radiation Instrumentation Inc., USA. [b]Manufactured by Far West Technology Inc., USA.

ing potential, signal lost by ion recombination and the effect of the stem of the ionisation chamber. To study the effect of gas flow stability, gas flow was varied and the change in chamber response was detected. At steady gas flow the linearity of dose response and repeatability were verified. For polarity effect and recombination the methods described in IAEA Code of Practice were followed [8]. The effect of the chamber stem was determined in air in a n/γ beam using a dummy stem beside the real stem. Air kerma and absorbed dose to water calibrations were performed in a ^{60}Co γ beam. Change of chamber responses relative to γ energy were determined in a 6 MV γ beam of the Varian Clinac linear accelerator in the Radiotherapy Department of Helsinki University Hospital.

At the reactor the useability of twin ionisation chambers for QC of beam monitors was studied by relative beam output measurements. For beam monitors the relative dose response, repeatability and the change of the beam output during the few first minutes from the start-up of the reactor were determined. The operation of beam monitors is presented in the work of Auterinen et al. [7]. The absolute dose distributions were measured with Exradin ionisation chambers at the beam central axis in a cylindrical PMMA phantom. Dose distributions were also determined by calculations by DORT (Two-Dimensional Discrete Ordinates Transport, Oak Ridge, USA) Code. For calculations the output of the beam was adjusted based on the activation foil measurements. Calculations and foil measurements are described in the work of Seppälä et al. [9] and Kaita et al. [10].

In measurements the epithermal neutron and γ doses were determined using the formalism presented in ICRU 45 [1] and extended by Raaijmakers et al. [5,6]. The basic equations can be written:

$$R_u = h_u D_g + k_u D_n + k'_u \phi$$

$$R_t = h_t D_g + k_t D_n + k'_t \phi \tag{1}$$

In Eqn. 1 D_g and D_n are the γ and neutron doses, quantities h_u, h_t are the responses of the detectors to the γ rays and k_u, k_t to fast neutrons in the mixed

Table 2. Performance test results of ionisation chambers.

Ionisation chamber	Dose linearity, $\leqslant 4$ Gy, ^{60}Co-beam (LSQ-corr.)	Repeatability ^{60}Co-beam (SD%)	Polarity effect (%)	Recombination ^{60}Co and n/γ beams (%)	Stem effect n/γ beam (%)
Exradin T2 and M2	1.00 ± 0.05	0.2	$0.9^{a,c}$ 1.5^b	$\leqslant 0.2$	$\leqslant 2.9^d$ $\leqslant 0.4^e$
FarWest 17 and 17M	1.00 ± 0.05	0.2	0.9^a 1.5^b	$\leqslant 0.3$	$\leqslant 0.3^d$

[a]In ^{60}Co γ beam; [b]in n/γ beam in air; [c]in n/γ beam in PMMA; [d]at the Bi surface in air; [e]17 cm from the Bi surface in air.

field relative to the responses to the γ rays used for calibration. Subscript u refers to detectors with a low neutron sensitivity and subscript t to detectors with approximately equal sensitivity to γ and neutron radiation. k_u', k_t' are the readings of the detectors due to thermal neutrons per unit of thermal neutron fluence, relative to the responses to the γ rays used for calibration.

Fast/epithermal neutron sensitivities were evaluated according to the formalism in ICRU and based on the calculated spectrum inside a phantom produced by the FiR1 epithermal beam and physical data (kerma factors, energy to produce an ion pair and stopping powers) available. Thermal neutron sensitivities were determined at a depth of 2.5 cm in a PMMA phantom using a 6 mm enriched ^{6}Li plastic cap on the ionisation chamber to exclude the thermal neutrons. Thermal fluence density was measured by activation foils [10].

Results and Discussion

The results of the performance tests of the ionisation chambers are presented in Table 2. In the performance tests no remarkable differences were found between the TE(TE) and Mg(Ar) ICs within each pair. Absorbed dose to water calibration factors and the relative sensitivities are presented in Table 3. In a 6-MV γ beam 1.7 and 2.9% increases in sensitivities were found for Exradin and Far West chamber pairs, respectively. In the mixed beam at reactor in a PMMA phantom most of the γ radiation is produced in neutron capture reactions of hydrogen with 2.23 MeV γ energy. The angular distribution of γ radiation in a reactor

Table 3. Absorbed dose to water calibration factors (N_w) for ^{60}Co γ radiation and the relative sensitivities for Exradin ionisation chambers.

Ionisation chamber	N_w (mGy/nC)	h_u, h_t	k_u, k_t	k_u', k_t' (10^{-13} Gy cm^2/n)
Exradin T2	54.8	1.00	0.83	5.42
Exradin M2	36.0	1.00	0.00	3.28

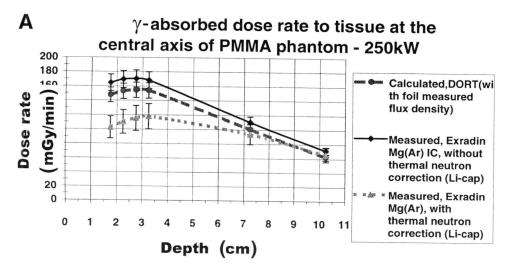

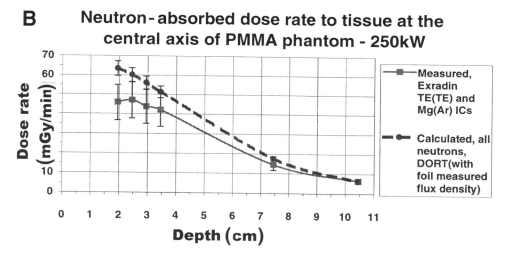

Fig. 1. Dose distributions at the beam central axis in a cylindrical PMMA phantom. **A:** γ-Dose distribution. Measured with Exradin M2 ionisation chamber (solid line), measured using Li-shield correction (dotted line), calculated (broken line). **B:** Epithermal neutron dose distribution. Measured with Exradin T2 ionisation chamber (solid line), calculated (broken line). Calculations were done by DORT-code.

beam is more isotropic than in ^{60}Co or 6-MV γ beams. For these reasons a relative gamma sensitivity of 1.00 was used.

Measured beam outputs and γ beam monitor readings correlated (R= 0.9999). For the epithermal neutron beam monitor about 2% nonlinearity was found relative LSQ-fit. The increase of the beam output during the start-up of the reactor showed similar behaviour for both beam monitors and ionisation chambers in a PMMA phantom. The rise time was detected between the 10 and 90% dose levels of the steady-state reactor output. The difference seen in rise time was about 10 s, which can be explained by the different integration times of detectors.

The calculated and measured dose distributions at the beam central axis in a PMMA phantom are presented in Fig. 1. For γ-dose distributions the calculated and measured curves coincide within 18% when no Li-cap is used on the chamber. The Li-cap reduces the signal by about 30% near the depth dose maximum and about 10% at 10 cm depth in phantom. Use of ^6Li shield on the detector leads to large disturbances in γ dose seen by the Mg(Ar) chamber. Compared to the calculated dose better agreement was found without the shield. The calculated and measured epithermal neutron dose distributions agree to within about 25% at the depth dose maximum and less than that deeper into the phantom.

Conclusions

Gas flow ionisation chambers are well suitable for relative dose measurements in Quality Control of beam monitors. The absolute absorbed dose determinations at reasonable uncertainty level ($\leqslant 5\%$) using the gas flow ionisation chambers require precise knowledge of the neutron spectrum. This is essential for determination of the cavity features (i.e., absorption, scattering and geometry) of the ionisation chamber.

References

1. ICRU Report 45. Clinical Neutron Dosimetry Part I: Determination of Absorbed Dose in a Patient Treated by External Beams of Fast Neutrons, 1989.
2. European protocol for neutron dosimetry for external beam therapy. Br J Radiol 1981;54: 882–898.
3. AAPM report No. 7. Protocol for neutron dosimetry 1980.
4. Rogus RD, Harling OK, Yanch JC. Mixed field dosimetry of epithermal neutron beams for boron neutron capture therapy at the MITR-II research reactor. Med Phys 1994;22:1611–1625.
5. Raaijmakers CPJ, Konijnenberg MV. Determination of dose components in phantoms irradiated with an epithermal neutron beam for neutron capture therapy. Med Phys 1995;22; 321–329.
6. Raaijmakers CPJ, Watkins PRD, Nottelman EL, Verhagen HW, Jansen JTM, Zoetelief J, Mijnheer BJ. The neutron sensitivity of dosimeters applied for boron neutron capture therapy. Med Phys 1996;23:1581–1589.
7. Auterinen I, Hiismäki P, Salmenhaara S, Tanner V. Operation and on-line beam monitoring of the Finnish BNCT station. In: Larsson B, Crawford J, Weinreich R (eds) Advances in Neutron Capture Therapy. Volume 1, Medicine and Physics. Amsterdam: Elsevier Science, 1997; 348–352 (these proceedings).
8. IAEA Technical Reports Series No. 277. Absorbed dose determinations in photon and electron beams 1987.
9. Seppälä T, Vähätalo J, Auterinen I, Savolainen S. Brain tissue substitutes for phantom measurements in NCT. In: Larsson B, Crawford J, Weinreich R (eds) Advances in Neutron Capture Ther-

apy. Volume 1, Medicine and Physics. Amsterdam: Elsevier Science, 1997;188—191 (these proceedings).

10. Kaita K, Seren T, Auterinen I. First characterisation of the Finnish epithermal neutron beam using activation detectors. In: Larsson B, Crawford J, Weinreich R (eds) Advances in Neutron Capture Therapy. Volume 1, Medicine and Physics. Amsterdam: Elsevier Science, 1997; 353—356 (these proceedings).

Brain tissue substitutes for phantom measurements in NCT

Tiina Seppälä[1], Jyrki Vähätalo[2], Iiro Auterinen[3] and Sauli Savolainen[1]

[1]Department of Physics and [2]Laboratory of Radiochemistry, University of Helsinki, Helsinki; and [3]VTT Chemical Technology, Technical Research Centre of Finland (VTT), Espoo, Finland

Introduction

The characterisation of the beam for dose planning in neutron capture therapy (NCT) is a demanding procedure consisting of free beam and phantom calculations and measurements. Phantoms of different shapes and materials are needed for calculation and measurement so that the neutron source can be defined as reliably as possible for the needs of dose planning.

There are no suitable international recommendations on radiotherapy dosimetry for low energetic neutrons used in NCT. In the first dosimetry protocols for boron neutron capture therapy (BNCT) at the beams at Petten and Brookhaven water phantoms have been used [1,2]. ICRU has recommended that water can be used as a reference phantom material for fast neutron dosimetry [3].

The therapeutic dose in BNCT is mainly caused by thermal neutrons interacting with boron containing tumour tissue (boron dose) in the reaction $^{10}B(n,\alpha)^7Li$. The main components of nondesired dose to the healthy tissue are γ dose, fast neutron dose, boron dose and nitrogen dose. The most important interactions of thermal neutrons in the head tissue are summarized in Table 1. These interactions have been chosen for calculating the reaction rates in the head tissue from the compositions of the head tissues [4] and the cross-sections [5].

Our reason to study the behaviour of the most important dose components in different tissue substitutes [3] was to optimise the composition of reference head phantom materials for measurements of performance, quality and acceptance tests in epithermal neutron beams.

Methods and Materials

The Monte Carlo based dose planning program rtt.MC was used in the calculations. The program was developed in Idaho National Engineering Laboratory (INEL) [7,8]. A simplified model of the Finnish FiR 1 epithermal beam in its basic configuration (see Fig. 1 in [9]) was used in the DORT modelling to determine the neutron and γ source for rtt.MC. At this stage the beam was not yet collimated. Our measurements showed later that the shape of the calculated spectrum seemed to agree quite well with measurements [10]. Only the intensity of the beam in the model was underestimated. The same calculated spectrum, but

Table 1. Most important interactions of thermal neutrons in the tissues of the head.

$^1H_{(H2O)}(n,n')^1H_{(H2O)}$ (thermal scattering)	$^{23}Na(n,\gamma)^{24}Na*$
$^1H_{(CH2)}(n,n')^1H_{(CH2)}$ (thermal scattering)	$^{31}P(n,\gamma)^{32}P*$
$^1H(n,\gamma)^2H$	$^{32}S(n,\gamma)^{33}S$
$^{12}C(n,\gamma)^{13}C$	$^{35}Cl(n,\gamma)^{36}Cl*$
$^{14}N(n,p)^{14}C*$	$^{35}Cl(n,p)^{35}S*$
$^{14}N(n,\gamma)^{15}N$	$^{39}K(n,\gamma)^{40}K*$
$^{16}O(n,\gamma)^{17}O$	$^{40}Ca(n,\gamma)^{41}Ca*$

intensity-corrected, was also used in modelling the first ionization chamber measurements [11]. A simple homogeneous cylindrical phantom model was used in the calculation. The transport of neutrons and photons was calculated in the different tissues defined by ICRU [4] and their substitutes. The effect of the background boron in these materials was also modelled.

When phantom materials are chosen for BNCT dosimetry the important thing is that the atomic densities (atoms/cm^3) of the most important reactions of the

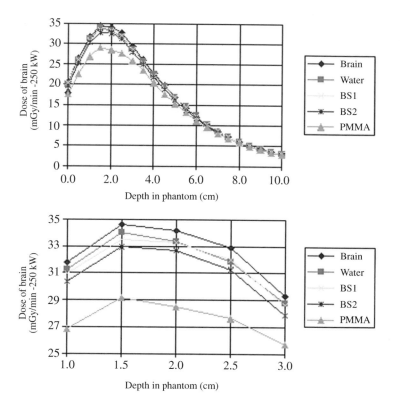

Fig. 1. **A**: Total doses in the brain and the brain substitutes along the central axis of the cylinder phantom. **B**: Total doses in the brain and the brain substitutes along the central axis of the cylinder phantom near the maximum of the total dose.

tissue substitutes compared to the tissue are as close to each other as possible. Different tissue substitutes as a phantom material can be compared to tissue when the flux distribution of neutron and photon irradiation is modelled in tissue substitutes and in tissue. In both cases the fluxes are converted to physical doses to the tissue. For example, when doses in the brain are calculated in all brain substitutes, the distributions of flux in brain substitutes can be compared to the distributions of flux in the brain.

For brain substitutes we developed two new liquids. The first proposed brain substitute liquid (we call it BS2) was based on the brain defined by ICRU [4], and into the other mixture (BS1) small fractions of P (0.4%), Cl (0.3%), K (0.3%), Na (0.2%) and S (0.2%) were added. BS1 and BS2 liquids were made of water, alcohol, urea and inorganic salts. The different dose components of brain in brain substitutes BS1, BS2, water and PMMA (polymethylmethacrylate, which is known also as lucite) and in the brain defined by ICRU [4] were compared. The depth of the maximum thermal flux in these materials were also compared.

Results

The total doses in these results are the physical doses of brain without any biological factors and consist of boron, γ, nitrogen and fast neutron doses. In the calculated results the background boron (10 ppm) was used in the brain and in the brain substitutes (Fig. 1A).

The calculated maximum thermal fluxes in all these materials were at the depth of 1.5 cm. In the maximum the total doses of brain differed in BS1, BS2 and water by less than 5% and in PMMA by 16% from the brain (Fig. 1B). The γ doses in the brain substitutes showed the greatest deviation compared to the γ dose in the brain. The fast neutron dose components of the brain substitutes differed less from the brain than did the boron, γ and nitrogen dose components [3,4].

Conclusion

BS1 and water are good choices for use as a phantom material for BNCT in epithermal beam characterisation. The different dose components and also the total dose of brain are closest to the brain in liquid BS1 developed by us and in water. In BS1, BS2, water and PMMA the γ doses of brain were smaller than in the brain, and were most significant in the PMMA because it has the smallest hydrogen density.

References

1. Raaijmakers CPJ, Konijnenberg MW, Verhagen HW, Mijnheer BJ. Determination of dose components in phantoms irradiated with an epithermal neutron beam for boron neutron capture therapy. Med Phys 1995;22:321−329.

2. Harling OK, Roberts KA, Moulin DJ, Rogus RD. Head phantoms for neutron capture therapy. Med Phys 1995;22:579–583.

3. ICRU Report 44. Tissue substitutes in radiation dosimetry and measurement, 1989.

4. ICRU Report 46. Photon, electron, proton and neutron interaction data for body tissues, 1992.

5. Erdtmann G. Neutron activation tables. Kernchemie in Einzeldarstellungen, Weinheim, 1976.

6. ICRU Report 30. Quantitative concepts and dosimetry in radiobiology, 1979.

7. Wheeler FJ. Radiation Transport in Tissue by Monte Carlo — Version X02. EGG-BNCT-11178, Idaho National Engineering Laboratory, January 1994.

8. Nigg DW. Methods for radiation dose distribution analysis and treatment planning in boron neutron capture therapy. Int J Radiat Biol Phys 1994;28:1121–1132.

9. Auterinen I, Hiisimäki P, Salmenhaara S, Tanner V. Operation and on-line beam monitoring of the Finnish BNCT station. In: Larsson B, Crawford J, Weinreich R (eds) Advances in Neutron Capture Therapy. Volume 1, Medicine and Physics. Amsterdam: Elsevier Science, 1997;348–352 (these proceedings).

10. Kaita K, Serén T, Auterinen I. First characterisation of the Finnish epithermal neutron beam using activation detectors. In: Larsson B, Crawford J, Weinreich R (eds) Advances in Neutron Capture Therapy. Volume 1, Medicine and Physics. Amsterdam: Elsevier Science, 1997;353–356 (these proceedings).

11. Kosunen A, Ylä-Mella H, Savolainen S. The twin ionisation chamber technique in quality control of a mixed epithermal neutron and γ beam for NCT. In: Larsson B, Crawford J, Weinreich R (eds) Advances in Neutron Capture Therapy. Volume 1, Medicine and Physics. Amsterdam: Elsevier Science, 1997;182–187 (these proceedings).

Characterisation and use of MOSFET γ dosimeters and silicon PIN diode neutron dosimeters for epithermal neutron beam dosimetry

M.G. Carolan[1,2], A.B. Rosenfeld[2], J.N. Mathur[2] and B.J. Allen[2,3]

[1]*Illawarra Cancer Care Centre, Wollongong, New South Wales;* [2]*Department of Physics, University of Wollongong, Wollongong, New South Wales; and* [3]*St. George Cancer Care Centre, Kogarah, New South Wales, Australia*

Introduction

Boron neutron capture therapy (BNCT) has presented new challenges for dosimetry due to the mixed γ and neutron field present and the epithermal energy range of the neutrons used. PIN diode neutron dosimeters and metal oxide field effect transistor (MOSFET) γ dosimeters permit the possibility of small (cubic millimetre size) detectors for routine BNCT dosimetry. They offer instantaneous read-out either on-line or immediately following exposure. This makes them attractive candidates for clinical dose monitoring applications. Here we will describe their operation and some experimental results obtained using them.

We have previously performed measurements in phantoms in the Petten HB11 beam [1] with the aim of verifying Monte Carlo calculations of dose distributions in the phantoms [2]. In those measurements we used PIN diodes as neutron dosimeters and MOSFETs as γ dosimeters. As a consequence of these experiments we embarked on a more detailed study of the response characteristics of these detectors in mixed fields and also of the behaviour of some of the phantoms we used in these experiments.

MOSFET and PIN dosimetry

A schematic representation of a MOSFET junction is shown in Fig. 1A. It consists of a silicon substrate upon which is deposited a layer of silicon oxide. An aluminium gate electrode is deposited on top of this oxide layer. Implanted into the silicon are source and drain electrodes. Any ionising radiation incident on the silicon oxide will cause the creation of electron-hole pairs in this layer ($E_g \sim 8$ eV). Positive holes will then be trapped in the oxide and induce an n-type channel thereby enhancing the effective source-drain conductivity. The threshold voltage, V_{th} is defined as that voltage which must be applied to the gate to initiate

Address for correspondence: Martin G. Carolan, Illawarra Cancer Care Centre, P.O. Box 1798, Wollongong, N.S.W. 2500, Australia.

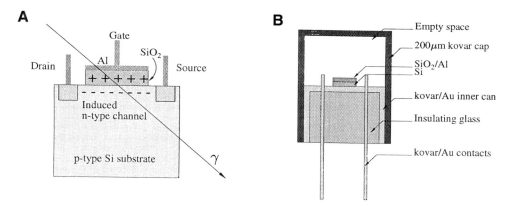

Fig. 1. **A**: A schematic of a MOSFET dosimeter showing generation of electron hole pairs in the SiO_2 layer and subsequent trapping of holes in this layer which draws carriers into the channel beneath the oxide layer. **B**: The geometry used in the MCNP4A model of the MOSFET (not to scale). A detailed model like this was necessary to determine the energy dependence of the MOSFET neutron response. Not shown is the ^{6}LiF shield around the MOSFET.

source-drain conduction. As the number of trapped holes in the oxide increases the V_{th} decreases. Thus the change in V_{th} is proportional to the dose received by the MOSFET. Applying a positive bias to the gate during irradiation will lead to a more efficient trapping of holes and thus to a greater sensitivity of the MOSFET. As the available traps become full the change in V_{th} per unit dose decreases.

The PIN diodes used consist of a layer of intrinsic silicon (~ 1.3 mm^3) with a resistivity of approximately 100 ohm.cm sandwiched between a p-type and a n-type layer of silicon. Neutrons incident on the silicon base section will interact with the silicon nuclei in the lattice and cause them to recoil, introducing defects into the lattice. The mean energy required to displace a lattice site is ~ 25 eV. Such defects introduce new energy levels into the lattice and act as recombination and compensation centres. These centres remove carriers and thereby decrease carrier lifetime with a consequent increase in the forward bias voltage of the diode, V_f. The change in V_f can be measured and is proportional to neutron dose. The production of defects by neutrons has an energy dependence which is described by the Si displacement KERMA function. This function is similar to tissue KERMA [1]. Although silicon and tissue KERMA are in approximately constant proportion for neutron energies above ~ 160 keV, this is not the case for all energies of interest in BNCT. Therefore PIN diode measurements will yield the silicon dose, i.e., more weighted towards the fast part of the spectrum than is the actual tissue dose.

Materials and Methods

The MOSFETs used were produced by INR, Ukraine. The substrate was p-type with a 1-μm thick thermally grown oxide layer. They were packaged in standard

TO-18 cases made of 200-μm thick kovar (29% Ni, 17% Co and 54% Fe). Read-out of V_{th} was done with a 42-μA pulsed current source. Calibration in a ^{60}Co photon field yielded sensitivities of ~ 1.8 mV·cGy^{-1}. A thermal neutron shield consisting of ^{6}LiF/polyester and $\sim 2-3$ mm thick was used to cover each MOS-FET. To determine the neutron response of the MOSFETs with and without this ^{6}LiF cover, MCNP4A simulations were done of a detailed model of the MOS-FETs using the geometry shown in Fig. 1B. The MOSFET was modelled in isotropic neutron fields of different energies using neutron, photon and electron transport and the Si KERMA was calculated at the point corresponding to the position of the SiO$_2$. This was assumed to be proportional to the SiO$_2$ dose. The resulting response functions were normalised to the MOSFET thermal neutron response, as measured in the TC10 thermal channel of the MOATA reactor at Ansto.

Epithermal beam measurements were performed in an 18-cm diameter cylinder phantom filled with tissue-equivalent gel, a 15-cm^3 perspex phantom, and a head and trunk phantom. These were exposed in the Petten JRC HFR HB11 BNCT beam with an aperture of 15 cm. MCNP calculations of the neutron and γ tissue doses, as well as the neutron silicon displacement dose in the cylinder and cube phantoms were performed. The MOSFET neutron response functions determined as described above were convolved with the neutron spectra at each point in these phantoms to determine the neutron component of the experimentally measured MOSFET change in V_{th}.

Gold, copper and manganese foils were exposed in the phantoms with and without cadmium covers to measure the thermal neutron activation and the epithermal resonance activation in order to confirm these parts of the neutron spectrum.

PIN diode dosimeters were also obtained from INR Ukraine and had a sensitivity of ~ 1.3 mV·cGy^{-1} (tissue dose) when measured in a ^{252}Cf spectrum. They were read out using a pulsed 1-mA current source. For the cylindrical gel phantom MCNP calculations were done with different concentrations of hydrogen in the model and with different mass densities of the gel. This allowed us to estimate the effect of dehydration of the gel and the small uncertainty in the measured density of the gel.

Results and Discussion

Figure 2 shows activation foil data in the cylindrical phantom. The Monte Carlo calculated activations assume that the hydrogen concentration of the gel in the phantom is decreased by 10%. Some shrinkage of the gel was observed over the ~ 6-month period between the construction of the phantom and when the measurements were carried out. When this is taken into account, good agreement is observed even for the resonance activations which are more sensitive to the neutron spectrum. This is supported by the consistency between PIN diode data and calculations when the same dehydration effect is taken into account (Fig.

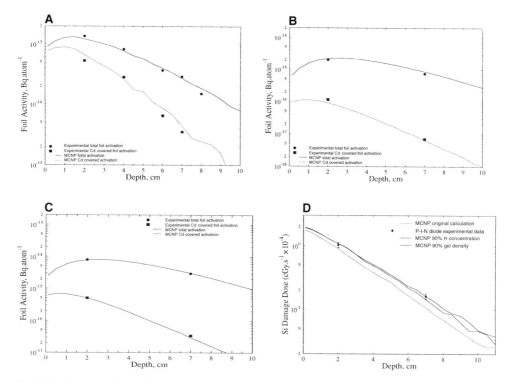

Fig. 2. In these results good agreement is observed between MCNP and experimental thermal and resonance foil activations for: Au (**A**), Cu (**B**) and Mn (**C**) along the central axis of a cylindrical phantom filled with TE gel assuming a H density of 0.9 relative to actual H density in tissue. Thermal activation was relatively insensitive to hydrogen concentration in the gel. This was not so for resonance activation. **D**: Silicon damage dose as measured using PIN diodes on the central axis of a gel filled cylindrical phantom. MCNP calculations show the effect of a 10% decrease in either the H concentration or the gel mass density.

2D). The other curve in Fig. 2D shows that a similar satisfactory agreement can be obtained if the density of the gel is assumed to be 10% less than originally measured. Figure 2D also shows the original calculated silicon damage where no account is taken of dehydration. This gives poor agreement between experiment and calculation at depth in the phantom. It is likely that a combination of these effects compromised our original measurements. Further support is lent to this hypothesis if the PIN measurements in a perspex cube phantom are considered. The density and H concentration in polymethyl methacrylate is well determined and yielded good agreement between MCNP and PIN diode measurements.

Figure 3A shows the neutron response calculated for MOSFET γ dosimeters using MCNP and the geometry shown in Fig. 1B. The response for a MOSFET without a ^{6}LiF cover is shown. Also shown is the response for MOSFETs covered

196

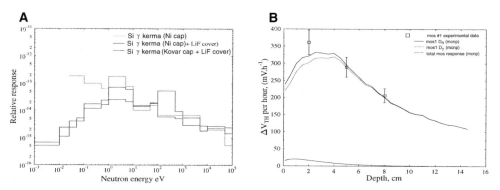

Fig. 3. **A**: Monte Carlo (MCNP4A) calculated energy-dependant neutron response functions for the MOSFETs used in our experiments with and without a ^{6}LiF thermal neutron cover. **B**: A comparison of the MCNP-calculated MOSFET response and the experimental MOSFET response observed along the central axis of a perspex cube phantom exposed in HB11. The calculated γ and neutron contributions are shown separately.

with ^{6}LiF as they were in our measurements. The effect of including the Co and Fe components of kovar in the model is also shown. This neutron response must be taken into account if MOSFETs (with kovar) covers are used in mixed fields with a large thermal and epithermal flux component.

Figure 3B is presented in terms of V_{th} shift in order to show the neutron and γ components and the total MOSFET response for MOSFETs placed along the central axis of the 15-cm perspex cube phantom. The relatively large uncertainties in the MOSFET measured data are primarily due to the thermal coefficient of V_{th}, which was found to be approximately 1.8 mV·K^{-1} at room temperature. This can be corrected for if the temperature is known. To use the MOSFET as a γ dosimeter it will be necessary to minimise any components of MOSFET packaging which lead to increased neutron response.

Conclusions

We have investigated the PIN neutron response and obtained agreement between PIN diode measurements and MCNP calculations of neutron dose in phantoms exposed in the HB11 beam. PIN response is not T.E., but small size and quick read-out indicates their use for patient neutron dose monitoring. We have determined the neutron response of MOSFETs using MCNP, and using this response obtained agreement between measured and calculated MOSFET response to γ and neutron dose in phantoms in epithermal neutron beams.

Acknowledgements

Thanks are due to the workshop team in the Physics Department at the University of Wollongong and the MOATA reactor operators for their assistance, and also to AINSE for grants which supported part of this work. Steven Wallace was responsible for the fabrication of the gel phantoms and was a central part of the team for the measurements done at Petten. We thank Ray Moss, Peter Watkins and their group for all their assistance.

References

1. Carolan M, Wallace S, Allen BJ, Rosenfeld A, Mathur J, Meriaty H, Stecher-Rassmussen F, Moss R, Raaijmakers C, Konijnenberg M. Validation of Monte Carlo dose planning calculations by epithermal beam dose distribution measurements in phantoms: In: Mishima Y (ed) Proceedings of 6th International Symposium on Neutron Capture Therapy. New York: Plenum Press, 1996.
2. Wallace SA, Allen BJ, Mathur JN. Monte Carlo neutron photon transport calculations: Road to modelling from CT scans. In: Mishima Y (ed) Proceedings of 6th International Symposium on Neutron Capture Therapy. New York: Plenum Press, 1996.

Macro- and microdosimetry for boron neutron capture therapy with a MOSFET

A.B. Rosenfeld[1], G.I. Kaplan[1], M.G. Carolan[1,3], B.J. Allen[1,2], C. Kota[4], M. Yudelev[4], R. Maughan[4] and J.A. Coderre[5]

[1]*Department of Physics, University of Wollongong, Wollongong, New South Wales, Australia;* [2]*St. George Hospital Cancer Care Center, Kogarah, New South Wales, Australia;* [3]*Illawarra Cancer Care Center, Wollongong, New South Wales, Australia;* [4]*Wayne State University, Harper Hospital, Detroit, Michigan, USA;* and [5]*Brookhaven National Laboratory, Upton, New York, USA*

Introduction

The radiation sensitivity of metal oxide semiconductor field effect transistor (MOSFET) is based on the build-up of charge in the SiO_2 layer when it is exposed to ionizing radiation. An application of MOSFET integral dosimetry in medicine has been studied in recent years [1—3].

The knowledge of average dose, which is quite good for characterizing the biological effect of radiation in a pure γ field, is inadequate in mixed radiation fields where high linear energy transfer (LET) radiation is present. Thus, for boron neutron capture therapy (BNCT), four dose components are present in the radiation field:

1. Recoil protons from the knock-on reaction of epithermal and fast neutrons on hydrogen nuclei.
2. Protons with energies of about 0.5 MeV from the $^{14}N(n,p)$ reaction.
3. γ Radiation from the reactor and from neutron reactions in the tissue.
4. Most importantly; high LET ions, ^4He and ^7Li from the $^{10}B(n,\alpha)^7Li$ reaction, having ranges in tissue of 7 and 5 μm, respectively.

The biological effects of the radiation field in such mixed fields demands microdosimetry which yields the spectrum of the energy deposited on the cellular level, i.e., LET spectrum.

Traditional microdosimetry is based on the use of gas proportional counters which are relatively large in size but, by variation of the gas pressure inside the detector, can simulate energy deposition by particles in sites with diameters of 2—100 μm [4]. Such systems have been applied for the evaluation of mixed γ-neutron fields in hadron therapy [5]. The use of T.E. gas proportional counters for in-phantom measurements is not always adequate, because, due to their size, they may significantly perturb the radiation field themselves. An approach to

Address for correspondence: Anatoly Rosenfeld, Department of Physics, University of Wollongong, Wollongong, NSW 2522, Australia.

microdosimetry based on actual cell morphology using high resolution quantitative autoradiography and two dimensional Monte Carlo simulation was first proposed for BNCT [6]. However, this method is time consuming and limited to [10]B dose only. Another approach to microdosimetry models a biological cell with a silicon microsize cell. The basis for this simulation is the similar ranges of 1.5 MeV α particles in tissue and in silicon. The quantitative measurement of deposited energy pattern by charge spectroscopy in a p-n junction the size of a typical biological cell is a further step in characterization of a mixed radiation environment. This approach has been applied in practical radiation protection for tha separation of γ and neutron radiation [7].

The aim of this work is to study a simplified Si structure, as a model of a micro-macro dosimeter for possible use in BNCT. Such a dosimeter incorporates integral MOSFET dosimetry and charge collection spectroscopy in practically the same geometric volume. The total integral dose has been measured using threshold voltage shift and the spectrum of deposited charge has been measured using the drain p-n junction as a *dE/dx* detector or E detector for stoppers.

Experiments

Charge spectroscopy with a single MOSFET.

The MOSFET silicon sensor, used in this study, has the effective sensitive area of drain p-n junction of $1.5 \times 10^{-2} mm^2$. The thickness of the depletion layer depends on the bias voltage and can be changed from 0.1 to 3.5 μm. The drain is surrounded by a 60-μm length silicon dioxide gate, which is sensitive to integral absorbed dose. For charge spectroscopy the drain of the MOSFET was connected to a charge sensitive preamplifier while the gate, source and substrate were grounded. Measurements were performed using a Canberra 7401 α spectroscopy system. Either [210]Po or [241]Am sources were placed inside the vacuum chamber with the MOSFET chip located immediately above them.

The pulse height spectrum for the [210]Po α source is shown in Fig. 1. The change of reverse bias voltage from 0.6 to 18 V did not significantly change the pulse height spectrum nor the maximum amplitude of the pulses. There is evidence that the change of depletion layer in the $n^+ - p$ junction from 1 to 3.5 μm is not effective in increasing the amplitude of the collected charge. It is possible to explain this as a contribution of slow diffusion charge collection, since the time constant of the preamplifier was of the order of microseconds.

The energy deposited by 5.3 MeV α particles in the drain $n^+ - p$ junction was 3.5 MeV. This is much higher than the energy expected to be deposited in the depletion layer of ∼ 4 μm. Our estimation showed that for this design of MOSFET the energy loss in the depletion layer should be about 0.6 MeV and an energy deposition of 3.5 MeV would correspond to a sensitive volume about 19 μm thick. For our MOSFET it is reasonable to assume a diffusion length of ∼ 14 μm, which together with the depletion layer provides the necessary thick-

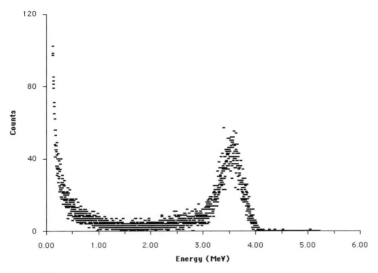

Fig. 1. ^{210}Po α particle pulse height spectrum measured by a MOSFET.

ness of the sensitive layer.

We investigated the effect of low LET radiation on the response of the drain n$^+$-p junction. To do this the MOSFET chip was irradiated with photons emitted by a ^{60}Co source and β particles from ^{90}Sr. It was shown that the small sensitive volume is not sensitive to γ photons and high energy electrons. This is important for separation of low and high LET radiation in hadron radiation oncology. Using MOSFET dosimeters in the single integral mode does not allow such separation.

Integral response of a MOSFET to high LET radiation.

To compare the integral response of a MOSFET (threshold voltage shift due to charge build-up in the SiO$_2$ layer) to high LET radiation with its low LET response, we irradiated a bare MOSFET chip with α particles from a ^{241}Am source (E$_α$ = 5.5 MeV) at a gate bias voltage from 0 to 100 V. The irradiation was carried out in air with the distance between the source and the MOSFET less than 1 mm.

For investigating a possible contribution to the threshold voltage change due to the ^{241}Am 59.9 keV X-ray the MOSFET was irradiated by an open ^{241}Am source and by the source covered by a sheet of paper. Figure 2 clearly shows that most of the contribution to the threshold voltage shift was due to the α particles. For bias voltages above 5 V the X-ray contribution was negligible.

Figure 3 shows the integral response of an MOSFET with a thick oxide layer to an ^{241}Am α particle flux of ~4×10^3 cm^{-2}.s^{-1}. A similar α particle flux is expected in BNCT. The irradiation was carried out with a gate bias of +18 V and showed good linearity up to the total fluence of 10^8 particles/cm^2.

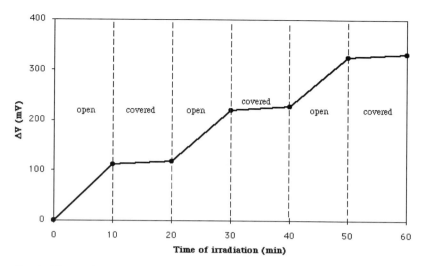

Fig. 2. Change in a MOSFET threshold voltage for open and paper covered [241]Am sources. The MOSFET threshold voltage was stable to ±1 mV during read-out.

Testing at BNCT Facility at BNL

The aim of the experimental research at the Brookhaven Medical Research Reactor (BMRR) was to obtain the main characteristics of the BNCT beam such as boron dose-depth distribution and the secondary particle spectrum in different

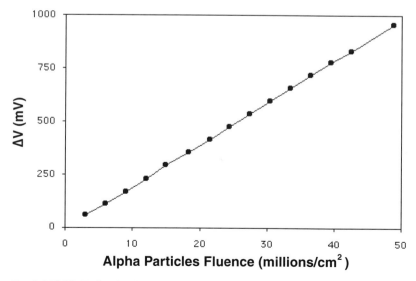

Fig. 3. MOSFET threshold voltage change vs. α dose. The MOSFET threshold range was stable to ±1 mV during read-out.

parts of the phantom using the MOSFET probe. The reactor was operated at 3 MW. The reactor power was maintained constant to within 3%. For our measurements we used a 15 cm perspex cube phantom with holes enabling the insertion of our MOSFET dosimeters at various depths along the central axis of the phantom.

Boric acid containing 95.5% enriched [10]B was mixed with epoxy and cast in the perspex cap which covered the MOSFET. The air gap between the silicon chip and the [10]B converter was < 1 mm. The concentration of [10]B in the cap was approximately 2% by weight. The 5 V bias was applied to the gate from a separate battery to avoid electrical interference between the drain n^+-p junction and the gate circuit. The Canberra 2003 charge sensitive preamplifier was mounted next to the phantom on the reactor wall next to the epithermal beam aperture. A standard spectroscopy setup and MOSFET reader were used.

The main contribution to the high LET part of the pulse height spectra would be from the products of the [10]B(n,α) reaction and recoil protons due to the fast neutron component of the beam. The paired detector method has been used for the evaluation of the radiation field in the perspex phantom. At points on the central axis of the phantom the pulse height spectrum and threshold voltage shift were measured over a range of depths from 0.5 to 9 cm using a MOSFET with a [10]B cover and one without.

All data were normalized to 10 min of irradiation and background spectra were subtracted. For the separation of the effect of [10]B a difference spectrum was calculated (Fig. 4). Figure 4 also shows the contribution to the pulse height spectra from α particles and [7]Li ions. Taking into account that the maximum range of

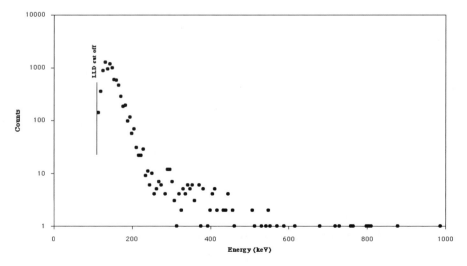

Fig. 4. Difference in spectrum between MOSFET with and without [10]B converter.

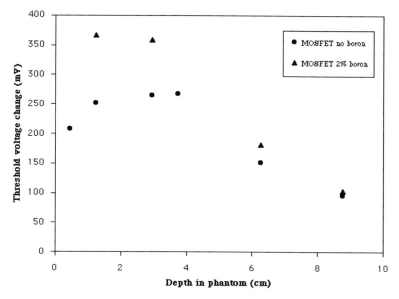

Fig. 5. MOSFET threshold voltage changes measured on the central axis of the perspex cube phantom exposed in the BNCT beam at BNL.

such particles in Si is about 7 μm, all of the ions were stoppers and the calculation of LET spectra for such a sensitive volume is useless. Figure 5 shows the change in threshold voltage of the same MOSFETs measured at the same points along the phantom axis.

Conclusion

For the first time a MOSFET dosimeter was used for simultaneous measurement of boron dose-depth distribution and microdosimetry in epithermal neutron beam. Advantages of the MOSFET macro-micro dosimeter include its small size, ability to be used under full reactor power, and separation of low and high LET dose using paired MOSFET's future work will be concentrated on reducing the geometrical size of silicon cells in MOSFET dosimeters.

Acknowledgements

We would like to thank C. Wu and D. Grinberg from BNL for their help with experiments on the reactor beam. One of the authors (AR) is thankful to his colleagues from KINR (Ukraine) for many years of fruitful collaboration in semiconductor dosimetry.

References

1. Gladstone DJ, Chin LM. Real time in vivo measurement of radiation dose during radio-immunotherapy in mice using a miniature MOSFET dosimeter probe. Radiat Res 1995; 141:330—335.
2. Rosenfeld AB, Carolan MG, Kaplan GI, Allen BJ. MOSFET dosimeters: The role of encapsulation on dosimetric characteristics in mixed gamma neutron and megavoltage X-ray fields. IEEE Trans Nucl Sci 1995;42 N6:1870—1877.
3. Butson M, Rosenfeld AB, Mathur JN, Carolan MG et al. A new radiotherapy surface dose detector: The MOSFET. Med Phys 1996;23(5):655—658.
4. Microdosimetry, ICRU Report 36, Issued 31 December 1983.
5. Wuu CS, Amols HI, Kliauga P, Reinstein LE, Saraf S. Microdosimetry for boron neutron capture therapy. Radiat Res 1992;130:355—359.
6. Solares GR, Zamenhof RG. A novel approach to the microdosimetry of neutron capture therapy. Radiat Res 1995;144:50—58.
7. Schröder O, Schmitz T, Pierschel M. Microdosimetric dosimeters for individual monitoring based on semiconductor detectors. Radiat Protect Dosimet 1994;52:431—434.

The distribution of neutron fluxes of the rat brain tumor model: A basic study

Hiroyuki Fujimori[1], Akira Matsumura[1], Yasushi Shibata[1], Tetsuya Yamamoto[1], Kunio Nakagawa[1], Yoshinori Hayakawa[2], Masahiko Isshiki[3], Yoshihiko Yoshii[1] and Tadao Nose[1]

[1]Department of Neurosurgery, [2]Proton Medical Center, University of Tsukuba, Tsukuba, Ibaraki; and [3]Japan Atomic Energy Research Institute, Tokai, Ibaraki, Japan

Purpose

In order to establish an in vivo rat brain tumor treatment model for the neutron capture therapy, we developed equipment for irradiation of the rats under general anesthesia and measured the distribution of neutron fluxes using normal rats.

Methods

Four F344 rats (350—500g) were used for this study. A burr hole was made on the coronal suture, and a 0.25-mm diameter gold wire was inserted into the brain for a 5 mm depth through the burr hole under general anesthesia. The next day the rats were killed by an overdose of pentobarbital and a 50-mm long gold wire was fixed on the scalp along the axis of the body and the thermal neutron beam (Fig. 1). The holder used for irradiation was made of teflon of 5 mm thickness with a neutron beam side of 2 mm thickness. The holder could hold four rats simultaneously and general anesthesia could be controlled from outside the room [1]. Each rat was provided a mask including ^{6}Li to protect the mouth and the eyes from the thermal neutron beam. The rats in the holder were irradiated using the thermal neutron beam for 84 mins (as 10MW steady state) from a JRR-2 reactor at the Japan Atomic Energy Research Institute. After irradiation,

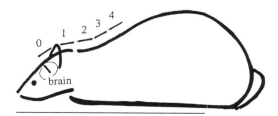

Fig. 1. The position of neutron flux measurement.

the neutron fluence was measured by the activation of the gold wires (0.25mm diameter) using the simultaneous β-γ analyzer (Fiji NSM15202, Aloka TGS 113) at JAERI.

Result

The mean neutron flux at 5 mm depth in the brain is $2.33 \cdot 10^8$ n/cm^2/s, on the scalp it is $4.64 \cdot 10^8$ n/cm^2/s and at 50 mm caudal on the skin is $3.49 \cdot 10^8$ n/cm^2/s. A 50% reduction in the neutron flux was observed at a 5 mm depth in the brain, and 25% reduction by 50 mm distance (Fig. 2). After irradiation, γ-rays from rat bodies had returned to the background level within 7 days (Fig. 3).

Discussion and Conclusion

For radiobiological neutron research, in vivo experiments are indispensable. In this study we developed an equipment for irradiation of the rat brain tumor model under general anesthesia. The experiments using the reactor need a lot of labor and time. Under these circumstances, our holder which can hold four rats simultaneously is more efficient than the holder for one rat [1,2]. After irradiation some animals have radiation injuries which may influence their survival in nontarget areas, especially their eyes and mouths. In previous studies, the animal's head was exposed totally [2,3]. Therefore we shielded the animal's eyeballs and oral mucosa with the ^{6}Li plate to avoid the disadvantage of irradiated animals. Under these conditions we indicated the distribution of neutron fluxes for this model to investigate boron neutron capture therapy experiments. The 50% decline of neutron flux at a 5 mm depth in the brain is thought to be partially

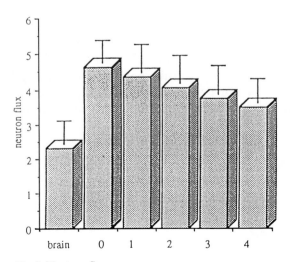

Fig. 2. Neutron flux.

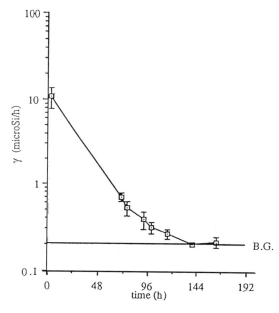

Fig. 3. γ ray from the rats after irradiation.

due to the ^{6}Li face mask since the neutron flux usually does not decrease so rapidly in the brain. Using this equipment, we intend to study the radiological effect of thermal or epithermal neutrons and also to investigate the therapeutic effect of new boron compounds.

References

1. Minobe T, Hatanaka H. Remote control anesthesia for neutron capture therapy for malignant gliomas. In: Hatanaka H (ed) Boron Neutron Capture Therapy for Tumors. Niigata: Nishimura 1986;451—456.
2. Joel DD, Fairchild RG, Laissue JA et al. Boron neutron capture therapy of intracerebral rat gliosarcomas. Proc Natl Acad Sci USA 1990;87:9808—9812.
3. Clendenon NR, Barth RF, Gordon WA et al. Boron neutron capture therapy of rat glioma. Neurosurgery 1990;26:47—55.

Three-dimensional determination of absorbed dose by NMR analysis of a tissue-equivalent phantom-dosimeter

G. Gambarini

Dipartimento di Fisica dell'Università and INFN, Milano, Italy

The three-dimensional determination of absorbed dose in a tissue-equivalent phantom simulating the situation of interest, is of great importance for the planning of treatments in boron neutron capture therapy (BNCT). The described method for the spatial determination of absorbed dose consists in inspecting with a nuclear magnetic resonance (NMR) imaging system, a phantom made with a tissue-equivalent material (typically a gel) in which a proper chemical dosimeter has been incorporated. The gel dosimeter we have experimented is mainly composed of a ferrous sulphate solution, which is the essential component of the Fricke dosimeter, incorporated Agarose SeaPlaque gel. Ionising radiation results in a conversion of ferrous ions into ferric ions, and a linear relation between Fe^{3+} yield and absorbed dose, in a certain dose interval, has been found. Fe^{2+} and Fe^{3+} ions are both paramagnetic, but they reduce (in different amounts) the spin relaxation times of hydrogen nuclei in aqueous solutions. In a proper dose interval, longitudinal and transversal relaxation rates, measurable by NMR analysis, result to be linearly correlated to the absorbed dose. Therefore, it is possible to make phantom dosimeters, i.e., phantoms in which the absorbed dose can be measured by NMR imaging after irradiation.

Irradiation and analysis facilities

The γ-irradiations were performed at a rate of about 0.14 Gy s^{-1} in a ^{137}Cs biological irradiator. The exposures to thermal neutrons were performed in the thermal column of Triga Mark II nuclear reactor (Pavia-Italy), at fluxes up to 10^{10} neutrons cm^{-2} s^{-1}.

The NMR measurements have been performed in a medical magnetic resonance imaging system (Somatom Siemens), which is a superconducting whole-body imager, operating at 1.5 T and 63 MHz. The transverse relaxation rates $1/T_2$ were determined, which in such a low magnetic field give higher sensitivity than the longitudinal relaxation rates $1/T_1$. A multiecho sequence with 16 echoes was employed. The T_2 values were calculated utilising a one-exponential fit with a nonlinear, least squares and three-parameter algorithm. For a good reproduc-

---

Address for correspondence: G. Gambarini, Dipartimento di Fisica dell'Università, via Celoria 16, I-20133 Milano, Italy.

ibility, the response (R) is defined as the difference between the relaxation rate measured in the irradiated sample and that measured simultaneously in a non-irradiated sample from the same gel preparation:

$$R = (1/T)_{irr} - (1/T)_{blank}$$

Ferrous sulphate gel composition

Initially, the gel composition was optimised and the protocol for gel preparation and analysis was settled, in order to achieve good sensitivity and good result reproducibility [1]. After having assembled a proper setup for gel preparation, which allows one to obtain dosimeters made up in the same conditions, in particular in regard to gel oxygenation and steam loss restrain, the gel composition giving the higher sensitivity was investigated.

The highest γ-sensitivity has been obtained with a dosimeter having the following composition: ferrous sulphate solution (1 mM $Fe(NH_4) \cdot 6H_2O$ — 50 mM H_2SO_4) in the amount of 50% of the final weight, Agarose SeaPlaque ($C_{12}H_{14}O_5(OH)_4$) in the amount of 1% of the final weight and highly purified water in the amount of 49% of the final weight. The obtained dose-response curve, linear up to about 40 Gy, has a slope equal to 0.2 s^{-1} Gy^{-1} and the ferric ion yield (G—value) results: G = 183 (Fe^{3+} ions per 100 eV absorbed energy). This dosimeter presents good tissue equivalence for γ-rays.

A proper gel composition has been studied for utilising the dosimeter in BNCT, in order to achieve a good tissue equivalence also for thermal neutrons [2]. In fact, in thermal neutron fields the absorbed energy derives from the nuclear reaction products, and consequently tissue equivalence is achieved only if the isotopic composition of the tissue-substitute is the same as that of the tissue to be simulated, at least for the elements which give the main contributions to the absorbed dose, that is H and N due to the reactions:

$$^{14}N(n,p)^{14}C \quad \text{and} \quad ^1H(n,\gamma)^2H$$

In small volumes the dominant contribution to the absorbed dose is due to protons (approximately 590 keV) emitted in the reaction with N. So, the percentage of N is of fundamental importance. C and O, the other main constituents of tissue, do not significantly contribute to the absorbed dose and only the total percentage (C+O) needs consideration. In this work, the composition of the gel-dosimeter was conveniently established to achieve good equivalence with brain tissue, because brain is the actual target of BNCT. The composition of the gel is the following: ferrous sulphate solution (1 mM $Fe(NH_4) \cdot 6H_2O$ and 50 mM H_2SO_4) in the amount of 50% of the final weight, Agarose SeaPlaque ($C_{12}H_{14}O_5(OH)_4$) in the amount of 1% of the final weight, area (CH_4N_2O) in the amount of 4% of the final weight and highly purified water (H_2O) in the amount of 45% of the final weight.

The elemental mass fractions of H, N, (C+O) for brain [3] and for this gel are reported in Table 1. The tissue equivalence of the gel for both γ rays and thermal neutrons is good. After exposure in the ^{137}Cs irradiator, the gel shows a slope of the dose-response curve equal to 0.065 s^{-1} Gy^{-1}; the resulting oxidation yield is $G = 60$ (Fe^{3+} ions per 100 eV absorbed energy). This value is lower than that of the gel optimised for γ rays, although higher than that of the Fricke dosimeter. The linearity is good up to 50 Gy. Samples made with the same gel, but augmented with 40 μg/g of ^{10}B, which is the quantity typically accumulated in tumours, were prepared and examined. Both dosimeters show the same γ sensitivity.

Results

Dosimeters with and without ^{10}B were exposed in the thermal column of the reactor, in the same position and to the same fluence. A fluence interval up to about 3×10^{13} neutrons cm^{-2} has been inspected. From differential measurements with borated and regular gels [4], the sensitivity to thermal neutrons, i.e., to secondary ionising radiation produced by thermal neutrons, has been found to be lower than that to ^{137}Cs γ rays. In borated gel, by evaluating the absorbed dose due to ^{10}B, the dosimeter sensitivity to ^{10}B secondary particles (α and ^{7}Li) has been found to be equal to 0.028 s^{-1}Gy^{-1}, corresponding to a G value equal to 26 (oxidised ions per 100 eV absorbed energy). This fact is a consequence of the dependence of the ferric ion yield on the linear energy transfer (LET) of the radiation. This question has received attention in Fricke dosimetry, and it requires a proper study in Fricke-gel dosimetry.

Finally, isodose curves were determined in phantoms consisting of the borated gel made up in the form of cylinders (8 cm diameter, 15 cm height) enclosed in thin Teflon containers. Teflon was also chosen for sample holders, in order to reduce the contribution to the dosimeter response coming from activation of the container and holder materials. Phantoms were exposed in the thermal column of the reactor with a thermal neutron fluence at the entrance of the phantom of about 10^{13} neutrons cm^{-2}. Then, the NMR imaging of the phantom was performed. In Fig. 1 a contour plot of transverse relaxation rates measured in the phantom is shown. Isodose curves have irregular shapes because of the low sensitivity of the dosimeter to thermal neutrons. From the fluence data at the central line of the reactor channel, however, good accord was found between the relaxation rate values in the phantom and the dosimeter response to thermal neutrons determined from a calibration of the same borated Fricke-gel contained in small vials.

Table 1. Elemental composition of brain tissue and the gel dosimeter.

	Percentage by mass			
	H	N	C + O	Others
Brain	10.7	2.2	85.7	1.4
Gel	10.9	2.2	86.8	0.1

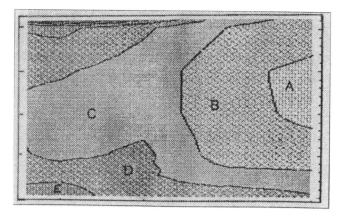

Fig. 1. Contour plot of the image of a cylindrical borated gel phantom exposed in the thermal column of the reactor. The dose values in the different regions, evaluated utilising gel calibration, are: **A:** 26–28 Gy, **B:** 24–26 Gy, **C:** 22–24 Gy, **D:** 20–22 Gy, **E:** 18–20 Gy.

Remarks

The promising results obtained with the described dosimeter for three-dimensional determination of absorbed dose in γ-irradiated phantoms, for the spatial determination of absorbed dose from thermal neutrons and for depth-dose profiling in a phantom exposed to a proton beam [5,6], encourage us to continue the research with the aim of increasing the sensitivity to thermal neutrons and of removing difficulties (such as ion diffusion), eventually by studying a new chemical dosimeter with suitable characteristics.

Acknowledgements

This work was partially supported by the Istituto Nazionale di Fisica Nucleare, Italy.

References

1. Gambarini G, Arrigoni S et al. Phys Med Biol 1994;39:703–717.
2. Gambarini G, Arrigoni S et al. Nucl Instr Meth 1994;A353:706–710.
3. ICRU Report 44, Bethesda, MD: ICRU Publications 1989.
4. Gambarini G, Birattari C et al. Radiat Protect Dosimet 1997;70:571–575.
5. Gambarini G, Monti D et al. Second International Symposium on Hadrontherapy, Switzerland 9–13 September, 1996.
6. Gambarini G, Monti D, Fumagalli ML, Birattari C, Salvadori P. Phantom-dosimeters examined by NMR analysis: a promising technique for 3-D determination of absorbed dose. Presented at the 3rd Topical Meeting on Industrial Radiation and Radioisotope Measurements and Applications (IRRMA'96). Raleigh (North Carolina) 6–9 October, 1996; Appl Radiat Isot (In press).

Advances in Neutron Capture Therapy.
Volume I, Medicine and Physics.
B. Larsson, J. Crawford and R. Weinreich, editors.

Thermoluminescent dosimeters in high fluxes of thermal neutrons

G. Gambarini[1], M. Sinha Roy[1,4], A. Scacco[2] and A.E. Sichirollo[3]

[1]*Dipartimento di Fisica dell'Università and I.N.F.N, Milan;* [2]*Dipartimento di Fisica dell'Università "La Sapienza", Rome;* [3]*Istituto Nazionale per lo Studio e la Cura dei Tumori, Milan; and* [4]*ICTP fellow, Trieste, Italy*

Thermoluminescent dosimeters (TLDs), widely experimented and utilized in personal dosimetry, have convenient characteristics which also encourage their employment in radiotherapy. In fact, for their small dimensions and tissue equivalence for most radiation fields, they allow mapping absorbed dose, without notably perturbing the radiation field.

In high fluxes of thermal neutrons, as those required for BNCT, some TLDs have shown a loss of reliability. Dosimeters having a high sensitivity to thermal neutrons have been shown to undergo irreversible radiation damage which affects their response [1,2]. Here we present some results obtained from the analysis of the TL emission, both for commercial and laboratory made phosphors exposed to high fluences of thermal neutrons.

Commercial LiF dosimeters

The commercial dosimeters we investigated were:
1. LiF:Mg,Ti (chips $3.1 \times 3.1 \times 0.9$ mm^3) from the Harshaw Chem. Co:
   TLD-600 (with 96.5% ^{6}LiF) and TLD-700 (with 99.99% ^{7}LiF)
2. LiF:Mg,Cu,P (circular chips 4.5 mm diameter, 0.8 mm thick) from the Beijing Radiation Detector Work, People's Republic of China:
   GR-206A (^{6}LiF:Mg,Cu,P) and GR-207A (^{7}LiF:Mg,Cu,P).

For all dosimeters the recommended annealing procedures were utilized:

LiF:Mg,Ti	400°C for 1 h, 100°C for 2 h
LiF:Mg,Cu,P	240°C for 10 min

followed by rapid cooling down to room temperature.

Owing to the high cross-section of ^{6}Li for the reaction with thermal neutrons, ^{6}Li(n,α)^{3}He, LiF dosimeters of different Li isotopic composition, exposed in thermal neutron fields, present different sensitivity and different shapes of glow curves. Therefore, ^{6}LiF-^{7}LiF pairs are advantageously utilized in personal dosim-

Address for correspondence: G. Gambarini, Dipartimento di Fisica dell'Università, via Celoria 16, I-20133, Milano, Italy.

etry for discriminating between the contributions of thermal neutrons and γ rays to the absorbed dose. The situation is very different in radiotherapy, where ^{6}LiF shows radiation damage effects.

TLD-600 and TLD-700 chips (response uniformity within 5%) exposed to various fluences of thermal neutrons, were analyzed with a Harshaw 2000 reader. The glow-curves were deconvoluted into Gaussian peaks (Fig. 1). In Fig. 2, TLD-600 peak areas vs. n_{th} fluence are shown. Peak 2 is not reliable, peaks 5, 6 and 7 are reliable. Peak areas are appreciably nonlinear from about 7×10^{11} neutrons cm^{-2}.

GR-206A and GR-207A dosimeters were exposed in thermal neutron fluxes (with various fluences up to about 10^{12} neutrons cm^{-2}) and then analyzed with a Harshaw-3500 reader. No interval of linearity was found for areas vs. thermal neutron fluence.

After their first exposure to thermal neutrons, all TLDs were annealed and irradiated with the same dose of γ rays (4 Gy); then they were annealed and exposed to the same thermal neutron fluence. The response, as shown in Fig. 3 for TLD-600, is clearly reduced by exposure to high fluences of thermal neutrons, and the effect is larger the higher the previous thermal neutron fluence has been. In GR-206A dosimeters, radiation damage not removed by annealing was shown to be higher than that of TLD-600. By relating the responses with those of dosimeters never exposed to thermal neutrons before, the reduction factor was determined as a function of thermal neutron fluence in the previous exposures. The results are shown in Fig. 4. TLD-700 and GR-207A do not show such an effect in the examined fluence interval. In their response, however, the contributions from n_{th} and γ rays have to be distinguished.

In conclusion, after thermal neutron exposures at a therapeutic level, TLDs with high sensitivity to thermal neutrons are irreversibly damaged; they can only be utilized once, and this fact makes a reliable dosimeter calibration difficult. TLDs with low sensitivity to thermal neutrons are not damaged, but they require discrimination between contributions from thermal neutrons and γ rays.

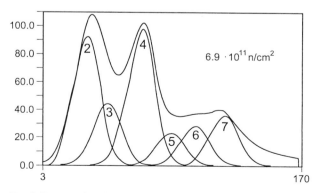

Fig. 1. Deconvoluted glow curve from a TLD-600 exposed to thermal neutrons.

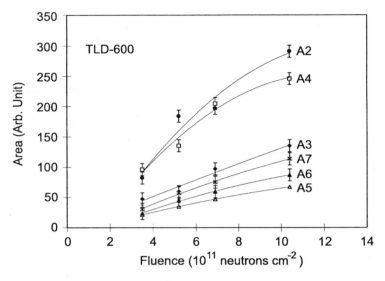

Fig. 2. Peak areas in deconvoluted glow curves from TLDs-600.

The determination of thermal neutron and γ-ray contributions in mixed (n_{th}, γ) fields with a high n_{th} component is worthy of further study.

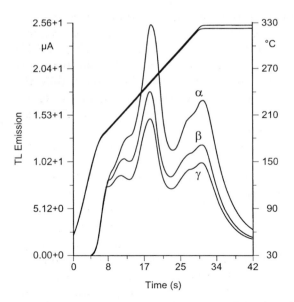

Fig. 3. Glow curves from TLDs-600 exposed to the same thermal neutron fluence. Before annealing the dosimeters were: (α) never exposed to neutrons, (β) exposed to $6 \cdot 10^{11}$ neutrons cm^{-2} and (γ) exposed to $1.2 \cdot 10^{12}$ neutrons cm^{-2}.

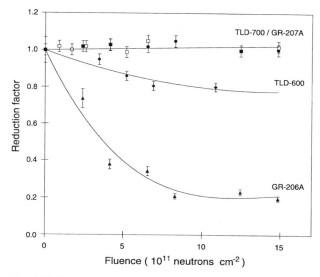

Fig. 4. TLDs-600 response to 1 Gy γ irradiation vs. thermal neutron fluence before annealing. The values are normalized to the response of dosimeters never exposed to thermal neutrons.

TL single crystals

With the aim of searching for phosphors which allow reliable dose determination in therapeutic radiation fields, and for which radiation damage does not hinder successive utilization, we have grown (using the Czochralski technique) single crystals, because of their peculiarity in allowing high annealing temperatures.

The investigated single crystals considered here are: lithium fluoride (LiF: Mg,Cu,P) and Fluoroperovskite ($KMgF_3$) doped with Tl, Eu or Ag. For all crystals the chosen annealing procedure was heating at 500°C for 30 min, followed by rapid cooling down to room temperature.

In LiF:Mg,Cu,P crystals the glow curves show many peaks differently populated by γ rays and by thermal neutrons, as shown in Fig. 5.

For $KMgF_3$ crystals, the emission features have been investigated. Tl and Ag doped crystals have shown their main emission in the spectral range 240–260 nm, that is outside the wavelength range (350–700 nm) of the commonly used commercial readers. $KMgF_3$:Eu samples show a high peak centered at 360 nm, so a large part of the emission is detected by commercial readers. The sensitivity of this phosphor is high, in fact, $KMgF_3$:Eu crystals, analyzed with Harshaw instruments, have shown a γ-ray response which is 3 times higher than that of TLD-700 chips. The response to thermal neutrons is 6 times higher than that of a TLD-700 (that is about 7 times lower than that of a TLD-600).

$KMgF_3$:Eu characteristics are promising and this material deserves further investigations regarding its reliability in high fluences of thermal neutrons.

216

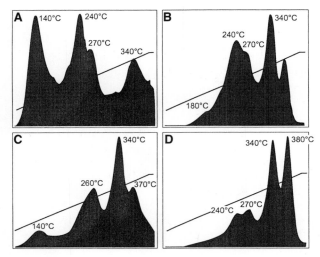

Fig. 5. Glow curves from LiF:Mg,Cu,P crystals after exposure to γ rays (at a: 5 Gy and b: 10^3 Gy) or to thermal neutrons (with fluence c: 10^{12} cm^{-2} and d: $2 \cdot 10^{13}$ cm^{-2}).

Acknowledgements

One of the authors (M. Sinha Roy) undertook this work with the kind support of the ICTP Program for Training and Research in Italian Laboratories, Trieste, Italy. This work was partially supported by Istituto Nazionale di Fisica Nucleare (Italy).

References

1. Gambarini G, Martini M et al. Radiat Prot Dosim 1997;70:175—180.
2. Gambarini G, Sinha Roy M et al. Dependence of TLD thermoluminescence yield on absorbed dose in a thermal neutron field. Presented at the 3rd Topical Meeting on Industrial Radiation and Radioisotope Measurements and Applications (IRRMA'96). Raleigh (North Carolina) October 6—9, 1996; Appl Radiat Isot (In press).

Dosimetric characteristics of an accelerator-based beam for boron cancer therapy — experimental results

S. Green[1], C. Kota[2], N. James[4], R. Maughan[2], D.A. Tattam[3], A.H. Beddoe[1], T.D. Beynon[3] and D.R. Weaver[3]

[1]Department of Medical Physics and Clinical Engineering, Queen Elizabeth Hospital, University Hospital Birmingham NHS Trust, Edgbaston, Birmingham, UK; [2]Gershenson Radiation Oncology Center, Harper Hospital and Wayne State University, Detroit, Michigan, USA; [3]School of Physics and Space Research, The University of Birmingham, Edgbaston, Birmingham, UK; and [4]CRC Institute for Cancer Studies, The University of Birmingham, Edgbaston, Birmingham, UK

Introduction

Initial design studies for an accelerator-based neutron source for BCT applications have been followed by experimental validation based on the system shown in Fig. 1. This is basically the Li target and moderator system described by Tattam et al. [1]. The experimental programme comprised the following elements:

1. Construction of a rectangular perspex-enclosed water phantom. Following the computational work of Gupta et al. [2] we have chosen a phantom of dimensions $17 \times 14 \times 15$ cm^3, which is the intermediate of the three phantoms which they investigated.
2. Measurements at four positions along the central axis of this phantom of:
   - fast neutron dose from a tissue-equivalent (TE) microdosimetric detector.
   - photon dose from a TE microdosimetric detector.
   - boron dose from a microdosimetric detector with TE wall loaded to 50 $\mu g \cdot g^{-1}$ with ^{10}B.
   - boron dose from gold foil activation.
3. Comparison of absolute experimental results (in terms of dose rate/mA of proton beam) with an absolute MCNP simulation of the exact experimental configuration.
4. Assessment of the clinical utility of this beam using the CBE factors derived for BPA and the fast neutron RBE from the Brookhaven group [3]. These are:
   - CBE, tumour + BPA   3.8
   - CBE normal brain + BPA   1.3
   - RBE, photons   1.0
   - RBE, neutrons   3.2

Address for correspondence: Stuart Green, Department of Medical Physics and Clinical Engineering, Queen Elizabeth Hospital, University Hospital Birmingham NHS Trust, Edgbaston, Birmingham, B15 2TH, UK.

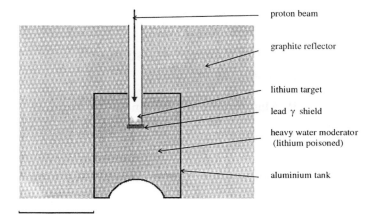

Fig. 1. The experimental beam moderation system.

— Tumour ^{10}B concentration   30 µg·g^{-1}
— Normal brain ^{10}B concentration   10 µg·g^{-1}

Results

The comparisons between experimental and MCNP simulation results are represented in Table 1 as ratios between the experimental and simulation results at each depth. Hence good agreement between experiment and calculation would result in a value of 1.0. It is clear from Table 1 that while the validation is successful for fast neutron, photon, and boron dose derived from gold foils, problems remain with the understanding of the boron dose derived from the microdosimetric detector. At this stage, dosimetric characterisation of our system continues on the basis of the successfully validated results, i.e., the microdosimetric measurements for photon and fast neutron dose, and the gold foil activation for boron dose.

Dosimetric data

In order to derive estimates of the likely biologically equivalent dose which will be delivered by the Birmingham beam, and to further understand its clinical utility,

Table 1. Ratio of experiment to MCNP simulation at different depths in a light water phantom.

Depth (cm)	Photon	Neutron	^{10}B (microdosimeter)	^{10}B (Au foils)
2.5	0.99 ± 0.07	0.97 ± 0.07	0.61 ± 0.04	0.98 ± 0.06
5.0	0.96 ± 0.10	1.00 ± 0.07	0.61 ± 0.05	0.99 ± 0.06
7.5	0.99 ± 0.10	0.94 ± 0.08	0.67 ± 0.05	0.91 ± 0.05
12.7	1.18 ± 0.13	0.83 ± 0.07	0.70 ± 0.06	1.23 ± 0.07

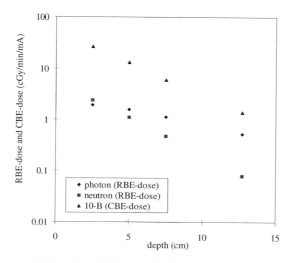

Fig. 2. Variation of RBE and CBE dose (for tumour) with depth in a light water phantom.

the factors listed above for concentration, CBE and RBE have been combined with the physical dose measurements to give the variation in tumour dose with depth shown in Fig. 2. In this plot the y-axis is in terms of a Gy-equivalent dose using CBE factors for tumour with BPA and RBE factors for fast neutron and photon dose. The data in Fig. 2, and the analogous data for normal brain assuming a ^{10}B concentration of 10 $\mu g \cdot g^{-1}$, can be used to derive the following relative doses at 5 cm depth.

Hence, from Table 2, the total dose to normal brain (in Gy-Eq) at 5 cm depth is only approximately 26% of the total dose to tumour at this depth, whereas the corresponding figure in terms of physical dose is 57%.

Microdosimetric distributions

The photon and fast neutron doses used in the analysis above were derived from the microdosimetric measurements shown in Fig. 3 (only the neutron dose region is plotted). In addition to facilitating the separate identification of photon and

Table 2. Relative doses at 5 cm deep in a water phantom exposed to an epithermal neutron beam.

Component	Physical dose		(RBE or CBE) × dose	
	Tumour	Normal brain	Tumour	Normal brain
^{10}B	64.5	21.5	83.2	9.5
Neutron	6.5	6.5	7.0	7.0
Photon	29.0	29.0	9.8	9.8
Total	100.0	57.0	100.0	26.3

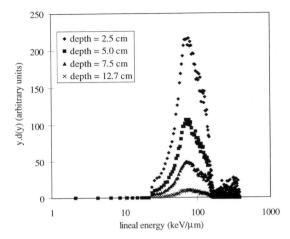

Fig. 3. Measurements with a tissue-equivalent microdosimeter at four depths in a light water phantom.

neutron dose components from a single measurement, this technique also gives information on the LET distribution of the individual ionisation events which make up the dose. The presentation of the data in Figs. 3 and 4 is such that physical dose is proportional to the area under the curve.

Figure 3 shows the partial microdosimetric measurements from the TE detector, derived from a single amplifier gain setting. These therefore include all of the neutron-induced events, but little of the photon component which extends down to approximately 0.1 keV/μm in lineal energy. These distributions show a change in magnitude with depth (reflecting reduced dose with depth), but there

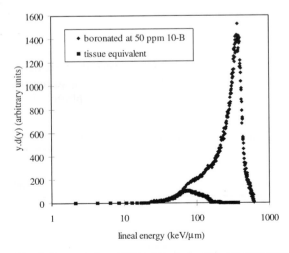

Fig. 4. Boronated and TE microdosimetric measurements at 5 cm depth in a light water phantom.

is little change in shape with depth. This suggests that the neutron RBE of our beam will remain approximately constant with depth.

The ^{10}B dose can be derived from measurements made with a boron-loaded microdosimetric detector and the comparison of the boronated and non-boronated detector response at 5 cm depth is shown in Fig. 4. While some problems remain with the computational validation of the results from the boronated detector, the comparison in Fig. 4 shows the clear dose enhancement due to the presence of ^{10}B (50 µg·g^{-1} in this case) and indicates the increased LET of the ionisation events resulting from neutron capture by ^{10}B.

Acknowledgements

The assistance of the members of the Brookhaven Group, particularly Jeff Coderre and Jacek Capala. Their openness in discussing their work is gratefully acknowledged. The assistance of the many members of the Birmingham group not named in this paper is also gratefully acknowledged, as is the financial help from the Radiological Research Trust for providing travel funds for SG.

References

1. Tattam DA, Allen DA, Beynon TD, Constantine G, Green S, Scott MC, Weaver DR. Preliminary neutron fluence measurements in the Birmingham BCT beam. In: Scientific Meeting and Biennial General Meeting, Univ. Birmingham, 1–3 April 1996. Programme Committee: Prof T.D. Beynon.
2. Gupta N, Niemkiewicz J, Blue TE, Gahbauer R, Qu TX. Effect of head phantom size on ^{10}B and ^{1}H(n,γ)^{2}H dose distributions for a broad field accelerator epithermal neutron source for BNCT. Med Phys 1993;20(2):395–404.
3. Coderre J. Private communication.

1997 Elsevier Science B.V.
Advances in Neutron Capture Therapy.
Volume I, Medicine and Physics.
B. Larsson, J. Crawford and R. Weinreich, editors.

Progress towards development of real-time dosimetry for BNCT

M. Bliss[1], R.A. Craig[1], D.S. Sunberg[1], Y.C. Harker[2], J.R. Hartwell[2] and J.R. Venhuizen[2]

[1] Pacific Northwest National Laboratory, Richland, Washington; and [2] Idaho National Engineering Laboratory, Idaho Falls, Idaho, USA

Introduction

Epithermal/thermal boron neutron capture therapy (BNCT) is a treatment method for malignant tumors. Because the doses and dose rates for medical therapeutic radiation are very close to the normal tissue tolerance, small errors in radiation delivery can result in ineffective treatment or overdose [1—3]. A substantial need exists for a device that will monitor, in real-time, the radiation dose delivered to a patient. Pacific Northwest National Laboratory (PNNL) has developed a scintillating glass optical fiber that is sensitive to thermal neutrons [4,5]. The small size of the fibers (150 μm diameter) offers the possibility of body surface or in vivo flux monitoring at multiple points within the radiation field. The count rate of such detectors can be as high as 10 MHz because the lifetime of the cerium activator is short (60 ns).

Previous reports [6,7] describe the current practice in measurement of neutron dose during BNCT and the need for real-time measurements of dose rate. Dose rates in BNCT are particularly difficult to calculate [8]. The therapeutic reaction is a $^{10}B(n,\alpha)^7Li$ reaction; the principal side reactions are $^{14}N(n,p)^{14}C$ and neutron capture by ^1H and, to a lesser extent, ^{23}Na. The cross-sections for the therapeutic reaction and reactions with natural nuclei in the patient are functions of the neutron energy and vary by several orders of magnitude for an epithermal beam mix. Predictive dose calculations must deal with incident beams that contain a spectrum of neutron energies [9]. Because of the variation of cross-section with neutron energy, the distribution of energies within the beam must be known to calculate the reaction rates accurately. Also, these reactions generate γ rays which contribute to the total radiation dose [8].

Figure 1 shows the essential features of the proposed real-time BNCT radiation sensor. The sensor consists of a short section of scintillating lightguide spliced to a passive lightguide. The passive lightguide carries the optical signal to a remote photon counter. The signal from the photon counter goes to a discriminator, which separates pulses which are greater than a predetermined threshold in amplitude from those that are smaller. Because neutron events produce approximately one order of magnitude more photoelectrons than γ-ray interactions do within the single scintillating lightguide (Fig. 2), the threshold is chosen such

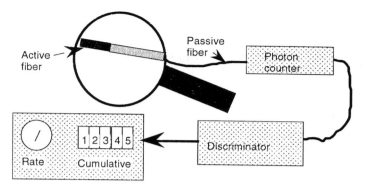

Fig. 1. Schematic showing the essential features of the real-time neutron dosimeter for use in BNCT relying on neutron-sensitive scintillating glass lightguides for the active element.

that the division represents a separation of neutron events from events arising from other ionizing radiation. These pulses then pass to a counting system which records pulse rates and total cumulative pulses for neutron and other interactions. The active and passive lightguides are suitably jacketed in a sterile, opaque, sheathing. The detector package, only a few hundred micrometers in diameter, can be inserted at the treatment site or other sites at which dose rate information is desired. Multiple sensors can be easily accommodated.

It is important to recognize that this sensor concept amounts to much more than simply placing a neutron scintillator on the end of a lightguide. The scintillator must be constructed as a lightguide in order to collect enough light to allow unequivocal separation of "neutron" and "other radiation" signals. The numerical apertures of the sensor and communications lightguides must be matched to reduce light loss at the interface.

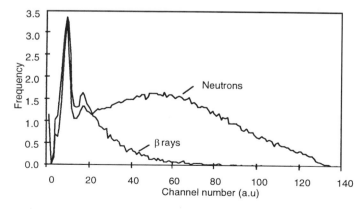

Fig. 2. Pulse-height spectra for a single fiber exposed to neutrons and β rays (representing γ-ray response) at low count rates.

Nuclear and optical considerations

When this detector concept was first proposed, there were a number of unresolved issues related to the application of this technology to the BNCT area. Because the fibers had been developed for large-area, low-flux situations, their use in the extremely high-flux environment presented by BNCT was problematic. Issues that required further study included the possibility of saturation and linearity, potential interference by γ-ray interactions, and the survival of the detector in the high-flux environment. The experiments reported here were designed to investigate the performance of fiber-based detectors in the BNCT setting and, in particular, to address these issues.

Experimental setup

The test detectors consisted of a segment of scintillating fiber-bonded or mechanically connected to the end of a passive fiber. The passive fiber is attached to a PMT, an electronics package, and a counting system. The smallest detector tested consisted of a fiber sensor 120 μm in diameter and 1 cm in length. Two types of sensor package were tested: in the first (design A), the active fiber was mounted in a commercial fiber optic connector; in the second (design B), the active fiber was attached to the end of the passive fiber within a glass capillary and glued into place (Fig. 3). The latter arrangement results in a sensor 0.5 mm in diameter. In each case, the sensor has to be enclosed within an opaque sheath.

The detector uses analog electronics. A commercial fiber optic fitting on the end of a photomultiplier tube (PMT) holds the passive fiber in place. The PMT

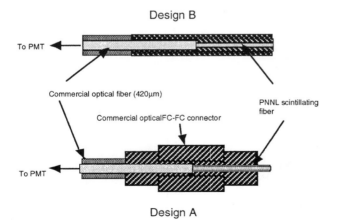

Fig. 3. The two detector designs tested. The lower design (**A**) has a short section of fiber mounted in a commercial fiber optic fitting which is then connected to an inactive high-numerical aperture commercial fiber. The upper design (**B**) has the fiber glued to the end of an inactive commercial fiber with silicone or UV-curing glue and protected with a silica capillary.

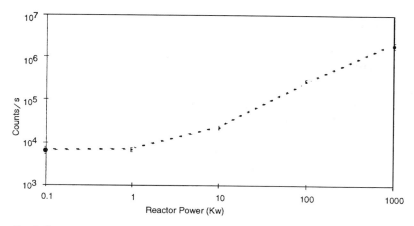

Fig. 4. Count rate vs. reactor power for design A-type detector.

is operated at a negative high voltage of 1000 V; the photoelectron signal is picked off the last dynode with a high-speed electronics circuit. A single photo-electron produces a shaped pulse of approximately 7 ns. The output of the pre-amplifier is run into a 60 ns integrator. The integrated signal is run into a dis-criminating and pulse-counting circuit. For most of the prototype tests, the discriminator was set at 1.25 photoelectrons to minimize the effect of PMT dark count and γ-ray sensitivity. (It was later recognized that the threshold needed to be set higher for the intense γ-ray fields found in the reactor environ-ment.)

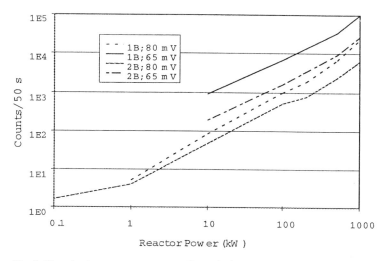

Fig. 5. Count rate vs. reactor power of two design B-type detectors for threshold settings of 65 and 80 mV. These are the same detectors that were used to study the effect of threshold setting in a γ-ray field.

The detector was inserted into a dry tube directly below the core of the Washington State University (WSU) TRIGA reactor, and the count rate compared to reactor power, which is proportional to neutron flux. The sensors were exposed to thermal neutron fluxes of up to 10^{10} neutrons/cm^2/s (as measured by gold-foil activation at a reactor power of 1000 kW) and the count rate recorded as a function of reactor power. The count rates were also measured for several pulse-height threshold settings.

Gamma ray sensitivity of the "neutron" count rate was measured using a ^{60}Co source in one of two dry tubes at the WSU irradiation facility. In one such tube the field could be varied up to 950 R/min without physically moving the sample; in the second, larger γ-ray fields were achievable but the sample had to be moved. In the first, the count rate was measured as a function of γ-ray field strength; in the second, the count rate was measured as a function of the pulse-height threshold setting. It was found that inconsistent results were obtained for successive measurements after the detector was moved; these data are not shown here.

Experimental results

Several detectors of each type were tested; in one case, a single detector was tested in the γ-ray field and then in the reactor tube. The detector response was found to be approximately linear with the reactor power over at least three decades for both detector designs (Figs. 4 and 5). The detector in the commercial fiber optic fitting (design A) at low threshold settings saturated at low reactor powers; this was attributed to the large γ ray to neutron flux ratio at low reactor power due to the residual fission product decay γ rays.

Design A detector response was found to be linear with the pure γ-ray flux (Fig. 6). A ^{60}Co field of ca. 950 R/min, is approximately equal to the γ-ray flux at maximum reactor power. The apparent neutron count rate in this flux is only

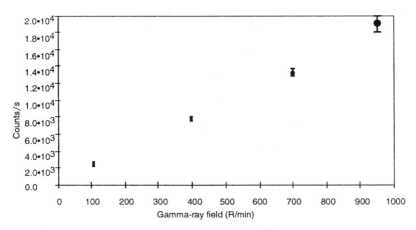

Fig. 6. Count rate vs. γ-ray field strength exposed to ^{60}Co field for design A-type detector.

2.5% of the neutron count rate observed from another design A detector in the reactor experiments at 1 MW of power. The variation of count rate for two design B detectors in a ~1100 R/min field is shown in Fig. 7; it is seen that the count rate varies over nearly three orders of magnitude for a 2.5-fold increase in threshold setting.

Conclusions

Preliminary experiments have been performed. Fluxes typical of those in BNCT (i.e., 10^{10} n/cm^2/s) have been measured with a single fiber. This prototype testing of a neutron-flux monitor indicates that dosimetry based on the tested detector concept, in support of the traditional calculations, is practical. The detector provides immediate neutron-flux information, and by implication, dose information. The data also indicate that γ-ray dose information may also be derived from the detector output.

The sensor showed no signs of saturation, even at the highest fluxes. The response of the sensor was linear with reactor power at the higher ($\geqslant 10$ kW) reactor powers. This indicates that the prototype can provide a proper measure of the flux and, by inference, the dose related to neutron reactions.

At lower powers (< 10 kW), the residual γ-ray flux was large enough that the detector response was not linear with reactor power. Even though the pulse-height threshold had not been optimized for γ-ray rejection, the γ-ray interference was still quite small. The γ-ray sensitivity can be reduced by more than one order of magnitude by increasing the threshold bias by 50%. This should, for practical purposes, eliminate γ-ray interference in the BNCT environment, for which the fields are many orders of magnitude smaller than in the reactor tube environment.

Detectors were operated in a thermal neutron flux of 10^{10} neutrons/cm^2/s and

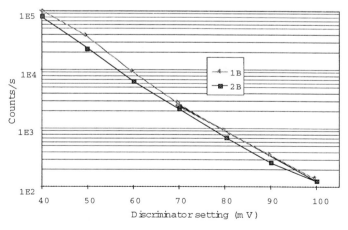

Fig. 7. Count rate vs. discriminator setting for two design B detectors in ~1100 R/min ^{60}Co field.

an epicadmium[1] flux of approximately the same order of magnitude for periods in excess of 1 h. A detector was left in the reactor γ-ray field for 16 h and showed no apparent degradation. Radioactive activation of various detector package components occurred, as expected.

There is some as yet unexplained inconsistency in the fast electronics; data drift was observed that may have been caused by feedback of intense signals. In addition, the observed sensitivity to position of the detector needs to be rationalized.

Overall, although further work remains, the concept appears viable for the clinical setting. The concept continues to have promise for measuring neutron fluxes for epithermal beams and can be readily adapted to provide real-time dose rate information for conventional γ-ray/X-ray therapy.

References

1. Matalka KZ et al. Radiation effects of boron neutron capture therapy on brain, skin, and eye of rats. Int J Radiat Oncol Biol Phys 1994;28:1089—1097.
2. Gavin PR et al. Large animal normal tissue tolerance with boron neutron capture. Int J Radiat Oncol Biol Phys 1994;28:1099—1106.
3. Morris GR et al. Boron neutron capture therapy: a guide to the understanding of the pathogenesis of late radiation damage to the rat spinal cord. Int J Radiat Oncol Biol Phys 1994;28:1107—1112.
4. Bliss M, Brodzinski RL, Craig RA, Geelhood BD, Knopf MA, Miley HS, Perkins RW, Reeder PL, Sunberg DS, Warner RA, Wogman NA. Glass-fibre-based neutron detectors for high- and low-flux environments. In: Johnson CB, Fenyves EJ (eds) Photoelectronic Detectors, Cameras and Systems. Proc SPIE 1995;2551:108—117.
5. Bliss M, Craig RA. A variety of neutron sensors based on scintillating glass waveguides. In: Udd E (ed) Pacific Northwest Fiber Optic Sensor Workshop. Proc SPIE 1995;2574:152—158.
6. Bliss M et al. A real-time dosimeter for boron-capture neutron radiation. Presented at the First International Workshop on Accelerator-Based Neutron Sources, September 11—14 September, 1994, Jackson WY, 269—278.
7. Bliss M, Craig RA, Reeder PL, Sunberg DS. Development of real-time dosimeter for therapeutic neutron radiation. IEEE Trans Nucl Sci 1995;42:639—643.
8. Nigg DW. Method for planning dose distribution analysis and treatment planning in boron neutron capture therapy. Int J Radiat Oncol Biol Phys 1994;28:1157—1166.
9. Liu HB et al. Enhancement of the epithermal neutron beam used for boron neutron capture therapy. Int J Radiat Oncol Biol Phys 1994;28:1149—1156.

---

[1]Epicadmium neutron flux is that measured by a detector shielded by cadmium. Typically, this is the flux of neutrons with energy greater than about 5 eV.

Advances in Neutron Capture Therapy.
Volume I, Medicine and Physics.
B. Larsson, J. Crawford and R. Weinreich, editors.

In vivo on-line ^{10}B (n,α) three-dimensional dosimetry using binary Gabor zone plate encoded γ-ray holography

D.A. Allen, T.D. Beynon and J. Perks

School of Physics and Space Research, University of Birmingham, Birmingham, UK

Introduction

Boron cancer therapy (BCT) utilises the reaction which occurs when thermal neutrons are absorbed by the ^{10}B nucleus: ^{10}B (n,α)^{7}Li. In 94% of cases the resulting ^{7}Li nucleus, which travels only a very short distance ($< 5\mu$m), decays from its excited state of 478 keV to its ground state by the emission of a γ ray of that energy. Thus 94% of reactions result in 2.313 MeV of high LET energy being deposited locally and 478 keV being released as a low LET photon, whilst for the remaining 6% it is 2.791 MeV of high LET radiation. This paper describes a method of determining the spatial distribution of the ^{10}B (n,α)^{7}Li reactions, within a patient undergoing treatment, by producing a three-dimensional image of the source of the 478 keV photons within the tumour and healthy tissue regions. This information can then be incorporated into an on-line treatment planning system in order to determine the required irradiation time necessary to deliver the prescribed dose. Monte Carlo simulations, using the code MCNP [1], have been used to calculate the photon source strength within a typical head phantom in the proposed Birmingham BCT beam [2]. As an example, at a depth of 4.3 cm into a phantom and with a proton beam on target of 5 mA, a tumour with a ^{10}B concentration of 45 µg/g will behave like a photon source of strength 15 µCi/cm^3.

To produce a three-dimensional image of the 478 keV photons, we propose to use a technique based on the development of a binary Gabor zone plate (BGZP) by Beynon et al. [3]. This method of incoherent holography has been successfully applied to white and infra-red light and a similar method has been used to image neutrons [4]. This paper discusses the potential of this technique for BCT dose mapping, and images produced by Monte Carlo simulations are presented, together with a real hologram of a ^{99m}Tc source.

Gabor zone-plate-encoded holography

In conventional holography, the hologram formed by the scattered spherical wave

---

Address for correspondence: D.A. Allen, School of Physics and Space Research, University of Birmingham, Birmingham B15 2TT, UK.

from a point object and a plane reference beam has the following form as a function of radius, r.

$$t(r) = \frac{1}{2}\left\{1 + \cos\left(\frac{\pi r^2}{r_1^2}\right)\right\}$$ (1)

where $t(r)$ is the intensity and r_1 is the radius of the first ring. When illuminated with monochromatic parallel light, such a hologram will act like a lens and it will focus the light to a single focal point, thus reconstructing the original point object. This is unlike the behaviour of a Fresnel lens, which has multiple foci.

If we can produce a lens which has a radial attenuation function for radiation with the same mathematical form as (Eqn. 1), then forming a shadowgraph of this lens from a point source is, in effect, like forming a hologram of a point object. The important point to remember is that we are not attempting to diffract the radiation coming from the source. In fact, the lens dimensions must be large enough so that no diffraction can occur — a condition which is easily satisfied with γ rays. Each point of an extended source casts a different shadowgraph of the lens onto the recording screen, which may be X-ray film or a γ camera or some other position sensitive area detection system.

The hologram formed by an extended source can be used to optically reconstruct the original source by reducing the shadowgraph down to optical dimensions and illuminating with monochromatic light. Alternatively, computer reconstruction may be used.

Binary Gabor zone plate

In practice it is very difficult to produce a lens which has the required transmission function, $t(r)$. To overcome this difficulty, we use a binary zone plate, which is constructed of 100% absorbing and 100% transmitting regions. These are shaped in such a way that if we take an average transmission around the zone plate at a given radius, then the transmission function at that radius is given by $t(r)$. Alternatively, if we spin the zone about its centre, then the time-averaged transmission as a function of radius is the same as a true Gabor zone plate.

Figure 1 shows a BGZP with 40 sectors and 80 zones. It is not strictly necessary for the black regions to be 100% absorbing. In fact, this is impossible with γ rays. Empirical observation has shown that around 50—70% absorption is sufficient, but results in a lower contrast image.

Performance

The image resolution achievable with a BGZP holography system is comprised of two components. One is due to the zone plate itself and the other is due to the finite resolution of the recording system. Furthermore, it is different in the transverse direction and the direction along the zone plate axis. The resolution due to

Fig. 1. A binary Gabor zone plate with 40 zones and 20 sectors.

the zone plate can be shown to be:

$$\delta x = \frac{1.64ar}{2b\sqrt{N}} \left(1 + \frac{b}{a}\right)$$

in the transverse direction and:

$$\delta z = \frac{a}{\epsilon b}(a + b)(\epsilon - 1)$$

along the axis. The recording-system-limited resolution is:

$$\delta x = \Delta c\left(\frac{a}{b}\right)$$

in the transverse direction and:

$$\delta z = \frac{a^2 \Delta c}{br_1\sqrt{N}}$$

in the longitudinal direction.

Here N is the number of zones in the plate, ε is 1.024 for $N = 30$, r_1 is the radius of the first zone and Δc is the resolution of the recording system. The object to zone plate distance a and b is the distance from the zone plate to the recording system. As an example, if we have a 30-zone plate with $r_1 = 10$ mm and we use a γ camera with an intrinsic (noncollimated) resolution of 3 mm, then with: $a = 300$ mm and $b = 400$ mm we can expect a combined resolution of $\Delta x = 3.5$ mm in the transverse direction and $\Delta z = 17.4$ mm in the longitudinal direction.

Computer simulations

In order to evaluate the performance of zone plate designs, Monte Carlo computer simulations, using MCNP, have been employed. Sources of various shapes and energies, both on their own and surrounded by scattering material, have been used. The lenses in the simulations did not have the azimuthal transmission variation of a BGZP, but had the same radial transmission that a BGZP would have if it were rotated about its centre. In fact, in a final system, it may be necessary to rotate the zone plate during hologram formation. The tally structure used was a 100×100 array of 3 mm^2 pixels.

Figure 2 shows the simulated reconstructed hologram using a 1-mm thick tungsten plate with 30 zones. There are two sources of 150 keV photons; one is a circle of 15 mm diameter at $a = 220$ mm, the other is a cross of length 20 mm at $a = 200$ mm. The plate to tally surface distance, b is 300 mm. The two sources can clearly be seen in their respective focal planes. This image contains some aliasing in its furthest planes. This is due to the large pixel size required in order to obtain a realistic field of view for the simulations.

Figure 3 shows the reconstructed holographic image from a 478 keV ellipsoidal source, surrounded by a head phantom, which represents a tumour volume. The zone plate used was 4-mm thick tungsten with 30 zones where $a = 400$ mm and $b = 600$ mm. The source is divided into two equal volume regions with a brightness ratio of 2:1. The effect of scattering within the phantom is accounted for in this simulation and, on comparison with a void phantom simulation, does not significantly degrade the image contrast. In practice, scattering will have to be taken into account to obtain quantitative information about source strengths. However, since patients will have undergone extensive CT, PET or MRI studies prior to treatment, there will be sufficient information available to perform an attenuation calculation. The main point to note from this image is that the bright and dark halves of the ellipsoid can be distinguished. In a clinical imaging system the tumour should appear as a bright region against the darker, low ^{10}B concentration, healthy brain.

A real hologram

A tungsten alloy zone plate with 30 zones and 12 sectors has been cut by laser

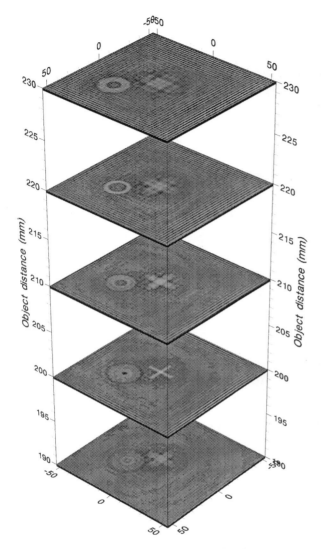

Fig. 2. The holographic image reconstruction from a Monte Carlo simulation using a 1-mm thick tungsten zone plate. This image is formed by two 150 keV sources, a cross at 200 mm and a circle at 220 mm.

from a 1-mm thick sintered sheet. This plate, designed for producing holograms from low-energy photons, has been used to produce a hologram from four ^{99m}Tc capillary sources arranged in the shape of an eccentric cross. The hologram was recorded at St Thomas' Hospital (London) using a Toshiba GCA-7200A γ camera, without its collimator, and with a plate to camera distance of $b = 230$ mm. The reconstructed image is seen in Fig. 4 and is in focus at $a = 215$ mm. The calculated transverse resolution of this image is $\Delta x = 4.5$ mm,

234

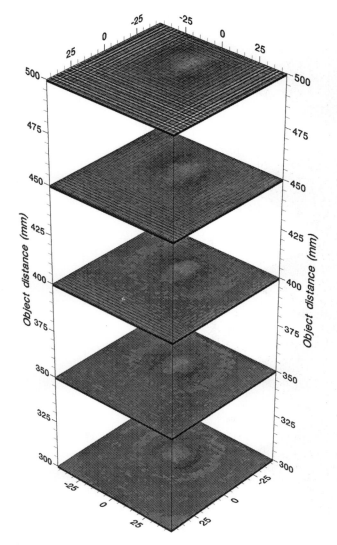

Fig. 3. Holographic image reconstructed from a Monte Carlo simulation with a 4-mm thick tungsten zone plate. Two-region 478-keV ellipsoidal source within a head phantom.

which is sufficient to pick out the central dark region of the cross which contains no radioisotope. This dark feature was too small to be visible with the collimated camera operating in its normal mode as a medical imaging γ camera.

Summary and further work

Three-dimensional imaging of γ-ray sources is possible using a γ camera and a BGZP-encoded incoherent holography system. The resolution achievable is suffi-

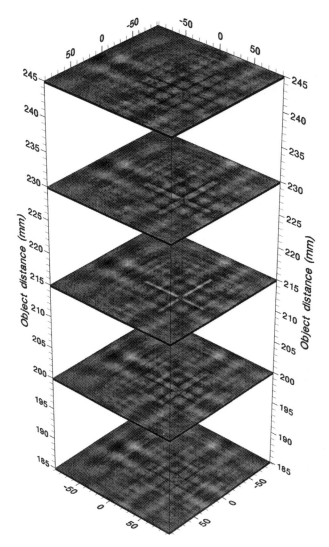

Fig. 4. Real γ-ray hologram reconstruction using a 1-mm thick tungsten zone plate and a standard noncollimated γ camera. The sources are four ^{99m}Tc capillaries arranged into a cross.

cient for macroscopic three-dimensional ^{10}B (n,α) dose mapping during BCT tumour irradiations. However, further work is needed to be able to use a γ-camera system within a neutron environment.

None of the images presented in this paper have been deconvoluted or received any form of image enhancement. Since the point spread functions are easily obtained it should be possible to improve the image quality of the hologram reconstructions by removing the satellite images. It should also be possible to produce images on an absolute brightness scale.

References

1. Briesmeister JF. MCNP — A general Monte Carlo n-particle transport code 4A. Los Alamos Nat Lab LA—12625—M, 1993.
2. Allen DA, Beynon TD. A design study for an accelerator-based epithermal neutron beam for BNCT. Phys Med Biol 1995;40:807—821.
3. Beynon TD, Kirk I, Matthews TR. Gabor zone plate with binary transmittance values. Optics Lett 1992;17:544—546.
4. Beynon TD, Pink AG. Neutron holography using Fresnel zone plate encoding. Nature 1980;283: 749—751.

A code of practice for the dosimetry of BNCT in Europe

F. Stecher-Rasmussen[1], I. Auterinen[2], A. Beddoe[3], I. Gonçalves[4], H. Järvinen[5], A. Kosunen[5], B. Larsson[6], M. Marek[7], B. Mijnheer[8], C.P.J. Raaijmakers[8], S. Savolainen[9], W.P. Voorbraak[1], P. Watkins[10] and E. Zsolnay[11]

[1]Netherlands Energy Research Foundation, ECN, Petten, The Netherlands; [2]VTT Chemical Technology, VTT, Espoo, Finland; [3]Queen Elizabeth Hospital, Birmingham, UK; [4]ITN Technology and Nuclear Institute, Sacavem, Portugal; [5]Finnish Centre for Radiation and Nuclear Safety, Helsinki, Finland; [6]Institute of Medical Radiobiology, Zürich, Switzerland; [7]Nuclear Research Institute, Rez near Prague, Czech Republic; [8]Netherlands Cancer Institute, Amsterdam, The Netherlands; [9]Helsinki University, Dept. of Physics, Helsinki, Finland; [10]Commission of the European Communities, JRC, Petten, The Netherlands; and [11]Technical University, Institute of Nuclear Techniques, Budapest, Hungary

Introduction

At the present state of development of boron neutron capture therapy (BNCT) worldwide a variety of different techniques is applied for the dosimetry related to preclinical studies or to clinical trials on human patients. As each BNCT research group performs the dosimetry in its own way, it is essential at this moment to introduce international uniformity of BNCT dosimetry.

The existing international recommendations on radiotherapy dosimetry are not applicable to BNCT due to the complexity of the mixed neutron- and γ-ray fields. Hence, guidelines on acceptable dosimetric procedures are urgently needed to provide credibility and reliability to the preclinical research and to the clinical trials on human patients. These guidelines will ensure the level of accuracy, reliability and reproducibility which is generally required in radiotherapy and which will be of crucial importance for the success and for the optimization of the BNCT treatment.

To arrive at such guidelines a European collaboration project has been defined.

Objective of the European collaboration

The objective of the collaboration is to prepare detailed guidelines for the dosimetry of epithermal neutrons to be used for treatment of cancer patients by BNCT at European research reactors and accelerators. This will be achieved through the basic characterization of the BNCT neutron beams:
— by theoretical review and analysis of the available knowledge;
— by systematic experimental investigations of the most promising methods in the available European BNCT beams;
— by verification of experimental results with theoretical calculations to deter-

mine the critical physical parameters affecting the overall accuracy of the measurements; and
— by systematic intercomparison of the selected dosimetry procedures in the available European BNCT beams.

The project is limited to the basic problems of physical dosimetry prior to clinical treatment.

The final outcome of the project will be a published code of practice for use by all European BNCT centres.

Work programme

In order to meet the objectives the collaboration project is divided into four work packages, in which the basic characteristics of the neutron beam (beam geometry, neutron and photon spectra, absorbed dose and fluence distributions) will be determined in a coherent and reproducible way.

Work Package 1: Beam characterization free in air
1.1 Beam geometry
1.2 Spectrum characterization of the neutron component
1.3 Spectrum characterization of the γ-ray component

Work Package 2: Beam calibration in phantom
2.1 Reference phantom material
2.2 Reference geometry
2.3 Absorbed dose to tissue
2.4 Nonreference conditions
2.5 Thermal neutron fluence rate
2.6 Intercomparison of methods

Work Package 3: On-line monitoring
3.1 Beam monitoring

Work Package 4: Writing the code of practice
4.1 Drafting and editing the text
4.2 Referee reading

The first two activities of Work Package 2 will result in the design and construction of a reference phantom. This phantom will be used for the intercomparison study of activity 2.6. All participants shall carry out measurements at two sites, starting with Petten and at a second stage at a centre with a BNCT beam with differing characteristics, to perform these measurements using their own equipment. The Petten facility shall be the common denominator in the intercomparison study. The results of the intercomparison will be analyzed with respect to measurement procedure, dosimeter calibration and values for the physical parameters required to convert the detector signal to dose or fluence. Sources of discrepancy will be traced and further investigated if necessary. The results of the intercomparison shall be used for a possible adaptation of the "Code of Practice for BNCT Dosimetry". Also the accuracy in dose determination in BNCT beams shall be assessed. The range of acceptability for the generated data will be defined in order to control the quality.

Benefits and Discussion

The aim of the project is a published and generally accepted code of practice for use by all European BNCT centres, which will ensure the accuracy, reliability and reproducibility of dosimetric measurements required for pretreatment BNCT as well as for the treatment of patients. With respect to the general requirements on traceable metrology in radiotherapy, the code will introduce the traceability of the dosimetric methods to the international measurement system.

The code of practice will ensure the comparability of the results of BNCT research and patient treatments in various beams, and will advance critical appraisal of the outcome of clinical trials. It also forms the basis for the comparison of the treatment results by BNCT and that of conventional therapy or other treatment modalities, thus promoting mutual and worldwide recognition of this new mode of radiotherapy.

Specific techniques and equipment are needed for dosimetric measurements in the complex radiation fields of BNCT. The international recommendations or codes of practice on dosimetry which are currently available for conventional photon and electron beam therapy and for neutron therapy are not applicable to BNCT. The European groups interested in BNCT are building up their competence and facilities with varying efforts, and cooperation between the groups is compulsory to produce an internationally acceptable firm basis of dosimetry. The coordination of the various efforts through the project would be highly beneficial by avoiding unnecessary duplication of effort, by verifying the methods applied or investigated, and by providing the means for effective communication and exchange of current experience between the groups. The available knowledge and experiences would then be effectively combined to produce a European recommendation for use by all European BNCT centres.

The need for the proposed code of practice has also been realized by the treatment centres outside Europe. To date, the somewhat scattered efforts of BNCT worldwide have not resulted in the creation of such a document. The relevant international organizations have at present no plans for this specific area, since their work for recommendations on dosimetry is usually based on sufficient flow of information available through published experience and recommendations by various researchers or research groups. The European code of practice, as a result of coordinated study between centres having reactors or accelerators, facilities and competence for multiple research and testing of BNCT dosimetry, would then later serve as a good basis for recommendation by the relevant international organizations.

The results of this work will also produce useful information to supplement some aspects of the existing codes of practice for conventional photon, electron and fast neutron therapy.

The code of practice will enable reliable verification of the new sophisticated treatment planning programmes in BNCT, which need to be verified and approved, based on measurements in phantoms using recommended dosimetry techniques.

In order to ensure maximum of completeness and acceptance, information will be collected from BNCT practice in the USA.

Theory

Monte Carlo modelling of packed cells used to evaluate dose in BCT

D.E. Charlton[1] and T.D. Utteridge[2,3]

[1]*Concordia University, Montreal, Canada;* [2]*Royal Adelaide Hospital, Adelaide, Australia; and* [3]*School of Applied Physics, University of South Australia, Pooraka, Australia*

Introduction

Boron capture therapy relies on the introduction of ^{10}B into the tumour and the irradiation of the tumour by thermal or epithermal neutrons. Accompanying the neutron fluence are γ rays and fast protons produced by the neutron source and nuclear interactions as the beam passes through the tissue. The dosimetry of these latter two components is reasonably well-understood, producing uniform distributions of dose over volumes comparable to that of the tumour (or with corrections for depth dose variations).

The therapeutic gain for this technique comes from the additional dose to the tumour from nuclear interactions in the ^{10}B. Here the high LET ions produced by the nuclear interactions in and close to the cell nuclei provide a higher differential dose to the tumour nuclei. However, because of the very short ranges of the ions, the local distribution of the ^{10}B becomes critical in estimating the dose. The dose to the tumour will only be equal to the dose to the cell nuclei of the tumour if the ^{10}B is uniformly distributed. It has been usual to assume that this is true (simplifying the dose calculation) but in this conference measurements by Chandra et al. [1] have shown that neither of the drugs most commonly used (BPA and BSH) produce uniform distributions. If this is the case, then in addition to the problem of calculating the dose, an additional difficulty is introduced. For a uniform distribution of ^{10}B the diameters of the cell nuclei need not be taken into account since all nuclei receive the same average dose. For a nonuniform distribution, the average doses to the cell nuclei are not equal and these cannot be averaged since this requires addition of doses to masses of different sizes.

Another problem is the contribution to the dose, both to the normal tissue and the tumour, by nuclear interactions in ^{14}N. The nitrogen distribution — external to the cells and in the cytoplasm and nuclei of cells — is not well known. In this presentation, dose to the nuclei (of varying diameters) of packed cells from uni-

---

Address for correspondence: D.E. Charlton, Physics Department, Concordia University, 1455 de Maisonneuve Blvd W, Montreal, PQ, Canada, H3G 1M8.

formly distributed ^{10}B will be calculated by Monte Carlo methods. The technique allows the introduction of nonuniform ^{10}B and ^{14}N distributions. In addition, detailed examination of the energy deposition will be presented.

Method

Structure of tissue

Cells and their nuclei as concentric spheres were placed in a cube 100 μm on edge and randomly packed to a 25% filling. Cell radii were chosen at random from a distribution of 5–7 μm in half micrometer intervals in the ratio 1:2:4:2:1. Spheres which overlapped previously positioned spheres were rejected. The spheres were then migrated towards the origin in small increments when the stepping did not produce overlap. In this way up to 50% of the volume was filled by the cells. Because we are interested in local effects (maximum ranges are in the order of 10 μm) only spheres in a cube 50 μm on edge were stored for scoring. The 200 different configurations of cells were generated and stored. For each configuration the smaller cube was scanned at a resolution of 1 μm^3 and the fraction of the volume occupied by cells and nuclei determined and stored with cell positions. The nuclear volume was set at 75% of the cell volume.

Sources of radiation

The thermal neutron cross section for ^{14}N and ^{10}B was used. Previous calculations [2] showed that for a neutron fluence of 10^{13} neutrons/cm^2 and 3.5 g/100g tissue of nitrogen there were 0.0272 interactions/μm^3 and for 20 ppm of ^{10}B there were 0.0462 interactions/μm^3. For other concentrations and fluences the numbers of interactions are proportional. The data were used to set the number of interactions in nitrogen and boron in the nuclei, cytoplasm and external to the cell for each set of cell configurations from the fractions of the volumes previously determined for each smaller cube. The stopping powers for the protons, the two α and the two Li ions were calculated from the programme TRIM [3] and used to calculate the ranges and energies at 0.1-μm intervals along their tracks. The calculations were carried out for a water medium.

Scoring hits in the nuclei and dose

In a separate programme the first set of cells was read as well as the fractions of the volume occupied by the cell cytoplasm and the nucleus for the particular cell configuration. From these fractions the number of interactions external to the cell, in the cytoplasm and in the nucleus were found for both the (n, α) and (n, p) reactions. Each interaction was placed at random in the appropriate compartment and given a direction using randomly assigned direction cosines. The simultaneous equations of the path and the surface of the nucleus were solved, a real solution giving the coordinates of the exit and entry points. From the distances to these points the energy deposited in the nucleus can be found from the data of distance travelled vs. ion energy. For stoppers and starters the partial chord length in the nucleus was used. The calculation was repeated (cycled) for the same cell configuration using new positions for the decays and new direction cosines. For the results presented the 200 configurations were each cycled 50 times giving data for 10,000 cells.

Results

Uniform distributions of nuclear interactions, the first calculations were performed for uniform distributions of 2 g nitrogen/100g tissue and 5 ppm of ^{10}B with a fluence of 5 × 10^{12} neutrons/cm^2. For the results presented here cells occupied on average 51% of the volume and nuclei 38%. The equilibrium doses for these conditions (averaged over 10,000 cells) are 0.75 Gy and 2.16 Gy for the nitrogen and boron, respectively (these results are independent of the fraction of the volume occupied by the cells). Equilibrium values calculated from the total energy liberated in the smaller box gave the same average values. The (n, p) reaction includes the contribution to the dose of the recoil ^{14}C when the reaction occurs in the nucleus. For this condition there are on average 9.7 nuclear hits by either α particles or Li ions and 12.2 passages by protons.

Using the Monte Carlo method it is possible to examine the dose and the LET at which the dose was delivered for the different ions for each passage in the nucleus. In Fig. 1 the dose and average LET (energy deposited/path length in

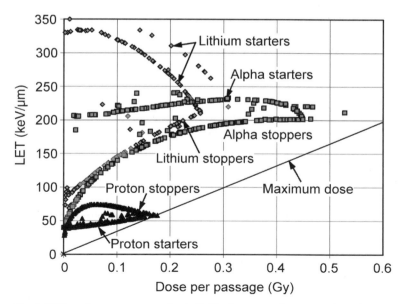

Fig. 1. LET vs. dose per passage for individual passages for one nuclear size.

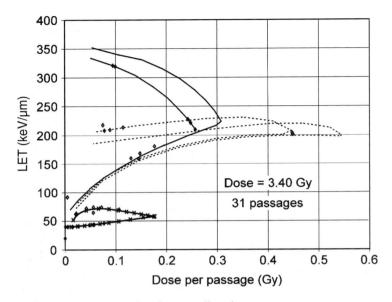

Fig. 2. Contributions to dose for one cell nucleus.

nucleus) for many individual crossings of the nucleus are shown. Each point is an energy deposition in the nucleus. There is a surprising structure to the figure which can be understood in terms of ions starting and stopping in the nuclei. As the ranges of the ions are very small most passages are either starters or stoppers with some Li ions starting and stopping in the nucleus. Fig. 2 shows the traces in Fig. 1 and the energy depositions for the dose to one nucleus. The total dose here (3.4 Gy) is made-up of 6 α, 10 Li and 15 proton passages. All but three or four of the passages start or stop in the nucleus. The dose to other cells will be made-up of different mixes of ions and stopping powers. Thus even though doses are added and averaged they are not of the same "quality" and the average dose is not a simple quantity.

Nonuniform distributions: Chandra et al. [1] have measured the distribution between the three compartments for BPA and BSH in T98G human glioblastoma cells after 4 h incubation. The data are shown in Table 1 with the equivalent concentration to give an average of 5 ppm in the tissue.

The calculated average dose (by summing and averaging doses to nuclei of different sizes) to the cell nuclei from the conditions given in Table 1 are 2.39 Gy for BPA (11% higher than uniform) and 2.04 Gy for BSH (6% lower than uni-

Table 1. Boron concentrations (ppm) of BPA and BSH in T98G human glioblastoma cells [1].

	Nucleus	Cytoplasm	External
BPA	156 ± 56 (5.8)	168 ± 71 (6.3)	110 (4.1)
BSH	90 ± 23 (4.3)	124 ± 45 (5.9)	110 (5.3)

form). The correct average dose is the ratio of total energy deposited in nuclei to the total mass of the nuclei. This figure is not significantly different from the incorrectly averaged dose.

Conclusions

A computer programme has been described which simulates cells in tissue and which is used to calculate the dose to cell nuclei from nuclear interactions in ^{10}B and ^{14}N for any distribution of these atoms. Several improvements can be included in the approach. The modelling of the cells and nuclei as concentric spheres is unsatisfactory in that the shape of the nuclei of tumour cells can be highly irregular. Low-grade astrocytomas have a packing similar to the one used here. Higher grade tumours have higher levels of packing. The cell and nuclear sizes used in the calculations are approximately correct. The nonuniform distributions described by Chandra et al. [1] were treated as averages but they have broad distributions and individual variations in the concentrations could be included in future. A copy of the programmes used in these calculations is available from DEC. Those who obtained copies during the Symposium are asked to contact DEC for improved versions of the programmes.

Acknowledgements

DEC wishes to thank the organisers of the Symposium for financial support.

References

1. Chandra S, Lorey DR, Smith DR, Morrison GH. Quantitative imaging of boron from BPA and BSH in glioblastoma cells with ion microscopy. In: Larsson B, Crawford J, Weinreich R (eds) Advances in Neutron Capture Therapy, Volume 2, Chemistry and Biology. Amsterdam: Elsevier Science, 1997;315–320 (these proceedings).
2. Charlton DE. Energy deposition in small ellipsoidal volumes by high-LET particles: Application to thermal neutron dosimetery. Int J Radiat Biol 1991;59:827.
3. Ziegler JF. TRIM, Transport of Ions in Matter, Yorktown, NY: IBM Research, 1992.

248

Advances in Neutron Capture Therapy.
Volume I, Medicine and Physics.
B. Larsson, J. Crawford and R. Weinreich, editors.

A coupled deterministic/stochastic method for dose computations in a filtered BNCT beam

T.R. Hubbard, R.A. Rydin and T.D. Burns
Department of Mechanical, Aerospace, and Nuclear Engineering, University of Virginia, Charlottesville, Virginia, USA

Introduction

BNCT is in need of computational methods for accurately estimating local body doses during treatment in a given NCT facility. This radiation transport problem is unique and challenging, and it is helpful to draw on the work of other laboratories which have shown good results in analogous problems. In particular, the ORNL's Monte Carlo adjoint shielding (MASH) code was examined.

Problem statement

We seek a method of computing the dose rate in various parts and organs of a human body during NCT treatments, given the source spectrum from the reactor and a description of the geometries and materials of the filter, collimator, room and patient. The transport of the neutron and γ radiation from the core through the beam port is well suited to discrete ordinates (S_n) methods owing to the deep-penetration (many MFPs) conditions and to symmetric geometries which are closely approximated in two-dimensional models. The patient and treatment room are suited to Monte Carlo techniques owing to the complicated geometries of biological systems which require asymmetrical three-dimensional models. Since neither method is capable of satisfactorily solving the entire problem, a method is desired to use S_n for the first part of the radiation transport, and Monte Carlo for the second part.

A direct coupling (i.e., "bootstrap") of an S_n solution to forward Monte Carlo is not practical, since few particles would reach areas of interest to give good "point" fluxes. An ideal method would couple a forward S_n solution of the filter/collimator to an adjoint Monte Carlo solution of the response at a point in the patient, thus making all adjoint particles contribute to the results.

Address for correspondence: Tom Hubbard, Nuclear Reactor Facility, University of Virginia, Charlottesville, VA 22903-2442, USA. E-mail: hubbard@virginia.edu

Theory

Given the steady-state neutron transport operator:

$$H = \hat{\mathbf{\Omega}} \cdot \nabla + \sigma_T(\mathbf{r}, E) - \int dE' \int d\hat{\mathbf{\Omega}}' \, \sigma_s(\mathbf{r}, E' \rightarrow E, \hat{\mathbf{\Omega}}' \cdot \hat{\mathbf{\Omega}}), \quad (1)$$

the associated adjoint operator can be shown to be [1]

$$H^+ = -\hat{\mathbf{\Omega}} \cdot \nabla + \sigma_T(\mathbf{r}, E) - \int dE' \int d\hat{\mathbf{\Omega}}' \, \sigma_s(\mathbf{r}, E \rightarrow E', \hat{\mathbf{\Omega}} \cdot \hat{\mathbf{\Omega}}'). \quad (2)$$

For a region surrounding the point of interest, assume that there is no neutron source, so that the angular flux ψ $(\mathbf{r}, E, \hat{\mathbf{\Omega}})$ is determined by solving:

$$H\psi = 0, \quad (3)$$

and define the adjoint problem as:

$$H^+\psi^+ = R(E)\delta(\mathbf{r} - \mathbf{r}_d), \quad (4)$$

where R is the appropriate response function (flux-to-dose conversion factor) at the point of interest, $\mathbf{r}_d$. By multiplying Eqn. 3 by ψ^+ and Eqn. 4 by ψ; integrating over all variables; and subtracting the results we get:

$$\langle \psi^+ H\psi \rangle - \langle \psi H^+ \psi^+ \rangle = \lambda, \quad (5)$$

where λ is the dose rate at the point of interest. It can easily be shown that the outscatter and inscatter terms will both cancel in Eqn. 5, leaving only:

$$\lambda = \langle \psi^+ \hat{\mathbf{\Omega}} \cdot \nabla\psi + \psi\hat{\mathbf{\Omega}} \cdot \nabla\psi^+ \rangle = \int d\hat{\mathbf{\Omega}} \int dE \int dV \nabla \cdot (\hat{\mathbf{\Omega}}\psi^+\psi). \quad (6)$$

By application of Green's formula this reduces to a surface integral,

$$\lambda = \int d\Gamma \int dE \int_{\hat{\mathbf{n}}\cdot\hat{\mathbf{\Omega}}<0} \hat{\mathbf{n}} \cdot \hat{\mathbf{\Omega}}\psi^+\psi + \int d\Gamma \int dE \int_{\hat{\mathbf{n}}\cdot\hat{\mathbf{\Omega}}>0} \hat{\mathbf{n}} \cdot \hat{\mathbf{\Omega}}\psi^+\psi. \quad (7)$$

If a no-return, flux-boundary condition is imposed on Eqn. 3, then the second term in Eqn. 7 will vanish. The dose response at a point within a bounded surface is thus the product of the inward-directed forward and outward-directed adjoint fluxes integrated over the surface.

Methods

The MASH code system normally uses the method outlined in "Theory" to calculate the dose to personnel in armored vehicles experiencing a nuclear attack [2]. In many ways the problem is similar to that of NCT computation, but some modifications are needed in order to accommodate the differences. As a first step towards development of the method, these differences are ignored in order to obtain preliminary results.

The DORT model

The UVAR pool and shield have been modeled in DORT with an optimized filter/collimator in RZ geometry [3] as shown in Fig. 1. To be consistent with the MASH package, the model must be rotated around a vertical Z axis. This results in a horizontal "slot" for the treatment portal, but it has been shown that the neutron spectrum is similar to that of a model with the correct RZ orientation and a circular portal.

The MORSE model

The ORNL multigroup Monte Carlo code, MORSE, was used to calculate the adjoint part of the problem by creating combinatorial geometry models with the material composition of tissue, as shown in Fig. 2. For these studies the man was placed horizontally aligned with the beam axis, with the head adjacent to the beam portal. Although this is not the ideal treatment orientation, because the body is in the line of the beam, it was sufficient to obtain qualitative results. Adjoint particles are started from various unique source positions within the body and are tracked until they leak from the coupling surface, whereupon the particle weight, position, and direction are recorded for coupling with the forward flux.

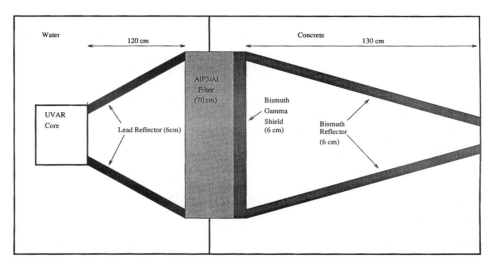

Fig. 1. DORT model of UVAR beam filter/collimator.

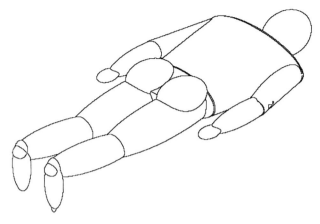

Fig. 2. Simple COM-GEOM model used for the MORSE model.

Results and Conclusions

Table 1 shows the relative dose rates and standard deviations (FSDs) for various positions within the model. From this data several observations are made:

1. For the slot configuration, the foot, etc., was in the direct beam, unshielded by the body, thus accounting for the high dose relative to the tumor.
2. Body orientations other than horizontal, in-beam line may provide lower dose rates to healthy tissue outside the head.
3. Deep-seated organs (e.g., heart) give higher FSDs than surface parts (e.g., hand).

Additional runs of various numbers of particles showed that the statistical accuracy is related to the problem run time as FSD α $1/\sqrt{cpu}$, and that good statistics can be achieved with reasonable run times on an IBM RS/6000 model 390 workstation.

The proposed method has merit and applicability to NCT geometries. Future work will involve writing new coupling routines so that the forward flux will

Table 1. Results for 50,000 adjoint source particles in various locations. Neutron dose is in arbitrary units relative to the dose rate at the tumor center (13 cm deep into brain on the centerline). "Forward" position is 10 cm deep and "aft" position is 16 cm deep.

Source position	Relative neutron dose	FSD (%)
Tumor	1.00	3.28
Forward tumor	1.52	6.56
Aft tumor	0.72	9.17
Heart	0.09	9.84
Gonad	4.48	2.89
Foot	7.95	6.38
Hand	5.37	1.79

retain spatial accuracy over the entire coupling surface. This will then be applied to a model with the correct RZ orientation of the DORT problem with a circular beam port and will be validated against benchmark data. The method will be enhanced with angle and source energy biasing and will also be compared with adjoint "flux estimators". Upon construction of an NCT facility at UVa, the method will be used to develop treatment planning protocols which will optimize patient position and beam characteristics based on the dose rates to the patient organs.

References

1. Lewis EE, Miller Jr WF. Computational Methods of Neutron Transport. New York: John Wiley and Sons, Inc., 1984.
2. Emmett MB, Rhodes WA et al. In: Johnson JO (ed) A user's manual for MASH 1.0 — a Monte Carlo adjoint shielding code system — ORNL/TM — 11778. Technical report, Oak Ridge National Laboratory, March 1996.
3. Burns TD, Hubbard TR, Reynolds AB, Rydin RA. Monte Carlo and deterministic analysis of a University of Virginia BNCT Facility. In: F. Vourropoulos (ed) Proceedings of the International Meeting for Neutron Applications, Crete. Bellingham, WA: SPIE, 1996.

Advances in Neutron Capture Therapy.
Volume I, Medicine and Physics.
B. Larsson, J. Crawford and R. Weinreich, editors.

A calculation of and sensitivity study for neutron RBEs for BNCT

Jeffrey E. Woollard and Thomas E. Blue (Nuclear Engineering Program)
Ohio State University, Columbus, Ohio, USA

Introduction

In boron neutron capture therapy (BNCT) of malignant brain tumors, the patient is irradiated in an epithermal neutron field. Hence, a knowledge of the energy dependence of the RBE of neutrons, $RBE(E_n)$, is important.

In this paper, the energy dependence of $RBE(E_n)$ is calculated using proton-fluence energy distributions resulting from $^1H(n,n')^1H$ and $^{14}N(n,p)^{14}C$ reactions in tissue, and using a measured relation between RBE and L, the linear energy transfer. The resulting relation for $RBE(E_n)$ is then normalized to the results of normal tissue-tolerance studies performed in the Brookhaven Medical Research Reactor (BMRR) epithermal neutron beam for BNCT. Also, the impact of different assumptions regarding the appropriate biological end points for our calculations of $RBE(E_n)$ is assessed.

Analysis

Previously, we have determined expressions for the energy distribution of the fluence (protons per unit area per unit energy) at a point, for protons born uniformly throughout an infinite medium, as a consequence of isotropic (in the center of mass system) scattering on hydrogen [1]:

$$\Phi^H(E_p) = \frac{\Phi(E_n)\Sigma_S^H(E_n)}{-dE/dx|_{E_p}} \left(1 - \frac{E_p}{E_n}\right), \quad E_p < E_n \tag{1}$$

and as a consequence of neutrons interacting with nitrogen via the $^{14}N(n,p)^{14}C$ reaction,

$$\Phi^H(E_p) = \frac{\Phi(E_n)\Sigma_a^N(E_n)}{-dE/dx|_{E_p}} \quad 0 < E_p < E_p^N \tag{2}$$

Address for correspondence: Jeffrey E. Woollard MS, Ohio State University, Columbus, OH 43210, USA.

where $\Phi(E_n)$ is the neutron fluence (neutrons per unit area) at neutron energy E_n, $\Sigma_S^H(E_n)$ is the macroscopic scattering cross-section for the $^1H(n,n')^1H$ reaction in tissue, $\Sigma_a^N(E_n)$ is the macroscopic absorption cross-section for the $^{14}N(n,p)^{14}C$ reaction in tissue, $-dE/dx$ is the average proton energy loss per unit pathlength traveled, and E_p^N is the kinetic energy of the proton emitted in the $^{14}N(n,p)^{14}C$ reaction, when the reaction is induced by thermal neutrons. If the reaction is induced by a more energetic neutron, some of its kinetic energy is transmitted to the recoil proton. This additional energy is small compared to E_p^N and is neglected in our analysis.

Summing $\Phi^H(E_p)$ and $\Phi^N(E_p)$ to obtain $\Phi(E_p)$, i.e.,

$$\Phi^H(E_p) = \Phi^H(E_p) + \Phi^N(E_p) \tag{3}$$

the absorbed dose, $D(E_n)$, can be calculated using the equation

$$D(E_n) = -\frac{k}{\rho}\int_0^\infty \Phi(E_p)\frac{dE}{dx}\Big|_{E_p} dE_p \tag{4}$$

where ρ is the mass density of tissue and k is a constant accounting for units. Substituting $\Phi(E_p)$ as given by Eqns. 1, 2, and 3 into Eqn. 4 for $D(E_n)$ yields

$$D(E_n) = \frac{k}{\rho}\Phi(E_n)\left\{\frac{\Sigma_S^H(E_n)E_n}{2} + \Sigma_a^N(E_n)E_p^N\right\}. \tag{5}$$

Note that despite its occurrence in Eqn. 4, dE/dx need not be known to calculate $D(E_n)$, since dE/dx in Eqn. 4 cancels dE/dx in the denominators of Eqns. 1 and 2.

The RBE-dose, $H(E_n)$, is defined by the following equation:

$$H(E_n) = -\frac{k}{\rho}\int_0^\infty \Phi(E_p)\frac{dE}{dx}\Big|_{E_p} RBE\left(L = \frac{-dE}{dx}\Big|_{E_p}\right) dE_p. \tag{6}$$

Substituting $\Phi(E_p)$ as given by Eqns. 1, 2, and 3 into Eqn. 6 for $H(E_n)$ yields

$$H(E_n) = \frac{k}{\rho}\Phi(E_n)\int_0^\infty \left\{\Sigma_S^H(E_n)\left[1 - (E_p/E_n)\right]\left[U(E_p) - U(E_p - E_n)\right] + \right.$$

$$\left. \Sigma_a^N(E_n) \times \left[U(E_p) - U(E_p - E_p^N)\right]\right\}\left(RBE\left[L = (-dE/dx)\big|_{E_p}\right]\right) dE_p \tag{7}$$

where $U(x)$ is the unit step function, which is used to account for the limited domains of Eqns. 1 and 2. Note that in calculating $H(E_n)$, a knowledge of the relationship between RBE and L is required. Since we are assuming $L = -dE/dx$, this further implies that a relationship between dE/dx and E_p must also be known. This latter relationship was obtained from data by Janni [2].

The RBE is conventionally a factor relating radiation damage to the absorbed dose. Therefore, we use for the definition of the RBE

$$RBE(E_n) = H(E_n)/D(E_n). \tag{8}$$

Substituting Eqn. 7 for $H(E_n)$ and Eqn. 5 for $D(E_n)$ into Eqn. 8 for $RBE(E_n)$ yields

$$RBE(E_n) = \int_0^\infty \left\{ \Sigma_S^H(E_n)\left[1 - (E_p/E_n)\right]\left[U(E_p) - U(E_p - E_n)\right] + \Sigma_a^N(E_n) \right.$$

$$\left. \times \left[U(E_p) - U(E_p - E_p^N)\right] \right\} \left(RBE\left[L = (-dE/dx)|_{E_p}\right] \right)$$

$$dE_p \Big/ \left\{ \left[\Sigma_S^H(E_n)E_n/2\right] + \Sigma_a^N(E_n)E_p^N \right\}. \tag{9}$$

In order to calculate RBE(E_n), values for $\Sigma_s^H(E_n)$ and $\Sigma_a^N(E_n)$ are required. These macroscopic cross-sections were calculated for two cases: 1) skeletal muscle [3] with a mass density of 1.05 g/cm^3, a hydrogen concentration of 10.2 weight percent, and a nitrogen concentration of 3.4 weight percent; and 2) adult brain tissue [3] with a mass density of 1.04 g/cm^3, a hydrogen concentration of 10.7 weight percent, and a nitrogen concentration of 2.2 weight percent. For both muscle and brain, the microscopic cross-sections used in the calculations were from the ENDF/B-VI cross-section library [4].

It is well-known that RBE is a function of end point, cell line, dose, and dose rate, as well as L. We first calculated RBE(E_n) based on the data for RBE(L), which was measured by Barendsen [5], for inactivation of cells of human origin for a surviving fraction of 10%. The analysis assumed that the effects of end point, dose, and dose rate affect the magnitude of RBE(E_n), but not its shape. The magnitude of RBE(E_n) was determined by normalizing RBE(E_n), according to Eqn. 10, below:

$$< RBE(E_n) > \equiv \frac{\int_0^\infty RBE(E_n)k_n(E_n)\Phi(E_n)dE_n}{\int_0^\infty k_n(E_n)\Phi(E_n)dE_n}. \tag{10}$$

The RBE for muscle (RBE^M(E_n)) was normalized to a different value than the RBE for brain (RBE^B(E_n)), using different values for $k_n(E_n)$ and $\Phi(E_n)$. The RBE(E_n) for muscle was normalized such that $<$RBE^M(E_n)$<$ = 4.5 (the value of the neutron RBE measured by Gavin [6] in the BMRR epithermal neutron beam for the end point of late skin necrosis in dogs) using $k_n(E_n)$ for skeletal muscle [3] and $\Phi(E_n)$ for the BMRR epithermal neutron beam in air. The RBE for brain was normalized such that $<$RBE^B(E_n)$>$ = 3.3, (the value of the neutron RBE reported by Phillip [7] for the BMRR epithermal neutron beam for the end point of late changes in the magnetic resonance images of dog brains) using $k_n(E_n)$ for brain [3] and $\Phi(E_n)$ for the BMRR epithermal neutron beam, at the depth of maximum RBE-dose in a dog head phantom.

Results

Performing the integrals in Eqn. 10, using the abnormalized $RBE(E_n)$ calculated in Eqn. 9, we found that $<(RBE^M(E_n)>= 2.63$, and $<RBE^B(E_n)>= 2.96$ normalization factors (c) of $c = 4.5/2.63 = 1.7$, and $c = 3.3/2.96 = 1.1$, for muscle and brain, respectively. A plot of the normalized RBE, $(RBE^M_{norm}(E_n)$ and $RBE^B_{norm}(E_n))$ vs. E_n is given in Fig. 1, where

$$RBE_{norm}(E_n) = cRBE(E_n). \qquad (11)$$

The calculations leading to the curve of $RBE^B_{norm}(E_n)$, which is shown in Fig. 1, were repeated, in the manner described above, using curves of $RBE(L)$ measured by Barendsen [5] for 1 and 80% survival. The resulting curves of $RBE^B_{norm}(E_n)$ vs. (E_n) are shown in Fig. 2.

Finally, a calculation was performed in order to assess the importance of the variations in $RBE^B_{norm}(E_n)$ which appear in Fig. 2. Specifically, the RBE-dose was calculated as a function of depth in an elliptical head phantom for each of the three curves of RBE shown in Fig. 2, using $\Phi(E_n)$ as a function of depth in phantom for our accelerator-based neutron source [8]. Due to the small contribution to the kerma rate, due to neutrons in the energy range where the three curves of $RBE^B_{norm}(E_n)$ differ, the differences among the resulting RBE-dose-depth curves are negligible.

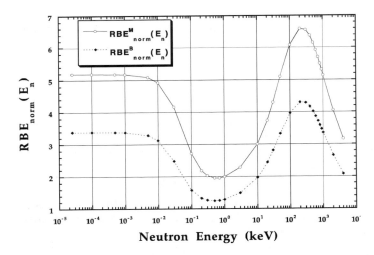

Fig. 1. Calculated curves of $RBE(E_n)$ vs. E_n for brain tissue and for muscle tissue.

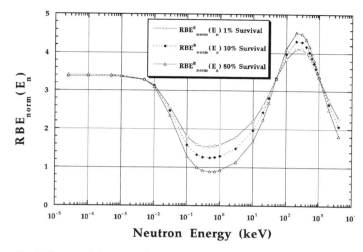

Fig. 2. Curves of the normalized RBE(E$_n$) for brain vs. E$_n$ calculated assuming cell surviving fractions of 1, 10, and 80%.

Conclusions

In conclusion, in this paper we have obtained reasonable estimates for the RBE of neutrons, as a function of neutron energy, for muscle and brain, for clinically relevant end points. The normalization of RBE(E$_n$) for muscle is useful for evaluating epithermal neutron beams based on in-air beam assessment parameters (neglecting spectrum modification of the beam at the skin's surface due to neutron moderation in the head); whereas the normalization of the RBE for brain is useful for evaluating epithermal neutron beams based on in-phantom beam assessment parameters.

Variations in our estimate of $RBE^B_{norm}(E_n)$, due to uncertainty in the appropriate level of survival, have a negligible effect on curves of predicted RBE-dose vs. depth in phantom.

References

1. Blue TE, Gupta N, Woollard JE. A calculation of the energy dependence of the RBE of neutrons. Phys Med Biol 1993;38:1693–1712.
2. Janni JF. Proton range-energy tables, 1 keV-10 GeV. Atomic Data Nucl Data Tables 1982;27: 147–339.
3. Photon, electron, proton and neutron interaction data for body tissue, ICRU 46. International Commission on Radiological Units and Measurements, 1992.
4. MCNPDAT6, MCNP4A standard neutron cross-sections (based on ENDF/B-VI), photon interaction and electron data libraries. DLC-181, RSIC Data Library Collection, Radiation Shielding Information Center, Oak Ridge National Laboratory, 1996.
5. Barendsen GW. Responses of cultured cells, tumors and normal tissues to radiations of different linear energy transfer. Curr Top Radiat Res 1968;4:293–356.
6. Gavin PR, Huiskamp R, Wheeler FJ, Kraft SL, DeHaan CE. Large animal normal tissue toler-

ance using an epithermal neutron beam and borocaptate sodium. Strahlenther Onkol 1993; 169:48—56.

7. Gavin PR, Kraft SL, Huiskamp R, Coderre JA. A review: CNS effects and normal tissues tolerances in dogs. J Neurol Oncol 1997;33:71—80.

8. Woollard JE, Blue TE, Gupta N, Gahbauer RA. Development and application of neutron field optimization parameters for an accelerator-based neutron source for boron neutron capture therapy. Nucl Tech 1996;155:100—112.

Neutron and γ-transport calculations for designing an irradiation field for BNCT

Sz. Czifrus

Institute of Nuclear Techniques, Technical University of Budapest, Budapest, Hungary

Introduction

In order to design a neutron and γ-filter arrangement, which can provide a thermal neutron field in the irradiation tunnel of the nuclear reactor of TUB, three-dimensional neutron and coupled neutron-γ transport calculations have been performed. Earlier, two-dimensional neutron transport calculations utilizing the code DOT 3.5 [1,2] were carried out for the reactor core and the results were compared with multifoil activation neutron spectrum measurements, showing relatively large discrepancies. These could be attributed to the asymmetrical core and reflector arrangement of a very small size, which cannot be modelled adequately in two dimensions. Therefore, in order to obtain reliable results, based on which the actual filter could be designed, both deterministic and Monte Carlo calculations have been performed using the codes TORT and MCNP4A, respectively.

Calculations with TORT

First, the neutron field was optimized. The preparation of a problem-dependent few (25) group cross-section set, utilized certain modules of the SCALE system and started from a 172 group AMPX master library, which was created from JEF 1.1 and 2.2 at IRI TU Delft. Among the steps of preparation were cross-section self-shielding using the Bondarenko and Nordheim methods for the unresolved and resolved resonance regions, a unit cell calculation and a cylindrical one-dimensional active core + reflector calculation, yielding a properly weighted (both in space and energy) ANISN type cross-section set. This was converted to the format usable for TORT using the program GIP.

A horizontal cross-section of the bodies used in the geometrical modelling can be seen in Fig. 1. To obtain the neutron source a P_1S_4 criticality calculation was carried out, followed by fixed-source P_3S_{10} optimization calculations. It was shown that for reliability the whole configuration must be divided into over

---

Address for correspondence: Institute of Nuclear Techniques, Technical University of Budapest, H−1521, Budapest, Hungary.

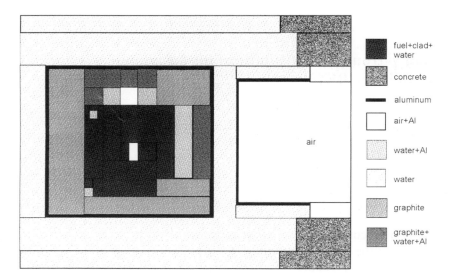

Fig. 1. Horizontal cross-section of the TORT model.

100,000 spatial mesh cells. To demonstrate the applicability of the modelling and calculational procedure, prior to the filter optimization several "supplementary" calculations were performed to compare the results with multifoil activation neutron spectrum measurements.

The coupled n-γ calculation followed a similar procedure, with the exception that here an ENDF/B-IV-based 27n-18γ library was applied, taken from the Scale 4.2 package. Since this set does not contain data for bismuth, data for this γ-shielding material were processed into the same format from JEF2.2 using NJOY91.91, again at IRI TU Delft.

Calculations with MCNP4A

For MCNP4A, the reactor core and surrounding regions have been modelled in fine detail (see Fig. 2). The final goal of the Monte Carlo calculations was to prove that the TORT results for the filter configuration are reliable. However, as with TORT, calculations aimed at comparing the results with measurements have also been carried out. The cross-section set applied was MCNPDAT5.

As a first computational step, a fixed surface source was generated from a criticality calculation[1]. Neutron spectrum in 25 groups and reaction rate values for the applied detector materials were calculated using point detectors during the criticality calculation for two irradiation positions inside the core and reflector. On the surface of the empty irradiation tunnel volumetric flux estimators were

---

[1]Note here that the k_{eff} value obtained by MCNP was 1.019, while TORT gave 1.024. The measured value is 1.011.

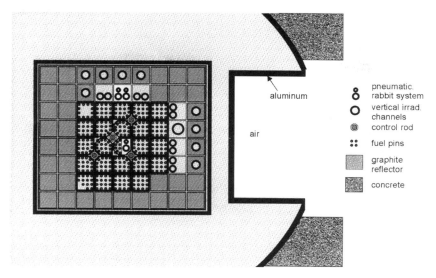

Fig. 2. Horizontal cross-section of the MCNP model.

placed and with the aid of the fixed source, weight-windows were generated and optimized in subsequent steps. For the irradiation position behind the filter arrangement volumetric and surface flux estimators were used. Application of point detectors could have been more advantageous because the final irradiation area is relatively far from the core region and thus, the problem being a considerably difficult deep-penetration one, volumetric detector results showed rather large standard deviations. However, for a point detector with a surface source a sphere surrounding all the fission material of sufficiently small radius should have been defined, which was not possible in the present case.

Results and Conclusions

The neutron spectra calculated using TORT and MCNP for an irradiation position located in the reflector region (G5) is shown in Fig. 3. It can be concluded that there is good agreement between the calculated spectra. In Table 1 a comparison between the calculated and measured reaction rate values is given for the position G5. A similar comparison can be found in [3]. The table shows not only that the two calculations agree well, but that there is good agreement between the calculations and measurements, too. Comparison of measured and calculated γ-dose rate values for the empty tunnel surface shows quite large discrepancies (over 70% for TORT and 50% for MCNP, in the same direction). Investigations are going on to determine the reasons for this disagreement.

During the calculational procedures certain advantages and disadvantages of both codes were noticed. On the one hand, for TORT the cross-section preparation is relatively complex and due to the large number of energy, spatial and

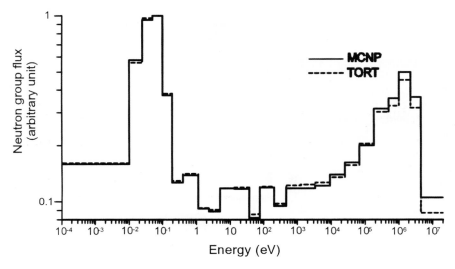

Fig. 3. Calculated neutron spectra for the irradiation position G5.

Table 1. Comparison of calculations with measurements for the irradiation position G5.

Reaction	Cover	MCNP C/M	TORT C/M
^{197}Au(n,γ)^{198}Au		0.89	0.97
^{59}Co(n,γ)^{60}Co		0.86	0.91
^{197}Au(n,γ)^{198}Au	Cd	1.08	1.18
^{59}Co(n,γ)^{60}Co	Cd	1.00	1.10
^{55}Mn(n,γ)^{56}Mn	Cd	0.78	0.85
^{58}Ni(n,p)^{58}Co		1.12	1.04
^{56}Fe(n,p)^{56}Mn		1.07	0.95
^{46}Ti(n,p)^{46}Sc		0.98	0.88
^{48}Ti(n,p)^{48}Sc		1.04	0.93
^{115}In(n,n')^{115m}In		1.49	1.41

angular mesh intervals, the calculations can be time-consuming. However, once an angular flux file is obtained, slightly different filter arrangements can easily and quickly be computed and thus optimized. On the other hand, MCNP has the advantage of offering very detailed geometry description and the use of continuous energy cross-section sets, correspondingly very accurate results. Nevertheless, obtaining reliable tally results with the optimization of weight windows and other variance reduction techniques also requires considerably long computer time.

Acknowledgements

The work was done in frame of the EC project on the Clinical Implementation of

Neutron Capture Therapy. Contract number: ERB-BMHI-CT92-0859. The author is very grateful to Dr J.E. Hoogenboom and P.F.A. de Leege of IRI TU Delft for their help in cross-section preparation.

References

1. Kloosterman JL. On gamma ray shielding and neutron streaming through ducts. IRI, TU Delft 1992.
2. Zsolnay ÉM. Recent investigations on neutron metrology at the Institute of Nuclear Techniques. Periodica Polytechnica, Ser. Physics 1993;1:17—32.
3. Zsolnay ÉM, Czifrus Sz. Thermal neutron field for BNCT experiments at the nuclear reactor of the TUB. In: Larsson B, Crawford J, Weinreich R (eds) Advances in Neutron Capture Therapy. Volume 1, Medicine and Physics: Amsterdam: Elsevier Science, 1997;386—390 (these proceedings).

Clinical significance of in-phantom evaluation parameters for epithermal neutron beams in BNCT

N. Gupta[1], R. Gahbauer[1], T.E. Blue[2] and J. Woollard[2]

[1]*Department of Radiation Oncology; and* [2]*Nuclear Engineering Program, The Ohio State University, Columbus, Ohio, USA*

Introduction

The task of optimizing an epithermal neutron beam for BNCT has been very challenging. Unlike X-rays, neutrons can be generated by only a few processes, each resulting in a wide energy spectrum. Moderating these neutrons down to a suitable energy window invariably results in a substantial loss in intensity, sometimes to a level that is so low that it is therapeutically unacceptable. To add to these problems, most neutron absorbers produce significant high-energy γ contamination. In epithermal beam optimization for BNCT, the three main questions that need to be considered are:

1. What neutron energy or range of neutron energies is most suitable for BNCT?
2. What is the minimum beam intensity acceptable for treatment?
3. How much γ contamination is acceptable in a beam?

There are no definite answers to the above questions, in part because the answers depend on many other factors, some of which are known imperfectly.

The basic goal of beam optimization is the delivery of a therapeutic dose to a tumor in a reasonable treatment time, subject to the constraint that the dose to the normal structures in the brain from the beam is a minimum and well below its tolerance. For a given beam, the maximum treatment time is limited by the normal tissue tolerance dose for that beam. In this paper, the overall philosophy of beam optimization with respect to normal tissue tolerances and treatment times are discussed. Clinically relevant beam optimization/evaluation parameters have been proposed and used, by way of example, to evaluate three different epithermal neutron beams to show the importance of choosing appropriate parameters for in-phantom optimization/evaluation of epithermal neutron beams.

Background

The dose distribution inside a head phantom from an epithermal neutron beam depends on a number of different factors, which complicate in-phantom beam

Address for correspondence: N. Gupta, Department of Radiation Oncology, The Ohio State University, Columbus, OH 43210, USA.

evaluation. The most important among these are shape and size of the head or head phantom [1], the size and collimation of the epithermal neutron beam used, and the directionality of the beam, (e.g., forwardly directed as opposed to isotropic in the forward direction) [2—7]. Besides, dose calculations in BNCT require the calculation of RBE-doses inside a head, using clinically relevant RBEs, which are not always known. Parameters chosen for evaluation of epithermal neutron beams should integrate the deleterious effects of the beam on normal tissues, and the potential effect of the beam on tumors.

Previously, an algorithm to estimate the normal tissue tolerance to mixed high and low LET radiations in BNCT was proposed by Gahbauer et al. [8,9,11]. A method was developed using it to compute the maximum allowable tumor dose or the maximum allowable treatment time as a function of boron load in the tumor [10]. From the perspective of beam optimization in phantom, such a method may be used to calculate the optimization parameters. The normal tissue tolerance restrictions under different treatment conditions, and for different boron compounds, may then be analyzed easily. At the end of this paper, one can easily visualize how it may very well be that for different boron compounds, different moderator assemblies may turn out to be the best.

Methods

Calculation methods

Fits of the distributions of various dose components with depth measured or calculated in a head phantom are the basis of our calculations and evaluation parameters. Various mathematical models were chosen to fit the different dose components. For the purposes of illustration for this paper, the dose components for three different epithermal neutron beams were fitted to these models. The data points from the measured beam data for the three beams (called for simplicity beams A, B, and C) are shown in Fig.1A—C. The fitted dose distributions for the three beams were used to calculate normal brain tolerance restrictions and corresponding treatment parameters as described earlier. Beam evaluation parameters, as described below, were also calculated to compare the three beams.

Evaluation parameters

One parameter for evaluating the beam intensity is the maximum treatment time (T) allowable before the normal brain tolerance is exceeded. However, one should not look at only the treatment time when evaluating a neutron beam. Another parameter is one that describes the effect of the beam in controlling a deep seated tumor. Since RBE's of different dose components and especially compound factors for the tumor are unknown, and because of the perceived ineffectiveness of low LET radiations in controlling high-grade brain tumors as reported by RTOG studies [12], we feel that a suitable parameter which would reflect the

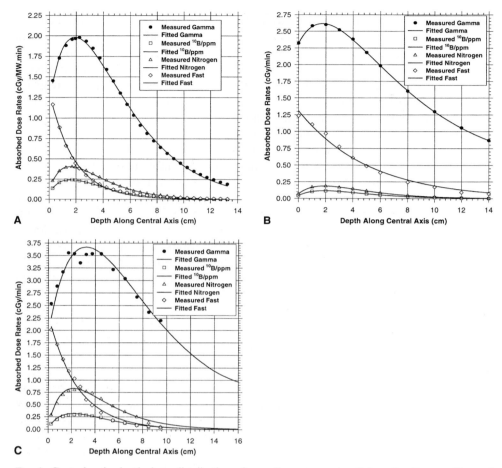

Fig. 1. Central axis depth-dose distributions from all components of dose for three epithermal neutron beams. **A**: Beam A; **B**: beam B; and **C**: beam C.

effectiveness of a given epithermal neutron beam in controlling a tumor is the total absorbed dose to tumor from all the high LET components delivered in the maximum allowable treatment time ($D_{T_{HIGH}}$). This evaluation parameter (not the total absorbed dose from all components (D_T)) is conservative with respect to its assessment to tumor damage, but it tests the success of a beam to treat tumors at different depths with BNCT alone.

Results and Discussions

General evaluation of the three beams

Table 1 shows a comparison of absorbed doses from different dose components of

Table 1. Comparison of absorbed dose distributions for three hypothetical beams shown in Fig. 1.

	Beam A	Beam B	Beam C
(γ dose at skin)/(peak ^{10}B dose/ppm)	4.88	20.22	6.19
(Peak γ dose)/(peak ^{10}B dose/ppm)	8.09	22.77	11.16
(Fast dose at skin)/(peak ^{10}B dose/ppm)	5.32	11.40	7.29
(Fast dose at 8cm)/(peak ^{10}B dose/ppm)	0.08	2.43	0.31
(^{10}B dose at 8cm)/(peak ^{10}B dose/ppm)	0.14	0.25	0.26

each beam, as a ratio of the peak ^{10}B dose/ppm for that beam. These data are presented as a qualitative comparison of the three beams. The rationale for choosing such a normalization was to assess the dose components for each beam per unit dose from the most desirable component (^{10}B(n,α)^{7}Li) to a tumor located at the depth D_{max} (or any other depth if so desired). The specific parameters that have been looked at are the entrance γ dose, γ dose at the peak, the fast dose at surface and at midline (8 cm, assuming a 16 cm deep head), and the ^{10}B dose at midline.

The γ dose within the head is comprised of primarily two components as described earlier: γs from hydrogen capture of thermal neurons, and external γs. The γ dose at the surface is proportional (in some manner) to the external γ contamination of the beam and the peak γ dose gives one an idea of the maximum γ dose received to normal brain. The fast neutron dose is maximum at the surface, and hence the fast dose at the surface is compared. The fast dose at midline is compared to get an idea of how energetic the fast neutrons in the beam are. For a well-moderated epithermal beam the fast dose at midline should be very small, whereas a large fast dose at midline would suggest that energetic neutrons are contaminating the epithermal beam. Finally, the ^{10}B dose at midline needs to be looked at to see if the epithermal beam is forwardly directed enough to be able to deliver enough thermal neutrons at midline.

From the numbers in Table 1, beam B seems to have the highest entrance γ dose, followed by beam C and beam A, suggesting that the external γ contamination from the three beams are in that order. The H capture γs ride on top of the external γs, as is evident from the fact that beam B has the highest peak γ dose/ peak ^{10}B dose per ppm. Secondly, beam B has the highest fast neutron dose at surface, followed by beam C and beam A. Finally, it looks like beam C is the most forwardly directed beam (since it has the highest thermal fluence at midline). Although beam B has an equally large thermal fluence at midline, it is probably due to the thermalization of the fast neutrons that persist to midline for beam B, and not from beam B being forwardly directed.

In-phantom evaluation of the three beams

Figure 2 are plots of $D_{T_{HIGH}}$ vs. tumor ^{10}B loading for the three beams shown in Fig. 1 for two different tumor/normal brain ^{10}B ratios (R), under similar fractio-

268

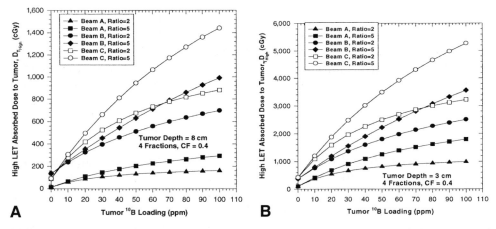

A

B

Fig. 2. Plots of the absorbed dose from all high-LET components ($D_{T_{HIGH}}$) to (**A**) a midline tumor, and (**B**) a tumor at 3 cm depth, for the three beams for two different tumor/normal brain [10]B ratios, and different tumor [10]B loadings.

nation schemes. Figure 2A is for a midline tumor (depth = 8 cm), and Fig. 2B is for a tumor at 3 cm depth. It can be seen from the graphs that for the configurations compared, beam A turned out to be the worst. It can also be seen how, under certain conditions (varying R in this case) one beam may look better than others, whereas this ordering may switch when conditions are changed. In Fig. 2 this can be seen in comparing beam B with beam C. Under most conditions beam C looks superior, whereas beam B looks superior for a few combina-

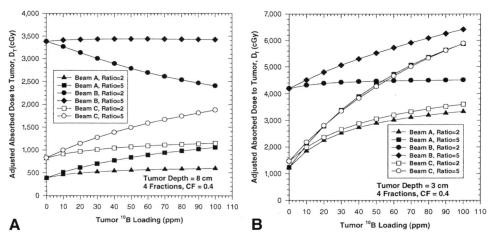

A

B

Fig. 3. Plots of the absorbed dose from all dose components (D_T) to (**A**) a midline tumor, and (**B**) a tumor at 3 cm depth, for the three beams for two different tumor/normal brain [10]B ratios, and different tumor [10]B loadings.

tions.

Figure 3 shows plots of D_T vs. tumor ^{10}B loading at two different tumor locations (midline, and 3 cm), for the three beams shown in Fig. 1. These plots have been included to show the extreme in choosing a beam optimization parameter, which is to give γ's full credit in controlling a tumor (as opposed to $D_{T_{HIGH}}$ which discounts the effect of γ's in controlling tumors). It can be seen from the graphs that for the three beams compared with D_T, beam B, because of its high γ contamination, looks much superior to the two other beams, under most conditions. However, because of the high γ and fast neutron contamination in beam B, an increase in tumor ^{10}B loading (and consequently in the normal tissue ^{10}B levels) results in less tumor dose, because the maximum allowable treatment time (to reach brain tolerance) gets shortened considerably and offsets the increased boron dose due to the increased ^{10}B levels. Beams A and C look identical for tumor depths of 3 cm, while beam C, because of its forwardly directed beam, looks superior to beam A for tumor depths of 8 cm.

Conclusions

In this paper we have shown the importance of choosing some clinically significant parameters for evaluation of epithermal beams in phantom. Choosing the appropriate parameters is crucial in evaluating an epithermal beam from a meaningful endpoint, rather than choosing unrealistic parameters, when embarking upon beam design and evaluation. This paper also shows some of the complex variables involved in evaluating a beam in phantom, and points out some unknowns that need to be identified in order to better evaluate neutron beams for BNCT.

References

1. Gupta N, Niemkiewicz J, Blue TE, Gahbauer R, Qu TX. Effect of head phantom size on 10b and 1h [n,γ] 2h dose distributions for a broad field accelerator epithermal neutron source for BNCT. Med Phys 1993;20(2:Pt1):395−404.
2. Yanch JC, Harling OK. Dosimetric effects of beam size and collimation of epithermal neutrons for boron neutron capture therapy. Radiat Res 1993;135(2):131−145.
3. Allen BJ. Maximum therapeutic depth in thermal neutron capture therapy. Strahlenther Onkol 1993;169(1):34−41.
4. Konijnenberg MW, Mijnheer BJ, Raaijmakers CP, Stecher-Rasmussen F, Watkins PR. An investigation of the possibilities of BNCT treatment planning with the Monte Carlo method. Strahlenther Onkol 1993;169(1):25−28.
5. Matsumoto T, Aizawa O. Head phantom experiment and calculation for boron neutron capture therapy. Phys Med Biol 1998;33(6):671−686.
6. Konijnenberg MW, Dewit LG, Mijnheer BJ, Raaijmakers CP, Watkins PR. Dose homogeneity in boron neutron capture therapy using an epithermal neutron beam. Radiat Res 1995;142(3):327−339.
7. Storr GJ. Assessment of ideal neutron beams for neutron capture therapy. Radiat Res 1992;131(3):235−242.

8. Gahbauer R, Goodman J, Blue T. Some thoughts on tolerance, dose, and fractionation in boron neutron capture therapy. Basic Life Sci 1989;50:81—85.

9. Gahbauer RA, Fairchild RG, Goodman JH, Blue TE. RBE in normal tissue studies. In: Gabel D, Moss R (eds) Boron Neutron Capture Therapy: Towards Clinical Trials of Glioma Treatment. New York: Plenum Press, 1991;123—128.

10. Gupta N, Gahbauer RA, Blue TE, Wambersie A. Dose prescription in boron neutron capture therapy. Int J Radiat Oncol Biol Phys 1994;28(5):1157—1166.

11. Gahbauer RA, Fairchild RG, Goodman JH, Blue TE. Can relative biological effectiveness be used for treatment planning in boron neutron capture therapy? In: Breit A (ed) Tumor Response Monitoring and Treatment Planning. Berlin: Springer Verlag, 1992.

12. Curran WJ, Scott CB, Horton J, Nelson JS, Weinstein AS, Fischbach AJ, Chang CH, Rotman M, Ashell SO, Krisch RE, Nelson DF. Recursive partitioning analysis of prognostic factors in three radiation therapy oncology group malignant glioma trials. Journal of the National Cancer Institute 1993;85:704—710.

Advances in Neutron Capture Therapy.
Volume I, Medicine and Physics.
B. Larsson, J. Crawford and R. Weinreich, editors.

Boron dose enhancement for ^{252}Cf brachytherapy

B.J. Allen and A. Ralston
St. George Cancer Care Centre, Gray St. Kogarah, New South Wales, Australia

Introduction

In Australia death rates from cervical cancer have decreased by a factor of two over the past 50 years, presumably as a result of screening. This improvement has not been shared by all Australians, with Aboriginal women having 6—7 times the incidence and mortality rates of all Australian women, a result similar to native Americans [1]. Further, the age-specific mortality rate increases rapidly with age, and approaches the incidence rate. Thus in Australia there are groups with poor prognoses that warrant improved treatment modalities.

In the Third World cervical cancer often presents at an advanced stage. Such bulky tumours are resistant to photon irradiation as a result of extensive hypoxia. As a consequence, cervical cancer has poor survival and poor local control rates. Survival at 5 years after treatment with external beam radiotherapy and high dose rate brachytherapy depends very much on the staging, i.e., stage I is 84%; II, 71%; III, 47% and IVa, 12% [2]. However, improved local control and survival has been achieved for advanced cervical cancer following neutron brachytherapy with Cf-252, when combined with external photon beam treatment, and without an increase in serious complications [3]. Cf-252 brachytherapy was also found to give a 91% 5-year control rate for stage Ib carcinoma of the cervix [4].

The potential of boron enhancement in Cf-252 brachytherapy was first examined by Schroy et al. [5] who irradiated Chinese hamster cells in vitro with Cf-252, and established a radiobiological boron enhancement. Beach et al. [6] carried out ANISN calculations and gold foil measurements in a head phantom. Dose enhancement was observed with increasing distance from the Cf source. Measurements by Wierzbicki et al. [7] in a multisource phantom showed a 10—20% dose enhancement, this being higher at the periphery of the planning target volume (PTV). Yanch et al. [8] reported Monte Carlo calculations in a phantom and assumed boron-10 concentrations to find a significant augmentation of dose which peaked at 10 cm from the source for [B] = 1—100 ppm. However, none of these authors investigated the region of efficacy which is governed by the PTV radius, wherein a lethal dose from fast neutrons is planned, and the BNCT margin, beyond which the total dose becomes nontoxic to cells.

Address for correspondence: B.J. Allen, St. George Cancer Care Centre, Gray St. Kogarah, NSW 2217, Australia. E-mail: b.allen@unsw.edu.au

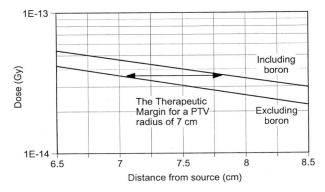

Fig. 1. Enhancement of total absorbed dose per neutron by neutron capture in boron-10 at a concentration of 30 ppm. The therapeutic margin is shown for a PTV radius of 7 cm.

Modelling method

Monte Carlo modelling of neutron and γ dose rates with various geometries of Cf-252 neutron sources have been previously reported [9,10]. The Monte Carlo code MCNP version 4a [11] was run on a 60-MHz Pentium computer. Each run used 100,000 source neutrons and took about 70 min for tally points at 1 cm spacing to achieve a statistical accuracy of 5% or less.

The pelvis phantom was a rectangular structure 40 cm long, 25 cm wide and 25 cm high, and filled with tissue-equivalent material. The Cf source was represented as a point source at the centre of the phantom, and hemispherical tissue inhomogeneities and tally cells were placed concentrically around the source. In this way the effect of bone, fat and air cavities on the neutron dose distribution can be readily investigated.

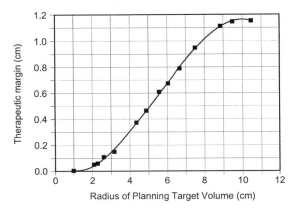

Fig. 2. The therapeutic margin is shown as a function of radius. In the radius range of 4—10 cm, the margin is typically 10% of the radius.

The neutron KERMA exhibits a minimum value at 35 eV. At lower energies, the N(n,p) is responsible for the energy transfer, while at higher energy proton recoils via the H(n,n)H reaction dominate. Thus the dose can be simply separated into low and high energy components, the latter being the major source of dose at all depths. As absorbed dose derives predominantly from hydrogen recoil reactions, the hydrogen content of tissue [12] is therefore a critical factor in determining dose distributions as a function of distance from the source.

These calculations assume a point source, have large voxels and do not include the γ-ray dose. They are made for comparative purposes and not for absolute absorbed dose accuracy.

Results

While the fast neutron dose dominates at all distances, the low-energy neutron flux (i.e., <35 eV) exceeds the high-energy flux at 3.5 cm from the source. This result suggests that thermal neutron capture in boron could enhance the dose to cancer cells at the periphery of large tumours. On the basis of 30 ppm of boron-10 in soft tissue, a small but increasing dose enhancement from boron capture is evident in Fig. 1. We define the therapeutic margin as the increase in PTV radius resulting from the boron for the same absorbed dose. This is calculated as shown for a PTV radius of 7 cm, where the margin is 0.7 cm or 10%. The therapeutic margin is shown as a function of radius in Fig. 2. In the radius range of 4–10 cm, the margin is typically 10% of the radius, which is equivalent to a 30% volume margin. Thus cancer cells beyond the PTV radius but within the margin which take up 30 ppm boron-10 would be eradicated and the probability of perilesional recurrence could be greatly reduced.

The median dose in the margin is calculated and the therapeutic ratio (TR) is obtained by dividing this by the neutron only dose at that radius. The TR is plotted as a function of radius in Fig. 3, and quite significant enhancements in the range 1.05 to 1.25 are found for PTV radii greater than 3 cm.

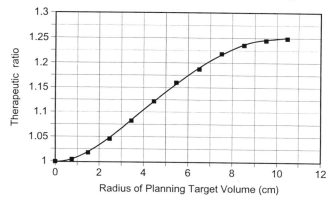

Fig. 3. Therapeutic ratio as a function of radius.

Conclusions

Selective uptake of boron by cervical cancer cells beyond the PTV would lead to significantly higher doses to such cells in the perilesional volume. This volume would represent a 30% increase in PTV, and as such improved local control might be expected. Currently there are no reports of boron compounds with selective uptake by cervical cancer. However, these calculations support the development and testing of such compounds.

References

1. Jeffs P. Cervical Cancer in Australia. Australian Institute of Health and Welfare Cancer, 1995 Series No. 3.
2. Hisao I, Kutuki S, Nishiguchi I et al. Radiotherapy for cervical cancer with high dose rate brachytherapy — correlation between tumour size, dose and failure. Radiother Oncol 1994;31: 240–247.
3. Maruyama Y, Van Nagell JR, Yoneda J, Donaldson E, Gallion H, Powell D, Kryscio R. A review of californium-252 neutron brachytherapy for cervical cancer. Cancer 1991;Sept.15: 1189–1197.
4. Maruyama Y, Van Nagell JR, Yoneda J, Donaldson E, Gallion H, Rowley K, Kryscio R, Beach JL. Phase 1-2 clinical trial of californium-252 treatment of stage 1B carcinoma of the cervix. Cancer 1987;59:1500–1505.
5. Schroy CB, Beach JL, Goud SN, Feola JM, Maruyama Y, Blue JW. Potential for boron neutron capture enhancement of Cf-252 brachytherapy treatment of localised tumours. In: Maruyama Y, Beach JL, Feola JM (eds) Californium-252 Brachytherapy and Fast Neutron Beam Therapy. Nuclear Science Applications B. New York: Plenum Press, 1986;2(3):763–769.
6. Beach L, Ashtari M, Harris M. Boron enhancement of high LET Cf-252 brachytherapy in the brain. In: Maruyama Y, Beach JL, Feola JM (eds) Californium-252 Brachytherapy and Fast Neutron Beam Therapy. Nuclear Science Applications B. New York: Plenum Press, 1986;2(3): 821–825.
7. Wierzbicki J, Maruyama Y, Alexander C. Boron neutron capture enhancement in Cf-252 brachytherapy. In: Allen BJ et al. (eds) Progress in Neutron Capture Therapy for Cancer. New York: Plenum Press, 1992;187–189.
8. Yanch JC, Zamenhof RG, Wierzbicki J, Maruyama Y. Comparison of dose distributions with B-10 augmentation near linear sources of Cf-252 obtained by Monte Carlo simulation and by experimental measurement. In: Allen BJ et al. (eds) Progress in Neutron Capture Therapy for Cancer. New York: Plenum Press, 1992;191–194.
9. Yanch JC, Zamenhof RG. Dosimetry of Cf-252 sources for neutron radiotherapy with and without augmentation by boron neutron capture therapy. Radiat Res 1992;131:249–256.
10. Bohm R, Nikodemova D, Fulop M, Pinak M. Monte Carlo simulation of ^{252}Cf dose distribution brachytherapy. Med Phys 1996;23(5):707–712.
11. Briesmeister JF. MCNP-a general Monte Carlo code for neutron and photon transport, LA7396-M Rev 2, Los Alamos Laboratory, Los Alamos NM 1986.
12. ICRP23 Report of the task group on Reference Man 1975.

© 1997 Elsevier Science B.V. All rights reserved.
Advances in Neutron Capture Therapy.
Volume I, Medicine and Physics.
B. Larsson, J. Crawford and R. Weinreich, editors.

The use of removal-diffusion theory to calculate neutron flux distributions for dose determination in boron neutron capture therapy

John Niemkiewicz[1] and Thomas E. Blue[2]

[1]*Department of Radiation Oncology, Grant/Riverside Methodist Hospitals, Columbus, Ohio; and*
[2]*Department of Nuclear Engineering, The Ohio State University, Columbus, Ohio, USA*

Introduction

This work investigates the use of removal-diffusion theory to calculate neutron flux distributions within a patient's head for BNCT treatment planning. The motivation for this work is a need to rapidly calculate dose distributions when doing routine treatment planning for BNCT. Calculational methods used to date include Monte Carlo simulation [1,2] and discrete ordinates [3] techniques. Each of these methods requires computer run times of many hours to achieve adequate results for a single distribution. Removal-diffusion theory [4] offers the potential advantage of a rapid calculation while giving results throughout the irradiated volume.

Methods

Removal-diffusion theory as implemented in this work involves the transport of the external source neutrons to their site of first collision. The resulting neutron first-collision rate distribution is then used as the source for standard diffusion theory and approximately satisfies the assumption of an isotropic source. This process is diagramed in Fig. 1. The left side of Fig. 1 shows the "removal" energy group structure that applies to the incident uncollided neutrons, while the right side shows the "diffusion" energy group structure. As indicated by the horizontal arrows, in their first scattering collision, incident uncollided neutrons can scatter into a diffusion energy group of approximately the same energy as their removal group or they can down-scatter into a diffusion group of lower energy. Subsequently, neutrons can then "diffuse" to a new location by additional scattering and may also down-scatter from their initial diffusion group into a lower energy diffusion group, as shown by the vertical downwardly directed arrows in the same figure.

Two source geometries were considered, a point isotropic neutron source and an accelerator-based neutron source. The energy spectrum, spatial distribution, and angular distribution of neutrons from the accelerator source were those pro-

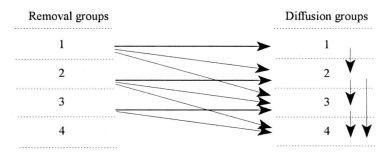

Fig. 1. Removal and diffusion energy group structure.

duced by an accelerator source optimized for BNCT, as designed at Ohio State University. Both neutron sources irradiated an ellipsoidal water phantom having the approximate dimensions of an adult human head (Fig. 2).

The "removal" part of the calculation involved the transport of the external source neutrons to their site of first collision. Removal parameters were determined from Monte Carlo calculations and included the total probability, per unit path length, that an uncollided neutron will have any interaction, and the probabilities per unit path length that an uncollided neutron, initially in one of four "removal" energy groups, will scatter in a single collision into one of four "diffusion" energy groups.

The neutron first-collision rate distribution, found as described above, was then used as the source for a standard diffusion theory calculation. Diffusion material parameters used for this calculation were determined by fitting analyti-

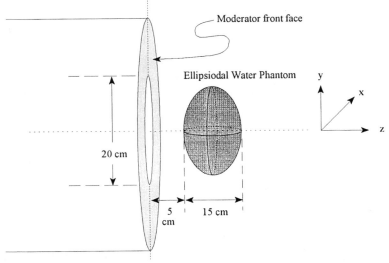

Fig. 2. Accelerator source calculational geometry.

cal solutions to the four-group, one-dimensional, removal-diffusion equation to neutron flux data found with Monte Carlo calculations for the same geometry and energy groups.

Finally, the neutron flux distributions found for the ellipsoidal phantom using removal-diffusion theory were compared to flux distributions that were determined by Monte Carlo calculations. The computer code MCNP was used for the Monte Carlo calculations, run on a Compaq Deskpro XL 590 PC. DIFF3D was used for the diffusion calculation and was run on a Sun SPARK Station IPC.

Results

The calculation of neutron flux in the ellipsoidal phantom using MCNP required many hours of CPU run time to achieve good statistics for neutron flux tallies at only 33 locations in the ellipsoid. The diffusion calculation required only 15 min of CPU time and resulted in neutron flux values at over 20,000 locations in the ellipsoid. Agreement was poor near the ellipsoid surface, as expected, since the diffusion approximation was not valid in that region. However, there was good agreement between the two calculational techniques, for both the point neutron source and the accelerator neutron source, throughout most of the ellipsoidal volume. The neutron fluxes calculated by both techniques for thermal neutrons are shown in Figs. 3 and 4. These fluxes were selected to be shown because most of the dose delivered in BNCT results from thermal neutron interactions.

Refinements to the removal-diffusion method in general, to the energy group structure and to boundary effects in particular, could lead to a practical method for calculating neutron distributions for NCT.

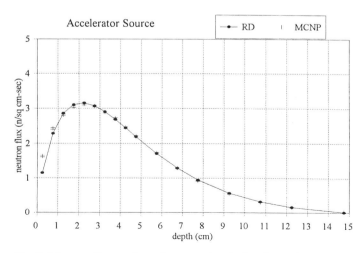

Fig. 3. Neutron fluxes along the central axis for thermal neutrons, calculated by both removal-diffusion (RD) and Monte Carlo (MCNP) methods.

278

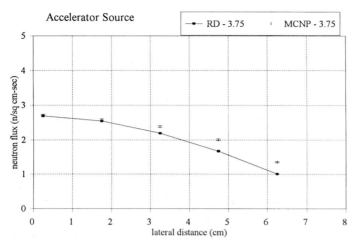

Fig. 4. Lateral profiles of neutron flux at depth (z) = 3.75 cm, calculated by removal-diffusion (RD) and Monte Carlo (MCNP) methods, for thermal neutrons.

References

1. Wheeler FJ, Griebenow ML, Wessol DE, Nigg DW. Analytical modeling for neutron capture therapy. Strahlenther Oncol 1989;165:186—188.
2. Zamenhof RG, Clement SD, Harling OK, Brenner JF, Wazer DE, Madoc-Jones H, Yanch JC. Monte Carlo based dosimetry and treatment planning for neutron capture of brain tumors. In: Harling OK, Bernard J, Zamenhof RG (eds) Neutron Beam Design, Development, and Performance for Neutron Capture Therapy. New York: Plenum Press, 1990.
3. Nigg DW, Randolph PD, Wheeler FJ. Demonstration of three-dimensional deterministic radiation transport theory dose distribution analysis for boron neutron capture therapy. Med Phys 1991;18:43—53.
4. Lamarsh JR. Radiation shielding. In: Introduction to Nuclear Engineering, 2nd edn. Menlo Park: Addison-Wesley, 1983;Sec. 10.9.

1997 Elsevier Science B.V.
Advances in Neutron Capture Therapy.
Volume I, Medicine and Physics.
B. Larsson, J. Crawford and R. Weinreich, editors.

BNCT dose sensitivity to the irradiation neutron spectrum

J. Arkuszewski

Paul Scherrer Institute, Villigen-PSI, Switzerland

The objective of this parameter analysis is to provide clear information about what energy of a neutron, entering the human head phantom, is the best from the BNCT point of view. This can be made with the MCNP Monte Carlo code [1] if the source neutrons are tagged according to their emission energy bins. The tallies are then binned in the same way and the performance of every source neutron can be calculated. The investigated angular and spatial neutron distributions at the phantom surface correspond to limiting cases of realistic irradiation facilities. The results can be interpreted in terms of the reaction-rate profiles across the head phantom as well as in terms of therapeutic gain (TG) defined as the ratio of the total dose deposited in boron-loaded tumor tissue and resulting from all radiation components (i.e., neutrons and neutron induced photons) to the maximum all-components dose deposited in the healthy tissue without boron. The ^{10}B is not assumed to be a component of the brain and does not take part in the neutron transport simulation. The energy deposition has been calculated for 30 µg/g ^{10}B in the tally spheres; no boron is present in the rest of brain where only ambient neutron and photon dose rates in the tissue are taken into account.

The ellipsoidal head phantom has been constructed according to the Snyder-Zamenhof model [2]. It consists of two ellipsoids; the inner one

$$\left(\frac{x}{6}\right)^2 + \left(\frac{y}{9}\right)^2 + \left(\frac{z}{6.5}\right)^2 = 1$$

contains the brain while the space between it and the outer one

$$\left(\frac{x}{6.8}\right)^2 + \left(\frac{y}{9.8}\right)^2 + \left(\frac{z+1}{8.3}\right)^2 = 1$$

is filled with bone representing the skull. Additionally there is a 12 cm long cylindrical neck with the radius of 6 cm along the superior-inferior or z-axis (Fig. 1). Strings of beads inside the brain are tally regions while the rest of the brain has been made transparent.

Address for correspondence: J. Arkuszewski, Paul Scherrer Institute, CH-5232 Villigen-PSI, Switzerland.

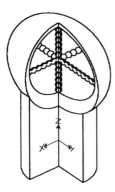

Fig. 1. Human head phantom with tally regions.

The composition of the phantom bone and brain components is shown below. Following the considerations of Zamenhof et al. [2], these data are based on both averaging the white and grey brain matter properties and on examination of CT scans of human skulls that can be considered as very reliable. The neck tissue is assumed to have the same composition as the brain (Table 1).

The neutron energy-source distribution is assumed flat between 0.1 eV and 21.5 MeV and binned in 3 equilethargy bins per decade, which amounts to the total of 25 bins. For every such energy distribution three kinds of spatial and angular source distributions are subject to analysis:

1) Collimated circular beams of 1 and 9.8 cm radius in the superior-inferior direction (z-axis);
2) inward cosine distribution on a ellipsoidal radius shell covering upper half of the skull; and
3) as above but with a shell covering the whole head except the neck.

The data used in the calculation taken from the standard MCNP library were based on the European Fusion File (EFF-1) evaluation [3], while the partial kerma factors were compiled from the ENDF-B/VI evaluation.

In order to get some more insight into the evaluation of results it will be helpful to scrutinize first a general dependence of various reaction rates on the neutron source energy. This is illustrated in Fig. 2 where various dose components are plotted at the phantom center for the half-shell source. The ordinate represents the source energy bins with the conversions shown in Table 2.

The total neutron dose has two major components: a mostly nitrogen (n,p)

Table 1. Phantom brain and bone composition,

	H	C	N	O	Ca	P	Cl	K	Na	g/cm^3
Brain	10.6	14.0	1.84	72.6	—	0.39	0.14	0.39	0.14	1.047
Skull	5.0	14.0	4.00	45.0	21.0	11.0	—	—	—	1.500

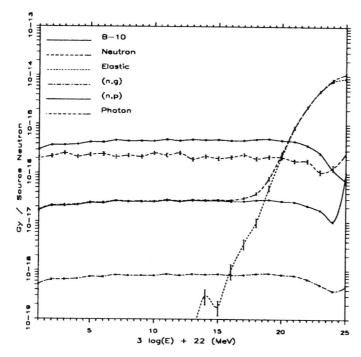

Fig. 2. Typical dose components vs. source energy (broad beam).

reaction and proton recoil. The intersection of curves corresponding to these two components determines the source energy above which the parasitic elastic energy deposition in hydrogen precludes the therapeutic use of the boron dose.

The maximum values of TG together with their space and energy location are summarized in Table 3. For all irradiation modes, TG is in the vicinity of three, the only exception being the Z-component of the narrow beam source, where TG is about six while for x- and y-axes the maximum occurs mostly at or near the phantom center. Only for the half-shell source and x-axis is it located near to the skull at 1 cm brain depth. Both collimated sources produce the z-axis maximum less than 1 cm from the irradiated surface while for both shell sources it occurs at 2 cm depth. The maximum TG values mostly occur in the energy bins 1–4.64 keV while for other, rather anomalous cases such as collimated beams and z-axis, the optimal neutron energy is less than 1 eV. Other source-axis configurations lay in between or slightly above. Figure 3 presents contours of therapeutic gain plotted against source neutron energy and z-axis. It can be concluded

Table 2. Energy conversion factors for Fig. 2.

Bin	1	4	7	10	13	16	19	22	25
MeV	10^{-7}	10^{-6}	10^{-5}	10^{-4}	10^{-3}	10^{-2}	10^{-1}	1	10

Table 3. Maximum therapeutic gain (TG).

Source	Axis	Location (cm)	Energy bin (MeV)	TG
Narrow beam	X	0	1.00E-3—2.15E-3	3.144
	Y	0	1.00E-3—2.15E-3	3.144
	Z	6	<1.E-7	6.396
Broad beam	X	0	2.15E-3—4.64E-3	3.074
	Y	1	4.64E-3—1.00E-2	2.911
	Z	5	4.64E-7—1.00E-6	3.547
Half shell	X	5	<1.E-7	3.139
	Y	0	2.15E-3—4.64E-3	2.932
	Z	2	2.15E-4—4.64E-4	3.129
Full shell	X	1	2.15E-4—4.64E-4	2.902
	Y	1	1.00E-3—2.15E-3	2.921
	Z	2	1.00E-3—2.15E-3	2.968

that the irradiation geometrical arrangement close to ideal is the half-shell source. In this case the incoming neutron current is assumed to be homogenous on the whole-shell surface which cannot be achieved in the real situation. Therefore it may be expected that the real half-shell source performance would be between

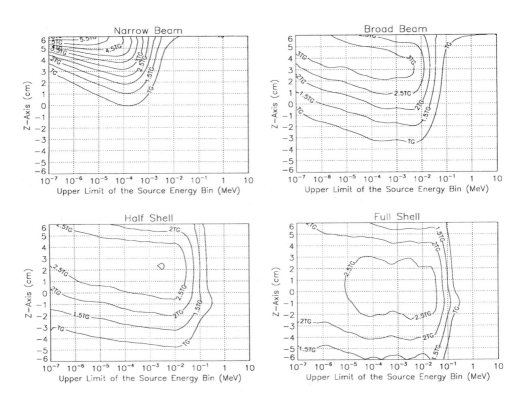

Fig. 3. Comparison of various sources TG contours for z-axis.

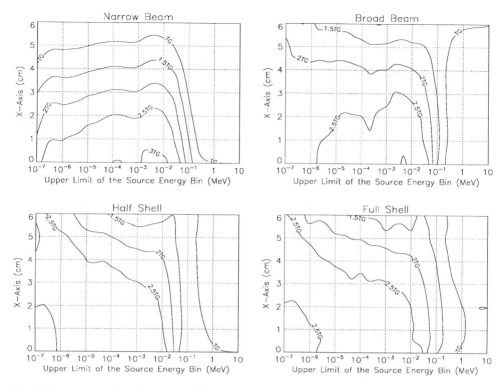

Fig. 4. Comparison of various sources TG contours for x-axis.

the broad beam and the idealized half-shell. Assuming a reasonable tumor-irradiation dose rate of 20 Gy/h, the requested neutron current on the skull surface amounts to about 10^{10}n/cm^2·s^{-1} for the half-shell source and is more than twice as large for the large collimated one. This is another important argument for the half-shell source. For the half-shell source there is a large range of neutron energy below ~ 5 keV where a relatively high value of TG can be attained even at the brain center. Moreover, a half-shell source irradiation cavity could make the positioning of the patients' head easier and, in principle, would permit the minimization of the harmful eye dose as compared to the full-shell geometry. The analogous x-axis results, presented in Fig. 4, corroborate the above conclusions: there is a considerable high value TG present along the x-axis for the half shell irradiation option. More detailed results can be found in [4].

References

1. Briesmeister JF. MCNP, A General Monte Carlo N-particle Transport Code, Version 4A. Los Alamos Report LA-12625-M, Rev.2, 1993.

284

2. Zamenhof RG et al. Monte Carlo based dosimetry and treatment planning for neutron capture therapy of brain tumors. In: Harling OK, Bernard JA, Zamenhof RG (eds) International Workshop on Neutron Beam Design, Development, and Performance for Neutron Capture Therapy. New York: Plenum Press 1990; 283.

3. Vontobel P. Assessment of NJOY Generated Neutron Heating Factors Based on JEF/EFF-1. PSI Report No.81, (1990), 1993.

4. Arkuszewski J. BNCT Dose Sensitivity to the Irradiation Neutron Spectrum. PSI Internal Report TM-23-95-04, 1995.

© 1997 Elsevier Science B.V. All rights reserved.
Advances in Neutron Capture Therapy.
Volume I, Medicine and Physics.
B. Larsson, J. Crawford and R. Weinreich, editors.

Space and energy distributions of the neutron dose field in a ^{10}B-loaded tissue-equivalent moderator

V.V. Kushin[1], E.A. Otroschenko[2], S.V. Plotnikov[1] and B.S. Sychev[2]

[1]*Institute of Theoretical and Experimental Physics; and* [2]*Moscow Radiotechnical Institute, Moscow, Russia*

Introduction

There are two main approaches nowadays to the problem of creation of epithermal neutron sources for BNCT. The first one is concerned with the use of fissionable materials, usually produced in nuclear reactors. Wide application of these technologies is considerably restricted by the problems of the safety of personnel working with fissionable materials and their storage, especially under modern conditions of ecological concern. An alternative approach of making neutron sources for BNCT is based on particle accelerators. The main attributes of this approach are the fast response and complete nuclear safety of these accelerator sources. Nevertheless, this approach requires significant power consumption and a substantial increase of operational complexity and cost of the source. Both approaches evidently have advantages and limitations.

The main purpose of the present paper is the search for an optimised scheme for a neutron source for BNCT, based on a combination of charged particle accelerator, subcritical multiplying assembly and filter-moderator [1]. In designing the scheme for a neutron source it is reasonable to take into account the following circumstances:

1. The use of a multiplying target of very high nuclear safety with $K_{eff} = 0.9$ increases the neutron beam intensity by a factor of 10 in comparison with usual nonmultiplying targets.
2. Additional reductions in power consumption can be achieved by using a convergent cascade scheme of neutron multiplication the series of subcritical cells separated by neutron gates [2]. For example, judging by estimates for 3-cell construction, it is possible to increase the neutron flux by a further factor of three.
3. It may be reasonable to use accelerated deuterons of rather high energy (e.g, 15 MeV) to produce a high neutron yield from the target.

Therefore, of special concern is the problem of the relative contribution of the

---

Address for correspondence: Sergey Plotnikov, Institute of Theoretical and Experimental Physics, B. Cheriomushkinskaya ul.25, GUS—117259, Moscow, Russia.

"fast" component of the neutron spectrum for the equivalent dose absorbed by boron-contained tumour tissue. The trade-off decision was based on the possibility of using epithermal neutron fluxes with the maximum therapeutically permissible upper neutron spectrum boundary.

Calculations

Model calculations were carried out for the reference geometry. The plane phantom (absorber) was considered to be a "3-layer pie" in the neutron beam direction. The neutron spectrum was taken to scale with $1/E$ in the range from E_{min} = 1 eV to E_{max} which was varied from 1 keV to 1 MeV. The compositions of the first and the third layers corresponded to soft tissue ($C_5H_{40}O_{18}N$) while the second layer contained a ^{10}B-load of concentration varying from 0 to 30 ppm (the thickness of this layer was assumed equal to 4 cm).

In Fig. 1 are shown the depth distributions of the total absorbed dose for various boron concentrations for the incident neutron spectrum with E_{max} = 100 keV. In Fig. 2 the depth distributions of absorbed dose at a boron concentration of 30 ppm in the second layer for various E_{max} is shown. Taking into account the RBE factors [3] the depth distributions of Fig. 3 are converted into the depth distributions of effective absorbed dose shown in Fig. 3. It is seen that the maximum value of the relative contribution of fast neutrons in effective absorbed dose in the second layer of 30 ppm boron does not exceed 10% when varying

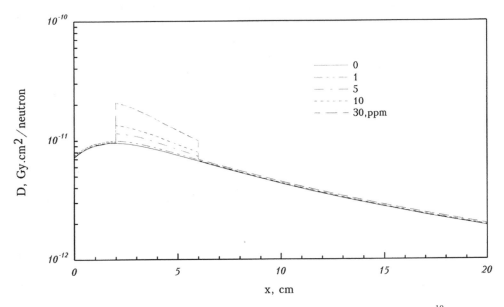

Fig. 1. Depth distributions of the absorbed dose in the three-layer composition at various ^{10}B contents of the second layer. E_{max} = 0.1 MeV.

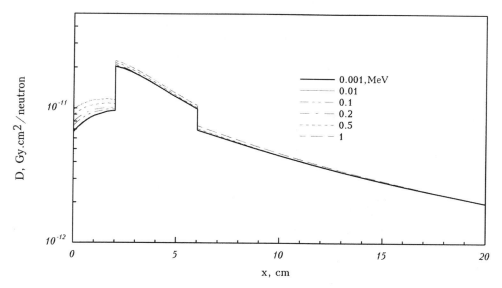

Fig. 2. Depth distributions of absorbed dose in the three-layer composition at various E_{max} values and the ^{10}B content of the second layer equal to 30 ppm.

E_{max} from 1 keV to 1 MeV. Calculations show that an absorbed dose rate of 0.01 Gy/s in the boron-contained layer may be reached by means of a 15 MeV deuter-

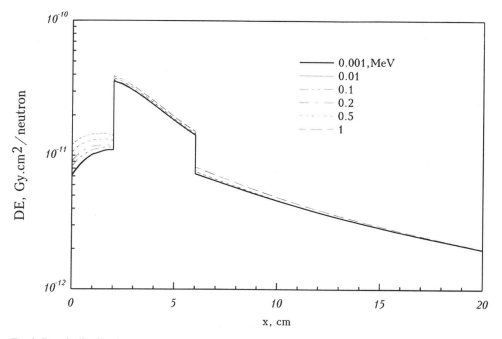

Fig. 3. Depth distributions of effective absorbed dose.

on linac and a moderator with a thickness not exceeding 40 cm.

Preliminary estimates show that the optimum combination of a relatively compact 15-MeV deuteron linac, with a neutron-multiplying assembly working in the deep subcritical regime ($K_{eff} = 0.8 - 0.9$) and with an appropriate moderator of 40 cm thickness reduces the required average accelerator current by a factor of 20—30. This leads to an accelerator current of only 1 mA, and a power in the multiplier assembly of 50 kW at a high level of nuclear safety.

References

1. Kushin VV et al. Spectral and dose characteristics of neutron field formed by a filter-moderator for BNCT. In: Proc. of the International Workshop on Accelerator-Based Neutron Sources for BNCT, vol II, Jackson, WY, USA. CONF-940976, 1994;279—290.
2. Chuvilo IV et al. A new BNCT-related possibility of original neutron flux density increase by use of multiplying cells chain separated by neutrons gates. In: Proc. of the International Workshop on Accelerator-Based Neutron Sources for BNCT, vol II, Jackson, WY, USA. CONF-940976, 1994;291—298.
3. Zhou XL, McMichael GE. Design of neutron beams at the Argonne Continuous Wave Linac (ACWL) for BNCT and Neutron Radiography. In: Proc. of the International Workshop on Accelerator-Based Neutron Sources for BNCT, vol II, Jackson, WY, USA. CONF-940976, 1994;427—440.

Advances in Neutron Capture Therapy.
Volume I, Medicine and Physics.
B. Larsson, J. Crawford and R. Weinreich, editors.

Three-dimensional back-projection reconstruction methods for Magnetic Resonance Imaging (MRI) of nuclei with short relaxation times

M. Flego[1], K. Nicolay[2] and P. Watkins[1]

[1]*European Commission, Joint Research Center, Petten; and* [2]*Bijvoet Center for Biomolecular Research, Utrecht University, The Netherlands*

Introduction

Clinical applications of nuclear MRI have developed rapidly in the past years, and the technique has become indispensable for the noninvasive imaging of soft-tissues which provides a high resolution and contrast. So far, most of the work on in vivo MRI has used H (protons). However, important biochemical information may be obtained by observing other nuclei as well. Here we report on the development of a three-dimensional (3D) back-projection reconstruction technique for imaging the spin density of nuclei with short transversal relaxation times, with potential application to imaging of boron-11 (^{11}B) in boron neutron capture therapy (BNCT). At present, the verification and quantification of in vivo boron content is a difficult problem and the development of a noninvasive method for measuring boron distribution in vivo would expedite BNCT investigations. An obstacle in the generation of NMR images for nuclei such as ^{11}B, is their very short transverse relaxation time (T2 < 1 ms), which is shorter than the minimal time-echo (TE) achievable in the standard spin-echo and gradient-echo imaging protocols. An additional problem for imaging boron in vivo is its low inherent NMR sensitivity. The signal-to-noise ratio (SNR) for ^{11}B imaging, at a concentration of 100 ppm boron in tissue, is about 1.6 million times lower than that achievable with proton imaging of tissue water [1]. To overcome these problems, the free induction decay (FID), rather than the echo signal, can be used to generate images in combination with 3D reconstruction methods. In this work a FID-based pulse sequence using a low angle nonselective excitation pulse [2], in combination with a 3D filtered back-projection reconstruction algorithm has been applied to proton MRI in rats and to ^{11}B imaging in phantoms to demonstrate its applicability to nuclei with long and short T2 times.

Materials and Methods

Measurements were carried out at the in vivo NMR facility of the Bijvoet Center for Biomolecular Research of Utrecht University on a 4.7 Tesla SISCO NMR spectrometer (200 MHz for protons) equipped with a 33 cm actively shielded gradient coil, producing maximal gradients of 3.2 G/cm. A male, Wistar rat (250–300 g) was used for proton imaging experiments. The rat head was positioned in a transmitter/receiver Helmholtz coil, 12 cm in diameter and 13 cm long, which provided a homogeneous B_1 field over the animal's brain. For boron-11 imaging a spherical phantom (6 cm diameter) containing a boric acid solution (100 ppm of ^{11}B), and a cylindrical phantom (2.5 cm in diameter, 5 cm long) filled with a solution of natural BSH (100 ppm of ^{11}B) in 4% bovine serum albumin (BSA) was used. The boron coil operating at 64 MHz was a Helmholtz type, 7 cm in diameter and 13 cm long.

The 3D back-projection sequence based on a FID acquisition protocol, used in these experiments, is depicted in Fig. 1. Here, a 3D read-out gradient is switched on and after a delay of 1 ms, in which the gradient is allowed to stabilize, a low flip angle ($\alpha < 90°$) radiofrequency pulse is applied to the sample. After the necessary dead time delay τ, the free induction decay is acquired in the presence of the field gradient. Following acquisition the gradient is switched off and after a delay d3, the sequence is repeated to collect a complete set of projections. Images of the spin distribution were reconstructed from the acquired profiles using a home-made implementation of a 3D filtered back-projection algorithm [3].

Experimental results

Figure 2 shows the reconstruction of transversal and coronal slices through the rat head (proton distribution) obtained using the method described above. An excitation pulse of 15 μs ($\alpha \approx 27°$ for a 90° pulse of 110 μs) was applied with a delay d3 of 50 ms. In total 4,096 projections were acquired with 64 sampling points and two transients per projection in a total time of 20 min. The field of view was 6 cm corresponding to a spectral width of 37 kHz for a gradient strength of 1.2 Gauss/cm. The pre-acquisition delay was 39 μs. Thirty-one slices in each direction (x, y and z) were reconstructed from the real part of the Fourier transform on a 64 × 64 matrix in about 5 min on a SUN computer, with an in-plane resolution of 0.93 × 0.93 mm^2. The low contrast between and within

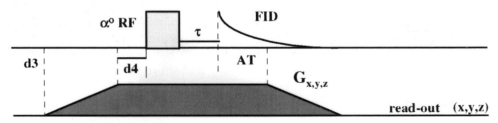

Fig. 1. The FID aquisition-based pulse sequence. The main features are low angle excitation, short repetition time and back-projection reconstruction.

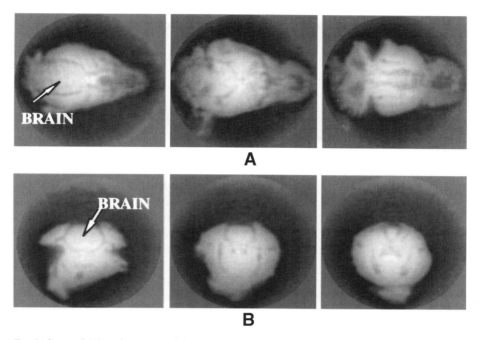

A

B

Fig. 2. Coronal (**A**) and transversal (**B**) sections of a rat head reconstructed from the FID signal by a 3D back-projection algorithm. 4,096 projections, 64 sampling points and 2 transients per projections. 64 × 64 image matrix. 0.93 × 0.93 mm³ in-plane resolution.

brain and muscles is due to similar proton density. Obviously, T2-weighting, which is inherent to most fast imaging methods and would introduce tissue contrast, is absent.

Figure 3(A) illustrates the reconstruction of the boron distribution in the

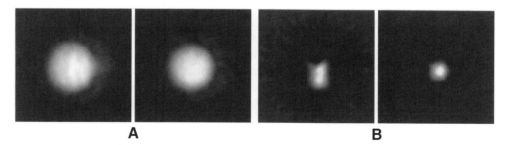

A   B

Fig. 3. **A**: Two sagittal sections of a boric acid phantom (100 ppm ¹¹B). 4,096 projections, 64 points, 256 transients with a field of view of 12 cm. 0.18 × 0.18 cm² in-plane resolution. **B**: Transversal (left) and coronal (right) sections of a cylindrical phantom containing BSH (100 ppm of ¹¹B) in 4% BSA. 4,096 projections, 32 points and 64 transients. Field of view of 20 cm. In-plane resolution of 0.625 × 0.625 cm².

spherical phantom (a glass bottle with a small neck, 1 cm long) containing boric acid. A 45 μs ($\alpha \approx 22°$ for a 90° pulse of 185 μs) RF pulse was applied to the sample with a d3 of 6 ms (repetition time of $\approx$ 7 ms). The short delay between pulses can be used because of the short T1 of ^{11}B (< 6 ms) and the small flip angle [4]. The line width of ^{11}B in this sample was about 170 Hz which corresponds to a minimum linear resolution of 0.14 cm (read-out gradient of 1.2 Gauss/cm) [4]. In total 4,096 projections were acquired in 2 h using 64 points and 256 transients per projection with a field of view of 12 cm; 31 slices were reconstructed along the (x), (y) and (z) directions in about 5 min; on a 64 × 64 matrix with an in-plane resolution of 0.18 × 0.18 cm^2. Figure 3(B) shows the cylindrical phantom filled with the BSH solution. In this case, since BSH was bound to the protein BSA [5], the line width was larger than in the previous experiment. It was about 500 Hz corresponding to a minimum resolution of 0.4 cm for a gradient strength of 1.2 G/cm. The experiment was performed applying an excitation pulse of 45 μs and a delay d3 of 4 ms with a dead time of about 37 μs. In total 4,096 projections were acquired in 80 min, using 32 sampling points and 64 transients per projection. The field of view was 20 cm; 32 slices were reconstructed in each direction in about 5 min resulting in a voxel size of 0.625 × 0.625 × 0.625 cm^3. Linear interpolation was used to display each slice on a 64 × 64 matrix.

Discussion

It has been shown above that MRI of short relaxing nuclei can be performed using a simple one-pulse back-projection sequence in combination with low angle excitation [2]. This sequence can be applied, in principle, to all samples irrespective of their T2 values. In the proton images, which have long T1 and high image resolution requirement with fairly strong signal, the 3D volume imaging technique is not satisfactory because of the long acquisition time even if only the read-out gradient is applied for signal encoding. However, boron imaging needs a much lower resolution due to the low SNR. In these conditions the 3D imaging technique with nonselective RF pulse excitation is desirable. Compared with traditional imaging methods the 3D scheme maximizes the SNR of the final images. Moreover, the FID-based acquisition protocol which avoids filtering of short T2 components, is essential for imaging fast relaxing nuclei such as boron. One problem with the described approach is related to the excitation bandwidth. Since the pulse is applied in the presence of the gradient, an unwanted slice selection effect may occur along the read-out direction especially for very low RF fields and strong gradients or big samples. However, since a small flip angle pulse is used, it normally can be made sufficiently short for any bandwidth required. This approach avoids signal sampling during the gradient ramp which would require careful data processing to avoid artifacts in the final image. A decrease in SNR due to the small angle excitation can be avoided using an optimum repetition time and an increased number of transients during acquisition [6]. In general, in each 3D experiment a compromise between the number of scans per projection and the SNR must be found in order to reduce the total acquisition time.

References

1. Bradshaw MK et al. Magnet Res Med 1995;34:48—56.
2. Hafner S. Magnet Res Imaging 1994;12(7)1047—1051.
3. Shepp J, J Comp Ass Tomogr 1980;4:94—107.
4. Callaghan P.Principles of nuclear magnetic resonance microscopy. Oxford: Clarendon Press, 1991.
5. Bauer WF et al. Progress in Neut Capt, Therapy for Cancer. Plenum Press, NY 1992;(In press).
6. Abragam A. Principles of nuclear magnetism. Oxford: Clarendon Press, 1961.

Nonuniformity of tumour dose from internally administered ^{211}At and ^{10}B

J. Stepanek, P. Cereghetti, B. Larsson and R. Weinreich

Institute for Medical Radiobiology (IMR) of the University of Zürich and the Paul Scherrer Institute, Villigen-PSI, Switzerland

Introduction

The use of compounds labeled by radioactive nuclides for therapy of tumours is receiving increasing attention. It is important to know the amount of labelled compounds required for a therapeutic effect. This depends on the spatial distribution of the tumour dose resulting from the nonuniform nuclide distribution in tumour. In order to protect normal tissue from irradiation, subcellular localization of sources of high LET radiation with very short ranges offers interesting prospects.

Attempts have been made to establish the α particle dosimetry of ^{211}At [1,2] and the α particle dosimetry of ^{10}B has been studied [3—6].

^{211}At is a therapeutically potent α particle and Auger-electron emitter. As indicated in the literature, approaches for applications of ^{211}At-labelled compounds are:

1. Intravascular therapy with microspheres or colloids.
2. Radioimmunotherapy with monoclonal antibody derivatives.
3. Intracellular metabolic trapping, for example with methylene blue or metastatobenzylguanidine.
4. Therapy using DNA ligands with astatodeoxyuridine or astatinated DNA markers.

No clinical trials with astatinated compounds have been performed so far. This is due to:

1. The hesitation of physicians to handle radioactive α particle emitters.
2. The poor availability of ^{211}At.
3. The instability of the astatine-carbon bond in vivo.
4. A general lack of toxicity studies.

In order to support the clinical approaches, we suggest substituting astatine for boron in some selected compounds, in the present phase of investigations and comparing the radiobiological properties of astatine with those of activated boron. The latter is the theme of the present contribution.

Methods, Calculations and Results

A three-dimensional random packing arrangement of cells was used as a model of a few-cell tumour [7]. A close-packed hexagonal spheroid was obtained by superposition of two orthorhombic face centred lattices. The position of the cells, the cell and nucleus radii as well as the thickness of their membranes can stochastically vary within certain limits.

The radiation spectrum of ^{211}At was obtained using the computer program IMRDEC [8]. The IMR version [9] of the Monte Carlo computer program GEANT from CERN was used to perform the particle transport calculations [10].

The ^{211}At decays with a half-life of 7.2 h, 41.8% to stable ^{207}Bi and 58.2% to unstable ^{211}Po, which decays with a half-life of 0.52 s to stable ^{207}Pb. Due to ^{211}Po having a much shorter half-life than that of its mother nuclide, the decay spectrum is fully additive, after multiplication by a factor of 0.582, to that of ^{211}At. In the decay chain to ^{207}Bi one α particle is emitted with an average energy of 5.869 MeV. ^{211}Po emits one α particle of average energy 7.441 MeV. In both cases these energies are almost equal to the most probable energy of the emitted α particles. Their stopping ranges are 69 and 97 μm, respectively. In all chains, including the decay of ^{211}Po, Auger and Coster-Kronig (CK) electrons are emitted, but prominently only in the decay of ^{211}At to ^{207}Bi. The detailed spectrum of Auger and CK electrons is given in [11]. 6.2 Auger and CK electrons with mean energy of 953.3 eV are emitted. Their stopping range is $\approx 1-170$ nm. Many of these electrons may therefore contribute considerably to DNA damage if the compound is attached to it. The total energy of recoiling atoms is 0.131 MeV. In the Monte Carlo calculations the total tracked energy was 6.837 MeV (without neutrino energy).

The total energy released in ^{10}B(n,$\alpha\gamma$)^{7}Li reaction is 2.79 MeV. This reaction branches, 6.3% resulting in an α particle of 1.78 MeV and a ^{7}Li ion of 1.01 MeV, and 93.7% producing a 0.48 MeV γ ray from an excited lithium state as well as a 1.47 MeV α particle and a 0.84 MeV ^{7}Li ion. The stopping range of the α particles is ≈ 8 μm.

The calculations have been performed for various distributions of ^{211}At or ^{10}B: a) homogeneously in the whole tumour (HT), b) on the cell membrane (CM), c) homogeneously in the cytoplasm (HC), d) on the nucleus membrane (NM), and e) homogeneously in the cell nucleus (HN). Spherical cells of 10-μm radii were considered with isocentric nuclei of 5-μm radii containing internuclear spacings varying between 10–100 μm. The spheroid model contained 136 cells in all cases. The approximate tumour radii were 70.1, 100.1, 130.1, 190.1 and 340.1 μm at the mean internuclear spacings of 10, 20, 30, 50 and 100 μm, respectively. The chemical composition was taken from ICRU report 46 (whole brain of adults).

Table 1 shows the average dose per disintegration to a nucleus and enhancement factors as a function of the mean internuclear distance for various com-

Table 1. Average dose (Gy) per disintegration to a nucleus and the enhancement factors as a function of the mean internuclear distance and compound distribution: HT—homogeneous in the whole tumour, CM — bound on the cell membrane, HC — homogeneous in the cell cytoplasm, NM — bound on the nucleus membrane, and HN — homogeneous in the cell nuclei.

Nuclide	Distribution	Mean internuclear distance (µm)									
		10		20		30		50		100	
		Dose	Factor	Dose	Factor	Dose	Factor	Dose	Factor	Dose	Factor
^{211}At	HT	$3.86 \cdot 10^{-3}$	1.0	$1.46 \cdot 10^{-3}$	1.0	$5.95 \cdot 10^{-4}$	1.0	$1.97 \cdot 10^{-4}$	1.0	$2.86 \cdot 10^{-5}$	1.0
	CM	$4.66 \cdot 10^{-3}$	1.16	$1.83 \cdot 10^{-3}$	1.25	$1.04 \cdot 10^{-3}$	1.75	$7.40 \cdot 10^{-4}$	3.76	$6.40 \cdot 10^{-4}$	22.3
	HC	$4.89 \cdot 10^{-3}$	1.27	$2.31 \cdot 10^{-3}$	1.58	$1.61 \cdot 10^{-3}$	2.71	$1.25 \cdot 10^{-3}$	6.35	$1.17 \cdot 10^{-3}$	40.9
	NM	$8.16 \cdot 10^{-3}$	1.60	$5.69 \cdot 10^{-3}$	3.90	$4.90 \cdot 10^{-3}$	8.24	$4.61 \cdot 10^{-3}$	23.4	$4.54 \cdot 10^{-3}$	159
	HN	$9.77 \cdot 10^{-3}$	2.53	$7.28 \cdot 10^{-3}$	4.99	$6.54 \cdot 10^{-3}$	11.0	$6.23 \cdot 10^{-3}$	31.6	$6.15 \cdot 10^{-3}$	215
^{10}B	HT	$2.56 \cdot 10^{-4}$	1.0	$8.83 \cdot 10^{-5}$	1.0	$3.96 \cdot 10^{-5}$	1.0	$1.29 \cdot 10^{-5}$	1.0	$2.15 \cdot 10^{-6}$	1.0
	CM	$3.40 \cdot 10^{-5}$	0.13	$3.04 \cdot 10^{-5}$	0.34	$3.04 \cdot 10^{-5}$	0.77	$3.04 \cdot 10^{-5}$	3.37	$3.04 \cdot 10^{-5}$	14.1
	HC	$3.11 \cdot 10^{-4}$	1.21	$3.11 \cdot 10^{-4}$	3.52	$3.11 \cdot 10^{-4}$	7.85	$3.11 \cdot 10^{-4}$	24.2	$3.11 \cdot 10^{-4}$	145
	NM	$1.97 \cdot 10^{-3}$	7.69	$1.97 \cdot 10^{-3}$	22.3	$1.97 \cdot 10^{-3}$	49.8	$1.97 \cdot 10^{-3}$	153	$1.97 \cdot 10^{-3}$	918
	HN	$3.14 \cdot 10^{-3}$	12.3	$3.14 \cdot 10^{-3}$	35.6	$3.14 \cdot 10^{-3}$	79.4	$3.14 \cdot 10^{-3}$	244	$3.14 \cdot 10^{-3}$	1462

pound distributions. It shows that it is much more important to incorporate ^{10}B than ^{211}At into the nucleus. The incorporation of ^{211}At becomes more important with growing distance between the cells. Because the stopping range of α particles emitted by ^{10}B is comparable with the nucleus size (8 µm), the dose to nucleus is the same in the NM and HN cases and almost the same in the HT and HC cases. In a previous study [11] it was shown that ^{10}B could be very efficiently placed in the cell cytoplasm if the cells were smaller than 10 µm in diameter and the nuclei smaller than 5 µm in diameter. In this case the α sources in the most peripheral regions of the cytoplasm still contribute to the dose to the cell nucleus.

With the exception of HT and CM compound distributions the ^{211}At enhancement factors are smaller than that of ^{10}B. This is because the more energetic α particles of ^{211}At distribute their energy more efficiently outside the cell nuclei. With ^{10}B distributed on the CM, the dose to nuclei is usually smaller due to the short range of the α particles (about 8 µm).

Also calculated were the minimum and maximum doses in the cell nucleus, in relation to the average dose in the case of a homogeneous compound distribution in the cell nucleus (20,500 disintegrations in 136 nuclei). This corresponds to a neutron fluence of $5 \cdot 10^{12}$ n/cm² at 25 ppm ^{10}B concentration, which is not very different to the present situation in neutron capture therapy of malignant glioma. In the case of ^{211}At the same number of disintegrations were considered for simplicity. They were 0.0095 and 3.0 in case of ^{211}At and 0.45 and 3.8 in case of ^{10}B. This implies that, especially, the ^{211}At-dose heterogeneity is large. A much higher concentration of ^{211}At has to be considered if all cells in tumour must obtain the desired dose.

Table 2. Spatial dose distribution.

Nuclide	Dose (Gy/disintegration) $0 \leqslant R \leqslant 10$ nm	Ratio of dose to that at $0 \leqslant R \leqslant 10$ nm	
		10 nm $< R \leqslant 100$ nm	100 nm $< R \leqslant 1$ μm
^{211}At	$3.00 \cdot 10^5$	$7.27 \cdot 10^{-3}$	$1.81 \cdot 10^{-5}$
^{10}B	$3.57 \cdot 10^4$	$1.10 \cdot 10^{-2}$	$5.55 \cdot 10^{-4}$
^{157}Gd	$1.03 \cdot 10^5$	$5.87 \cdot 10^{-5}$	$7.71 \cdot 10^{-7}$
Without Auger, Coster-Kronig and stripped electrons			
^{211}At	$7.04 \cdot 10^4$	$3.08 \cdot 10^{-2}$	$7.56 \cdot 10^{-5}$
^{10}B	$4.33 \cdot 10^3$	$8.96 \cdot 10^{-2}$	$4.57 \cdot 10^{-3}$
^{157}Gd	$5.82 \cdot 10^2$	$9.42 \cdot 10^{-2}$	$9.18 \cdot 10^{-5}$

Taking the Maxwellian-averaged cross-section of the reaction ^{10}B(n,αγ)^{7}Li to be 3,400 barns, then a ^{10}B concentration of 25 ppm corresponds, at a neutron fluence of $5 \cdot 10^{12}$ cm^{-2}, to a charged particle dose of 9.6 Gy. It is important to realize that the same dose can be obtained in 1 h at only $3.2 \cdot 10^{-5}$ ppm concentration ^{211}At.

Table 2 shows the radial dose distribution around a point source in three radial zones: 0—10 nm, 10—100 nm and 100 nm—1 μm. A strong decrease of the dose can be observed. Comparison of the results, with and without inclusion of the Auger and Coster-Kronig electrons in the case of ^{211}At, as well as of the stripped electrons in the case of ^{10}B indicates their large contribution to the dose in the nearest vicinity of the nuclide. Also included are doses from ^{157}Gd [10]. This demonstrates the advantage of ^{157}Gd over ^{10}B if they both were incorporated into DNA. Furthermore, ^{157}Gd has, at thermal neutron energy, a much larger (n,γ) cross-section than the (n,α) cross-section of ^{10}B, ca. 250,000 vs. 3,800 barns and the dose per disintegration is higher than that of ^{10}B at radii < 10 nm. Therefore, the use of ^{157}Gd would require much smaller atomic concentration.

In the above calculations it was assumed that, during the (n,α)-reaction of ^{10}B, five electrons would be stripped from the disintegrating nucleus. Furthermore, we considered that these electrons would have the same kinetic energy as they had in the electronic shells of ^{10}B, i.e., two electrons have energy of 306.23 eV, two have energy of 30.71 eV and one electron has energy of 21.72 eV.

Conclusions

The microdosimetrical calculations have shown that, in the case of cells with radius $\geqslant 10$ μm, it would be favourable to incorporate both ^{211}At and ^{10}B, into the tumour cell nuclei. This is increasingly evident with growing distance between the cells. The effect is less important in the case of ^{211}At due to the large stopping range of the emitted α particles. The heterogeneity of the dose to tumour nuclei is, for the same reason, much larger than in case of ^{10}B. These nanodosimetrical calculations have demonstrated the advantage of incorporating the considered nuclides into the DNA. Including the energy of stripped electrons leads to an increase of the ^{10}B-dose in the radius $\leqslant 10$ nm by a factor of about eight. An accurate measurement of the energies of stripped electrons of ^{10}B would enable more precise numerical investigations.

References

1. Humm JL. A microdosimetric model of Astatine-211 labelled antibodies for radioimmunotherapy. Int J Rad Oncol Biol Phys 1987;13:1767.
2. Humm JL, Cobb LM. Nonuniformity of tumor dose in radioimmunotherapy. J Nucl Med 1990; 31:75.
3. Gabel D, Foster S, Fairchild RG. The Monte Carlo simulation of the biological effect of the ^{10}B(n,α)^{7}Li reaction in cells and tissue and its implication for boron neutron capture therapy. Radiat Res 1987;111:14.
4. Charlton DE. Energy deposition in small ellipsoidal volumes by high-LET particles: application to thermal neutron dosimetry. Int J Radiat Biol 1991;59(3):827.
5. Stepanek J, Larsson B. Heterogeneity of the energy deposition by high-LET particles in the cell in the framework of BNCT. In: Hadrontherapy in Oncology. Proceedings of the First Int Symp on Hadrontherapy, Como, Italy, 18–21 October 1993.
6. Hartman T, Carlsson J. Radiation dose heterogeneity in receptor and antigen mediated boron neutron capture therapy. In: Hadrontherapy in Oncology. Proceedings of the First Int Symp on Hadrontherapy, Como, Italy, 18–21 October 1993.
7. Cereghetti P. A method to generate a close-packed hexagonal spheroid. Internal PSI document TM-29-94-4, 1994.
8. Stepanek J. A program to determine the radiation spectra due to a single atomic-subshell ionisation by a particle or due to deexcitation or decay of radionuclides. Comp Phys Commun 1996; (In press).
9. Knespl D, Reist HW, Stepanek J. Particle Track Simulation in Nanometer Range for Radiotherapy and Radiation Protection, Proceedings of SGSMP/SGBT annual meeting 1993.
10. Stepanek J. Radiation spectrum of ^{158}Gd and radial dose distribution. In: Larsson B, Crawford J, Weinreich R (eds) Advances in Neutron Capture Therapy, Volume 2, Chemistry and Biology. Amsterdam: Elsevier Science, 1997;425–429 (these proceedings).
11. Stepanek J, Larsson B, Weinreich R. Auger-electron spectra of radionuclides for therapy and diagnostics. Acta Oncol 1996;35(7):863–868.

Existing facilities

Advances in Neutron Capture Therapy.
Volume I, Medicine and Physics.
B. Larsson, J. Crawford and R. Weinreich, editors.

The physics and technology of NCT — an overview

Geoff Constantine

School of Physics and Space Research, University of Birmingham, Birmingham B15 2TT, UK

Introduction

Since the Kobe meeting, worldwide interest in epithermal NCT has been stimulated by the start of clinical trials in the USA. To satisfy potential demand for NCT for glioblastoma alone will require many powerful hospital-based neutron sources, but in the short term, development of the therapy must rely on research reactors currently in operation. Several papers at this symposium feature plans to use existing reactors to provide intense beams of NCT quality. Some of the physics principles involved in achieving this aim will be reviewed. I will also comment briefly on areas in which physics and technology are making their mark in the development and implementation of NCT.

Physicists and technologists — our role in NCT

It is worth reminding ourselves that the aim of the physics and technology fraternity is to provide the clinician, on behalf of his patients, with the radiation field best suited to the proposed treatment. A broad consensus has been reached of an epithermal neutron fluence rate of 10^9 cm^{-2}.s^{-1} or greater, with neutrons and photon doses per useful neutron fluence not exceeding 9×10^{-11} cGy cm^2 and 2×10^{-11} cGy cm^{-2}, respectively. Figures of merit (FOM), used to characterise beams, include E_m, the dose-weighted mean energy of the neutron spectrum, and a more refined FOM formulated by David Nigg of INEL. In his FOM the current to flux ratio J/ϕ forms the numerator, while the denominator sums the neutron and photon doses per incident neutron. An approach to FOM closer to reality includes a phantom in the beam description. Parameters such as advantage depth, advantage ratio and advantage depth dose rate indicate the range of treatable tumour locations, likely tumour dose at normal tissue tolerance level, and treatment time.

These descriptions of the therapy environment gloss over the question of the energy-dependent relative biological efficiency (RBE) for the processes involved. Physicists are helping to throw light into this dark corner by modelling interaction events at a microscopic level. Corinne Vroegindeweij and co-workers at ECN, Petten and INEL, Blue and colleagues at Ohio State University, and Pöller and Sauerwein at Essen report valuable contributions in this important area.

Neutron sources

At present only nuclear reactors can provide enough neutrons for capture therapy, although accelerator sources should soon become competitive. Let us look at the physics involved in converting neutrons produced at high energy from reactors or accelerator sources to an NCT-suitable spectrum. Most research reactors have been designed to supply neutrons to external experiments. The necessary penetration in the biological shield can be of any shape, but is usually either a broad chamber, normally graphite-filled to generate a well-thermalised spectrum, or a cylindrical hole of restricted size, to give access for samples or to extract neutrons from close to the core. The difference in aspect ratio between these designs, "thermal column" and "beam" reactors, respectively, necessitates very different strategies in generating an epithermal neutron spectrum.

Thermal column reactors

The first stage in adapting a thermal column is to replace the graphite by a less effective moderator, or more appropriately "spectrum shifter", since we only want slowing down to proceed partway between the source energy (a mean of ~ 2 MeV but extending to ~ 20 MeV for fission neutrons) and thermal energies (say 0.03 eV). Adequate penetration with minimum proton recoil damage to the surface (skin-sparing) requires a neutron spectrum predominantly in the range 1 eV to 10 keV. The ideal spectrum shifter will slow fission neutrons down very effectively to ~ 10 keV and rather more gently thereafter. While inelastic scattering can take part in slowing neutrons of high energy, for the lighter elements we are involved with here, elastic scattering plays the major role. The average relative decrease in the neutron's energy on scattering from a nucleus of atomic weight A, is given by

$$\xi = ln\left(\frac{E\ after}{E\ before}\right) \sim \frac{2}{A + 2/3} \tag{1}$$

(N.B. This is not applicable to H, but is only 3% in error for A = 2 (deuterium)).

ξ is constant over the whole energy range down to a few eV, the onset of chemical binding effects. The requirement for a spectrum shifter more effective at high energies can only be met therefore by a material having a cross-section that falls with decreasing neutron energy. Figure 1 shows the energy-dependent cross-section of aluminium, with energy plotted on a logarithmic scale. The horizontal bar at the top shows the energy loss for 10 average collisions. Seventy-three average collisions in aluminium will slow neutrons from 2 MeV to 10 keV. Each successive collision sets the neutron off in a random direction uncorrelated with its direction prior to the collision. This is the well-known "drunken man's walk" problem. The mean distance travelled from the source in (n) steps is proportional

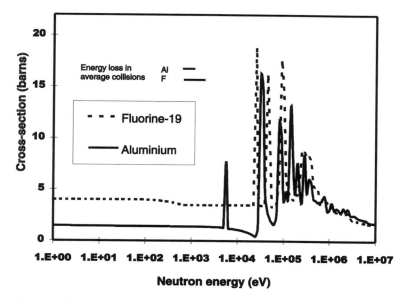

Fig. 1. Total cross-sections for Al and F.

to $\sqrt{n}$ but with a very large variance. This falls down when we realize that the aluminium cross-section shows considerable resonance structure. The drunken man not only moves in random directions but takes steps of wildly varying length, from a mean free path (step length) of ~1 cm at 30 keV, where the cross-section peaks at 17 barns, to 33 cm at 27 keV (0.5 barns in the antiresonance "window"). Movement of neutrons through aluminium while slowing from 2 MeV to 10 keV is thus dominated by window effects.

A solution to this difficulty lies in adding other components. Thus aluminium oxide Al_2O_3 as used in the current BMRR spectrum shifter, brings the fairly uniform oxygen cross-section to the mixture and partially fills the window. It was Baiba Harrington of ANSTO in Australia [1] who first noted that fluorine has resonances at neutron energies where aluminium has windows and proposed the use of aluminium fluoride in her therapy facility design for HIFAR. Figure 1 shows this fortunate match. Fluorine also has a very low inelastic scattering threshold (115 keV) which augments its effectiveness for slowing higher energy neutrons. Further slowing down occurs of course below 10 keV where the cross-sections become fairly uniform. Barring the few neutrons absorbed by the spectrum shifter material during slowing down, their fate is decided by diffusion, either back to the reactor, laterally into the biological shield or forwards to the output port, or alternatively if they undergo sufficient collisions, thermalising completely. A thermal neutron absorber, usually cadmium, will prevent them reaching the patient.

Since there is a high γ-ray content to the radiation leaving the core, and spectrum shifter materials must be of fairly low atomic weight, all the thermal column reactor NCT facilities incorporate a bismuth γ shield as the final layer. Photons are absorbed in this, while neutrons diffuse through it by multiple scattering, with inevitable intensity loss, but because of its high atomic weight negligible change in spectrum. The fact that the final collision takes place close to the surface of the bismuth results in a broad angular spread of the emerging neutrons. The design of a spectrum shifter is a compromise to achieve an optimum mix of flux intensity and spectrum. Both the reactors at which epithermal neutron capture therapy is undergoing clinical trials are of the thermal column type. The BMRR at Brookhaven has a spectrum shifter of aluminium and aluminium oxide, while the MITR employs predominantly sulphur with additional aluminium. The 250 kW Triga II reactor at Helsinki in Finland is the first at which aluminium fluoride is being incorporated in the spectrum shifter, while designs including it are being studied at Georgia Tech in the USA and at Studsvik in Sweden.

Beam reactors

Here the shape of the penetration through the shield precludes the possibility of filling it with spectrum shifter material. Virtually all the neutrons would be scattered out into the biological shield before reaching the patient. The only strategy available is to use a filter material whose cross-section is high for fast neutrons and low in the epithermal range. For instance if the fast neutron cross-section was twice that for epithermal neutrons, a filter that scattered 99% of fast neutrons out of the beam would only scatter out and lose 90% of the epithermal neutrons. The spectrum would be considerably improved, at the expense of intensity. Neutron filtering clearly puts a premium on availability of a high flux reactor, with a beam as wide and short as possible to maximise the solid angles subtended by the source, nominally the core end of the beam tube.

The final emergent spectrum is the product of the spectrum entering the core end of the beam tube and the transmission function of the filter. Light water reactors have an inherent disadvantage in that H's cross-section falls significantly above 100 keV, leading to hardening of the spectrum with distance from the fission source. This adverse effect is offset in the HFR, Petten by the 50 mm thick aluminium core vessel acting as a partial spectrum shifter before the filter stage. There is clearly an overlap in requirements for spectrum shifter and filter materials but, in addition, a filter needs to have a very low cross section in the sub-10 keV region. Oxygen and fluorine are thus precluded. Fortunately Ti has a large cross-section resonance around 25 keV which effectively closes the gap left by the Al window there and S has resonances that coincide with Al's windows at higher energies. With a suitable combination of these, with cadmium to exclude thermal neutrons, an output spectrum with a mean energy of $E_m \sim 10$ keV can be attained.

As in thermal column reactors, the low atomic weight materials in a filter do not address the γ problem. The original suggestion by John L Russell Jr and Denise Noonan, then at Georgia Tech, to use liquid argon was adopted by the author in building a beam for radiobiology studies on PLUTO at Harwell in the late 1980s. Its ratio of γ attenuation per atom to neutron cross-section sub-20 keV is at least a factor two higher than for any other material. It also has a useful high cross-section for fast neutrons and its window at 55 keV is adequately covered by the other materials in the filter. Because of its low density (1.4 g cm^{-3}) a considerable length is required (1.5 m in the HFR Petten filter), but this has the merit of minimising multiple scattering close to the patient, resulting in a high J/ϕ ratio.

A significant problem with Ar lies with the ^{36}Ar isotope which has a low cross-section for fast neutrons but a very high value below 20 keV, completely wrong for a filter. Although of only 0.34% isotope fraction, it is responsible for a factor of two intensity reduction. At Petten, the possibility of isotopic separation was examined but the cost of removing ^{36}Ar from 150 l of liquid Ar was prohibitive.

Fission plates

Many "thermal column" reactors can support a spectrum shifter NCT facility. In a design study for the Pavia Triga reactor by Rief of JRC Ispra in the 1980s a fission plate fed by thermal neutrons from the reflector gave an extended plane source of fission neutrons that could be optimally spectrum shifted in a favourable geometry, i.e., tall, wide and much reduced distance to the output port. A lower reactor power would suffice. Alternatively the concept can be employed to generate a higher flux and improved energy spectrum. This latter approach has been adopted by authors from both BNL and MIT. At the MIT reactor, an entirely new fission plate facility is proposed which gives a horizontal beam with a very large increase in epithermal flux over the present subreactor facility. The 30% Al/70% AlF$_3$ spectrum shifter is followed by 20 mm of Ti, cadmium to absorb thermal neutrons and a bismuth photon shield. The Ti resonance not only covers the Al window incompletely compensated by the fluorine resonance, but extending downwards impedes diffusion of neutrons of 10—25 keV while allowing easier passage for sub-10 keV neutrons. A significantly improved spectrum results. Sacrificing part of the intensity available by adding a conical, lead-lined collimator beyond the bismuth shield leads to useful improvements in the J/ϕ characteristics.

Accelerator sources

Following a dedicated workshop in 1994 [2], this symposium has attracted a number of excellent papers setting out plans and proposals for accelerator-based NCT facilities. Three basic areas must be covered: the accelerator/projectile choice, the target with its material, heat removal and induced radioactivity problems and finally converting neutrons emitted by the target into an NCT-favourable spectrum. Charged particles under consideration include protons and deuterons, impinging on the target materials Li, Be, D and W to induce (p,n), (d,n) and spallation reactions. Not every projectile/target combination from the above matrix is feasible of course but on the grounds of neutron yield the most favoured is the ^{7}Li (p,n) reaction, although some authors prefer Be to Li because its higher melting point eases the target design problem.

Authors recognise that currents of the order 10 mA will be required, and in session L several papers are devoted to the development of suitable accelerators including Van de Graaf, superconducting cyclotron, high current tandem electrostatic and electrostatic quadruple accelerators. Photoneutron production in D_2O from bremsstrahlung, emitted when relativistic electrons fall on a W target, is also examined. The target design problem is addressed by several authors. It is particularly acute for Li, with a melting point of only 179°C. Reducing the heat load by beam defocussing, rastering and oblique incidence are considered, together with heat removal by conventional liquid cooling and from Ohio State, ingenious use of heat pipe technology. There is close interaction between target design and the beam energy and current combination. Unlike the fission process with its isotropic emission of a fixed neutron spectrum, the spectrum and yield of neutrons emitted as a function of angle to the incident particle beam depend on its incident energy. Calculations are generally adequate for predicting such distributions for input to neutronic calculations of spectrum shifters, and measurements reported at the symposium for the ^{9}Be (p,n) reaction support this view, at least for total yield, with some shortcomings in detail at lower energies.

Most of the reactions proposed are endothermic, so the upper energy limit of the neutrons is given by the difference between the incident-charged particle energy and a reaction threshold, neutrons at the highest energy being emitted in the forward direction. A balance must be struck between the falling yield as the particle energy is reduced towards the threshold, and the reduction in size of the spectrum shifter needed and thus better utilisation of the available neutrons. Several papers explore this intriguing area. Because the target of an accelerator is generally much smaller than a reactor core, a much more compact spectrum shifter is called for from geometrical considerations. This, coupled with the limited upper neutron energy, brings D_2O into favour. Although, like H, deuterium's cross-section falls with rising neutron energy, this is insignificant below 1 MeV, and because of the high ξ value, only a few collisions will bring the neutrons to NCT-favourable energies. Photon production can be discouraged by suitable choice of materials, and waste neutrons absorbed in ^{6}Li compounds, either dissolved in the D_2O or as surface coatings, so that a bismuth photon shield is no longer necessary close to the patient.

Neutrons can also be made by a variety of reactions at rather higher energy. It is then a natural extension to use ^{10}B—loaded chemicals to enhance the fast neutron dose [3,4,5]. In spallation the physics of neutron production is completely different. Here a beam of (usually) protons hits a target of some convenient material, usually a heavy metal such as W, Pb or U. The impact of a proton on a target nucleus heats the latter, which then cools down by a process similar to evaporation in which neutrons, protons, etc., of MeV energies are emitted. The charged particles are of course immediately brought to rest nearby; neutrons can emerge to be moderated for various uses, including NCT [6]. The advantage is that the neutron yield, which depends on the energy of the bombarding beam, can be much larger than in the ^{7}Li (p,n) ^{7}Be reaction. On the other hand, the accelerator has to be capable of producing currents of the order of a µA at 600 MeV ranging to 300 µA at 30 MeV [7]. This represents a much larger investment than the machines required to produce the currents of up to tens of mA of 2−3 MeV protons needed for the ^{7}Li(p,n)^{7}Be reaction. If the spallation source could be combined with another process that also needed similar beams (such as isotope production) this disadvantage would of course be very largely reduced.

A difficulty is that the contamination of unwanted high-energy neutrons, whose energy extends up to the bombarding proton energy, is higher than from either fission reactors or from low-energy accelerators. The effect gets worse with increasing proton energy, which is therefore limited in practice to less than about 250 MeV, at which a few µA would be required [7]. It is also possible to use artificial radioactive sources to produce neutrons. While there are in principle several candidates, the consensus today is that ^{252}Cf, which has an energy spectrum similar to that from fission, is the most convenient. There are several established programs using it in brachytherapy [8,9]. It is again a natural extension to use ^{10}B-loaded chemicals to enhance the dose from ^{252}Cf. A variant of this idea is to use a small linac to produce neutrons within the patient using the ^{7}Li (p,n) ^{7}Be reaction [8,10].

Physics calculations — neutronics

Whether designing a spectrum shifter for a reactor or accelerator, or a filter for a beam reactor, a reliable method of calculation is vital. Many calculations will be needed to explore different parameters — dimensions, materials, etc., to gain physical insight and hence to optimise the design. Among authors at this symposium Monte Carlo has proved the most popular with MCNP the universal workhorse, with its acknowledged capability for point energy, coupled neutron photon calculations in complex geometries. The Achilles heel of Monte Carlo is the difficulty of achieving good statistical accuracy in deep penetration systems, which comes to the fore in extending calculations to remote parts of the problem, in phantoms fed by a spectrum shifter and assessing doses to organs in parts of the patient distant from the target tumour. However, with advances in computing speed this problem is constantly in retreat.

Several papers in the symposium undertake useful comparisons of MCNP with other methods, such as discrete ordinates codes, including DOT 3.5, ANISN, DORT and TORT. Deterministic codes can cope with deep penetration involving many orders of magnitude variations in fluxes across the problem, which raises acute running time difficulties for Monte Carlo, even with sophisticated acceleration techniques. The need to subdivide the neutrons into energy groups, restrictions on geometric complexity of the problem, angular discretisation of fluxes, etc., distance the discrete ordinates model increasingly from physical reality. However, it is usually found that running times are shorter than those needed to obtain satisfactory statistics on doses in an MCNP model. The Monte Carlo vs. discrete ordinates rivalry, and the pressing need for rapid computing, surface again in the treatment planning area. Excellent accounts are presented of the current treatment planning codes developed by INEL and MIT and their collaborators, and directions of further development discussed, including the use of removal-diffusion theory and optimisation techniques for summing the results of approximate three-dimensional dose patterns in choosing aperture sizes and beam orientations for multilateral irradiations.

Validation

Confirmation of calculations is vital in developing therapy facility designs and treatment planning systems. A number of papers give accounts of measurements of free beams emerging from spectrum shifters and filters, and yet more of neutron and photon fluxes and kerma doses in phantoms. A wide variety of techniques have been employed or are under development; resonance activation foils, silicon PIN diode, Bonner spheres and BF_3 and fission chambers for neutrons and TLD's, ionisation chambers and MOSFET detectors for photon fields. Dose rates have been evaluated in head phantoms using plain and ^{10}B-loaded tissue equivalent plastic microdosimeters.

While accelerator-based NCT facilities have yet to be built, a number of designs are under development, and measurements have been undertaken at various stages under low beam current conditions. These range from angle- and energy-dependent neutron yield determinations from a thick Be target, through flux distributions within a spectrum shifter, to a fully representative system including phantom measurements.

Technology

Since reactors involved in NCT are mostly 30+ years old, most technology problems have long since been solved at least for spectrum shifters. The liquid Ar filter circuit at HFR, Petten, presented some challenges; Ar, being close to its triple point, has a limited temperature range in the liquid phase. Initial operation revealed instabilities and boil-off of active Ar gas. Extensive investigations led to a rebuild of the heat exchanger with a two-pass feature, cooling the Ar both before and after its passage through the circulating pumps. Apart from the accelerator designer's difficulty in achieving and reliably transporting high enough beam currents, target design is destined to be the foremost problem in accelerator-based NCT. Neutron economy demands a compact target embedded in a spectrum shifter, while heat transfer is better served by a large target surface area. The Birmingham design is based on a D_2O cooled, Al structure supporting an intermediate gold layer, plated with Li on which a 10 mA proton beam, rastered at 2 kHz, falls obliquely.

New developments in physics and technology

Many innovative papers presented at this symposium are focussed on a wide range of problems. One aimed at the question of in vivo ^{10}B location during treatment comes from ECN, Petten, where a γ telescope views photons from ^{10}B and H capture events in a phantom. Addressing the same question is the "γ lens" of Birmingham University, featuring a W Gabor lens, a position sensitive γ detector and computer reconstruction of the three-dimensional distribution of capture events.

Other projects reported include MRI of the in vivo ^{11}B isotope distribution with back-projection reconstruction techniques, development of thermal neutron sensitive, small diameter glass fibres for surface and in vivo dosimetry, and in areas parallel to NCT, boron capture enhancement to ^{252}Cf fast neutron brachytherapy, ^{157}Gd as an alternative to ^{10}B and use of thermal neutrons from accelerator sources for extracorporeal treatment of liver tumours and alleviation of knee joint rheumatoid arthritis.

Current and projected facilities

The Brookhaven and MIT facilities, BMRR and MITR, respectively, are well-described as they are currently configured and operating during their ongoing clinical trials. A rounded account is given of the completed High Flux Reactor facility at Petten, which awaits the go-ahead to start the first clinical trials in Europe. Turning to the future, the front runner among reactor facilities is the Finnish research reactor FiR 1 at Helsinki with its enthusiastic team drawn from all disciplines who are pioneering the use of AlF_3 as a spectrum shifter material.

Although probably further away in time, the first among the accelerator-based NCT facilities to reach therapy conditions is likely to be that at Birmingham University, which has a flying start with the 1 mA capability Dynamitron proton accelerator already in existence, with plans for upgrading to 10 mA well advanced.

Conclusions

On the evidence of this symposium, assuming favourable outcome of clinical trials, NCT is on course for rapid expansion by the millennium. Demand, outstripping the capacity of reactors, will stimulate widespread provision of hospital-based accelerator-driven NCT facilities.

310

References

1. Harrington BV. A calculational study of tangential and radial beams in HIFAR for Neutron Capture Therapy. In: Harling OK, Bernard JR, Zamenhof RG (eds) Neutron Beam Design, Development and Performance for Neutron Capture Therapy, vol 54, Basic Life Science Series. NY: Plenum Press, 1990;97−107.
2. Jackson WY. First international workshop on accelerator-based neutron sources for BNCT. Idaho National Engineering Laboratory Report 1994;11−14 September:CONF−940976.
3. Hideghety K et al. Optimization of fast neutron therapy by neutron capture reactions. In: Larsson B, Crawford J, Weinreich R (eds) Advances in Neutron Capture Therapy. Volume 2, Chemistry and Biology. Amsterdam: Elsevier Science, 1997;621−625 (these proceedings).
4. Maughan RL et al. Feasibility of boron neutron capture enhancement of fast neutron therapy utilizing a superconducting cyclotron In: Larsson B, Crawford J, Weinreich R (eds) Advances in Neutron Capture Therapy. Volume 1, Medicine and Physics. Amsterdam: Elsevier Science, 1997;490−495 (these proceedings).
5. Langen K et al. Feasibility of the utilization of BNCT in the fast neutron therapy beam at Fermilab. In: Larsson B, Crawford J, Weinreich R (eds) Advances in Neutron Capture Therapy. Volume 1, Medicine and Physics. Amsterdam: Elsevier Science, 1997;501−504 (these proceedings).
6. Teichmann S, Crawford JF. Theoretical study of a spallation neutron source for BNCT. In: Larsson B, Crawford J, Weinreich R (eds) Advances in Neutron Capture Therapy. Volume 1, Medicine and Physics. Amsterdam: Elsevier Science, 1997;555−559 (these proceedings).
7. Arkuszewski J, Crawford JF, Teichmann S, Stepanek J. Neutron production for BNCT by protons of different energies. First Int Workshop on Accelerator-Based Neutron Sources for BNCT. Idaho National Engineering Laboratory Report 1994;11−14 September: CONF−940976.
8. Californium − Isotope for 21st Century Radiotherapy, NATO Advanced Technologies Workshop, Detroit, Michigan, April 1996; Proceedings to be published in the NATO ASI Series.
9. Lorvidhaya V et al. Boron neutron capture therapy in advanced cancer of the cervix. In: Larsson B, Crawford J, Weinreich R (eds) Advances in Neutron Capture Therapy. Volume 2, Chemistry and Biology. Amsterdam: Elsevier Science, 1997;540−544 (these proceedings).
10. Crawford JF. The potential of internal neutron sources in capture therapy. In: Allen BJ, Moore DE, Harrington BV (eds) Progress in NCT for Cancer. New York: Plenum Press, 1992.

NCT facilities at the Brookhaven Medical Research Reactor

Hungyuan B. Liu[1,3], Jacek Capala[1], Darrel D. Joel[1], Robert M. Brugger[1] and David C. Rorer[2]

[1]Medical Department and [2]Reactor Division, Brookhaven Natl. Lab., Upton, New York; and [3]McClellan Nuclear Radiation Center, McClellan AFB, California, USA

Introduction

The Brookhaven Medical Research Reactor (BMRR) is a 3 MW tank-type reactor designed for medical and biological studies [1,2]. Figure 1 depicts the horizontal schematic view of the BMRR facilities with the reactor core in Fig. 1,1 at the center, the epithermal neutron irradiation facility (ENIF) (Fig.1,9) on the east side, the thermal neutron irradiation facility (TNIF)(Fig. 1,10) on the west side, the broad beam facility (BBF) (Fig. 1,11) located at the end of the thermal column on the south face, and three experimental thimbles (Fig. 1,7) on the north side.

The reactor core is light water-cooled, water-moderated, and graphite-reflected. Heat generated in the graphite reflector (Fig. 1,2) surrounding the reactor vessel is removed by the forced flow of filtered air. The control rod system consists of four natural boron stainless steel rods which fit between the fuel elements. Nuclear instrumentation consists of a three-channel safety system which will setback or scram the reactor if two of the three channels are tripped.

The ENIF and TNIF include shielded (Fig. 1,6) rooms, each equipped with a special neutron beam port. Placement of the neutron beam port is 91 cm above the floor and almost centrally in the reactor wall, which provides clearance for a wide range of irradiation positions. Access to either facility is through a pair of hand-operated steel shielding doors (not shown in Fig. 1), each 106 cm wide, 212 cm high and 12.7 cm thick, with a space between. Cables and instrumentation wires can be snaked through two offset conduits in the 61 cm thick shielding walls of either irradiation room. There is a 20 ton beam shutter (Fig. 1,5) for each port. Each beam shutter can be raised or lowered hydraulically inside a vertical cavity to control the neutron irradiation. Each beam shutter is either open or closed and is monitored by interlock switches at the beam shutter control console outside either irradiation room and in the reactor control room. When a beam shutter is down, a high-density concrete section of the beam shutter blocks the neutron beam between the reactor core and the neutron beam port. When a

---

Address for correspondence: Hungyuan B. Liu, SM−ALC/TIR 5335 Price Avenue, McClellan AFB, CA 95652−2504, USA.

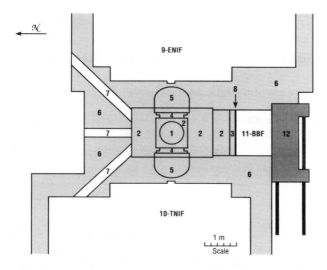

Fig. 1. Horizontal schematic view of the Brookhaven Medical Research Reactor (BMRR) facilities, showing 1) reactor core; 2) graphite reflector; 3) Pb shield; 4) Bi shield; 5) neutron beam shutter; 6) high-density concrete; 7) experimental thimble; 8) Cd screen; 9) epithermal neutron irradiation room; 10) thermal neutron irradiation room; 11) broad beam irradiation room; 12) high-density concrete rolling door.

beam shutter is raised, a filter/moderator section of the beam shutter is between the reactor core and the neutron beam port, and either an epithermal or a thermal neutron beam is extracted for irradiations.

The primary use of the BMRR at this time is for NCT experiments, including the current dose-escalation clinical trials at the ENIF. The following sections will review the specific functions of these existing facilities and possible upgrades in the future.

ENIF

A clinical trial of NCT for patients with glioblastoma multiforme started in September 1994. The trial uses the existing epithermal neutron beam for brain tumor irradiations and p—boronophenylalanine-fructose complex (BPA) as the ^{10}B delivery agent. The current collimator [3], made of a mixture of polyethylene and Li_2CO_3 ($\approx 93\%$ enriched isotopic ^6Li, 45 wt%), is 15.2 cm thick with a conical cavity 20 cm in diameter on the reactor core side tapering to 12 cm facing a patient's head. The collimated epithermal neutron beam has an intensity of 0.84×10^9 n_{epi}/cm^2.s at 3 MW reactor power and a beam directionality of $J_{epi}/\phi_{epi.} \approx 0.8$, with fast neutron and γ contamination of 4.8 and 2.0×10^{-11} cGy/(n_{epi}/cm^2), respectively. Current irradiation times for patients range from ≈ 40 min for unilateral up to ≈ 60 min for bilateral irradiations.

Depleted U fission chambers were mounted upward and downward at the corners of the irradiation port (reactor core side of the collimator), in a nonperturbing and nonperturbable configuration for neutron beam intensity monitoring during patient irradiations. These chambers are shielded by the collimator and give stable readings regardless of the position of a patient's head against the irradiation aperture. These chambers monitor the epithermal neutron flux ($\approx 70\%$ of total signals) in the beam, are calibrated to respond to the reactor power and also serve as reactor power monitors. During neutron irradiations, these chambers monitor the intensity and stability of the epithermal neutron beam, and integral chamber readings and appropriate ratio computations are displayed and recorded at 20-s intervals.

TNIF

The existing TNIF can be arranged for either small animals (rats and mice) or cell culture irradiations for NCT compound screening and normal tissue tolerance studies. The current collimator [4,5], made of a mixture of polyethylene and Li_2CO_3 ($\approx 93\%$ enriched isotopic ^6Li, 45 wt%), is 10.2 cm thick with a conical cavity 12 cm in diameter on the reactor core side tapering to 2 cm facing the animals. The collimated thermal neutron beam has an intensity of 17×10^9 n_{th}/cm^2.s with fast neutron and γ contamination of 4.0 and 2.5×10^{-11} cGy/(n_{th}/cm^2), respectively. The current irradiation time required to deliver a thermal neutron fluence, for instance 5×10^{12} n_{th}/cm^2 at an implanted tumor, 0.5 cm deep ($\phi_{th.} \approx 8.4 \times 10^9$ n_{th}/cm^2.s) in the head of a rat, is ≈ 10 min at 3 MW reactor power. Cell culture irradiations are performed by positioning a rotating device, made of Lucite with eight locations for mounting eight 1.5 ml vials, in the beam center line at 25.4 cm away from the irradiation port face. There is no collimator used during cell culture irradiations. The average thermal neutron flux inside the cell vials is 17×10^9 n_{th}/cm^2.s with fast neutron and γ contamination of 3.2 and 1.4×10^{-11} cGy/(n_{th}/cm^2), respectively.

An upgrade [6,7] was proposed to build a new beam shutter with a fission-plate assembly to produce an enhanced epithermal neutron beam. Design review of the new beam shutter system has been completed. This upgrade would produce an uncollimated epithermal neutron beam of intensity 19×10^9 n_{epi}/cm^2.s with fast neutron and γ contamination of 2.3 and 0.6×10^{-11} cGy/(n_{epi}/cm^2), respectively, compared to the existing uncollimated beam at the ENIF, which has an intensity of 2.7×10^9 n_{epi}/cm^2.s with fast neutron and γ contamination of 4.3 and 1.0×10^{-11} cGy/(n_{epi}/cm^2), respectively.

BBF

The BBF's irradiation hutch is much smaller than the irradiation rooms of the ENIF and the TNIF. It is heavily shielded on the top, bottom, and two sides. The facility is open to the entire south face of the graphite reflector. A 20 ton, 91 cm thick high-density concrete rolling door (Fig. 1,12) provides full access to the room and completes the shield when closed. To control diffusion of thermal neutrons into the room, a Cd screen (Fig. 2,8), which can be retracted, extends over the entire face of the facility. When the Cd screen is dropped, a broad γ beam is produced. In the past, this facility was used for whole-body irradiation experiments but currently is not used.

The existing uncollimated wide-field thermal neutron beam has an intensity of 12×10^9 $n_{th}/cm^2.s$ with fast neutron and γ contamination of 0.2 and 11×10^{-11} $cGy/(n_{th}/cm^2)$, respectively. As an alternate source of thermal neutrons, a proposed design [5] would transform the BBF to become a small-animal and cell-culture irradiation facility. Multiple rats, mice or cell-culture samples could be irradiated simultaneously. Another modification of the BBF, which deploys a fission-plate assembly, would prepare this facility for radiobiologic studies by animal whole-body irradiations and also for moderator testing experiments in designing neutron beams. The design goal for radiobiologic studies is to produce a clean and uniform radiation source with the capability of adjusting the weight between the dominant radiation dose components, i.e., fission neutrons and γ rays. There is no immediate plan for modification of the BBF at this time.

Experimental Thimbles

The three 10.2 cm diameter thimbles (Fig. 1,7) on the north side of the BMRR were cast into the biological concrete shield with no beam shutters. The radial thimble [8] is currently used to irradiate samples for evaluating ^{10}B uptake in samples by the method of prompt γ neutron activation analysis (PGNAA). The facility is equipped with a Ge detector, an automatic sample exchanger, and an IBM-486 computer-based control system to sequentially irradiate and measure up to a hundred samples in a day, changing samples manually or automatically. The tangential thimble that leads to the TNIF is for moderation experiments and is currently blocked. The other tangential thimble has a pneumatic system to convey samples to the edge of the graphite reflector zone and is currently used for radioisotope production and neutron activation analysis.

Acknowledgements

This Research is supported by the US Department of Energy under contract DE−AC02−76CH00016 with Brookhaven National Laboratory.

References

1. Godel JB (ed). Description of Facilities and Mechanical Components, Medical Research Reactor (MRR), BNL 600(T−173), Brookhaven National Laboratory, 1960.
2. Liu HB, Brugger RM, Greenberg DD, Rorer DC, Hu JP, Hauptman HM. Enhancement of the epithermal neutron beam used for BNCT at the BMRR. Int J Radiation Oncol Biol Phys 1994; 28:1149−1156.

3. Liu HB, Greenberg DD, Capala J, Coderre JA, Wheeler FJ. An improved neutron collimator for brain tumor irradiations in clinical boron neutron capture therapy. Med Phys 1997;(In press).
4. Liu HB, Joel DD, Slatkin DN, Coderre JA. Improved apparatus for neutron capture therapy of rat brain tumors. Int J Radiation Oncol Biol Phys 1994;28:1167—1173.
5. Liu HB. Design of a small-animal thermal-neutron irradiation facility at the Brookhaven Medical Research Reactor. Nucl Tech 1996;115:311—319.
6. Liu HB, Brugger RM, Rorer DC, Tichler PR, Hu JP. Design of a high-flux epithermal neutron beam using ^{235}U fission plates at the Brookhaven Medical Research Reactor. Med Phys 1994; 21(10):1627—1631.
7. Liu HB, Patti FJ. Epithermal neutron beam upgrade with a fission plate converter at the Brookhaven Medical Research Reactor. Nucl Tech 1996;(In press).
8   Fairchild RG, Gabel D, Laster BH, Greenberg D, Kiszenick W, Micca PL. Microanalytical techniques for boron analysis using the ^{10}B (n,α) ^{7}Li reaction. Med Phys 1986;13(1):50—56.

© 1997 Elsevier Science B.V. All rights reserved.
Advances in Neutron Capture Therapy.
Volume I, Medicine and Physics.
B. Larsson, J. Crawford and R. Weinreich, editors.

The irradiation characteristics of the upgraded heavy water facility of the Kyoto University Reactor

Yoshinori Sakurai, Tooru Kobayashi, Keiji Kanda and Koji Ono
Research Reactor Institute, Kyoto University, Kumatori-cho, Sennan-gun, Osaka, Japan

Keywords: control of depth dose distribution, epithermal neutron enhancement region, epithermal neutron irradiation, heavy water neutron irradiation facility, Kyoto university reactor (KUR), mixing ratio of epithermal neutrons to thermal neutrons, spectrum shifter, thermal neutron filters, thermal neutron irradiation.

Introduction

It is very important in NCT to get sufficient thermal neutron flux at the tumor without exceeding the tolerance dose of normal tissue. For thermal neutron irradiation, thermal neutron flux rapidly decreases in human tissue, which mainly consists of water, due to absorption and scatter in H. For epithermal neutron irradiation, the incident epithermal neutrons are thermalized mainly by H. Thermal neutron flux distributions in human tissue have peaks between 2 and 3 cm depth. So, the relative thermal neutron flux distribution due to epithermal neutron irradiation is more suitable for deep-seated tumor than that due to thermal neutron irradiation [1]. Thus, it is expected that thermal neutron flux distribution can be controlled by changing the mixing ratio of epithermal neutrons to thermal neutrons.

The heavy water neutron irradiation facility of the Kyoto University Reactor (KUR) was remodeled in May 1996 for neutron capture therapy [2]. In order to control the neutron energy spectrum, the epithermal neutron enhancement region (Al 80% / D_2O 20%), the spectrum shifter (D_2O) and thermal neutron filters (boral and cadmium) are employed at the updated facility. The facility is useful for neutron irradiations, offering energy spectra ranging from nearly pure thermal neutrons to epithermal neutrons, by controlling the heavy water thickness of the spectrum shifter and employing thermal neutron filters of cadmium and boral.

Experiments for depth dose distributions

Depth distributions of thermal neutron fluxes, cadmium ratios and γ-ray dose equivalent rates in a head phantom were measured for several irradiation modes at the updated facility. Thermal neutron fluxes and cadmium ratios were measured using gold wires of 0.25 mm diameter and cadmium tube of 0.5 mm thickness. γ-ray dose rates were measured using TLDs of BeO. Here, the results are shown for the "standard thermal mode", the "standard mix mode" and the "standard epithermal mode", whose cadmium ratios are almost 150, 9.4 and 1.1, respectively.

Figure 1 shows the comparison of the measured depth distributions of thermal neutron flux among the standard irradiation modes and the old thermal irradiation field (the cadmium ratio is approximately 5,000). The distributions are normalized at the peak. As the cadmium ratio of the incident neutron beam is smaller, the distribution shape is more gentle, the distribution peak position is deeper, and the relative fluence at the deeper part is larger. For the old thermal irradiation field, the depth where the relative flux is 20% of that at the peak position, is about 3.7 cm. At the updated facility, it is about 4.5 cm for the standard thermal mode, 5.3 cm for the standard mix mode, and 8 cm for the standard epithermal mode. Not only the depth distributions but also the radial distributions are expected to be improved.

Figure 2 shows the comparison of the measured depth distributions of γ-ray dose equivalent rate among the standard irradiation modes and the old thermal irradiation field. The distributions are normalized to thermal neutron flux at the peak. The γ-rays in the phantom are almost always the secondary γ-rays generated from $^{1}H(n,\gamma)^{2}D$ reactions. So, the γ-ray dose rate depends on the thermal neutron flux. Figure 3 shows the measured depth distributions of thermal neutron flux and cadmium ratio in the phantom for the standard epithermal mode. The cadmium ratio increases as a quadratic function of the depth. However, at a depth of over 10 cm, the measured values decrease. This is thought to be due to the influence of the high-energy components of the incident neutron beam.

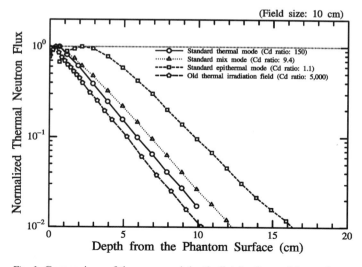

Fig. 1. Comparison of the measured depth distributions of thermal neutron flux.

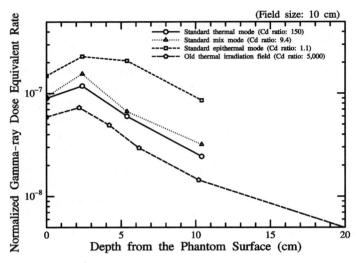

Fig. 2. Comparison of the measured depth distributions of γ-ray dose equivalent rate normalized by thermal neutron flux at the peak.

Control of depth dose distribution

At the updated facility, the mixing ratio of thermal and epithermal neutrons can be controlled by employing D_2O spectrum shifters and thermal neutron filters of cadmium and boral. As shown in Fig. 1 it is expected that the thermal neutron flux distribution can be controlled between the standard mix mode and the standard epithermal mode by employing the cadmium filter. Thermal neutron fluxes,

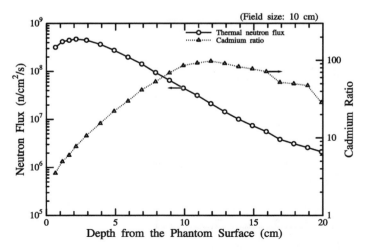

Fig. 3. Measured depth distributions of thermal and cadmium ratio in the phantom for the standard epithermal mode.

cadmium ratios and γ-ray dose equivalent rates were experimentally estimated by changing the aperture of the cadmium filter.

Figure 4 shows the relative intensities of neutrons and γ-rays, and cadmium ratios at the standard irradiation point as functions of the cadmium filter aperture. It is assumed that the epithermal neutrons have a pure $1/E$ spectrum and the energy range is from 0.6 eV to 10 keV. The epithermal neutron intensity hardly changes. On the other hand, the thermal neutron intensity, the γ-ray dose and the cadmium ratio decrease as the cadmium filter aperture decreases. From the results, it was found that the γ-rays were almost generated from the (n,γ) reactions of the bismuth with thermal neutrons. For the cadmium filter aperture of smaller than about 5 cm, the γ-ray intensity increases as the aperture decreases. The reason is thought to be that the γ-rays generated from the cadmium filter exceed those from the core-side and the bismuth layer.

It was confirmed that the cadmium ratio can be controlled from almost one to the maximum value of the irradiation mode by changing the cadmium filter aperture. It is expected that the relative thermal neutron flux distribution in a human body can be controlled employing both the spectrum shifter and the cadmium filter.

Conclusion

The following conclusions were confirmed from the experimental results:
1. By varying the D_2O thickness of the spectrum shifter, mainly epithermal and fast neutron components can be changed.
2. By changing the aperture of the thermal neutron filters of cadmium, the mixing ratio of thermal neutrons to epithermal neutrons can be changed without reducing the epithermal neutron intensity.

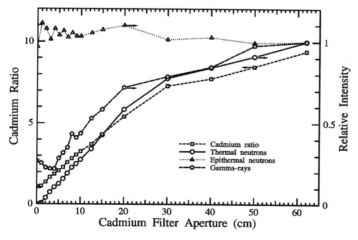

Fig. 4. Measured relative intensity of neutrons and γ-rays, and cadmium ratio as functions of the cadmium filter aperture.

3. Using both the spectrum shifter and the thermal neutron filters, the depth dose distribution is expected to be controllable.

Acknowledgements

The authors would like to thank Prof Hiroshi Utsumi of Kyoto University Research Reactor Institute (KURRI) for helpful advice from the side of radiation biology. The authors also thank Mr Daniel Osborne of Purdue University and Mr Masayori Ishikawa of Kyoto University Graduate School for their assistance in the experiments. Lastly, the authors would like to thank Dr Hannah Mitchell of Georgia Institute of Technology for helpful comments.

References

1. Fairchild RG. Development and dosimetry of an 'epi-thermal' neutron beam for possible use in neutron capture therapy. Phys Med Biol 1965;10:491–504.
2. Kobayashi T, Sakurai Y, Kanda K, Fujita Y, Ono K. Remodeling of the heavy-water facility of the Kyoto University Reactor for biomedical uses (neutron energy spectrum shifter from thermal to epi-thermal neutrons). In: Proc. of 10th Pacific Basin Nuclear Conference. Tokyo: Atomic Energy Society of Japan, 1996;1506–1513.

Advances in Neutron Capture Therapy.
Volume I, Medicine and Physics.
B. Larsson, J. Crawford and R. Weinreich, editors.

The upgrade of the heavy water facility of the Kyoto University Reactor for neutron capture therapy

Tooru Kobayashi, Keiji Kanda, Yoshiaki Fujita, Yoshinori Sakurai and Koji Ono

Research Reactor Institute, Kyoto University, Kumatori-cho, Sennan-gun, Osaka, Japan

Introduction

The heavy water thermal neutron irradiation facility of the Kyoto University Reactor (KUR) has been utilized in several fields, such as medical biology and physical engineering since first criticality in June 1964. The facility was designed as a high-quality thermal neutron irradiation field for biomedical purposes [1,2]. Fundamental studies for the advancement of neutron capture therapy (NCT) have been aggressively pursued at the KUR since 1970. On May 4, 1974, the first NCT clinical treatment for brain tumor at the KUR was carried out by Dr H. Hatanaka. Based on the accumulated data from fundamental studies, regular clinical treatment began in February 1990. To date, 61 NCTs have been carried out for 48 brain tumors and 13 melanomas at the KUR.

At the old facility, only thermal neutrons were employed, and a halt in the KUR operation was required for each clinical irradiation. Through NCT experiences and studies, the following requests were made by the clinical doctors:

1. Clinical utilization during continuous operation of the KUR.
2. Utilization of epithermal neutron irradiation for the treatment of deep-seated tumors.

The remodeling study of the facility required almost 6 years [3—5]. In the spring of 1993, it was decided that the facility would be remodeled by March 1996. In July 1993, a report entitled "The Status of Research Reactor in University" was released by the Science Council of Japan. In the report, "the utilization of epithermal neutrons for NCT" was specified as a subject which should be tackled at the KUR. Following this report, the remodeling plan for the facility materialized with the utilization of epithermal neutron irradiation, in addition to thermal neutron irradiation.

Updated KUR heavy water neutron irradiation facility

Figure 1 shows a vertical cross-section of the updated KUR heavy water neutron irradiation facility. The core tank and the heavy water tank are separated by a cooling light water jacket of 10 mm thickness. The epithermal neutron enhance-

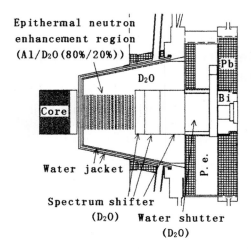

Fig. 1. The updated KUR heavy water neutron irradiation facility.

ment region was added to the inside of the heavy water tank to enhance the epithermal neutron component and to reduce the fast neutron component. A mixture of Al and heavy water (Al—D_2O), with a volume ratio of 80:20 was selected. The configuration was chosen to be a cylinder of 60 cm diameter and 66 cm thickness.

The neutron energy spectrum shifter of heavy water was added to the outside of the epithermal neutron enhancement region. The neutron energy spectrum shifter is comprised of three parts, with thicknesses of 10, 20 and 30 cm, in order from the core side. The total thickness of the heavy water layer can be controlled from 0 to 60 cm in 10 cm increments. Additionally, a heavy water shutter of about 30 cm thickness was located outside of the spectrum shifter. Thermal neutron filters of boral and cadmium are used to improve the beam characteristics for epithermal neutron irradiation. In order from the core side, the boral and cadmium filters, with thicknesses of 6.4 and 1.5 mm, respectively, were installed at the core-side of the bismuth layer to eliminate secondary γ rays. The bismuth layer is 23.4 cm in thickness and 54 cm in diameter. As parts of the center of the bismuth block are removable, the bismuth thickness at the center is changeable from 0 to 23.4 cm. The standard irradiation position is the center of the surface of the 23.4 cm thick bismuth layer.

Irradiation characteristics

Several kinds of neutron energy spectra can be obtained at the updated facility using both the spectrum shifter and the thermal neutron filters. We defined symbols to express the irradiation modes, such as "OO—0011". The first and second characters represent the conditions of the cadmium and boral filters. The character "O" means the filter "opened", and the characters "C" and "B" mean the cadmium and boral filters "full-closed", respectively. The four numbers represent the conditions of the heavy water shutter and the spectrum shifters three, two and one in order. The number "0" and "1" mean "empty" and "full", respectively.

In order to confirm the irradiation conditions for several irradiation modes shown in Table 1, thermal neutron fluxes, cadmium ratios and γ-ray dose equivalent rates at the bismuth surface were experimentally estimated using gold foils of 50 μm thickness, cadmium covers of 0.7 mm thickness and TLDs of BeO, respectively. The bismuth thickness at the center is 18.4 cm in the area of 25 cm^2. For the standpoint of biomedical uses, we defined three groups of the irradiation modes as follows:

1) thermal neutron modes: the cadmium ratio is over 100;
2) mixed neutron modes: the cadmium ratio is below 100; and
3) epithermal neutron modes: the cadmium or boral filters are fully closed (the cadmium ratio is approximately 1).

The standard modes for the groups 1, 2 and 3 are "OO−0011", "OO−0000" and "CO−0000", respectively.

Radiation shielding system

Figure 2 shows a layout of the advanced clinical irradiation systems of the updated facility. Radiation shielding system was designed to allow irradiation room entry under continuous 5 MW operation. A design criterion of the room entry was a dose equivalent rate less than 100 μSv/hr at the working area in the irradiation room. The radiation shielding system was designed in the following two conceptions:

1. Fast neutrons are moderated to lower energies and are absorbed with boron.
2. The γ rays are shielded with iron and lead.

Table 1. The measured values of the neutron fluxes and the γ-ray dose equivalent rates at the bismuth surface during 5 MW operation for several irradiation modes.

Irradiation mode	D$_2$O thickness (cm)	Cadium ratio	Neutron flux (n/cm^2/s)		γ-ray dose equivalent rate (cSv/h)
			Thermal (less than 0.6 eV)	Epithermal* (0.6 eV - 10 keV)	
OO−0111	60	780.0	5.9E + 8	1.9E + 6	40
OO−0110	50	580.0	7.6E + 8	3.2E + 6	50
OO−0101	40	320.0	9.1E + 8	6.8E + 6	50
OO−0011	30	150.0	2.0E + 9	3.2E + 7	100
OO−0010	20	49.0	2.3E + 9	1.2E + 8	120
OO−0001	10	22.0	3.3E + 9	4.0E + 8	210
OO−0000	0	9.4	4.9E + 9	1.5E + 9	330
CO−0000	0	1.1	−	1.5E + 9	70

Measurements were carried out using the "irradiation rail device". It is assumed that the epithermal neutrons have a pure 1/E spectrum.

324

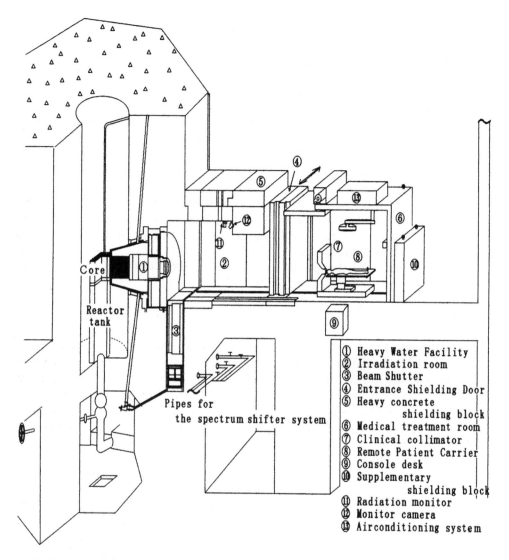

Fig. 2. Layout of the advanced clinical irradiation system of the updated facility.

For the radiation shielding system, the heavy water shutter including the spectrum shifters and the boral filter play the role of fast neutron moderators and neutron absorbers, respectively. In addition, the bismuth layer, and the beam shutter which consists of polyethylene, borated polyethylene, Pb and Fe, act as shields against γ rays. The total thickness of the beam shutter is 710 mm. The irradiation room (2.4^w 2.4^h 3.6^l m^3) consists of heavy concrete blocks of 1,000 mm thickness and the entrance shielding door with 1,200 mm thickness consists of Pb, polyethylene and borated polyethylene.

A procedure for clinical irradiation is as follows:
1) The beam shutter is closed;
2) Preparation for the clinical irradiation is completed in the irradiation room;
3) The entrance shielding door is closed;
4) The beam shutter is opened;
5) The heavy water shutter and the boral filter are opened; and
6) The remote patient carrier moves to the irradiation point, and the clinical irradiation is started. After the clinical irradiation, the process is reversed.

Conclusion

The remodeling construction of the KUR heavy water thermal neutron irradiation facility was completed at the end of May 1996. Neutron irradiations with several energy spectra ranging from nearly pure thermal neutrons to epithermal neutrons, can be provided by the updated facility. Further, the neutron energy spectra can be changed and also clinical irradiations can be performed under the continuous operation of the KUR at 5 MW.

Acknowledgements

The authors thank Dr Yoshifumi Oda of Kobe Central Citizen Hospital for helpful advice from the side of neutron capture therapy, Prof Hiroshi Utsumi of Kyoto University Research Reactor Institute (KURRI) for helpful advice from the side of radiation biology, and Prof Kaichiro Mishima of KURRI for helpful comments from the side of thermal-hydraulics. Special thanks are due to the users of this facility, the collaborators of the remodeling studies, and the cooperators of the remodeling construction.

References

1. Kanda K, Kobayashi T. Development of reactor neutron field for neutron capture therapy and its related studies. Atomkernenergie Kerntechnik 1984;(Suppl 44):585−591.
2. Kobayashi T, Kanda K, Ujeno Y, Ishida MR. Biomedical irradiation system for boron neutron capture therapy in the Kyoto University Reactor. In: Harling OK, Bernard JA, Zamenhof RG (eds). Neutron Beam Design, Development and Performance for Neutron Capture Therapy. New York: Plenum Press, 1990;321−339.
3. Aoki K, Kanda K. Effect of (,n) reactions of heavy water moderator on beam quality in biomedical irradiation facility. Nucl Sci Technol 1983;20:812−821.
4. Fujihara S, Kobayashi T, Kanda K. Reevaluation of thermal neutron field of the KUR Heavy Water Facility for biomedical uses (graphite layers). Annu Rep Res Reactor Inst Kyoto Univ 1990;23:12−13.
5. Sakurai Y, Kobayashi T, Kanda K, Fujita Y. Feasibility study on neutron energy spectrum shifter in the KUR Heavy Water Facility for neutron capture therapy. Annu Rep Res Reactor Inst Kyoto Univ 1993;26:8−25.

Advances in Neutron Capture Therapy.
Volume I, Medicine and Physics.
B. Larsson, J. Crawford and R. Weinreich, editors.

A new medical irradiation facility at JRR-4

K. Yokoo, T. Yamada, F. Sakurai, T. Nakajima, N. Ohhashi and H. Izumo
Department of Research Reactor, Tokai Research Establishment, Japan Atomic Energy Research Institute, Tokai-mura, Naka-gun, Ibaraki, Japan

Introduction

A medical irradiation facility for boron neutron capture therapy (BNCT) was installed at JRR-2 in August 1990. Thermal neutron flux at the beam port was about 1×10^9 n/cm^2/s. Since then 31 medical irradiations were performed in 5 years for clinical trials of BNCT. The operation of JRR-2 will be terminated at the end of 1996.

The operation of JRR-4 using HEU fuel was terminated at the beginning of 1996, and will be resumed using LEU fuel with a new medical irradiation facility in September 1998. The mission of JRR-2 for BNCT is transferred to JRR-4, after suspension of about 1.5 years.

The new facility at JRR-4 is planned to be capable of providing both thermal and epithermal neutron beams with enhanced neutron fluxes. The existing heavy water tank and thermal column facility will be remodeled into the new medical irradiation facility. A medical treatment room and patient-monitoring area are also to be prepared adjacent to the irradiation facility.

New medical irradiation facility

General arrangements

The general arrangement of the facility is shown in Fig. 1. The irradiation room and the adjacent medical treatment room are located in the basement. Patients are received at the entrance of the administration building and are transferred to the basement using the elevator.

Design of the facility

The cross-section of the medical irradiation facility is shown in Fig. 2. The heavy water tank plays the role of neutron beam moderator with aluminium and heavy water. The heavy water layers are separated and optimum heavy water thickness can be chosen for both thermal and epithermal beams according to the needs of each treatment. The tank is arranged with a cadmium shutter.

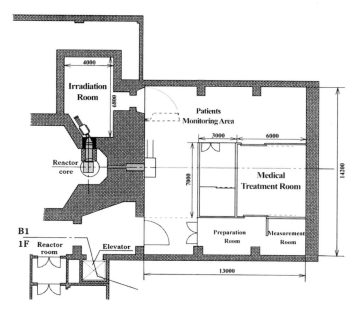

Fig. 1. General arrangement of the medical irradiation facility.

The beam's experimental elements consist of: 1) a bismuth filter for reducing γ ray dose, 2) lead and graphite for beam reflectors, 3) LiF and B_4C for decreasing activation of structural materials, 4) a LiF collimator at the beam port, and 5) borated polyethylene and lead blocks for shielding around the beam port. The beam port is not equipped with a beam shutter.

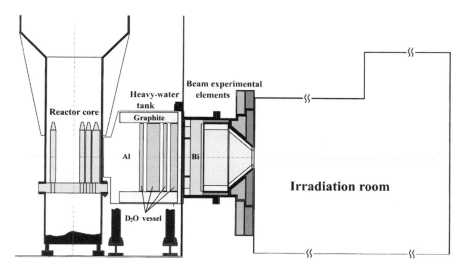

Fig. 2. Cross-section of the medical irradiation facility.

It is possible to adjust the irradiation angle of the patients within 90° to the left side, and 60° to the right side.

Operation of the facility

The rated output of the reactor is 3.5 MW, and the operation mode is daily operation (6 h/day). During the reactor's operation for medical irradiation, other utilization of the reactor is not foreseen. The facility can provide a wide variety of neutron beams. The changeover of neutron spectrum is realized by changing the thickness of heavy water in the heavy water tank, by inserting/removing a thin cadmium plate in the beam line, and by changing the thickness of the graphite reflector in the beam hole.

Beam design and analysis

Calculational method and benchmarking

Two-dimensional calculations using DOT3.5 code and library data based on JENDL3.1 were performed for several alternative design concepts. Twenty-one groups of neutron and nine groups of γ-ray energy structure were used in the calculations.

Beam analyses were performed for both free beam and phantom models. A cylindrical head phantom (16 cm diameter and 25 cm height) with ICRU44 brain tissue was assumed.

Bench marking was performed against thermal neutron fluxes and γ-ray dose rates measured at an existing beam hole. C/E values were 1.36 and 0.70 for thermal neutron flux and γ dose rate, respectively.

Objectives of beam design

The basic policy of the beam design was to provide a variety of neutron beams by easy changes to the configurations mentioned above. While thermal neutron beams are needed to continue the conventional BNCT in Japan, epithermal neutron beams are requested by users for the treatment of deep-seated tumours.

The objectives of the beam design were set as follows for the free beam model:
1. Thermal neutron flux at beam port (thermal beam mode): $\geqslant 1 \times 10^9$ n/cm^2/s.
2. Epithermal neutron flux at beam port (epithermal beam mode): $\geqslant 1 \times 10^9$ n/cm^2/s.
3. γ dose contamination: $\leqslant 3 \times 10^{-13}$ Gy/n-cm^2.
4. Fast neutron contamination: $\leqslant 5 \times 10^{-13}$ Gy/n-cm^2.
5. Size of beam port: 200×200 mm.
6. Estimated irradiation time: $\leqslant 2$ h.

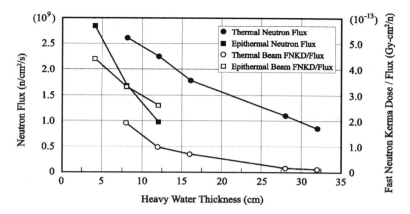

Fig. 3. Neutron flux and FNKD/flux vs. heavy water thickness.

Design optimization and results

Design optimization studies were performed for the aluminium and heavy water thickness of the heavy water tank, position and thickness of the bismuth shield,

Table 1. Beam performance of typical mode.

	Items	Unit	Epithermal Beam Mode	Thermal Beam Mode I	Thermal Beam Mode II
General Condition	Aluminium thickness	cm	75	75	75
	D_2O thickness	cm	8	12	33
	Bismuth thickness	cm	15	18	18
Free Beam Performance at Beam Port	ϕ_{f1} (> 821 keV)	n/cm²/s	$4.5 \cdot 10^6$	$2.0 \cdot 10^6$	$1.4 \cdot 10^5$
	ϕ_{f2} (3.35−821 keV)	n/cm²/s	$1.4 \cdot 10^8$	$5.0 \cdot 10^7$	$8.9 \cdot 10^5$
	ϕ_{epi} (0.53 eV−3.35 keV)	n/cm²/s	$1.7 \cdot 10^9$	$8.8 \cdot 10^8$	$3.4 \cdot 10^7$
	ϕ_{th} (< 0.53 eV)	n/cm²/s	$4.4 \cdot 10^8$	$2.3 \cdot 10^9$	$8.5 \cdot 10^8$
	γ ray dose/flux	Gy-cm²/n	$3.0 \cdot 10^{-13}$	$2.5 \cdot 10^{-13}$	$2.0 \cdot 10^{-13}$
	Fast neutron Kerma dose/flux	Gy-cm²/n	$3.3 \cdot 10^{-13}$	$9.7 \cdot 10^{-14}$	$1.1 \cdot 10^{-14}$
	J/ϕ		0.75	0.76	0.77
	Cadmium ratio		1.5	5.9	43
Dose Distribution in Phantom	Maximum B.G. dose	RBE-Gy/h	42	61	18
	Maximum tumour dose	RBE-Gy/h	107	178	54
	Advantage depth	cm	6.2	5.2	4.7
	Irradiation time	h	0.72	0.49	1.69

Assumptions for dose evaluation:
1. Phantom composition: brain tissue (ICRU44).
2. Phantom dimension: 16 cm diameter and 25 cm height (cylindrical).
3. RBE: 1.0 (γ), 2.7 (thermal), 5.0 (fast, epithermal), 2.3 (boron). C-RBE: 0.4 (boron).
4. Boron-10 concentration: 30 ppm (tumour), 3 ppm (normal tissue), 30 ppm (blood).

thickness of the graphite reflectors in the heavy water tank and the beam hole, etc.

Aluminium, of 75 cm thickness, was chosen to reduce fast neutron contamination in epithermal neutron beams, while the remaining total heavy water thickness of 33 cm was enough to provide a thermal neutron beam almost equivalent to the JRR-2 beam.

The thickness of the heavy water layer can be arbitrary, chosen from 0—28 cm in 4-cm steps. The maximum thickness is 33 cm. The dependence of beam performance on heavy water thickness is shown in Fig. 3.

Beam performances are shown in Table 1 for three typical beam modes, epithermal beam mode, thermal beam mode I, and thermal beam mode II. Thermal beam mode I provides a thermal neutron beam with more epithermal neutrons and its advantage depth is larger than that of thermal beam mode II. The latter mode provides a thermal neutron beam with less epithermal neutrons.

Conclusions

It has been shown that the facility can provide a wide variety of neutron beams by changing the thickness of heavy water in the heavy water tank, by inserting/removing a thin cadmium plate in the beam line, and by changing the thickness of the graphite reflector in the beam hole.

All modes mentioned above satisfy the design objectives: Epithermal beam mode, with its larger advantage depth, is suitable for the treatment of deep-seated tumours, thermal beam mode I, with its higher neutron flux, is suitable for shallow-seated tumours, and thermal beam mode II provides users with the ability to continue the conventional thermal neutron BNCT being performed at JRR-2.

Advances in Neutron Capture Therapy.
Volume I, Medicine and Physics.
B. Larsson, J. Crawford and R. Weinreich, editors.

The completed boron neutron capture therapy facility at the HFR Petten

R.L. Moss[1], J. Casado[1], K. Ravensberg[2], F. Stecher-Rasmussen[2] and P. Watkins[1]

[1]HFR Unit, Institute for Advanced Materials, Joint Research Centre; and [2]Department of Nuclear Energy, Netherlands Energy Research Foundation (ECN), Petten, The Netherlands

Introduction

In 1987, the European Collaboration on boron neutron capture therapy (BNCT), currently consisting of over 40 research centres in 14 European countries, and including members in the disciplines of radiobiology, chemistry, physics and medicine, set itself two priority tasks [1]:

1. To initiate clinical trials of glioma at the earliest possible date at the high flux reactor at Petten in The Netherlands.
2. To create conditions that other tumours can be treated at Petten and at other European sites.

The integral component in task 1 has been the design, development and construction of an irradiation facility at the high flux reactor (HFR) in Petten, The Netherlands. Under the auspices of the European Collaboration, an extensive series of experiments have been performed in recent years and presented at previous NCT Symposia. The experiments had the objective to determine the preconditions for BNCT treatment of glioma patients, using the Petten epithermal neutron beam and using BSH as the boron carrier. The irradiation room and ancillary facilities are now complete and await the start of the first European clinical trials of BNCT.

Figure 1 displays the features of the room, which is not only a well-engineered, shielded radiation facility, with efficiently designed beam shutters and on-line beam monitoring systems, but includes features such as cameras and microphones, shielded lighting, antistatic floor covering, electro-optical laser alignment devices, a custom-built therapy table, complete interlocking safety systems and full radiation monitoring.

Furthermore, adjacent to the facility, an observation or control area is located with TV + video recording systems and PCs displaying graphically the beam monitoring parameters and the system control parameters. At a neighbouring beam tube, a prompt γ-ray analysis facility is available where blood-boron concentration measurements can be obtained within a few minutes. Outside and adjacent to the reactor building, a connecting set of four temporary building

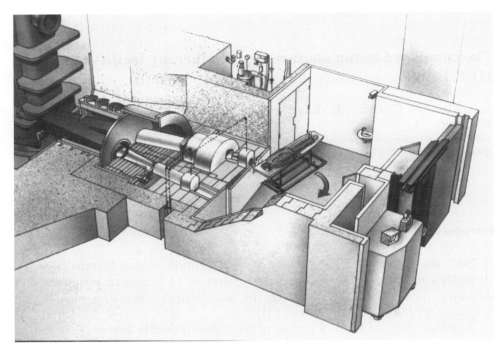

Fig. 1. An artist's impression of the BNCT treatment room at the HFR Petten, indicating reactor, beam tube, and patient on therapy table in the beam.

units, aptly named the BNCT-Wing, has been built. The wing houses rooms for patients, reception, preparation, office space for medical staff and a waiting room.

High flux reactor at Petten

The high flux materials testing reactor (HFR) at Petten is owned and managed by the Commission of the European Communities and has, for the last 25 years, been utilised for the irradiation testing of materials and nuclear fuel for the European civil nuclear power programme. The reactor operates at 45 MW and is cooled and moderated by light water. The standard core configuration consists of 33 fuel assemblies, six control rods, 16 beryllium reflector elements and 17 free positions for experimental facilities. The reactor is also equipped with 12 horizontal beam tubes, used mainly for nuclear physics and solid state physics research.

With respect to BNCT, to obtain a sufficient and adequate flux of neutrons, the beam tube arrangement, HB11/12 at the north side of the reactor vessel, satisfies the necessary physical requirements, i.e., a large diameter beam and facing a large source area of a high flux reactor. In addition, the exit side of the beam can accommodate a large working area for developing an irradiation room. Furthermore, the facility faces the reactor building's emergency exit, giving in effect, unhindered access from outside.

Beam characteristics

Following an extensive series of design calculations, and thereafter, extensive experimental and characterisation work, the beam characteristics at 1 cm from the beam opening are:

total neutron flux	$3.8 \times 10^8 \text{ cm}^{-2} \text{ s}^{-1}$
thermal flux (<1 eV)	$2.6 \times 10^6 \text{ cm}^{-2} \text{ s}^{-1}$
epithermal flux (1 eV to 10 keV)	$3.3 \times 10^8 \text{ cm}^{-2} \text{ s}^{-1}$
fast flux ($>$ 10 keV)	$4.9 \times 10^7 \text{ cm}^{-2} \text{ s}^{-1}$
"average" neutron energy	10.4 keV
fast neutron dose	1.04 Gy/h
incident photon dose	1.25 Gy/h
current: flux ratio	>0.81

The beam is also highly forward directional (parallel), with a divergence of $<5°$.

Irradiation room

The irradiation room has been built to reflect as well as possible, and within reason, a hospital-type environment. A list of items installed is given below. Although some of the items may appear to be trivial, they do reflect the thoroughness in adapting a reactor facility into a hospital-like environment:

1. Two cameras (one camera is fixed in the upper corner of the room, with the second placed on a tripod close to the patient).
2. Two—way intercom (for communication with the observation area).
3. Microphone (to hear the patient during treatment).
4. Electro-optical laser positioning devices, type: ILEE LDA 2011, 670 nm, class 3A (which produce cross-hairs along the beam centre line, enabling positioning of the patient correctly in the beam).
5. Lighting (four units, with special nonreflecting shades, plus dimmer).
6. Transparent, lighted exit signs at each entrance point.
7. Wash-basin, plus warm water.
8. Antistatic, low conducting, nonactivating, floor covering.
9. Various electrical (earthed) sockets placed around the room, specially wired to satisfy hospital standards.
10. Al rack, for storage of collimators and other provisions.
11. Therapy table, made of Al, with a wooden top, and able to move in all three orthogonal directions, each with its own braking system, and with an electric motor to move the table in the vertical direction.
12. A radiotherapist's "yellow" button, to initiate the procedure to start treatment.
13. Air conditioning.

14. Infra-red sensors, located in the labyrinth to detect presence of unauthorised personnel (persistent violation automatically causes closure of the beam shutters).
15. Numerous microswitches on the main door and labyrinth door to detect the open/close status of the doors, plus electrical connection box and alarm unit to oversee all the interlock system.

An overview of the radiation room, with patient in position on the therapy table is shown schematically in Fig. 1.

Observation/control area

The observation/control area is located between the outside wall of the irradiation room and the reactor containment wall. The area houses the instrumentation and control panels for the filtered neutron beam and beam shutters, and the monitoring devices for the patient, including a TV monitor, video recorder and intercom. The beam is monitored via a PC, which displays the on-line beam monitoring parameters. The functioning of the facility is governed by a so-called facility timer, where the duration of the radiation is preset for one or two fractions per session, and on which the beam open button is engaged. The area is enclosed in an office-type environment, with swing doors at each side to give unhindered access to the emergency exit (if required). All walls, floor areas and ceilings in the area and the entrance to the emergency exit are painted in bright (hospital) colours.

Outside building — BNCT wing

The BNCT-wing consists of an interconnecting structure of three and a half temporary units, located outside the reactor building, and connected to the emergency exit on the north side of the reactor containment building. The units contain three areas for the reception and preparation of the patient for treatment, a waiting room and an office for the medical staff. In addition, a WC and wash basin, and an interconnecting corridor, which serves doubly as access to the BNCT facility, as well as the evacuation route from the reactor, are available. Communication means are available, such as telephones, a direct intercom to the BNCT observation/control area, and an HFR intercom for contact with the HFR control room.

Concluding remarks

After many years of development, and great financial investment, the facility is now in its completed state. The structure inside the radiation area has had to satisfy very rigorous constraints with respect to radioprotection of personnel, while at the same time, the facility has been set up to reflect as closely as possible, a hospital-type environment, with all the associated medical and health provisions. The facility waits to play its role in man's endeavour to destroy a most malignant disease.

Reference

1. Gabel D. Approach to Boron Neutron Capture Therapy in Europe: Goals of a European collaboration on Boron Neutron Capture Therapy. Particle Accelerator Conf, Nice. Proc 2nd Eur 1990.

The technical aspects of treating patients at the Petten BNCT facility

R.L. Moss[1], J. Casado[1], K. Ravensberg[2], F. Stecher-Rasmussen[2], P. Watkins[1], B. Mijnheer[3], N. Raaijmakers[3], E. Nottelman[3], W. Sauerwein[4] and D. Gabel[5]

[1]HFR Unit, Institute for Advanced Materials, Joint Research Centre; [2]Department of Nuclear Energy, Netherlands Energy Research Foundation (ECN), Petten; [3]Department of Radiotherapy, Netherlands Cancer Institute, Amsterdam, The Netherlands; [4]Radiological Centre, University Clinic, Essen; and [5]Department of Chemistry, University of Bremen, Bremen, Germany

Introduction

The first European clinical trials on boron neutron capture therapy (BNCT) of glioma will take place at the high flux reactor in Petten. The patient protocol and the medical infrastructure to perform the study and the facility itself and its various features are described elsewhere at this symposium. To perform such a treatment at a research reactor is highly complex, and involves health, safety, security, radioprotection and simple logistical aspects, that may differ considerably from conventional hospital treatment, let alone straightforward radiation experiments.

The procedure starts with patient accrual at one of the European hospitals in the programme, who as part of the accrual procedure, contact Petten to ascertain beam availability. Following inclusion into the study, a patient, some 3—5 weeks later, arrives in The Netherlands, where action has been taken to ensure that hospital space is available for 1 week at the designated hospital within easy travelling distance to the Petten site. During this period, preparatory actions at Petten, apart from the medical matters, ensure that the Petten BNCT group is informed punctually, that calibration of the beam and the prompt γ facility is performed, and that the checkup procedures of all apparatus takes place. The security and radioprotection services must be informed in order to prepare for patient arrival and to assist in the flow of the patient and accompanying vehicles on to the site without undue delays. These procedures take place on 4 consecutive days for each patient. Technically, the procedure is not completed at Petten, until all post-irradiation analyses and all documentation has been completed and submitted to the principal clinical investigator (Dr W. Sauerwein). As part of the clinical practice at Petten, all procedures are documented according to written standard operating procedures, following the guidelines given in the Good Clinical Practice handbooks [1].

Proposed study of BNCT in Europe [2]

The phase I treatment of glioma patients consists of a dose escalation scheme from a starting dose determined from the healthy tissue tolerance study. BNCT is given 3–5 weeks after surgery. Boron concentration at the time of treatment is kept constant for all patients. The protocol is designed and established with the active involvement of all participating clinics throughout Europe, so that a uniform protocol for all patients in the study is applied. The three principal steps and basic conditions are:

Presurgical inclusion

— Age, between 50 and 70 years;
— Karnovsky index > 70;
— presumptive diagnosis of glioblastoma and;
— availability of Petten beam within next 3–5 weeks.

Surgery with BSH uptake study, to

— Debulk the tumour mass, offering the patient the benefit of a proven treatment modality and allowing for maximum radiation effect; and
— to establish that the stipulated boron uptake in tumour and boron concentration in blood, as well as a stipulated tumour-to-blood concentration ratio, can be expected during the subsequent radiotherapy.

Postsurgical inclusion for irradiation with BNCT instead of conventional radiotherapy or other therapy

— Confirmation of glioblastoma by histology;
— blood boron concentration and boron uptake satisfy criteria;
— good recovery from surgery; and
— ability to travel to Petten.

Following the necessary treatment planning [3], BNCT is performed as a treatment in four fractions. The boron carrier, borocaptate sodium (BSH) is infused prior to each fraction, at prescribed time intervals and amounts. Whilst the patient is in the trial, other anticancer therapies will not be planned for the present tumour, except the main surgery and BNCT, unless required for the treatment of recurrence.

BNCT treatment at Petten

The actual treatment at Petten is of course far more complex and structured than the brief description above. All operations at the facility are described by the standard operating procedures, which give the step-by-step actions and instructions, starting from the entrance to the Petten site, and ending with return of the patient to the hospital. At the facility itself, the safety interlocks and other provisions that have been provided, ease the complex operation of the overall system and make the facility as safe as possible. On each day of treatment, the following chronological procedures are performed:

1) Checkups of safety interlock systems, Ar system, beam shutters, communication channels, patient treatment table, laser positioning system, the timer and the general medical provisions.
2) Performance of the reference beam phantom measurements.
3) All beam shutters are closed.
4) Arrival of the patient at the BNCT wing.
5) Measurement of the blood-boron concentration.
6) Calculation of the radiation time.
7) The patient is brought into the reactor building to the radiation room.
8) The patient is accurately positioned as required in front of the beam.
9) Activation foils are placed on the patient.
10) All personnel, apart from the radiotherapist and patient, leave the room.
11) The radiotherapist, then:
    — checks that all personnel have left the room and that the main door is closed;
    — engages the treatment initiation button next to the labyrinth exit;
    — vacates the room via the labyrinth;
    — properly closes the labyrinth door;
    — engages, within 10 s of engaging the initiation button, the second treatment button outside the labyrinth entrance;
    — ensures that the patient I.D., the estimated dose and radiation time have been correctly preset on the beam monitoring program (LABVIEW) and on the timer control unit; and
    — engages the beam open button to start the radiation.
12) On completion of the radiation, the beam shutters automatically close, the main door is opened, and the radiotherapist and staff enter the room.
13) The health physicist measures the (radio) activity of the patient.
14) The patient returns to the BNCT-Wing for eventual return to the hospital, where a brief physical examination is taken. During the coming night, boron is infused and blood samples taken at regular intervals.
15) The procedures are repeated on the following 3 consecutive days.

Technical issues

Approval to use the Petten facility has been subject to a rigorous assessment by numerous Governmental authorities, including the Ministries of Health (for medical issues), Economic Affairs (HFR Licensing issues), Environment (buildings issues) and Social Affairs (working conditions). The following issues have all been reported, assessed and finally approved.

Safety approval

Approval to use the facility, within the conditions associated with experiments performed within the reactor's existing operating licence, was granted by the Dutch Ministry of Social Affairs in January 1996, and was based on the project's justification, its radiation protection measures, its quality assurance and its managerial infrastructure.

Safety protocol

The facility was assessed as a system of units, each having its own safety protocols, instructions and instrumentation:

the reactor —
> the safety of the reactor is guaranteed at all times by its standard safety provisions. In particular, for a reactor scram, the cooling of the Ar must react accordingly to prevent freezing of the liquid Ar. For reactor hall evacuation, special provisions are taken, including immediate closure of all beam shutters.

The water shutter —
> can be opened during normal reactor operation, only if the Ar cryostat is full, and both beam shutters are closed.

The S filter component —
> if this overheats, this is detected via thermocouples that warn the beam operator to close the water shutter.

The liquid Ar system —
> has a multiple fault detection system which, if violated, automatically shuts down all beam shutters.

The beam shutters —
> only may be opened if the liquid Ar cryostat is full, and the labyrinth and main doors closed. The main beam shutter can only be opened if the radiotherapist follows the procedure described earlier.

The main door —
> only can be opened if the main beam shutter and the γ shutter are closed. If one or both of the shutters are open, an interlock system prevents the door from opening. If the main door should be (partly) opened manually, then the beam shutters close automatically.

The labyrinth —
> infrared sensors detect the presence of someone entering the labyrinth causing both visual (flashing light) and acoustic (buzzing) alarms to activate. Further

advance into the labyrinth results in the automatic closure of the main and secondary beam shutters.

The above alarms and actions are written in a clear and concise form and follow the guidelines, where applicable, of the Standard Operating Procedures in good Clinical Practice. Instructions are displayed in English and Dutch, and if required, could be in other languages of the European Union.

Radioprotection

Following standard radioprotection practice for nuclear facilities, all personnel are allocated a personal dosimeter. The area around the radiation room is monitored at all times. Following patient treatment, the patient will be radioactive. Measurements are taken and noted prior to the patient leaving the reactor building. Further measurements are taken before the patient leaves the Petten site.

Due to the nature of neutron radiation, the materials of the therapy table and the masks and fixation plates have been carefully chosen. The table itself has a wooden top and, at the patient's head, has a lithiated polyethylene sheet, in order to minimise neutron activation of the table. The patient is fixed in position by means of a perspex plate (type: posifix-5, Sinmed bv) fixed to the table, and a thermoplastic mask (type: posicast, Sinmed bv) which covers the patient's head. The fixation materials were especially chosen for their minimal activation characteristics following radiation in the beam. To ascertain this, a variety of materials, supplied by all the participating hospitals in the clinical trials, were collected and irradiated in the neutron beam.

Reactor operation, security and communication

Normal reactor operations continue uninterrupted 24 h per day even when patient treatment is in progress. Personnel involved in BNCT, including the patient, who are not classified as nuclear workers, must be accompanied at all times. Consequently, security procedures have to be followed, including prompt notification of all users at least 1 day prior to treatment. All movement of personnel on site must be monitored, especially movement of medical staff and patient through the reactor boundary, the emergency exit/entrance to the facility and on leaving each exit.

Concluding remarks

Final approval to start clinical trials at Petten is still pending (1996). Nevertheless, with the recent completion of the radiation facility and a variety of approvals already obtained at the various levels within the national authorities, including the patient protocol at the hospitals involved in the trial, it is evident, as also experienced at other BNCT facilities in the USA and Japan, that the effort and complexity to arrive even at the present position should never be underestimated.

This paper, along with the similar ones presented by other BNCT operators, should always serve as a forewarning to managers of new facilities. The procedures are even more complex when treated on an international scale, which even here in Europe, with the European Union and its so-called freedom of movement from country to country of its professions and businesses, raises untold anomalies in procedures.

References

1. Bohaychuk W, Ball G. Good clinical research practices, an indexed reference to international guidelines and regulations, with practical interpretation. GCRP Publications January 1994.
2. Sauerwein W, Gabel D, Fankhauser H. Glioma BNCT. Postoperative treatment of glioblastoma with BNCT at the Petten irradiation facility. 1. Phase I clinical trial. EC-BNCT August 1995.
3. Watkins P R D, Vroegindeweij C, Aaldijk K, Wheeler FW, Wessol DE. Use of the BNCT.Rtpe/ rtt.MC treatment planning system for BNCT irradiations of human patients at Petten. In: Larsson B, Crawford J, Weinreich R (eds) Advances in Neutron Capture Therapy. Volume 1, Medicine and Physics: Amsterdam: Elsevier Science, 1997;112–117.

The Finnish boron neutron capture therapy program — an overview on scientific projects

Sauli Savolainen[1], Iiro Auterinen[4], Merja Kallio[5], Marjatta Kärkkäinen[3], Antti Kosunen[7], Carita Aschan[1], Judit Benczik[3], Markus Färkkilä[6], Pekka Hiismäki[4], Karoliina Kaita[4], Martti Kulvik[5], Päivi Ryynänen[1], Tiina Seppälä[1], Tom Serén[4], Vesa Tanner[4], Matti Toivonen[7], Jyrki Vähätalo[2] and Hanna Ylä-Mella[1]

[1]Department of Physics, [2]Laboratory of Radiochemistry and [3]Faculty of Veterinary Medicine, University of Helsinki (HU), Helsinki; [4]VTT Chemical Technology, Technical Research Centre of Finland (VTT), Espoo; [5]Clinical Research Institute and [6]Departments of Neurology, Helsinki University Central Hospital (HUCH), Helsinki; and [7]Department of Inspection and Metrology, Finnish Centre for Radiation and Nuclear Safety (STUK), Helsinki, Finland

Keywords: beam collimator, boron bulk-analysis, boron carrier, dosimetry, ionization chambers, labeling procedure, moderator material, monitoring system, normal tissue tolerance, radio labeled, reference phantom materials, TLD-dosimeters, tissue-equivalent, tissue-substitute, trace element distribution, treatment facility, treatment planning.

Introduction

A research group for carrying out clinical application of boron neutron capture therapy (BNCT) was established in Finland in the early 1990s. The work started with the planning of modifications to the thermal column of the VTT research reactor towards a BNCT neutron source, and with clinical research for boron carriers in HUCH [1]. Now the project is a multidisciplinary research project involving scientists from different departments of HU, HUCH, VTT, STUK and of the Helsinki University of Technology (HUT). The aim of this project is to start BNC treatment in Finland with malignant brain tumors by the end of the century. This overview focuses on the present scientific projects on BNCT in Finland.

Neutron source

The Finnish research reactor (FiR 1) operated by the Technical Research Center of Finland is a 250 kW TRIGA II open tank reactor with the inherently safe special TRIGA uranium-zirconium hydride fuel. Based on numerical modelling a new optimal neutron moderator material composition was developed for

Address for correspondence: Sauli Savolainen, Department of Radiology, Helsinki University Central Hospital, Haartmaninkatu 4, FIN—00290 Helsinki, Finland. E-mail: sauli.savolainen@hyks.mail-net.fi

epithermal generation [2]. The patented material (FLUENTAL™) is a composition of AlF$_3$ (69 m-%), Al (30 m-%) and LiF. The manufacturing process based on the hot isostatic pressing (HIP) technique has been developed for the material pressing solid blocks with 100% density. The manufacturing of the needed moderator material was completed in February 1996.

In April 1996 the new FLUENTAL™ neutron moderator was installed in the thermal column space. The new moderator constituted a major step in turning the reactor into a BNC treatment facility. This basic configuration with opti-

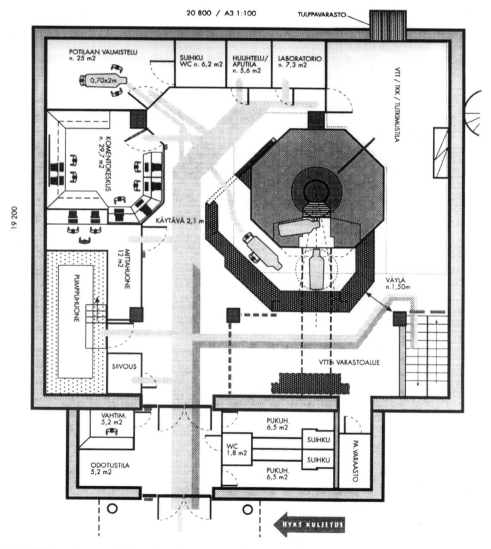

Fig. 1. Schematic ground floor view of the FiR 1 BNCT research treatment facility.

mized core loading and on-line beam monitors for the epithermal field (see Fig. 1 in [3]) was then used to characterize the epithermal source using activation detectors [4] and to test the dosimetric methods [5]. Also measurement teams from Nuclear Research Institute Rez, Czech Republic and INEL in the USA participated in this characterization effort. The performance of the basic epithermal facility turned out to be close to the design values, the epithermal flux at the bismuth face being $1.26 \cdot 10^9 n/cm^2.s$ and the fast flux $2.6 \cdot 10^7$ $n/cm^2.s$ [4].

In September 1996 a conical beam collimator was installed [3]. This collimator enables the use of epithermal field for animal and human experiments. In October 1996 a thorough renovation of the reactor building has started. The ground and second floor will be converted into a BNCT research and treatment facility (Fig. 1). An irradiation space suitable for human size studies will be constructed including widening of the irradiation column for transverse irradiations of human patients. A control center and auxiliary rooms for patient/animal preparation for irradiation will be built.

Dosimetry and dose control plans

The existing international recommendations on radiotherapy dosimetry are not applicable to BNCT due to the complexity of the mixed neutron and γ fields. Characterization of the treatment beam is the basis of the dosimetry in BNCT. It also provides an experimental verification of the computer models of the beam. The thermal and epithermal and part of fast neutron spectra is measured with foil activation analyses [4]. A lithium-covered Si-detector is used to estimate the actual capture dose in BNCT.

The monitoring system is designed to give information about the epithermal and thermal neutron fluxes and γ dose rates at the free-field source plane outside the neutron moderator close to the irradiation position. This is the primary and independent system to register and control the neutron beam properties during treatment. The particles coming from the TRIGA-reactor core through the Al fluoride moderator are monitored with two neutron sensitive fission chambers and one γ-sensitive ionization chamber [3]. The computer simulated doses due to the neutron and γ components have to be measured in the circumstances identical to the clinical situations. Respectively, utilization of a combination of tissue-equivalent (TE) and magnesium chambers filled with TE and Ar gas for the measurements gives the neutron/γ dose relation in the desired geometry [5,6].

Standard sources (^{60}Co and ^{137}Cs) of the Secondary Standard Laboratory of STUK have been used for calibration and testing of the ionization chambers used for BNCT. The air kerma rates of the standard sources are traceable to the International Standard at Bureau International des Poids et Mesures in France and National Physical Laboratory in UK. At present four types of ionization chambers for BNCT dosimetry are available. Ge detectors are planned for the use of measuring the capture of ^{10}B in the phantom or patient. All the dosimetric measurements are referenced to on-line monitoring of the epithermal source where fission and ionization chambers are used [3]. The posttreatment dose control in patients can be improved by using TLD dosimeters parallel to other techniques. The utility of TL detectors for BNCT dosimetry is studied by performing in and on phantom measurements with several types of TL detectors. LiF: Mg, Cu and P detectors of enriched ^{7}Li are less sensitive to neutrons than any other TL detectors and therefore an interesting alternative for the traditional Li (natural) enriched LiF: Mg, Ti detectors. Measurement of the neutron-specific 275°C glow peak instead of the whole glow area of the LiF: Mg, Ti detectors (glow curve analysis) is another method of improving the abilities of detector pairs in separating the radiation components in the mixed γ/neutron fields. Self-absorption of neutrons inside the detector must also be considered as an essential source of uncertainty in BNCT dosimetry. This uncertainty is minimized by using detectors with a thin active layer of LiF: Mg, Ti (natural isotope composition) on a passive LiF basis.

Treatment planning and phantom designs

The behavior of the most important dose components in NCT was modeled in different tissue equivalents and substitutes to optimize the composition of reference phantom materials for measurements of performance, quality and acceptance tests in epithermal neutron beams. Calculations of the distribution of the absorbed dose for BNCT are more complex than for photon and electron therapy. The Idaho National Engineering Laboratory (INEL) with university collaborators has developed the first functioning treatment planning program for BNCT [7]. The software was installed for the use of Finnish BNCT research group in December 1994. The treatment planning program for BNCT takes as input anatomical regions of the patient. A software was developed in collaboration with the Laboratory for Biomedical Engineering at HUT for doing segmentation of the medical image, contour tracing of segmented image, and B-spline fitting.

The dimensions of the phantom should simulate the anatomy and the materials of the phantom should be close to tissue-equivalent (TE). The compartments for a BNCT head-like phantom are elliptical covering shapes of skin, skull and brains [8]. We have constructed a solid cylindrical PMMA phantom with an axial measurement channel and a liquid phantom with a computer-controlled scanning mechanism. The liquid phantom incorporates different types of target parts, heads: a round cylinder and a double elliptical cylinder for human head models and dog head models. For a tissue-substitute (TS), liquid in a BNCT head-like phantom the simplest choice is water and the most precise choice is brain substitute (BS)-liquid [9].

Analysis of boron and BPA

The Finnish BNCT research group has studied boronated LDL as a potential ^{10}B carrier. In an early clinical study it was found by single photon emission tomography that [99mTc]-labeled LDL accumulates in brain tumors in vivo [10]. Boronated LDL reconstructed by the present methods proved, however, to be so deformed that for clinical use new reconstruction methods need to be developed. Proton-induced γ emission analysis (PIGE), secondary ion mass spectrometry (SIMS), inductively coupled plasma mass spectrometry (ICP-MS), and inductively coupled atomic emission spectrometry (ICP-AES) were tested to measure boron in LDL matrix. It was concluded that PIGE can be an appropriate control method for chemical analysis [11].

The planned treatment approach will be based on the use of BPA as the boron carrier. The current efforts on boron bulk analysis with PIGE and ICP-AES are therefore focused on BPA-matrix. In order to analyze boron distribution at cellular level, SIMS and nuclear reaction analysis (NRA) will be used combined with freeze-drying and cryosectioning, thus preserving the original trace element distribution. To verify reliable quantification, a set of ^{10}B-enriched standard slices will be prepared using an isotope separator. Boron concentration, distribution and localization in vivo can be determined by radiolabeled boron carriers. A potential labeled marker for probing the effectiveness of the current boron carrier is radiofluorinated derivate of BPA, i.e., 4-borono-2-[^{18}F] fluorophenylalanine (FBPA). BPA can be radiofluorinated directly by carrier-added electrophilic methods. However, the scientific radiochemical goal of the Finnish BNCT program is to label BPA with a nucleophilic regioselective no-carrier-added (NCA) method. The labeling procedure is based on the method for 4-[^{18}F]-fluorophenylalanine described by Lemaire et al. [12].

Radiobiology

Normal tissue tolerance studies will contribute towards the verification of the treatment planning, radiation doses, biological effects, and radiation safety of BNCT before proceeding to therapies of patients. Both in Brookhaven National Laboratory, USA and Petten, Holland, epithermal neutron radiation with dogs using Na borocaptate as a boron carrier have been performed. As the boron carrier in Finland is going to be BPA the normal tissue tolerance studies will be performed with BPA as boron carrier. For the studies adult dogs will be given BPA and different radiation doses. A prolonged follow-up of the dogs will be carried out. During the follow-up the dogs will be evaluated clinically and also radiologically utilizing MRI-scans. The studies will be done in collaboration with the Faculty of Veterinary Medicine at the University of Helsinki.

Acknowledgements

The financial support from the Finnish Academy, University of Helsinki, and Helsinki University Central Hospital is acknowledged.

References

1. Hiismäki P, Auterinen I, Färkkilä M. The Finnish BNCT program, an overview. In: Kallio M, Auterinen I (eds) Proceedings of the CLINCT BNCT Workshop. Helsinki: Helsinki University of Technology series TKK−F−A718, 1994;2−4.

2. Auterinen I, Hiismäki P. Epithermal BNCT neutron beam design for a Triga II reactor. In: Soloway H, Barth RF (eds) Advances in Neutron Capture Therapy. Proceedings of the 5th International Symposium on Neutron Capture Therapy, Columbus, OH, September 14−17 1992. New York: Plenum Press, 1993;81−84.

3. Auterinen I, Hiismäki P, Salmenhaara S, Tanner V. Operation and on-line beam monitoring of the Finnish BNCT station. In: Larsson B, Crawford J, Weinreich R (eds) Advances in Neutron Capture Therapy. Volume 1, Medicine and Physics: Amsterdam: Elsevier Science, 1997; 348−352 (these proceedings).

4. Kaita K, Serén T, Auterinen I. First characterization of the Finnish epithermal neutron beam using activation detectors. In: Larsson B, Crawford J, Weinreich R (eds) Advances in Neutron Capture Therapy. Volume 1, Medicine and Physics: Amsterdam: Elsevier Science, 1997; 353−356 (these proceedings).

5. Kosunen A, Ylä-Mella H, Savolainen S. The twin ionization chamber technique in quality control of a mixed epithermal neutron and γ beam for NCT. In: Larsson B, Crawford J, Weinreich R (eds) Advances in Neutron Capture Therapy. Volume 1, Medicine and Physics: Amsterdam: Elsevier Science, 1997;182−187 (these proceedings).

6. Savolainen S, Järvinen H, Kosunen A, Anttila K, Auterinen I, Forss M. Dosimetry and dose control plans for BNCT at FiR-1 TRIGA II reactor in Otaniemi. In: Kallio M, Auterinen I (eds) Proceedings of the CLINCT BNCT Workshop. Helsinki: Helsinki University of Technology series TKK-F-A718, 1994;46−48.

7. Nigg DW. Methods for radiation dose distribution analysis and treatment planning in boron neutron capture therapy. Int J Radiation Biol Phys 1994;28:1121−1132.

8. Harling OK, Roberts KA, Moulin DJ, Rougs RD. Head phantoms for neutron capture therapy. Med Phys 1995;22:579−583.

9. Seppälä T, Vähätalo J, Auterinen I, Savolainen S. Brain tissue substitutes for phantom measurements in NCT. In: Larsson B, Crawford J, Weinreich R (eds) Advances in Neutron Capture Therapy. Volume 1, Medicine and Physics: Amsterdam: Elsevier Science, 1997;188−191 (these proceedings).

10. Leppälä J, Kallio M, Nikula T, Nikkinen P, Liewendahl K, Jääskeläinen J, Savolainen S, Gylling H, Hiltunen J, Callaway J, Kahl S, Färkkilä M. Accumulation of 99m-Tc-LDL in human malignant glioma. Br J Cancer 1995;71:383−387.

11. Savolainen S, Räisänen J, Eteläniemi V, Abo Ramadan U Kallio M. Analysis of 10-B by PIGE with factor analytical γ-ray peak identification. Appl Rad Isot 1995;46:855−958.

12. Lemaire C, Guillaume M, Christiaens L, Palmer AJ, Cantineau R. A new route for the synthesis of [^{18}F]-fluoroaromatic substituted aminoacids: no carrier added L-p-[^{18}F]-fluorophenylalanine. Appl Radiat Isot 1987;38:1033−1038.

Operation and on-line beam monitoring of the Finnish BNCT station

Iiro Auterinen, Pekka Hiismäki, Seppo Salmenhaara and Vesa Tanner
TT Chemical Technology, Technical Research Centre of Finland (VTT), Espoo, Finland

Keywords: FLUENTAL[TM], neutron moderator, reactor neutron source, epithermal irradiation, epithermal moderator, reactor core, beam on-line monitoring, ionisation chamber, beam collimator.

Introduction

In April 1996 the new FLUENTAL[TM] aluminium fluoride — aluminium (AlF_3 69m-%, Al 30m-% and LiF) neutron moderator [1] was installed in the thermal column space of the TRIGA research reactor FiR 1 at VTT, in Otaniemi (Fig. 1). The new moderator constituted a major step in turning the reactor into a epithermal BNCT treatment facility. Also, this was the first experimental test of the new moderator material with a reactor neutron source. The material had been tested earlier with an accelerator photoneutron source by Nigg et al. [2,3]. In the first construction phase enough space was allocated for free beam and phantom experiments. The existing thermal column space was elongated with additional concrete block walls around the heavy concrete sliding door. In this first configuration the epithermal irradiation facility was operated for free-beam characterisation [4] and phantom dose measurements [5], from May to the end of August 1996, mostly 5 days a week and 5–12 h/day.

Optimisation of the reactor core loading

The fast and epithermal flux towards the moderator was maximised by positioning six fresh fuel elements closest to the moderator, followed by the fuel elements with the lowest burn-up. The control rods were reorganised so that the rod on the beam side was withdrawn during operation. The result was that the bias towards the epithermal column was approximately 50% when measured with the Ni activation produced by the fast (> 1 MeV) flux (Fig. 2).

Neutron beam on-line monitoring

The monitoring system was designed to give information about the epithermal neutron flux and γ-dose rate at the free field source plane outside the neutron

Address for correspondence: Iiro Auterinen, VTT Chemical Technology, Technical Research Centre of Finland (VTT), P.O. Box 1404, FIN-02044 Espoo VTT, Finland. Email: iiro.auterinen@vtt.fi.

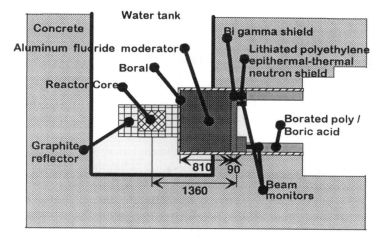

Fig. 1. Basic installation of the new epithermal moderator at FiR 1. The total depth of the moderator installation is 81 cm, of which 75 cm is of FLUENTAL™.

moderator and the Bi γ shield close to the irradiation position. This is the primary system to register and control the neutron beam properties during treatment, i.e., to make sure the patient gets the specified amount of dosage. The system built so far is the basis for a complete and redundant system for the actual medical treatments. The readings from this reduced system were used as beam intensity reference when the beam properties were analysed with dosimetric and nuclear spectroscopy techniques during the summer of 1996.

The monitors are two neutron-sensitive fission chambers and one γ-sensitive ionisation chamber. ^{235}U fission chambers were selected for good discrimination between neutrons and γ radiation. These pulse mode detectors have an extremely

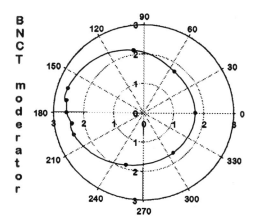

Fig. 2. Angular distribution of ^{58}Ni(n,p) reaction rates $(10-14/s)$, eq. fast flux > 1 MeV, in the irradiation ring of FiR 1.

large operating range, which facilitate measurements at a wide range of reactor power levels. Of the ^{235}U response, 95% is from the thermal and 5% from the epithermal neutron component. One fission chamber is in free field and shielded with cadmium foil to cut off the thermal neutrons, the other is mounted inside plastic, at a depth of 2.5 cm, to monitor the thermal field produced by epithermal neutrons. The γ-sensitive unit is a nitrogen-filled ionisation chamber, which can be operated in its current mode at γ dose levels from 0.002 mSv/min to 2 Sv/min.

The fission chamber pulses are fed through single-channel analyser units into a computer counter interface. The γ-sensitive ionisation chamber electronics include a current-to-voltage converter and an AD converter. All the data processing and visualisation is done with PC virtual instrumentation software. The important parameters are displayed on the screen together with the necessary alarms and interlocks. The counts and count rates from every channel are also stored on hard disk.

The facility does not have any beam shutters between the core and the moderator so the output of the beam always follows the reactor power. A typical operation cycle is presented in Fig. 3. The linearity of the beam monitors relative to the reactor instrumentation power reading has been studied (Fig. 4).

Further construction

In September 1996 a conical beam collimator with a basic 60° Bi cone and

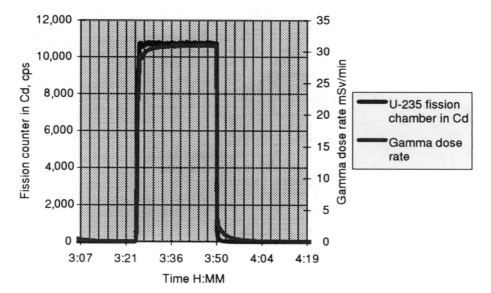

Fig. 3. Beam monitor readings during a typical operation cycle for an ionisation chamber measurement in a solid phantom.

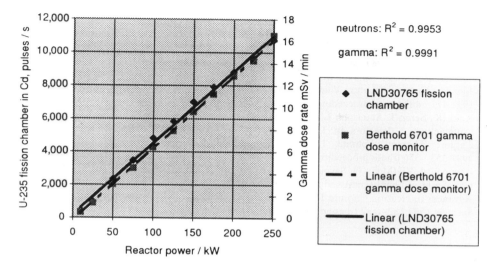

Fig. 4. The linearity of the beam monitor signals relative to the reactor instrumentation power reading.

lithiated polyethylene apertures was installed. This collimator enables the use of the epithermal field for animal and human experiments. The estimated healthy tissue tolerance limited (12.6 Gy-Eq) treatment time with 10 ppm BPA in a normal brain is about 1.5 h.

Conclusions

The modular construction concept for the moderator turned out to be successful. Core optimisation gave a significant gain for the epithermal beam. From the very beginning, all measurements at the beam have been referenced to both beam monitor and reactor power readings. An irradiation cycle is started by driving to full power in about 3 min. The residual γ after shut down needs some consideration from the personnel safety point of view.

Acknowledgements

The construction of the BNCT station has been carried out at VTT under contract with the Radtek Inc., Espoo. Radtek is a company formed to combine private capital and state technology development funding (TEKES, Sitra) for this purpose.

References

1. Hiismäki P, Auterinen I. Patent FI-92890 (1995), National Board of Patents and Registration in Finland, Helsinki, Finland, P.O. Box 1160 FIN-00101 Helsinki.
2. Nigg DW, Mitchell HE, Harker YD, Harmon JF. Computational and experimental studies of an

accelerator based epithermal photoneutron source facility for boron neutron capture therapy. In: Venhuizen JR (ed) INEL BNCT Research Program Annual Report 1995. Idaho National Engineering Laboratory, Idaho Falls, Idaho, 1996;27.

3. Nigg DW, Mitchell HE, Harker YD, Harmon JF. Experimental investigation of filtered epithermal photoneutron beams for BNCT. In: Larsson B, Crawford J, Weinreich R (eds) Advances in Neutron Capture Therapy, Volume 1, Medicine and Physics. Amsterdam: Elsevier Science, 1997;477—482 (these proceedings).

4. Kaita K, Serén T, Auterinen I. First characterisation of the Finnish epithermal neutron beam using activation detectors. In: Larsson B, Crawford J, Weinreich R (eds) Advances in Neutron Capture Therapy, Volume 1, Medicine and Physics. Amsterdam: Elsevier Science, 1997;353—356 (these proceedings).

5. Kosunen A, Ylä-Mella H, Savolainen S. The twin ionisation chamber technique in quality control of a mixed epithermal and γ beam for NCT. In: Larsson B, Crawford J, Weinreich R (eds) Advances in Neutron Capture Therapy, Volume 1, Medicine and Physics. Amsterdam: Elsevier Science, 1997;182—187 (these proceedings).

© 1997 Elsevier Science B.V. All rights reserved.
Advances in Neutron Capture Therapy.
Volume I, Medicine and Physics.
B. Larsson, J. Crawford and R. Weinreich, editors.

First characterisation of the Finnish epithermal neutron beam using activation detectors

Karoliina Kaita[1], Tom Serén[2] and Iiro Auterinen[2]

[1]*Department of Technical Physics, Helsinki University of Technology; and* [2]*VTT Chemical Technology, Technical Research Centre of Finland (VTT), Espoo, Finland*

Introduction

In April 1996 the new FLUENTAL^{TM} aluminium fluoride-aluminium (AlF$_3$-Al) neutron moderator [1] was installed in the place of the graphite in the thermal column at the TRIGA research reactor FiR 1 at VTT, Otaniemi, Espoo. The new moderator constituted a major step in turning the reactor into a BNCT brain tumour treatment facility. After installing the moderator several measurements have been made to characterise the free-beam neutron field as well as the flux distribution in various phantoms. The main measurement campaign in May 1996 was carried out in close cooperation with INEL (USA) and NRI Rez (Czech Republic). In addition to activation measurements, the US and Czech visitors performed proton recoil, Bonner sphere and semiconductor detector measurements.

The energy distribution (i.e., energy spectrum) as well as the intensity of the neutron flux are essential parameters for the treatment planning and the patient dose rate calculations. The epithermal neutron flux (from 0.5 eV to 10 keV) should preferably exceed 10^9 n/cm^2.s [2]. The measurements were carried out in the free field close to the Bi shield surface outside the FLUENTAL^{TM} moderator without the beam delimiter cone, which was installed later. The measurement point was in the middle of the 50 cm^2 uncovered area of bismuth surface. See Fig. 1 in [3].

Activation detectors

Activation detectors (thin foils or wires of pure or diluted neutron capturing elements) are the main tool for characterising the neutron field, both qualitatively and quantitatively. By irradiating multiple activation detectors with different energy-dependent cross-sections and measuring the induced activities, the calculated (S$_N$ or Monte Carlo) neutron spectra can be adjusted to be consistent with the measured reaction rates. With new cross-section libraries, e.g., IRDF-90 [4],

---

Address of correspondence: Karoliina Kaita, Department of Technical Physics, Helsinki University of Technology, FIN-02150 Espoo, Finland.

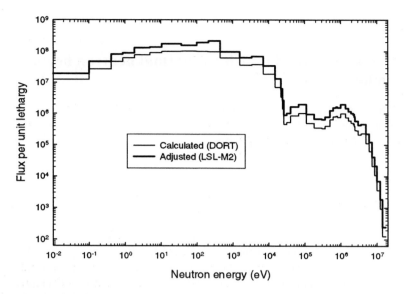

Fig. 1. Calculated and adjusted neutron flux in 47 energy groups.

the cross-section uncertainties have been significantly reduced and provide a sound basis for neutron spectrum adjustment.

Measurements and analysis

Extensive activation measurements have been carried out, mainly to characterise the free beam neutron field, but also, e.g., to check the effect of changes in the reactor core loading pattern on the source distribution and the flux distribution in phantoms. We have mainly used the Petten foil set [5] with Cd cover to characterise the epithermal neutron flux. The Petten set consists of 12 Al-diluted foils, eight of which (Au, pure Sc, Mn, Cu, In, La, W and ^{238}U) were used in the epithermal beam measurement in May 1996. An additional foil of enriched ^{58}Fe obtained from Russia was also used. The other four, Au, pure In, Ni and Al, which were bare, were left out of this first irradiation. For measuring the thermal flux a separate irradiation was carried out in August 1996 with bare Dy, Au and Mn foils. For flux mapping around the reactor core we have used Au (thermal + epithermal flux) and Ni (fast flux). All activation measurements have been carried out at the full reactor power of 250 kW.

The measured reaction rates were used to adjust input spectra based on transport calculations (DORT code). The same DORT source model was used in this work and in [6]. The generalized least-squares code LSL-M2 [7] was used to adjust the neutron spectra. A 47-group energy structure (same as in the DORT calculations) was used in the adjustment procedure. The cross-sections with uncertainties were condensed from IRDF-90 vs. 2 [4] and ENDF/B-VI (Dy, La and W, no uncertainties).

The groupwise input uncertainties were evaluated conservatively and the group-to-group correlations were assumed exponential on a lethargy-distance scale as recommended in [8]. The Sc reaction gave inconsistent results and was deleted from the final analysis.

The fast region turned out to be very difficult to measure with activation methods. The only way to achieve measurable response was by irradiating pure In foils of fairly large mass in an enriched Bi sphere with additional Cd cover (INEL) to suppress the activation from the dominating thermal-neutron reaction. The results of the analysis for the free-beam neutron field at the Bi surface (see Fig. 1) are:

Epithermal flux (0.5 eV − 10 keV): 1.26×10^9n/ cm^2.s^{-1} ± 4.4%
Thermal flux (<0.5 eV): 2.55×10^8 n/ cm^2.s^{-1} ± 9.8%
Fast flux (> 10 keV): 2.63×10^7 n/ cm^2.s^{-1} ± 25.8%
Total flux 1.55×10^9 n/cm^2.s^{-1}

The adjustment ratio in each energy group is presented in Fig. 2. It stays inside the interval 1.4−2.2, which means that the calculated flux is systematically lower than the adjusted flux. This can be explained by the homogeneous core model used in these calculations. The homogeneous core model gives smaller total flux than a heterogeneous core model. Preliminary calculations with the improved core model have been performed and they show an increase of 50% in total calculated flux compared to the previous calculations. The shape and absolute value of the adjusted spectrum remain essentially the same even when the new calculated spectrum is used as an LSL-M2-input.

Conclusions

The free-beam neutron field at the Finnish BNCT facility has been determined

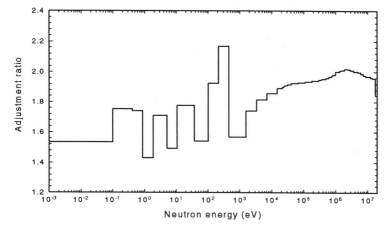

Fig. 2. Adjustment ratio (adjusted/calculated flux) in 47 energy groups.

with very good accuracy. It was verified that the neutron field created by the new moderator is eminently suited for epithermal BNCT. The epithermal component is sufficiently large, both in absolute terms and compared to the thermal and fast components.

References

1. Hiismäki P, Auterinen I. Patent FI-92890 1995.
2. Auterinen I, Hiismäki P. Epithermal BNCT neutron beam design for a TRIGA II reactor. In: Soloway AH et al. (eds) Advances in Neutron Capture Therapy. New York: Plenum Press, 1993;81—84.
3. Auterinen I, Salmenhaara S, Tanner V. Operation and on-line beam monitoring of the Finnish BNCT station. In: Larsson B, Crawford J, Weinreich R (eds) Advances in Neutron Capture Therapy. Volume 1, Medicine and Physics: Amsterdam: Elsevier Science, 1997;348—352 (these proceedings).
4. Kocherov NP, McLaughlin PK. The International Reactor Dosimetry File (IRDF-90). IAEA-NDS-141, Rev. 2 1993.
5. Netherlands Energy Research Foundation ECN, P.O. BOX 1, 1755 ZG Petten, The Netherlands.
6. Seppälä T, Vähätalo J, Auterinen I, Savolainen S. Brain tissue substitutes for phantom measurements in NCT. In: Larsson B, Crawford J, Weinreich R (eds) Advances in Neutron Capture Therapy. Volume 1, Medicine and Physics: Amsterdam: Elsevier Science, 1997;188—191 (these proceedings).
7. Stallmann FW. NUREG/CR-4349, ORNL/TM-9933 1986.
8. Standard guide for determining neutron energy spectra from neutron sensors for radiation-hardness testing of electronics. In: American Society for Testing & Materials, Philadelphia, PA 19103-1187, USA. Director, Editorial Services: R.A. Storer. Annual Book of ASTM Standards, Vol 12.02.ASTM E 721—93, 1993.

Advances in Neutron Capture Therapy.
Volume I, Medicine and Physics.
B. Larsson, J. Crawford and R. Weinreich, editors.

Considerations for patient positioning in static beams for BNCT

L. Wielopolski[1], J. Capala[1], M. Chadha[2], N.E. Pendzick[1] and A.D. Chanana[2]

[1]*Medical Department, Brookhaven National Laboratory, Upton;* and [2]*Department of Radiation Oncology, Beth Israel Medical Center, New York, USA*

Introduction

Boron neutron capture therapy (BNCT) is a binary treatment modality that may selectively irradiate tumor tissue. BNCT utilizes compounds containing the stable isotope of boron, ^{10}B, to sensitize tumor cells to irradiation by low energy thermal neutrons. The interaction of the ^{10}B with a thermal neutron, through a capture reaction, causes the boron nucleus to split, releasing an α particle and a Li ion. These high LET particles are very damaging to cells containing ^{10}B. Thermal neutrons in the brain are derived from the attenuation and moderation of an incident epithermal neutron beam, obtained from filtered neutrons emanating from a nuclear reactor.

Phase I/II clinical trials of BNCT for patients with a highly malignant brain tumor, glioblastoma multiforme, are underway using p-boronophenylalanine-fructose and the epithermal neutron beam of the Brookhaven Medical Research Reactor (BMRR). Since the neutron beam is permanently oriented horizontally, there is a need to properly position and immobilize the patient for treatment. The objective of this short communication is to provide a guideline for patient positioning, verification and immobilization for BNCT. Although the guideline is based on the experience gained at BMRR it should be applicable to any static beam for BNCT.

General conditions

At the BMRR a collimated beam is emitted horizontally from the biological shielding wall into the treatment room. It is into this fixed beam that a patient has to be maneuvered for proper treatment. Because of the rapid loss of neutron intensity at every incremental increase in the distance from the beam port, the head of the patient must be kept contiguous with the beam port, rendering patient positioning difficult. The beam port wall is equipped with three conventional positioning lasers, identical to those used in conventional radiation oncology facilities for triangulation. Three lasers, each with cross-hairs, are

---

Address of correspondence: Lucian Wielopolski PhD, Medical Department, Brookhaven National Laboratory, Upton, NY 11973, USA.

orthogonally mounted so as to project at the isocenter virtually located 10 cm distal from the beam port. Each of the laser beams intercepts the beam central axis. Typical treatment times of about 40 min require that patients be immobilized securely but comfortably.

For patient positioning purposes a mock-up room, identical to the treatment room, was constructed with an opening in a wall simulating the beam port. A cross-hair laser, additional to the three orthogonal lasers, was positioned with the axis along the central beam axis shining into the port from the neutron beam direction. The mock-up room is otherwise identical with the treatment room. The opening in the wall allows one to check the patient position from the beam's eye view. A hydraulic table or a chair are employed to provide adjustable patient support during BNCT. Another instrument was designed for stereotactic marking of patients prior to the treatment planning MRI scans of the brain. Cardinal to BNCT therapy are three processes that are closely coupled, namely patient marking, treatment planning and patient positioning. These processes are described in the following sections.

Patient marking

The heads of patients scheduled for BNCT are marked with fiducial marks at anterior, posterior, right lateral, left lateral and vertex points with a surgical pen using the in-house built stereotactic frame. The four other surface marks are located at a plain which is about 5 cm inferior to the vertex. This marking is accomplished by placing the patient (with the stereotactic frame placed on the same surface and around the head) on a flat firm surface so that orthogonal compatibility with that of the positioning lights and patient couch in the MRI scanner is maintained. Vitamin E capsules are placed on the surface marks to provide an MRI image of the fiducial marks that are used during the treatment planning to establish patient coordinates. The four fiducial marks in the cross-sectional plane (excluding the one at the vertex) are coplanar. Similarly, anterior, vertex and posterior marks are coplanar in the sagittal plane. Subsequent to surface markings MRI brain scans are carried out, with and without contrast enhancing material. The head is scanned from C4 to the vertex contiguously with 5-mm thick slices.

Treatment planning and patient positioning

MRI images are transferred electronically to the treatment planning computer and are used to create a three-dimensional model of the head for isodose calculations employing the MNCP code. In addition the MCNP code provides the coordinates of the beam central axis intercepts of the different regions in the patient head, e.g., scalp, skull, brain and target. Using this information, the coordinates of the entry and exit points of the beam central axis on a patient's head are calculated relative to the fiducial marks. In addition the distances from the fiducial marks to the beam port are also calculated. Using these coordinates the entry point and whenever possible the exit point are marked on a patient's head.

For the purpose of BNCT simulation, the patient is placed on a table or in a chair in the mock-up room. The table or the chair with the patient are maneuvered until the entry point mark is contiguous with the center of the beam port and the laser lines intercept the exit point. This positioning is confirmed by viewing the patient's head and entry point through the opening in the wall. Once a final satisfactory position is achieved, i.e., the beam entry and exit marks on the patient are collinear with the beam central axis as represented by the laser lines, the patient is immobilized using a variety of supporting accessories and materials such as foams and Velcro strips. These materials are preselected following irradiation in the reactor to assure minimal neutron activation. The final patient position is verified by checking the distances of the fiducial marks from the beam port as calculated by the treatment planning software. At this configuration, laser lines on the patient head are marked with a pen and are used as the final set of marks for patient positioning in the treatment room. In addition the height of the table or chair are measured and the laser lines are marked on all the items used for patient support.

In the treatment room the table or the chair and all the supporting and immobilization items are assembled according to the laser marks. Then the patient's position is secured according to the laser marks on the head and verified again by measuring the distances of the fiducial marks from the beam port. The outline of the patient's head and other features such as the nose are marked on a closed loop video monitor for observing any movement. If movement does occur during treatment the patient is instructed through the audio intercom system to take corrective action.

Discussion

As opposed to conventional radiotherapy where the clinical accelerator moves isocentrically around the patient, for BNCT the reactor provides a fixed beam. Therefore, the patient has to be maneuvered so that the superior, posterior and lateral parts of the head can be placed in contact with the beam port. Due to this unique requirement and because of the need to reduce the distance between the patient and the beam port, no space is left between the beam port and the patient for conventional verification devices, e.g., X-ray machine. The procedure described above evolved during our clinical trials of treating patients with glioblastoma multiforme. This procedure has been found to be quite reproducible and verifiable. It is our experience that small errors in positioning of the patient have small effects on the isodose distribution, on the coordinates of the positioning points and on the verification distances. We are conducting systematic analysis on error propagation in the isodoses and in the coordinates due to errors in fiducial marks and patient positioning.

Acknowledgements

This work was supported by the Office of Health and Environmental Research of the US Department of Energy under Contract DE-AC02−76CH00016.

Proposed facilities

Status of epithermal neutron beam design for neutron capture therapy at THOR

Yen-Wan Hsueh Liu[1], H.J. Chu[1] and H.M. Liu[2]

[1] *Department of Nuclear Engineering and Engineering Physics, National Tsing Hua University, Hsinchu; and [2] Nuclear Science and Technology Development Center, National Tsing Hua University, Hsinchu, Taiwan, ROC*

Introduction

Previous design calculations using TORT [1] and BUGLE-80 [2] library showed that by replacing the removable portion of the graphite blocks in the thermal column of Tsing Hua Open-pool Reactor (THOR) with a properly designed moderator, an epithermal neutron beam suitable for neutron capture therapy (NCT) could be obtained [3]. The beam configuration (configuration 1) is given in Table 1. Continuous efforts were made to verify the calculational results.

Sensitivity study

First, the effect of the cross-section library used by TORT is examined. The use of individual cross-section data for the fuel assemblies of THOR instead of the cross-sections of LWR core in BUGLE-80 library results in a $\sim 10\%$ decrease of the neutron/γ-ray fluxes at the beam exit. The use of problem-dependent cross-section sets derived from VITAMIN-C library through the AMPX-77 [4] routines results in 16, 5 and 11% increases for fast, epithermal and thermal neutron fluxes, respectively, at the beam exit. The use of BUGLE-93 [5] (ENDF/B-V-based) cross-sections except for cadmium, results in a 20% increase of thermal neutron flux at the beam exit. Half of the effect is due to the smaller thermal absorption cross-section of lead in BUGLE-93.

The effect of the number of discrete angles used in the three-dimensional transport calculation is also examined. When the beam is designed as a void region followed by a moderator region, the use of S_{16} angular approximation instead of S_8 in the TORT calculation results in an increase of fast neutron dose rate at the beam exit by a factor of three. The increases of epithermal neutron flux, thermal neutron flux and γ-ray flux are 50, 30 and 24% respectively. The effect would be slightly smaller for the beam design with a moderator region followed by a void region. It appears that when there is a large void region, the use of S_8 is not suffi-

---

Address for correspondence: Yen-Wan Hsueh Liu, Department of Nuclear Engineering and Engineering Physics, National Tsing Hua University, Hsinchu, Taiwan, R.O.C.

Table 1. Description of configurations.

Configuration 1

Core + H_2O (1 cm) + Pb (5 cm) + 243 cm phantom area
243 cm = Cd (0.018 cm) + void (178.7 cm) + moderator (55 cm) + Cd (0.02 cm) + Pb (10 cm)
Moderator = Al (19.64 cm) + Al_2O_3 (7.86 cm) + Al (19.64 cm) + Al_2O_3 (7.86 cm)
Cross-sectional area of beam = 4040 cm^2
Surrounding material = Pb (15 cm) + Li_2CO_3 (3.8 cm)

Configuration 2

Core + Al (0.7 cm) + H_2O (1 cm) + Pb (9 cm) + Al (4.8 cm) + Air (12 cm) + 241 cm phantom area
241 cm = Al (1 cm) + Cd (0.01 cm) + Air (176 cm) +Al (15.32 cm) + Al_2O_3 (8.84 cm) + air (3.4 cm) +Al (17.04 cm) + Al_2O_3 (8.84 cm) + Cd (0.01 cm) + air (1.7 cm) + Pb (8.5 cm)
Cross-sectional area of beam = 4040 cm^2
Surrounding material = Cd (0.01 cm) + Pb (12.3 cm) + Li_2CO_3 (6 cm)

Configuration 3

Core + Al (0.7 cm) + H_2O (1 cm) +Pb (9 cm) + Al (4.8 cm) + air (12 cm) + 241 cm phantom area
241 cm = Al (1 cm) + Cd (0.1 cm) + air (185.4 cm)
+ Al (14 cm) + Al_2O_3 (8 cm) + Al (14 cm) + Al_2O_3 (8 cm) + Cd (0.1 cm) + Pb (10 cm)
Cross-section area of beam = 3533 cm^2
Surrounding material = Cd (0.1 cm) + Pb (12.3 cm) + borated PE (6 cm)

Configuration 4

Core + Al (0.7 cm) + H_2O (1 cm) + Pb (9 cm) + Al (4.8 cm) + air (12 cm) + 243 cm phantom area + beam stopper
243 cm = Al (1 cm) + inner box 1 (76 cm) + air (90 cm) + inner box 2 (76 cm)
Inner box 1 = Al (1 cm) + Cd (0.1 cm)
+ Al plate region (15.5 cm) + two Al_2O_3 containers (10.4 cm)
+ Al plate region (15.6 cm) + two Al_2O_3 containers (10.4 cm) + air (23 cm)
Inner box 2 = Al (1 cm) + air (52 cm) + Cd (0.1 cm)
+ three bi shot containers (15.5 cm) + air (7.4 cm)
Al plate region = Al (11.9 cm) + air (3.6 or 3.7 cm)
Al_2O_3 container = air (0.2 cm) + Al (0.2 cm) + Al_2O_3 (4.4 cm) + Al (0.2 cm) + air (0.2 cm)
Bi shot container = air (0.1 or 0.2 cm) + Al (0.2 cm) + bi
shot (4.4 cm) + Al (0.2 cm) + air (0.2 cm)
Cross-sectional area of beam = 3533 cm^2
Surrounding material = Cd (0.1 cm) + Pb (12.3 cm) + borated PE (6 cm)

---

cient due to the ray effect pertinent to the multidimensional discrete-ordinate methods.

The inclusion of more water surrounding the core and more graphite surrounding the moderator region, in the modeling of the calculation, will result in an increase of thermal neutron flux and γ-ray flux, by a factor of two, at the beam exit. Despite all the above effects, the quality of the beam designed for THOR meets the design criteria.

Due to the extra structural material present at the core exit and a 12 cm air region in front of the to-be-built 243 cm moderator region, the calculations were repeated. The epithermal neutron flux at the beam exit was found to be reduced to 27% of its original value under a similar but slightly thinner moderator design (configuration 2 of Table 1). By further reducing the thickness of the moderator (configuration 3 of Table 1), the epithermal neutron flux at the center line of the beam exit can reach $\sim 0.6 \times 10^9$ n/cm^2.s^{-1} at the core power of 1 MW when S_{16} is used. The fast neutron dose and γ-ray dose per epithermal neutron are 9.85×10^{-11} cGy cm^2/s and 3.34×10^{-11} cGy cm^2/s, respectively, both of which are within the design limit ($< 10^{-10}$ cGy cm^2/s). The cross-sectional area of the beam, in this case, is reduced to 35×33 cm^2 to reflect the more realistic situation of the to-be-built beam.

Comparisons of TORT results with MCNP4A on the present test beam configuration

A test beam was built in August 1995 in the removable portion of the thermal column of THOR. The beam design was based partly on the above conceptual design consisting of cadmium, aluminum, Al$_2$O$_3$ and bismuth. The Al$_2$O$_3$ powder and bismuth shot were placed inside the aluminum containers (configuration 4 of Table 1); the densities of which turned out to be only one-fifth and one-half of their theoretical densities. This made the beam quality deviate from the design goal. The beam, however, can still be used for the purpose of bench marking the calculational and experimental results.

Comparisons of calculational results of TORT with MCNP4A [6] were made at five different locations along the test beam. The five locations correspond approximately to the core exit, the entrance and exit of inner box 1, and the entrance and exit of inner box 2. The BUGLE-80 library and S_{16} were used in the TORT calculation. ENDF/B-V-based data, MCNPDAT [7], is used in the MCNP4A calculation. The fast, epithermal and thermal neutron fluxes at the core exit calculated by the two methods are fairly close to each other. The differences are 34, 20 and 7%, respectively, due to the slightly different modeling of source distributions in the core. The descending rates of neutron fluxes along the beam, calculated by the two methods, are quite consistent up to the entrance of inner box 2. The descending rates of neutron fluxes along inner box 2 are different by factors of 1.9, 1.26 and 0.87 for fast, epithermal and thermal neutrons respectively. As a result, at the beam exit, the fast and epithermal neutron fluxes predicted by TORT are ~ 50 and $\sim 25\%$ lower than those calculated by MCNP4A. The thermal neutron flux predicted by TORT is $\sim 10\%$ higher. This difference remains to be resolved.

Measurement of the thermal and epithermal neutron fluxes are performed by using gold foils, both with and without cadmium covering. The experimental epithermal and thermal neutron fluxes at the beam exit are found to be $\sim 50\%$ and $\sim 20\%$ lower than the TORT results.

Conclusions and Future work

So far, the calculational results of TORT have been examined carefully through various sensitivity studies. It has been found that S_{16} will be necessary in the design calculations. Due to the change of structural material at the core exit and an additional 12 cm air region in front of the to-be-built filter/moderator region, the epithermal neutron flux at the beam exit, under a similar moderator design, is found to be only $\sim 0.6 \times 10^9$ n/cm^2.s^{-1} at the core power of 1 MW. The TORT result of the present test beam has been compared with that of MCNP4A and the measurements. The thermal neutron and the epithermal neutron fluxes obtained by the two calculational methods agree quite well. The measurements, however, are ~ 20 and $\sim 50\%$ lower. The 50% discrepancy in the fast neutron flux, between the two calculational methods, remains to be resolved.

In the coming year, a new beam will be built based on the optimum designs calculated by TORT and MCNP4A. Biased quadrature sets will be used in the TORT calculation in the hope of solving the discrepancy of fast neutron fluxes between the two calculational methods. Aluminum Fluoride will be considered to lower the fast neutron dose. Further measurements will be carried out to help in characterizing the beam quality.

Acknowledgements

The authors would like to express their gratitude to Mr T.F. Liaw in providing the experimental data. The work is supported by National Science Council of Taiwan, Republic of China, under contract no. NSC84−2212−E−007−005 and NSC85−2212−E−007−079.

References

1. TORT: Three-Dimensional Discrete-Ordinates Transport, v.1.5.15. Oak Ridge National Laboratory, RSIC CCC-543 1992.
2. BUGLE-80, Couple 47 Neutron, 20 Gamma-Ray P$_3$ Cross Section Library for LWR Shielding Calculation by the ANS-6.1.2 Working Group on Multigroup Cross Sections. Oak Ridge National Laboratory, ANS 6.1.2 and EG&G Idaho, Inc., RSIC DLC-75 1992.
3. Su L, Liu YWH, Peir JJ, Liaw TF. Epithermal neutron beam design for neutron capture therapy at Tsing Hua open-pool reactor. In: Mishima Y (ed) Cancer Neutron Capture Therapy, New York: Plenum Press, 1996;337−342.
4. Greene NM, Ford III WE, Petrie LM, Arwood JW. AMPX-77: A Modula Code System for Generating Coupled Multigroup Neutron-Gamma Cross Section Libraries from ENDF/B-IV and/or ENDF/B-V. ORNL/CSD/TM/283, RSIC PSR-315 1992.
5. BUGLE-93, Couple 47 Neutron, 20 Gamma-Ray Group Cross Section Library Derived from ENDF/B-V for LWR Shielding and Pressure Vessel Dosimetry Applications. Oak Ridge National Laboratory, RSIC DLC-175 1994.
6. MCNP: Monte Carlo N-Particle Transport Code System, Version 4A. Oak Ridge National Laboratory, RSIC CCC-200 1993.
7. MCNPDAT, MCNP,Version 4, Standard Neutron Cross Section Data Library Based in Part on ENDF/B-V, RSIC DLC-105 1994.

Design of a facility for NCT research in the IEA-R1 reactor

M.A.P. Camillo[1], P.R.P. Coelho[1], M. de A. Damy[1], D.B.M. Ferreira Jr[1], J.R. Maiorino[1], R.N. de Mesquita[1], N. Nascimento[1], R. Pugliesi[1], J.R. Rogero[1], W.J. Vieira[2] and G.S. Zahn[1]

[1]*Nuclear Reactor Department, Technology Applications Department, IPEN-CNEN, São Paulo; and* [2]*IEAv/CTA/EAN, São José dos Campos, Brazil*

Introduction

For several years, the possibility to use the IEA-R1 reactor to make research on neutron capture therapy (NCT) has been evaluated. Also, some studies have been developed in order to obtain a suitable neutron beam. This work describes the conceptual design for a facility using a radial beam hole of IEA-R1 research reactor.

Irradiation facility design

The IEA-R1 reactor is a 2-MW pool-type research reactor and nowadays its power is being increased to 5 MW. This reactor is mainly used in radioactive material production. It has several beam holes and the neutron flux that exits in it is small. The basic idea is to build a device to be introduced into the beam hole, in such a way that neutron and γ filters (Al, Si, Fe, Bi, etc.) can be arranged and easily changed, in order to make different emergent neutron spectra (thermal or epithermal) possible. Also, a flexible setup should be obtained, in order to meet the needs of several types of studies. To enhance the neutron intensity entering the device, a fission plate will be installed between the BH and the reactor core. Calculations to determine the neutron flux gain and the heat generation in the plate are in progress, using ANISN transport radiation codes [1]. In these calculations, parameters like the thickness of the plate and its material (metallic uranium, U_3O_8 or UO_2), as well as two different degrees of enrichment in ^{235}U (20 and 93%), are being taken into account.

Beam hole number three (BH-3 — Fig. 1) was chosen because of its 8-inch inner diameter (the highest available). As it is difficult to obtain a computational model of this reactor, because there is a mix of fuel (two different enrichment and several burn-up levels), several measurements of neutron flux inside the beam hole and in the edge of the core, near the BH entrance, have been made

Address for correspondence: Paulo Rogério P. Coelho, Departamento de Física de Reatores, IPEN-CNEN/SP, Caixa Postal 11049, CEP 05422-970, São Paulo, SP, Brazil.

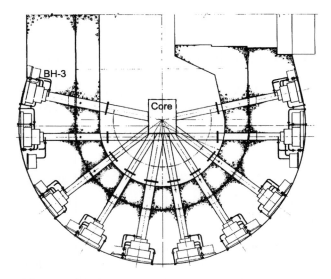

Fig. 1. Top view of the IEA-R1 reactor showing the relative position of the BH-3.

using both activation and scintillation detectors. The data will serve as the basic input for the design. With BH-3 empty, a thermal flux of 10^{10} neutrons/cm^2.s^{-1} was obtained in a position 90 cm away from the edge of the core (entrance of the beam hole) [2]. To obtain sufficiently high neutron flux for the purpose of biological experiments, the "irradiation cell" will be placed inside BH-3 (see Fig. 2), consisting of a box with an 8 cm^2 cross-section which can be inserted just after the filters. The calculations to define the basic dimensions of the device and shield are being made using transport (ANISN) and Monte Carlo (MCNP) codes [3]. Finally, a beam catcher outside the beam hole will be designed to isolate the experimental facility.

Proposed experiments

This facility will allow studies with different combinations of neutron filters to assess neutron spectra, dose rates, etc., suitable for use in neutron capture therapy. The optimization of filter combination will be obtained using the DOT 3.5 transport radiation code [4] and MCNP Monte Carlo Code, and the calculations will be evaluated using experimental measurements. The "irradiation box" will be used for phantom irradiation on dose distribution studies, as well as "in vitro" and "in vivo" biological sample irradiations.

Also, this facility will allow assays of cell growing curves (gliomas and melanomas in culture) in the presence of ^{10}B compounds, and tumor regression assays in mice. In addition, some studies of the effects of NCT in neurophysiological systems using rats as models will be developed.

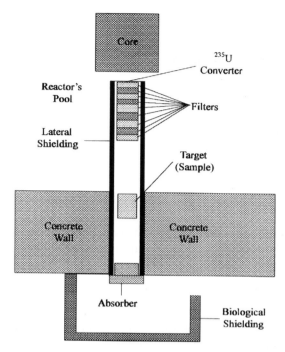

Fig. 2. Preliminary sketch of the facility to be mounted in the beam hole.

References

1. Engle WW Jr. ANISN - A one-dimensional discrete ordinate transport code with anisotropic scattering. ORNL-CCC-254, 1973.
2. Bitelli U, Alves MAP, Damy MA, Coelho PRP. Thermal neutron flux mapping in the irradiation tube 8 in the IEA-R1 reactor (in portuguese). Proceedings of the VIII ENFIR 1991; 249–252.
3. Briemeister J (ed). MCNP - A general Monte Carlo Code for Neutron and Photon Transport, Version 3A. LA-7396-M Rev. 2, 1986.
4. Rhoades WA, Mynatt FR. The DOT III two-dimensional discrete ordinate transport code. ORNL-TM-4280, 1973.

Development of irradiation facility for BNCT at the "Jozef Stefan" Institute TRIGA Research Reactor

Marko Maučec and Bogdan Glumac
"Jozef Stefan" Institute, Reactor Physics Division, Ljubljana, Slovenia

Introduction

It has been reported [1−4] that satisfactory thermal/epithermal neutron beams for boron neutron capture therapy (BNCT) could be designed at TRIGA research reactors. These reactors are generally considered as quite safe, for installing and operating in populated areas. Therefore a decision has been made that similar epithermal beams could be developed at the "Jozef Stefan" Institute TRIGA Mark-II research reactor as well.

The first step of the development was the study of appropriate configuration of thermal/epithermal neutron and γ filters using the Monte Carlo simulation code MCNP4B. As an emerging point for calculation we decided to use a simple spherical reactor, filled with a homogenised mixture of the materials contained in the TRIGA fuel unit cell. Dimensions of the sphere were picked out in such a manner that the bare sphere (without graphite reflector) was approximately critical (k_{eff} was 1.011). Particular filter configurations were simply arranged as concentric spheres.

Epithermal irradiation facility design with MCNP4B

It is obvious that the spherical model mentioned above did not have much in common with the real TRIGA reactor core from the geometrical point of view, but was only used as an abundant neutron source for the filter configuration optimisation. It was quite suitable, because it provided very good statistics and reasonable computing times (estimated tally relative errors were less than 1%, and computer times used varied around 350 min). Because of the simplicity of this geometry we were able to use a criticality calculation which provides a most reliable reactor spectrum calculation.

We performed an extensive number of parametric studies, altering the length of the scatterer, particular filter elements and the density of the alumina used. With reference to the density of Al_2O_3, which is approximately 1.5 g/cm^3 it has to be

---

Address for correspondence: Marko Maučec, "Jozef Stefan" Institute, Reactor Physics Division, Jamova 39, POB 100, 1111 Ljubljana, Slovenia.

emphasised that this value could be raised to 3.9 g/cm^3, if alumina sand is sintered. This density was found to be almost ideal for epithermal filter but the procedure of sintering is quite expensive (special tools would have to be machined), so we used an alternative of keeping the density of Al$_2$O$_3$ around 2.0 g/cm^3 (with pressing it into a compact cylindrical tablet), and increasing the length of the spectrum shifter.

Selecting the best spectrum shifter material

Considering technical and financial feasibility we decided to adopt two different combinations of epithermal column, precisely described in [2] and [5]. After analysing the results we are in a position to confirm that the most appropriate configuration of the irradiation facility for the BNCT at our reactor would be composed of:
- 1.5 cm of D$_2$O;
- 40 cm of Al;
- 80 cm of alumina with density 2.0 g/cm^3 (or 40 cm with density 3.9 g/cm^3, if sintered);
- 0.05 cm of Cd; and
- 15 cm of Pb.

Source intensity normalisation

According to the recommendations for normalising a criticality calculation (chapter 5 in [6]) and considering that the maximum operating power of IJS TRI-GA reactor is 250 kW, 180 MeV of energy is released during each fission of U-235 and approximately 1.53 new neutrons emerge from it, the average number of neutrons being born in the TRIGA reactor core was estimated to be 1.326 × 10^{16}. We simply multiply the neutron flux densities in each energy bin by that constant, using one of MCNPs input options. Now all the neutron spectra calculated are presented in appropriate flux units (n/cm^2.s^{-1}). It was not necessary to repeat the procedure with photon tallies, because we do not need the actual number of photons at the irradiation port, but only the energy distribution which has to be minimised.

The detailed MCNP model of the TRIGA Mark II reactor with irradiation channel

As already mentioned, the spherical models were quite useful for the purpose of optimising the filters of the irradiation facility, but were inconvenient for determination of the complete dose rate at the irradiation point, the activation of particular parts and materials of the facility, fast neutron leakage rate, evaluation of the influence of the collimator, etc.

For this purpose we developed a complete Monte Carlo model, where we considered all important details about the reactor core, graphite reflector, thermal and thermalising column and all irradiation channels. Our goal was to prepare a faithful copy of the real core and its surroundings. The core has cylindrical, although not periodical, configuration. It consists of 20% enriched TRIGA fuel elements, B_4C control rods and graphite elements. All radial and axial dimensions are precisely described according to the experimental benchmark specifications from [7].

With the use of an improved TRIGA reactor core model, we were able to study the optimum core configuration for the purpose of BNCT. An emerging point was the most recent core labelled 147, appropriately modified, to assure the maximum neutron flux level at the beginning of the radial channel. Therefore, the final core shape, adjusted for BNCT treatment, has one new fuel element added and two moved from the diametrically opposite outer positions of the original core, to the beginning of the radial channel. It has to be emphasised that the reactor operational condition of maximum excess reactivity of 2,620 pcm (pcm is "percent mil" = 10^{-5} of $(k-1)/k$, where k is the multiplication factor) had to be retained during the study.

Particular attention was given to the radial channel, which leads through the graphite reflector, right to the Al casing, and where the irradiation facility is inserted. After an extensive number of calculations and considering technical feasibility and particularly safety requirements, we prepared the final shape of the epithermal part of the irradiation facility:

— 30 cm of Al and 40 cm of Al_2O_3 joined together in one piece (the pins at the front and the back of the filter elements contribute an additional 14.4 cm of Al); and

— 30 cm of Al_2O_3 with 0.05 cm of Cd foil.

All the elements stated above are in the shape of a cylinder, with a diameter of 136.2 mm. Alumina (Al_2O_3) was compressed to the final density of 2.3 g/cm^3. Final elaboration of epithermal and γ filters is thoroughly presented in [5] so no details will be given here. The model of the irradiation facility, already inserted in the radial channel, is presented in Fig. 1. Comparison of neutron spectra of the original to the modified core is presented in Fig. 2. It shows that the latter, with fuel elements concentrated at the very beginning of the channel, provides a higher level of total neutron flux, with an amplifying factor of about 1.32 (+32%).

Analysing the results from Table 1 and Fig. 2, we can determine, that this column assures very successful shifting of neutron spectra to epithermal energies, and decreasing of fast neutrons (estimated tally relative error is 4.6%). Unfortunately, rather high attenuation of neutron flux is observed; more than seven orders of magnitude. Nevertheless, the column provides an epithermal neutron flux of 1.71×10^5 n/cm^2.s^{-1}, with the fast/epithermal flux-ratio of 0.093 (compared to the relevant values obtained with standard 147 and modified core, which are 1.81 and 2.18, respectively). As seen in Fig. 3, 15 cm of Pb is also rather efficient at minimising the γ flux at the irradiation point; the attenuation factor of the total flux is almost 1.62×10^6.

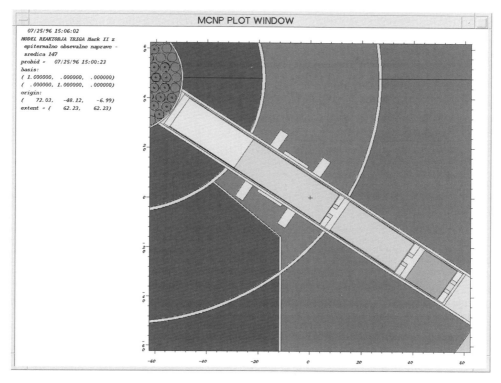

Fig. 1. MCNP model of the epithermal filter for BNCT treatment, inserted into the radial channel.

Conclusions

The first computational results presented in this contribution show that the modelled irradiation epithermal facility at the IJS TRIGA reactor produces good epithermal neutron spectra with extensive decrease of fast neutrons and

Table 1. Calculated integral values of neutron and γ flux at different points of irradiation (at maximum reactor power of 250 kW).

Point of calculation	Total neutron flux (n/cm²s)	Epithermal neutron flux (n/cm²s)	Fast neutron flux (n/cm²s)	Fast-to-epithermal neutron ratio	Total γ flux (/1 source p.)
Before epithermal and γ filter (standard core 147)	$3.13 \cdot 10^{12}$	$2.54 \cdot 10^{10}$	$4.61 \cdot 10^{10}$	1.81	$3.10 \cdot 10^{-4}$
Before epithermal and γ filter (modified core)	$4.13 \cdot 10^{12}$	$4.22 \cdot 10^{10}$	$9.20 \cdot 10^{10}$	2.18	$3.07 \cdot 10^{-4}$
Irradiation point (after traversing filters)	$2.14 \cdot 10^{5}$	$1.71 \cdot 10^{5}$	$1.59 \cdot 10^{4}$	0.09	$1.90 \cdot 10^{-10}$

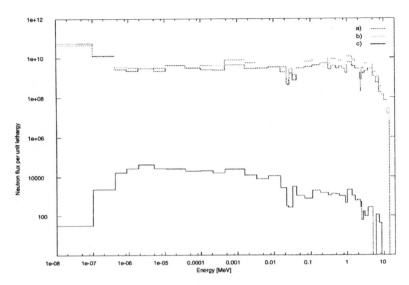

Fig. 2. Comparison between neutron spectra, calculated before and after traversing epithermal filter: a) neutron spectrum before traversing filter: standard core configuration; b) neutron spectrum before traversing filter: modified core configuration; and c) neutron spectrum after traversing epithermal filter.

minimised γ irradiation. But, unfortunately, the suitable shape of neutron and γ spectra is not good enough for successful treatment — a sufficiently high level of

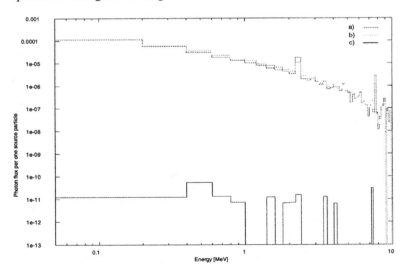

Fig. 3. Comparison between photon spectra, calculated before and after traversing γ filter: a) photon spectrum before traversing filter: standard core configuration; b) photon spectrum before traversing filter: modified core configuration; and c) photon spectrum after traversing γ filter.

neutron flux at the irradiation point is also one of the most important facts. According to the results of the Japanese experiments [8], the distance from the core to the irradiation point is a very important factor to design a neutron irradiation field for BNCT. We can get an acceptable dose with only 1 h irradiation by using a 100 kW reactor if we can get the irradiation port at a distance of 120 cm from the core side. In our case the maximum power of TRIGA reactor is 250 kW, but on the other hand the irradiation point is almost 360 cm from the core. So, unfortunately the irradiation times would probably be much longer than 1 h, but the exact numbers will be available after the first experiments. Nevertheless, the irradiation channel can of course be used for in vitro studies; boronated malignant tissue will be inserted into the channel, where fluxes are much higher.

Since a detailed geometry model of the reactor is already prepared, the focal point of our future work will be to reach for suitable and efficient variance reduction techniques, necessary for successful calculations on geometrically demanding Monte Carlo models. The construction of the thermal beam in the tangential channel is also one of our future plans. The reason why we decided to use tangential channel instead of thermal column is obvious; diagonal channel leads through the thermalising graphite column, but due to its position relative to the core it is far less "poisoned" with hard γ rays.

References

1. Auterinen I, Hiismäki P. Epithermal BNCT neutron beam design for a TRIGA II reactor. In: Soloway AH, Barth RF, Carpenter DE (eds) Advances in Neutron Capture Therapy. Columbus, Ohio, Sept, 1992: Proceedings of the 5th Int Symp on Neutron Capture Therapy. New York: Plenum Press, 1993;81—84.
2. Liu HB. Design of neutron beams for neutron capture therapy using a 300 kW slab TRIGA reactor. Nucl Tech March 1995;109:314—326.
3. Matsumoto T. Design studies of an epithermal neutron beam for neutron capture therapy at the Musashi reactor. Nucl Sci Technol 1995;32(2):87—94.
4. Rief H et al. Generating epithermal neutron beams for neutron capture therapy in small reactors. In: Soloway AH, Barth RF, Carpenter DE (eds) Advances in Neutron Capture Therapy. Columbus, Ohio, Sept, 1992: Proceedings of the 5th Int Symp on Neutron Capture Therapy for Cancer. New York: Plenum Press, 1993;13—17.
5. Maučec M et al. Development of Irradiation Facility for BNCT Treatment of Tumors at the IJS TRIGA Research Reactor. NSS 2nd Regional Meeting, Nuclear Energy in Central Europe, Portoroz, Slovenia, 11—14 September 1995;153—160.
6. Briesmeister JF (ed) MCNP — A General Monte Carlo N-Particle Transport Code version 4A. Los Alamos, NM: Los Alamos National Laboratory CCC-200, 1993.
7. Mele I et al. TRIGA Mark II benchmark experiment, Part I: steady-state operation. Nucl Tech 1994;105:37—51.
8. Aizawa O. Evaluation of neutron irradiation field for boron neutron capture therapy by using absorbed dose in a phantom. Int J Radiat Oncol Biol Phys 1994;28(5):1143—1148.

1997 Elsevier Science B.V.
Advances in Neutron Capture Therapy.
Volume I, Medicine and Physics.
B. Larsson, J. Crawford and R. Weinreich, editors.

BNCT filter design studies for the ORNL Tower Shielding Facility

Daniel T. Ingersoll, Charles O. Slater and Larry R. Williams

Oak Ridge National Laboratory, Oak Ridge, Tennessee, USA

Keywords: beam filter, filter designs, filter materials, neutron sources, reactor facilities, Tower Shielding Facility, treatment facility.

Introduction

Boron neutron capture therapy (BNCT) in the USA has entered into a new phase with the initiation of clinical trials using neutron sources at the Brookhaven National Laboratory [1] and the Massachusetts Institute of Technology [2]. If these trials are successful in demonstrating the efficacy of BNCT as a viable treatment for glioblastoma multiforme, then there will be an immediate demand for several additional neutron sources in order to treat the several thousand patients currently diagnosed with glioblastomas in the USA each year. However, the requirements for an acceptable neutron source for BNCT are rather severe in terms of the need to provide a sufficient number of epithermal neutrons to a patient-accessible location in a reasonable time with minimal thermal-neutron, fast-neutron, and γ-ray backgrounds. A few reactor facilities in the USA have been studied for potential conversion to BNCT applications, most notably the Idaho Power Burst Facility (PBF) [1] and the Georgia Institute of Technology Research Reactor (GTRR) [3]. A recent study of potential neutron sources at the Oak Ridge National Laboratory (ORNL) has been completed, which concludes that another available source, the Tower Shielding Facility (TSF), also appears very well suited for BNCT.

Facility description

The TSF was built in 1954 to support the shielding design for the Aircraft Nuclear Propulsion Project. The current reactor, the TSR-II, was put into operation in 1960 and is configured in a unique above-ground, partially shielded environment. The reactor core is made of Al-U alloy plates, which are assembled to form a spherical annulus surrounding a central control "ball" mechanism. The light-water-cooled reactor is contained in an Al pressure vessel and located in a large concrete "bunker" referred to as the big beam shield (BBS). The BBS

Address for correspondence: Daniel T. Ingersoll, Oak Ridge National Laboratory, P.O. Box 2008, Oak Ridge, TN 37830-6363, USA.

contains a 77-cm-diameter beam collimator, which permits access to a broad beam neutron flux exceeding 4×10^{11} cm^{-2}.s^{-1} at the operational power of 1 MW. A plan view of the BBS is given in Fig. 1.

The collimated beam emerges horizontally onto an unenclosed test pad area on which shield mock-ups were assembled. Conversion of the reactor to BNCT application is straightforward, since no modifications to the existing reactor pressure vessel system are needed. The appropriate beam filter and collimator system can be easily constructed in the expansive area previously used for the large shield mock-ups. Additional engineering of the beam shutter mechanism and the construction of treatment support facilities will be needed but can be easily accommodated on the remote dedicated site.

Filter design analysis

Several preliminary one- and two-dimensional analyses have been performed to determine if the TSR-II is a viable source, i.e., one that can produce a suitable epithermal beam while maintaining sufficient flux to treat patients in a reasonable exposure time (less than 1 h). Calculations were performed using the ANISN [4] and DORT [5] discrete ordinate codes and using well-characterized boundary source data generated for analyses of previous shielding benchmark experiments. The initial calculations assumed that the filter materials would be placed adjacent to the current beam shutter and collimator mechanism, which is approximately 90 cm from the center of the reactor core or approximately 50 cm from the outer surface of the core.

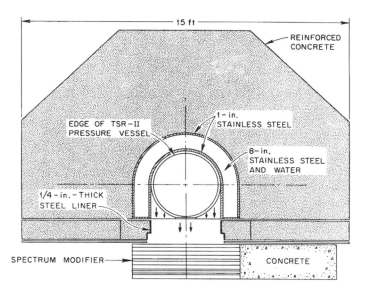

Fig. 1. Plan view schematic of the big beam shield at the Tower Shielding Facility.

Numerous filter designs were investigated using an assortment of materials commonly considered in other BNCT filter design studies. These include Al, heavy water, S, Bi, Pb, Cd, boral, and lithiated polyethylene. The best balance between beam intensity and energy spectrum was achieved using an Al/Al fluoride material developed for BNCT applications in Finland [6]. Several designs achieved a patient-incident epithermal flux of equal or greater strength than that of the Brookhaven Medical Research Reactor (BMRR) and provided a comparable or better neutron energy spectrum.

The preferred beam filter design selected from these preliminary calculations contains 80 cm of Al/AlF_3 (in a 1:1 mixture), followed by 9.2 cm S, 0.02 cm Cd, and 10 cm Bi. Two-dimensional calculations indicated that a 10-cm-thick lithiated polyethylene collimator provides acceptable beam definition while minimizing beam loss. The reference configuration yields an epithermal flux of 2.4×10^9 cm^{-2}.s^{-1} with a nonepithermal neutron kerma of 1.4×10^{-11} cGy.cm^2 and a γ-ray kerma of 8.5×10^{-12} cGy.cm^2. Figure 2 compares the flux spectrum of the TSR-II unfiltered beam with the flux spectrum on the patient side of the reference beam filter. Although the epithermal flux is attenuated by a factor of 40 across the filter, the thermal and fast fluxes are attenuated substantially more. In the filtered spectrum, approximately 98% of the total neutron flux is in the epithermal energy range of 0.5 eV to 10 keV.

An assessment of how the TSF source compares to other actual or proposed BNCT facilities is shown in Fig. 3. The patient-incident epithermal flux is plotted against a figure-of-merit parameter called "beam purity" [7]. The beam purity parameter is defined to be larger (better) for beams with good collimation and low background radiations (thermal neutrons, fast neutrons, and γ rays). The

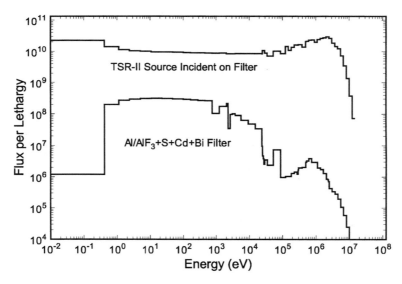

Fig. 2. Comparison of unfiltered and filtered neutron spectra at the Tower Shielding Facility.

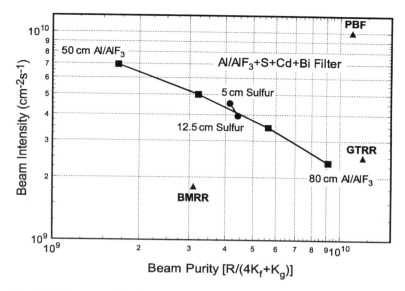

Fig. 3. Performance of various TSF filter options compared to other BNCT facilities.

reference filter design described above yields a beam purity of 9.1×10^9 $cGy^{-1}cm^{-2}$. The results plotted in Fig. 3 show the sensitivity of the beam intensity and purity to changes in the thickness of some of the key filter materials. In particular, the Al/AlF_3 was varied from 50 to 80 cm and the S was varied from 5 to 12.5 cm. The different series of data show clearly the classic trade-off between beam intensity and beam quality. The superior performance of the proposed PBF treatment facility is due to the relatively high power level of that reactor (10 MW).

Conclusions

Our analyses have shown that a beam which meets or exceeds the magnitude and spectral quality of the BMRR beam can be achieved using the TSR-II. Other attractive features of the TSF site include its close proximity to key medical and research facilities, especially at ORNL and at the University of Tennessee, its relative separation from the main ORNL site, and the unconstrained space surrounding the reactor system. Hence, it appears that this facility is very well-suited for potential dedication to BNCT research and clinical treatments. Future analyses are planned to further optimize the filter and collimator design.

References

1. Wheeler FJ, Parsons DK, Rushton BL, Nigg DW. Epithermal neutron beam design for neutron capture therapy at the PBF and BMRR reactor facilities. Nucl Tech 1990;92:106–117.

2. Choi JR, Clement SD, Harling OK, Zamenhof RG. Neutron capture therapy beams at the MIT research reactor. In: Harling OK (ed) Neutron Beam Design, Development, and Performance for Neutron Capture Therapy. New York: Plenum Press, 1990.

3. Klee KA, Nigg DW, Wheeler FJ, Karam RA. Conceptual Design for an Advanced Epithermal-Neutron Beam for Boron Neutron Capture Therapy at the Georgia Institute of Technology Research Reactor. Knoxville, TN: Proceedings of the 1994 Topical Meeting on Advances in Reactor Physics, vol III 1994;72—82.

4. Engle WW Jr. ANISN, A One-Dimensional Discrete Ordinates Transport Code with Anisotropic Scattering. Report K-1693, March 1967.

5. Rhoades WA, Childs RL. The DORT two-dimensional discrete ordinates transport code. Nucl Sci Eng 1988;99(1):88—89.

6. Auterinen I, Hiismaki P. Design of an epithermal neutron beam for the TRIGA reactor in Otaniemi. In: Auterinen J, Kallio M (eds) CLINCT BNCT Workshop Helsinki 1993. Helsinki University of Technology Series ISBN 951-22-1980-8, ISSN 0355-7790 TKK-F-A718, 1994.

7. Wheeler FJ, Wessol DE. Radiation Transport Requirements for Clinical Application of Neutron Capture Therapy: The rrt.MC Monte Carlo Module. Portland, OR: Proceedings of the International Conference on Mathematics and Computations, Reactor Physics, and Environmental Analyses. April 30 — May 4, 1995;876—883.

Design and calculation of rebuilt No. 1 neutron beam of Tsinghua University Pool-Reactor for BNCT

Mo Da-wei[1], Cai Qing-sheng[1] and Tian Bo[2]
[1]*INET Tsinghua University, Beijing; and* [2]*Shenzhen OUR science Development Co. Ltd. Shenzhen, PRC*

Requirement of BNCT for neutron beam

The neutron beam required for boron neutron capture therapy (BNCT) depends not only on the kind of cancer, position, size, shape and depth in the patient body, theoretically, but also on the character of the boronated chemical. If the chemical has better affinity for tumour cells, and the cancer contains more ^{10}B, the neutron flux could be decreased. Following early work on the treatment of brain tumours by BNCT with the drug BSH, the neutron beam is required to have the following properties [1]:
— epithermal neutron (0.4 eV — 0.02 MeV) flux about 1×10^9n/cm^2.s;
— epithermal neutron /thermal neutron (< 0.4 eV) about 100;
— epithermal neutron /fast neutron (> 0.02 MeV) about 20–30.
This is the basis of our calculation.

Description of the INET reactor

Reactor and neutron beam port

There are two reactor cores in the same pool at INET Tsinghua University. The pool section is oval-shaped with a length of 3.5 m, a width of 2 m and a height of 8.35 m. No. 1 neutron beam penetrates into the pool and faces towards the core. The axis of the neutron beam is horizontal and aligned on the center of the reactor. The height of the axis is 1.3 m. There are seven horizontal neutron beam ports and eight vertical neutron beams in the INET pool reactor. Number 1 and No. 7 are large scale horizontal neutron beam ports. No. 1 was designed for a shielding experiment, and No. 7 is for a thermal column. In front of No. 1 the neutron beam port is a 1 m^2 area, which is near the reactor core (Fig. 1). The No. 7 neutron beam port is almost the same size as the No. 1 neutron beam. Both are suitable for BNCT. Of course, the reactor is old, dating back to 1963. It is difficult to rebuild the core. This means that neither the neutron spectrum nor the neutron flux from the reactor can be changed. Only the neutron

---

Address for correspondence: Mo Da-wei, INET Tsinghua University, Beijing, 100084, PRC.

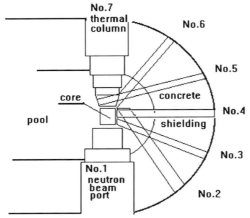

Fig. 1. Horizontal cross-section of the reactor.

beam port can be rebuilt to meet the requirements for BNCT. So, in this work, we plan to design only the neutron filter and shifter to satisfy the demand of BNCT.

Reactor specification

Core:

Thermal Power	1 MW	Active core height	50 cm
Average L.H.R.	53.3 W/cm	Cooling type	Forced cooling

Fuel:

Fuel material	UO_2 + Mg	^{235}U enrichment	10%
^{235}U loading charge	3,008 g	Diameter of fuel rod	7 mm
Cladding material	Al	Number of assembly	16
Number of fuel rods	376	Lattice geometry	square
Reflector	BeO and C		

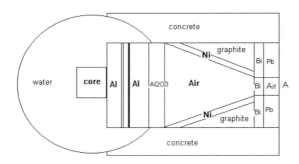

Fig. 2. Scheme 1: (A) is the position of the patient.

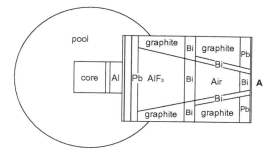

Fig. 3. Scheme 2: (A) is the position of the patient.

The reconstruction of the reactor

The BNL [2], MURR [3], MIT [4] and Petten JRC [5] work on neutron beam design has been studied. There are three possible drafts in our plan. The first one is to use Al and Al_2O_3 as filter and shifter materials (Fig. 2). In the second, AlF_3 is used as both filter and shifter (Fig. 3). The third is to make use of No. 7 thermal column to produce an epithermal neutron beam for BNCT (Fig. 4).

All of these schemes can meet the basic needs of BNCT. The calculated results are listed in Table 1. All calculations are done with MCNP. In brief, the 1 MW pool-type research reactor of INET Tsinghua University can be used to supply enough epithermal neutron for BNCT. But a large-scale neutron beam port close to the core is essential.

Discussion

The above-mentioned calculation points to the following conclusions:
— Al is quite a good material for neutron filter and spectrum shifter. Because it can be shaped easily, Al should be the first selection.
— AlF_3 is better than Al, but obtaining high quality AlF_3 is difficult in China.

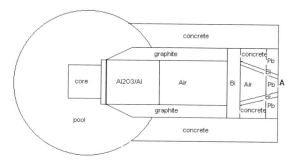

Fig. 4. Scheme 3: (A) is the position of the patient.

Table 1. The results of the calculations.

	Scheme 1	Scheme 2	Scheme 3
Filter and shifter materials	50 cm Al + 24 cm Al$_2$O$_3$ + 14 cm Bi	54 cm AlF$_3$ + 15 cm Bi	D$_2$O 5.5 cm + 43.5 cm Al$_2$O$_3$ + 10 cm Al + 15 cm Bi + Graphite
Collimator wall materials	Ni and Graphite	Bi and Concrete	Bi and Concrete
Distance from Point A to core center (cm)	264.55	187	238.4
Fast neutron flux (n/cm^2.s)	$(5.83 \pm 1.46) \times 10^7$	$(4.53 \pm 0.41) \times 10^7$	$(5.83 \pm 0.47) \times 10^7$
Epithermal neutron flux (n/cm^2.s)	$(1.12 \pm 0.06) \times 10^9$	$(9.57 \pm 0.21) \times 10^8$	$(9.63 \pm 0.17) \times 10^8$
Thermal neutron flux (n/cm^2.s)	$(1.32 \pm 0.39) \times 10^7$	$(6.80 \pm 1.15) \times 10^5$	$(7.48 \pm 0.52) \times 10^7$
γ dose (Rem/h)	$(4.20 \pm 0.46) \times 10^2$	$(1.05 \pm 0.04) \times 10^2$	$(2.06 \pm 0.06) \times 10^2$

— The scale and length of the cave collimator and the material of its wall are very important. The neutron spectrum, neutron flux and neutron beam divergence all depend on them. Figures 2, 3 and 4 show our choice. While it may not be the best, it can meet our needs.

All of this work is a preliminary, conceptual study. More detailed studies should be done. For example, the γ and fast neutron doses, scattered radiation, induced radiation, etc., should be considered. The shutter, patient bed, position, phantom experiment, treatment plan and other engineering design remains to be done. We hope that the engineering design of the No. 1 neutron beam port can be started this year.

Experimental tests

To verify the reliability of the computations, experimental results in the reactor and the No. 1 neutron beam were compared with calculated results. Table 2 shows the comparison.

Table. 2 Comparison with experiment.

Parameter comparison	Experimental results	Computed results
Neutron flux n.s^{-1}cm^2		
Core thermal	$(1.42 \pm 0.11) \times 10^{13}$	$(1.272 \pm 0.044) \times 10^{13}$
No. 1 fast (>0.5 MeV)	$(5.81 \pm 0.46) \times 10^9$	$(3.925 \pm 0.076) \times 10^9$
No. 1 fast (>0.01 MeV)	$(6.57 \pm 0.53) \times 10^9$	$(6.040 \pm 0.056) \times 10^9$
Average energy of No. 1 Neutron beam (MeV)		
E1 (>0.5 MeV)	2.14	2.09
E2 (>0.01 MeV)	1.90	1.43
K_{eff}	1.0293	1.0265 ± 0.0011

Acknowledgements

The authors express their thanks to Prof Dong Duo, Prof Shan Wenzhi and Mr Wang Yiaqi, and especially to Prof Hukai who gave us so much advice about MCNP calculations. We thank them for their suggestions and for commenting kindly and frankly on our efforts.

References

1. Brugger RM, Constantine G, Harling OK, Wheeler FJ. Neutron Beam Design, Development and Performance for NCT. MIT, Cambridge, MA: Rapporteurs Report March 1989, Plenum Press 1990;3—12.
2. Wheeler FJ et al. Epithermal neutron beam design for NCT at the Power Burst Facility and the Brookhaven Medical Research Center. Nucl Tech 1990;92:106—117.
3. Brugger RM, Jing-Luen A, Liu SB, Liu HB. An epithermal neutron beam for NCT at the Missouri University Research Reactor. Nucl Tech June 1992;98:322—332.
4. Harling OK et al. Preparation for Phase I Clinical Trials of BNCT at MIT Reactor and the New England Medical Center. Radiat Oncol Invest 2 1994;109—118.
5. Moss RL, Casado J, Ravensberg K, Stecher-Rasmussen F, Watkins P. The completed boron neutron capture therapy facility at the HFR Petten. In: Larsson B, Crawford J, Weinreich R (eds) Advances in Neutron Capture Therapy, Volume 1, Medicine and Physics. Amsterdam: Elsevier Science, 1997; 331—335 (these proceedings).
6. Moss RL. Review of reactor-based neutron beam development for BNCT applications. In: Soloway AH, Barth RF, Carpenter DE (eds) Advances in Neutron Capture Therapy. Columbus, Ohio, Sept. 1992: Proceedings of 5th International Symposium of NCT. New York: Plenum Press, 1993.

Thermal neutron field for BNCT experiments at the nuclear reactor of TUB

É.M. Zsolnay and Sz. Czifrus

Institute of Nuclear Techniques, Technical University of Budapest, Budapest, Hungary

Keywords: experiments, filter arrangement, spectrum measurements, neutron/γ filter, thermal beam, transport calculations.

Introduction

Besides the epithermal neutrons from high flux reactors applied for the treatment of glioma, thermal neutrons from the much smaller and less expensive low-power research reactors have an important role in the further development and application of boron neutron capture therapy (BNCT). One part of the study of the fundamental radiobiological processes, responsible for the achievement of the therapeutic gain of BNCT, consists of the irradiation of cell cultures and small test animals with thermal neutrons.

BNCT studies with thermal neutrons in Hungary started at the 100 kW power nuclear reactor of the Technical University of Budapest (TUB) several years ago. The work has been done in cooperation with the Institute of Nuclear Techniques (INT) of TUB and a number of national institutes and universities, and resulted in the following:

1. The development of a preliminary irradiation field at one of the horizontal beam channels of the reactor for chemical and biological experiments for BNCT [1].
2. Chemical and biological studies: synthesis of boron compounds, preparation of boron-containing monoclonal antibodies and the development of experimental model systems for the biological evaluation of BNCT [2].
3. Preliminary calculations and a feasibility study on the development of a pure thermal neutron beam at the irradiation tunnel of the reactor for BNCT experiments [3,4].

In February 1994 we joined the Concerted Action of the European Collaboration on BNCT with the aim of developing a thermal neutron irradiation field at the irradiation tunnel of the reactor for preclinical radiobiological studies and elaborating the biological evaluation of BNCT in human melanomas. This paper presents the results of the activity of designing the irradiation field.

Address for correspondence: E.M. Zsolnay, Institute of Nuclear Techniques, Technical University of Budapest, H—1521 Budapest, Hungary.

Development of the thermal neutron irradiation field

Description of the facility

The facility of the reactor suitable for BNCT experiments is the large irradiation tunnel passing the biological shielding. The tunnel starts from the outer boundary of the reactor shielding with an aperture of 130×170 cm^2 and, after a stepwise decrease, it approaches the core with a surface area of about 50 cm^2. There is a water gap of 9 cm between the core and this inner surface. The tunnel is equipped with a carriage running on a railway. The carriage is able to transport different experimental arrangements or large samples (e.g., animals) into the irradiation zone.

Calculations for designing the neutron/γ filter — experimental verification of the results

Earlier feasibility studies [4] have shown that the leakage spectrum of the irradiation tunnel can be converted into a thermal neutron source by the application of a special neutron/γ filter. Therefore, neutron and γ transport calculations have been performed to determine the composition and arrangement of the filter leading to the optimum spectral characteristics for BNCT (thermal neutron beam with negligible epithermal, fast neutron and γ radiation background).

The geometrical complexity of the reactor core, the reflector arrangement and the irradiation tunnel made it necessary to perform three-dimensional calculations. In order to obtain reliable results, on which the actual filter arrangement can be built, two different transport codes (TORT and MCNP4A [5,6]) were used and the results obtained were compared with each other and with the experiments. The neutron spectrum measurements were performed with multifoil activation methods, while in the γ dose rate measurements TLDs were used.

Several different filter arrangements were investigated, in each case primarily focusing on the thermal and fast neutron flux. The TORT calculations were performed in 25 neutron energy groups. Thereafter coupled neutron-γ calculations were done (using 27 neutron and 18 γ energy groups) for the most promising filter compositions. Details of the calculations can be found in [7]. The TORT and MCNP results showed good agreement: the deviations between the corresponding spectrum characteristic data were less than 30% in each case.

The ratios of the calculated to measured reaction rates for the leakage neutron spectrum of the irradiation tunnel and for the filter arrangement shown in Fig. 1 are given in Table 1. The data illustrate very good agreement between the calculations and measurements.

The deviation between the measured and calculated γ dose rate values at the inner surface of the tunnel without the filter was within a factor of 2 for both the TORT and MCNP results.

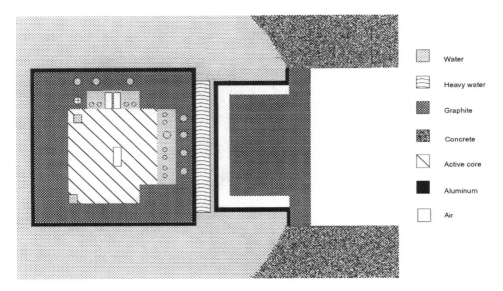

Fig. 1. Heavy water premoderation + graphite filter of 40 cm thickness in the irradiation tunnel.

The final configuration of the irradiation field

The final configuration of the thermal neutron irradiation field can be seen in

Table 1: Comparison of calculations with the measurements.

Reaction	Cover	C/E for reaction rates		
		Leakage spectrum of the irradiation tunnel		D$_2$O premoderation + 40 cm graphite in the tunnel
		MCNP	TORT	MCNP
^{197}Au(n,γ)^{198}Au	—	0.98	1.09	0.95
^{115}In(n,γ)^{116}In	—	0.92	1.09	0.90
^{55}Mn(n,γ)^{56}Mn	—	0.86	1.01	0.95
^{197}Au(n,γ)^{198}Au	Cd	1.19	1.19	1.10
^{115}In(n,γ)^{116}In	Cd	1.00	1.24	—
^{45}Sc(n,γ)^{46}Sc	Cd	1.14	1.32	—
^{55}Mn(n,γ)^{56}Mn	Cd	0.92	1.03	0.86
^{58}Ni(n,p)^{58}Co	—	1.14	0.83	1.20
^{54}Fe(n,p)^{54}Mn	—	1.04	0.75	—
^{56}Fe(n,p)^{56}Mn	—	0.93	0.92	—
^{47}Ti(n,p)^{47}Sc	—	1.07	0.81	—
^{115}In(n,n)^{115m}In	—	1.05	0.93	1.12

Note: The thermal to fast (E > 1 MeV) neutron flux ratio, in the case of the leakage spectrum of the tunnel, is ∼ 2.8, while in case of the configuration in Fig. 1 it is ∼ 50.

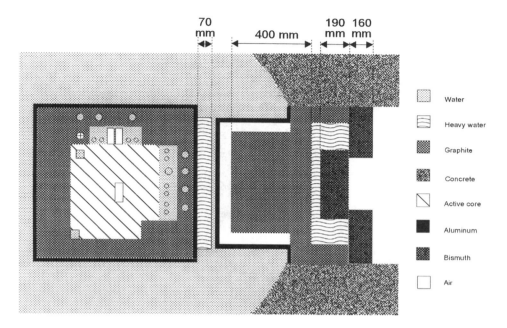

Fig. 2. Final configuration of the BNCT irradiation field.

Fig. 2. The neutron and γ filter in the tunnel consists of the combination of graphite, heavy water and bismuth. Premoderation by heavy water is used between the core and the inner surface of the tunnel.

According to the calculations the irradiation field will have the following parameters:

1. Thermal neutron flux at the position of irradiation $\sim 2 \times 10^9$ n/cm²s
2. Thermal to fast neutron flux ratio ~ 280
3. γ-Dose rate ~ 0.5 Gy/h
4. Dose rate of (fast neutrons + γ radiation) $\leqslant 1.4$ Gy/h

The technical implementation of the designed configuration is in progress.

Acknowledgements

The work was done in the framework of the EC project on the Clinical Implementation of Neutron Capture Therapy. Contract number: ERB-BMHI-CT92-0859.

References

1. Csom Gy et al. Investigation on the neutron beam for realization of boron neutron capture therapy. In: Allen BJ, Moore DE, Harrington BV (eds) Progress in Neutron Capture Therapy for Cancer. New York: Plenum Press, 1992.

2. Csuka O et al. Boron neutron capture therapy of mouse and human melanomas. In: Vermorken A, Durieux L (eds) Proceedings of EC-Hungary Joint Workshop on Cancer Research, EUR 13482 EN. Commission of the European Communities, 1991.

3. Zsolnay ÉM. Recent investigations on neutron metrology at the Institute of Nuclear Techniques. Periodica Polytechnica Ser Phys 1993;1:17—32.

4. Zsolnay ÉM et al. First Progress Report on the Preclinical Investigation of Cancer Treatment with BNCT Using Thermal Neutrons from Small Nuclear Reactors, to the EC project of Clinical Implementation of Neutron Capture Therapy. Report, Budapest, February 1995.

5. TORT-DORT, Two- and three-dimensional discrete ordinates transport. Version 2.7.3. Report CCC543. Radiation Shielding Information Center, Oak Ridge, TN (Current version).

6. MCNP4A Monte Carlo N-Particle Transport Code System. Report CCC-200. Radiation Shielding Information Center, Oak Ridge, TN (Current version).

7. Czifrus Sz. Neutron and γ-transport calculations for designing an irradiation field for BNCT. In: Larsson B, Crawford J, Weinreich R (eds) Advances in Neutron Capture Therapy, Volume 1, Medicine and Physics. Amsterdam: Elsevier Science, 1997;259—263 (these proceedings).

The BNCT facility at the Nuclear Research Institute (NRI) reactor in the Czech Republic

J. Burian[1], M. Marek[1], J. Rataj[1], K. Prokes[2], L. Petruzelka[2], V. Mareš[3], B. Gruner[4] and P. Stopka[4]

[1]Nuclear Research Institute Rez, plc (NRI), [2]Department of Oncology, Faculty Hospital of Charles University; [3]Institute of Physiology, Academy of Sciences; and [4]Institute of Inorg Chem, Academy of Sciences, Prague, Czech Republic

Introduction

The efforts of the Czech interdisciplinary group are concentrated on the installation of boron neutron capture therapy (BNCT) at the LVR-15 reactor of the NRI in Rez, for treatment of brain glioblastomas. This paper presents the technological and physical characteristics of the BNCT facility, constructed on the LVR-15 reactor of NRI and the biological effectiveness of the epithermal beam, tested on a simple animal model. In addition, a new molecular mechanism of the BNCT reaction and purity tests of sodium borocaptate (BSH) from a new producer, Katchem, Ltd., Prague, are reported.

Results

Neutron beam

The principal disadvantage of LVR-15 geometry, is the long distance (4 m) between the core of the neutron source and the irradiation point. A beam of epithermal neutrons were obtained by filtration of neutrons from the reactor core by 4 cm of graphite, 55 cm of Al, 15 cm of S and 1 cm of Ti. The inner conic collimator, made of Al and graphite, was designed by using MCNP and DORT codes [1]. The configuration used is shown in Fig. 1 and the characteristics of the beam are summarized in Table 1.

Dosimetry and irradiation room

A physical dosimetry monitoring system collects information from four detectors for neutrons and γ rays by an on-line system based on CAMAC modules and computer control. Measurements of thermal neutron distributions were performed inside the head of a human whole-body, water-filled phantom (artificial skeleton with plexiglass cover). Thermal neutron distributions were measured with a Si semiconductor detector [2] through channels placed along the spinal

392

column and in the head. The thermal neutron distribution inside the head irradiated by epithermal and pure thermal neutrons, is presented in Fig. 2. A new irradiation room, $4 \times 4 \times 2.2$ m in size, was built from concrete blocks. The thickness of the walls and the ceiling is 40 cm. The inner surface is covered with boronated polyethylene.

Biological effectiveness

The effects of the above-described neutron beam were tested on the brains of 1-week-old rats. The neutrons (8.8×10^7 n/cm^{2}s) were thermalized by a 2.5-cm-thick polyethylene block and the times of irradiation were 5, 10 and 20 min. The brains of animals injected intracranially with 150 µg BSH (in 3 µl phosphate buffered saline, pH 7.2, calculated ^{10}B content 29.56 µg/g w.w.), or the same volume of saline, were examined histologically 8 h after the irradiation. Irradiation of the saline-injected animals, as well as those entirely intact, damaged solitary cells in the dividing populations of the external granular layer of the cerebellum and periventricular region of the forebrain hemispheres. In the animals injected with BSH and irradiated for 5—10 min, the number of lethally damaged cells in these regions significantly increased. After 20 min irradiation, the damaged cells occurred in the postmitotic and more differentiated regions

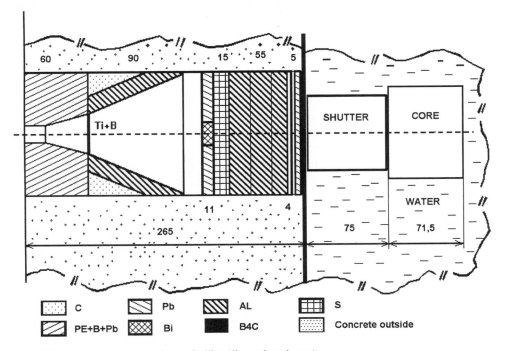

Fig. 1. The epithermal neutron beam facility (dimensions in cm).

Table 1. Characteristics of the epithermal neutron beam at the LVR-15 reactor (10 MW power).

Total neutron flux	1.47×10^8	$cm^{-2}.s^{-1}$
Thermal neutron flux (<0.414 eV)	2.43×10^7	$cm^{-2}.s^{-1}$
Epithermal neutron flux (0.414 eV to 10 kev)	1.07×10^8	$cm^{-2}.s^{-1}$
Fast neutron flux (>10 keV)	1.57×10^7	$cm^{-2}.s^{-1}$
Ratio of fast to epithermal flux	0.15	
Ratio of fast to total flux	0.11	
"Average" neutron energy	13.30	keV
Fast neutron dose rate	0.50	Gy/h
Fast neutron dose per epithermal neutron	1.30×10^{-12}	$Gy.cm^2$
Incident γ dose rate	2.25	Gy/h
Incident γ dose per epithermal neutron	7.30×10^{-12}	$Gy.cm^2$

as well, namely the deeper parts of the cerebellar cortex, hippocampus and layers two and three of the cerebral cortex [3,4].

Formation of free oxygen radicals in the BNCT reaction

Two types of mercaptoborates ($Na_2B_{12}H_{11}SH$, $[N(CH_3)_4]_2B_{12}H_{11}SH$) and $Na_2B_4O_7$ in 2.10^{-3} molar aqueous solutions were irradiated by thermal neutron flux at the LVR-15 reactor using total doses of 5 and 18 Gy. The generation of hydroxyl radicals ($\cdot OH$), superoxide anion-radicals ($O_2\cdot$) and oxygen singlets ($^1O_2$) was determined by EPR spectroscopy [5]. The quantity of radicals generated in mercaptoborate solutions was significantly higher and dependent on the oxygen concentration in the irradiated solutions and energy of the neutron

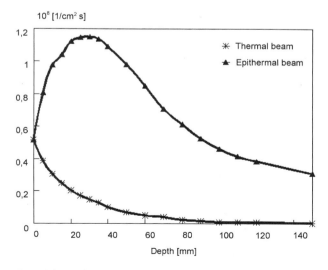

Fig. 2. Thermal neutron distribution inside the human head phantom.

beam. The generation of free oxygen radicals could represent additional cytotoxic mechanisms important for the therapeutic effects of BNCT.

Sodium borocaptate (BSH)

Purity of the BSH compound produced by a new supplier (Katchem Ltd., Prague) was tested by HPLC methods [6], and high-field ^{10}B and ^{1}H NMR techniques. It was shown that the provided samples were free of BSH oxidation products and other organic impurities. In agreement with the results of chemical analysis, cytological effects of this product, tested on glioma cells in culture, were the same as of BSH from another source (Centronic, Ltd, New Addington).

Conclusions

An irradiation facility with a beam of epithermal neutrons for BNCT of brain tumors has been constructed at the LVR-15 reactor in the NRI in Rez near Prague, and its efficiency verified on a sensitive immature rat brain model. Formation of the free oxygen radicals was shown in in vitro irradiated solutions of two mercaptoborate compounds. BSH produced by Katchem, Ltd, Prague, was found to be chemically pure and suitable for preclinical studies. A further increase of neutron fluxes is expected to be achieved by optimization of filter composition, removing of the Be reflector and adding a fuel element(s) at the edge of the core in the near future.

Acknowledgements

Supported by Contract PECO-ERB-BMH1-CT92-5008 (EU) and IGA-MZ (CR) No. 2204−3.

References

1. Burian J, Marek M, Rataj J, Mareš V, Stopka P, Štrouf O. Preclinical tests for neutron capture therapy on the LVR-15 reactor. In: Soloway AH, Barth RF, Carpenter DE (eds) Advances in NCT. London, New York: Plenum Press, 1993;25−28.
2. Marek M. Small Si-Li detectors for Thermal neutron on-line measurements. Safety Nucl Energy 1995;3:165.
3. Mareš V, Lisá V, Drahota J, Burian J. Mercaptoborate neutron capture reaction (BCNR) in the biological models in vivo and in culture. Physiol Res 1966;45:4P.
4. Mareš V, Lisá V, Drahota Z, Bacakova L, Spanova A, Kvítek J, Hnatowicz V, Burian J. Toxicity, uptake and retention of mercaptoborate (BSH) in glial and glioma cells in culture. Proc of 7th Internatl Symp on NCT for Cancer, Zurich, 1997. In: Larsson B, Crawford J, Weinreich R (eds) Advances in Neutron Capture Therapy, Volume 2, Chemistry and Biology. Amsterdam: Elsevier Science, 1997;210−215 (these proceedings).
5. Stopka P, Burian J, Štrouf O. ESR study of hydroxyl radicals, superoxide anion radicals and molecular singlet oxygen generated by mercaptoundeca-hydro-closo-dodecaborate (2-) solution irradiated by neutrons under conditions of BNC reaction. Kobe, Japan: Proceedings of the 6th

Int Symp of Neutron Capture Therapy. New York: Plenum Press, 1996;615.

6. Grûner B, Plzák Z, Vinš I. Purity assay of sodium mercaptododecaborate by high-performance liquid chromatography. Chromatography 1992;595:169–177.

Medical irradiation facility based on a fluid fuel reactor with low power

V.M. Litjaev[1], V.A. Pivovarov[1], N.A. Soloviev[1], A.S. Sysoev[2] and S.E. Ulyanenko[2]

[1]*Institute of Physics and Power Engineering (IPPE); and* [2]*Medical Radiological Research Center (MRRC), Obninsk, Russia*

Introduction

Beam therapy continues to remain one of the main methods for the treatment of malignant tumours. In recent years all growing attention has been attracted to neutron radiation [1—5].

Main requirements to neutron beams and to a medical reactor

For boron neutron capture therapy (BNCT), a well-collimated beam of epi-thermal neutrons ($E_n = 10$ eV $-$ 10 keV) with an intensity of $\sim 10^{10}$ n/cm$^2 \cdot$s^{-1} is required. The fast neutrons ($E_n > 10$ keV) in the spectrum of the neutron beam should be such that the absorbed dose from these neutrons does not exceed 2 Gy. At present the beams for BNCT are realized on research reactors with powers from 3 to 20 MW; in the USA the project of a specialized medical reactor MTR with five beams for BNCT and with a power of 10 MW is being developed. The second method for treating malignant tumours with the help of neutron radiation is therapy by fast neutrons (TFN). The main requirements for a beam are that proportion neutrons with energy $E_n > 100$ keV should be $\sim 90\%$ and the flux at the patient should be $\sim 10^9$ n/cm$^2 \cdot$s^{-1}. We shall formulate the requirements, which need to be met by the reactor used for irradiation of people:
1. Maximum safety on the basis of properties of inherent self-protection, and use of well-justified technical decisions, checked by practice.
2. Simplicity and reliability of operation in conditions of variable mode of operations. The reactor must work at maximum power for 10—20 min during irradiations; power must then be reduced to a minimum ($\sim 0.1\%$) while the patient is being exchanged.
3. Low reactor power, simplifying the problems of heat-removal, minimizing radiation consequences of serious accidents, and making procedures of li-

Address for correspondence: V.A. Pivovarov, Institute of Physics and Power Engineering, 1 Bondarenko Sq., Obninsk, Kaluga Region, 249020, Russia.

censing easier.

4. Absence of reloads of fuel during the full life of the reactor, or at least, long (15–20 years) reload periods.

5. Low cost of the reactor facility, the irradiation complex, its operation and minimum operational staff.

As a possible variant, capable of satisfying the above-mentioned requirements, a fluid fuel reactor is offered. Specified properties permit us to design a reactor with a high level of safety, which is easily adaptable to variable regimes, inexpensive, simple and reliable in operation.

Conceptual design of the irradiation facility

Figure 1A shows the core of the specialized medical fluid fuel reactor. The form of the core and position of the heat exchanger are determined from conditions of a creation of a plain "radiative" stain on the side surface of a reactor vessel with a size of 30 cm^2 and maximum neutron flux near these surfaces. The main characteristics of the reactor are shown in Table 1.

The irradiation facility contains three beams; two horizontal and one vertical.

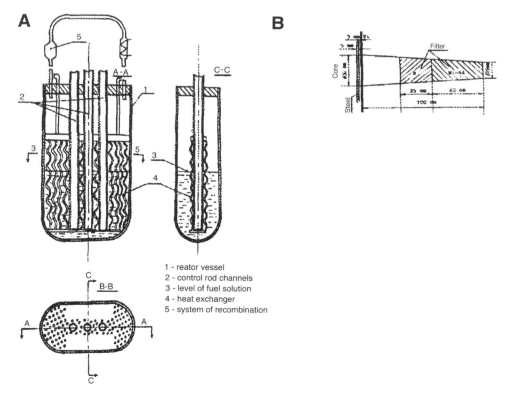

1 - reator vessel
2 - control rod channels
3 - level of fuel solution
4 - heat exchanger
5 - system of recombination

Fig.1. The scheme of core (**A**) and the scheme of horizontal channel for neutron capture therapy (**B**).

For the formation of a beam for BNCT with the required characteristics it uses special filters. Such filters can conditionally be named as "scattering" filters. The necessary spectrum is formed with the help of multiple scattering.

As calculations have shown, conventional scattering filters cannot be used for formation of a beam for BNCT as the fluid fuel reactor has a comparatively low average core power density and accordingly lower neutron flux. It is therefore appropriate to use another type of a filter, which can conditionally be named as a "transmitting" filter. This filter forms the required neutron spectrum at the exit of a channel, mainly at the expense of a direct flux of neutrons (without collisions) in a required range of energy and neutrons scattered from the beam. The most suitable material for this purpose is the isotope ^{64}Ni. The total neutron cross-section of this isotope is depicted in Fig. 2A. Due to the resonance structure (a deep minima in cross-sections at high energy) the transmitting filter cannot be built as monoisotopic, therefore the isotope of S inserts itself into a structure of a filter (Fig. 1B). It is clear from this figure that the function of a filter in our design is combined with the function of a collimator. This approach permits us to reduce the distance between the position of the patient and the reactor.

Figure 2B shows a spectrum of neutrons at the exit from a horizontal channel behind this filter calculated by the code MCNP4A. The spectra of therapeutic beams from the medical reactor MTR with an operating power of 10 MW and research reactor PBF with an operating power of 20 MW with scattering filters Al/D$_2$O/Li are also shown in Fig. 2B. The value of the flux of epithermal neutrons on the exit of a beam (105 cm from the core) for a fluid fuel reactor with a nickel filter is $4.8 \cdot 10^9$ n/cm$^2 \cdot$s^{-1}. Damaging doses from fast neutrons for a single irradiation is ~ 2.5 Gy. For comparison, on the MTR beam epithermal flux is equal to $1.7 \cdot 10^{10}$ n/cm$^2 \cdot$s^{-1}, on the beam PBF-$5.8 \cdot 10^9$ n/cm$^2 \cdot$s^{-1} at a damaging dose from fast neutrons of ~ 2 Gy.

Conclusion

The basic practicality is shown for the creation of a fluid fuel reactor for BNCT. The main advantages of this reactor are its safety, profitability, convenience and

Table 1. Main characteristics of the reactor.

Characteristic	Significance
Power (kW)	200
Initial enrichment (wt%)	90
^{235}U inventory (g)	3572
Average solution temperature ($^\circ$C)	80
Volume of fuel solution UO$_2$SO$_4$ at 20°C (l)	44.6
Overall dimensions of the reactor vessel (cm)	
— height	100
— max size in horizontal section	30×60
Maximum flux of neutrons in core (n/cm$^2 \cdot$s^{-1})	$1.8 \cdot 10^{13}$

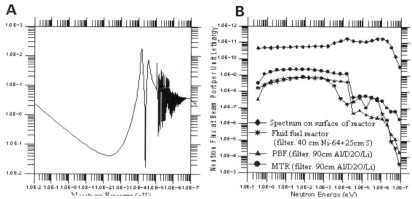

Fig. 2. The total neutron cross-section of ^{64}Ni (**A**). The neutron spectrum of the beam for neutron capture therapy (**B**).

reliability in operation, stipulated by low power, simplicity of a design and by inherent properties of self-protection. The special filter based on ^{64}Ni is necessary for formation of a beam for BNCT on the fluid fuel reactor. This filter permits the compensation of a small average power density of this reactor. The cost of this filter will be reasonably high in comparison with conventional scattering filters. However, for the lattert, operating power 15—100 times higher is required, and therefore the reactors are more expensive and more dangerous. So, the choice is as follows: a simple, cheap, safe reactor with low power and with an expensive filter, or a powerful, expensive and potentially more dangerous reactor with a simple and cheap filter. For a reasonable choice between these variants a deeper technical and economic study is necessary.

References

1. Koester L, Breit A, Wagner FM et al. Neutron converter for medical use. Atomkernenergie Kerntechnik 1984;N44:592.
2. Oka Y, Sh. An. Design study of facilities for BNCT. In: Fairchild RF, Brownell FL (eds) Proceedings of the 1st Int Symposium on Neutron Capture Therapy. MIT, USA. New York: Brookhaven National Laboratory, BNL—51730, 1983;57.
3. Fairchild R, Kalef-Ezra J, Fiarman S. Physics aspects of boron neutron capture therapy: epithermal neutron beam optimization. In: Lineberry MJ, McFarlane HF (chairpersons) Proceedings of the International Reactor Physics Conference, Sept 18—22. Wyoming, USA. American Nuclear Society, 1988; vol II, 423—432.
4. Bondarenko AV, Litjaev VM, Matveev YuV, Pivovarov VA, Soloviev NA, Sysoev AS. Concept of economic and safe reactor with low power for neutron therapy. Preprint FEI-2449 (in Russian) 1995.
5. Galanin AN, Litjaev VM, Pivovarov VA, Soloviev NA, Sysoev AS, Sharapov VN. Medical beam for fast neutron therapy with liquid fuel reactor. Preprint FEI-2450 (in Russian) 1995.

© 1997 Elsevier Science B.V. All rights reserved.
Advances in Neutron Capture Therapy.
Volume I, Medicine and Physics.
B. Larsson, J. Crawford and R. Weinreich, editors.

Remote therapy by fast neutrons at the fluid fuel reactor with power of 50 kW

A.V. Bondarenko[1], A.N. Galanin[1], V.V. Dolgov[1], V.M. Litjaev[1], Yu.V. Matveev[1], V.A. Pivovarov[1], V.P. Radchenko[1], N.A. Solovjev[1], V.N. Sharapov[1], A.S. Sysoev[2] and S.E. Ulyanenko[2]

[1]*Institute of Physics and Power Engineering (IPPE); and* [2]*Medical Radiological Research Center (MRRC), Obninsk, Russia*

Keywords: boron polyethene filter, code MCNP4A, fluid fuel reactor, neutron source, operating power, special filter, therapy by fast neutrons, vertical channel.

Introduction

At present clinical therapy by fast neutrons (TFN) on reactors is only available in two countries: Russia (Obninsk) and Germany (Munich) [1].

The clinical research of the treatment of various malignant tumours shows appreciable advantages in comparison with conventional γ therapy. The widest research on TFN is conducted in Obninsk, due to the close cooperation of two institutes: Institute of Physics and Power Engineering (IPPE), having the reactor BR-10, and Medical Radiological Research Center (MRRC) RAMS, developing the techniques of beam therapy. At present more than 200 patients with various forms of malignant tumours have passed a series of treatments. TFN is executed on the beam B-3 of BR-10. The beam B-3 has a sufficiently wide spectrum with intensity of fast neutrons at the patient position of $5.1 \cdot 10^8$ n/cm^2·s. The boron polythene filter with a thickness of 1 cm is used for formation of a hard neutron spectrum.

Beam for TFN at the fluid fuel reactor

At present the fluid fuel (solution UO_2SO_4 in water) reactor with a power of 50 kW for Mo-99m production is designed in IPPE. In this paper we shall consider the fluid fuel reactor as a neutron source for TFN [2].

The fluid fuel reactors have the following advantages over other types of reactors:
1) a high level of safety;
2) simplicity and reliability in conditions of variable operational modes;
3) it is not necessary to reload the fuel in current life-time of the reactor; and

---

Address for correspondence: V.A. Pivovarov, Institute of Physics and Power Engineering, 1 Bondarenko Sq., Obninsk, Kaluga Region, 249020, Russia.

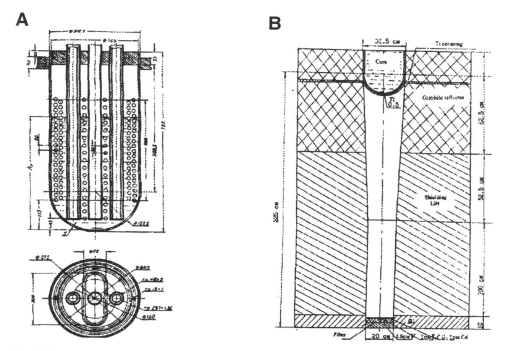

Fig. 1. The scheme of the core (**A**) and the scheme of the irradiation facility for therapy by fast neutrons (**B**).

4) low cost and a minimum of operational staff.

The scheme of the reactor is represented in Fig. 1A. The UO_2SO_4 solution in this reactor is simultaneously fuel and moderator. The core has approximately 2 kg of uranium with 90% enrichment. The volume of the solution in the reactor is 20 l. The reactor vessel is placed in a graphite reflector. The power level in the

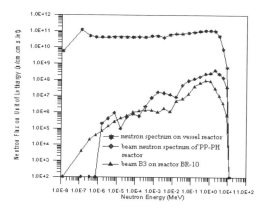

Fig. 2. The neutron spectra of beam for therapy by fast neutrons at the patient position.

reactor is controlled by the control rods.

The scheme of the irradiation facility is shown in Fig. 1B. For TFN a vertical channel is used. The "radiating" surface of the neutron beam is the hemispherical bottom of the reactor. A neutron channel passes through the graphite reflector and shielding, which consists of lithium hydride and bismuth layers. The maximum diameter of the beam is 20 cm.

Because the unfiltered neutron energy spectra in the fluid fuel reactor and BR-10 differ, the boron-polyethene filter turned out to be unsuitable.

A special filter has been designed, which consists of 0.5 cm titanium (second vessel of the reactor), 1 cm boron carbide (B-10 enriched up to 80%), 1.5 cm vanadium and 0.1 cm cadmium. The calculation of the characteristics of the neutron beam was made by the code MCNP4A [3].

The calculated intensity of fast neutrons at the patient position, located on the distance about 2 m from a surface of a reactor is about 10^9 $n/cm^2 \cdot s$, similar to B-3, and with a similar proportion of fast neutrons of 0.87. Figure 2 shows the neutron spectrum on the surface of the fluid fuel reactor vessel, the neutron spectrum on the channel exit behind the offered filter (0.5 cm Ti + 1 cm B_4C + 1.5 cm V + 0.1 cm Cd), and the neutron spectrum of the beam B-3 with a boron polyethene filter. It can be seen that the spectral structures of filter beams of neutrons are identical, thus providing the opportunity for implementation of medical beam for therapy by fast neutrons on the fluid fuel reactor with an operating power of 50 kW.

References

1. Koester L, Breit A, Wagner FM et al. Neutron converter for medical use. Atomkernenergie Kerntechnik 1984;44:592.
2. Galanin AN, Litjaev VM, Pivovarov VA, Soloviev NA, Sysoev AS, Sharapov VN. Medical beam for fast neutron therapy with liquid fuel reactor. Preprint FEI-2450, 1995 (In Russian).
3. Breismeister JF (ed) MCNP — 4, A General Monte Carlo N-Particle Transport Code, Version 4A. LA-12625-M, 1993.

Advances in Neutron Capture Therapy.
Volume I, Medicine and Physics.
B. Larsson, J. Crawford and R. Weinreich, editors.

Design studies for the MIT fission converter beam

W.S. Kiger III and O.K. Harling

Nuclear Reactor Laboratory, Massachusetts Institute of Technology, Cambridge, Massachusetts, USA

Keywords: Al, AlF_3, collimator, converter, ellipsoidal head phantom, epithermal neutrons, epithermal neutron beam, fission converter, fission converter beam, MCNP, reflector, specific dose.

Introduction

To meet the anticipated demand for boron neutron capture therapy (BNCT) irradiations, a high intensity, high quality fission converter-based epithermal neutron beam has been designed for the MITR-II Research Reactor. This epithermal neutron beam, capable of delivering treatments in a few minutes with negligible background contamination, would be installed in the present thermal column and *hohlraum* of the 5 MW MITR-II Research Reactor. In this approach to epithermal neutron production, thermal neutrons from the MITR-II core induce fissions in the converter, producing fission neutrons which are filtered and moderated to the appropriate energy range and collimated onto the patient or target position (Fig. 1).

Neutronic design studies for this epithermal neutron beam have been carried out using the general purpose Monte Carlo radiation transport code MCNP [1]. The Monte Carlo model of the MITR-II, which has been extensively benchmarked both in the core [2] and in the region where the converter will be located [3], was used as the basis of these calculations. The designs of the fission converter [4], filter/moderator, reflector, photon shield, and collimator have been analyzed to determine optimal configurations. This paper will present some results from these design studies and summarize beam performance for one "optimal configuration".

Design goals

Although the dose profile in a realistic phantom is the ultimate figure of merit for an epithermal neutron beam, for simplicity and computational speed, in-air figures of merit, (i.e., $\dot{D}_{fn}/\phi_{epi}$ and $\dot{D}_{\gamma}/\phi_{epi}$) were used to measure beam performance in these analyses. Design goals for beam intensity, contamination and directionality were derived from the following considerations:
1. Beam intensity should be sufficiently high so that irradiation times are com-

---

Address for correspondence: W.S. Kiger III, Nuclear Reactor Laboratory, Massachusetts Institute of Technology, 138 Albany St., NW 13-252, Cambridge, MA 02139, USA. E-mail: wskiger@mit.edu

404

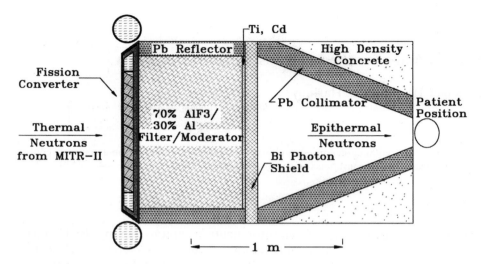

Fig. 1. Plan view of the MIT fission converter-based epithermal neutron beam. The fission converter, composed of 11 burned MITR-II fuel elements, is cooled by D_2O and enclosed in a double-walled Al tank. Fission neutrons produced in the converter are filtered and moderated by 68 cm of 70% AlF_3/30% Al and 2 cm Ti. A 0.4 mm Cd layer which filters out thermal neutrons is followed by an 8 cm thick Bi photon shield. A 102 cm long collimator lined with 15 cm Pb directs the high purity epithermal neutron beam onto the patient position.

parable to or preferably shorter than patient setup time;
2. the specific dose from beam contamination should be small compared to the irreducible background photon dose from H and N capture in tissue ($\sim 2 \times 10^{-10}$ cGy cm^2/n) so that contamination does not adversely affect beam performance; and
3. in order to help achieve deep effective beam penetration (i.e., deep advantage depth), adequate collimation is also desirable [5,6].

Results

Parametric analysis of the bismuth photon shield, shown in Fig. 2A, indicates that 5–8 cm is the optimal bismuth thickness since the specific photon dose is much less than the $\sim 2 \times 10^{-10}$ cGy cm^2/n irreducible photon dose from H capture. At greater thickness, the loss of epithermal intensity outweighs the marginal reduction in photon contamination.

Examination of the design for the reflector (surrounding the filter/moderator) shows that a reflector can provide substantial benefit, increasing epithermal flux at the patient position by as much as 50%. Analysis of reflectors of Ni, Pb, and AlF_3 (see Fig. 2B) leads to selection of a 10 cm thickness of Pb as optimal. Due to the high cost and photon contamination associated with Ni, we have rejected this material.

Neutron scattering by the collimator lining contributes significantly to intensity

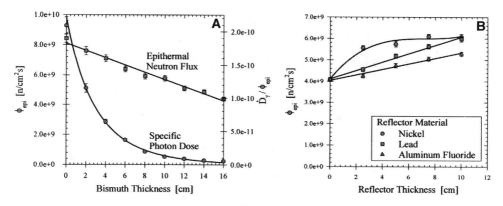

Fig. 2. Parametric analyses showing (**A**) ϕ_{epi} and specific photon dose $\dot{D}_\gamma/\phi_{epi}$ vs. bismuth photon shield thickness and (**B**) ϕ_{epi} vs. reflector thickness.

at the patient position, but also tends to degrade directionality somewhat; without the contribution from neutrons scattered in the collimator lining, $\phi_{epi} = 2.5 \times 10^9$ n/cm^2.s^{-1} and $J_{epi}/\phi_{epi} = 0.9$. The epithermal neutron flux for the optimal collimator lining (15 cm Pb) is 4 times higher than this case and has a current-to-flux ratio of 0.52. Figure 3 shows epithermal neutron flux and specific photon dose as a function of collimator thickness for pyramidal collimators of Bi, Pb, Ni, and graphite. Photon contamination is highest with Ni because of its high photon production. The relative photon contamination decreases with depth of the other materials, which have much lower photon production cross-sections, because of the augmented epithermal flux at the patient position, increased shielding against photons produced in the concrete, and reduction of the flux reaching the concrete which in turn lowers photon production.

Although all of the analyses presented in this section are internally consistent,

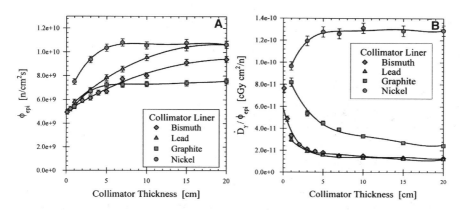

Fig. 3. Epithermal neutron flux (**A**) and specific photon dose (**B**) as a function of collimator liner thickness for pyramidal collimators of bismuth, lead, graphite, and nickel.

because some employ earlier beam designs which were not fully optimized, the beam performance results reported in these parametric studies are not as favorable as those reported for the optimized beam design below.

Performance of the optimized beam design

With the MITR-II reactor core at 5.0 MW, the fission converter produces 78.1 kW fission power, resulting in a calculated epithermal neutron flux (in air) at the patient position of 1.3×10^{10} n/cm^2.s. In-air fast neutron and photon contamination, with respective specific doses $(\dot{D}/\phi_{epi})$ of 1.3×10^{-11} cGy cm^2/n and 1.2×10^{-11} cGy cm^2/n, are negligible compared to the irreducible background dose of 2.0×10^{-10} cGy cm^2/n due to H neutron capture photons and the N (n,p) reaction in the patient. If higher beam intensity is desired, using fresh rather than spent MITR-II fuel increases power to 102.9 kW and increases epithermal flux by $\sim 30\%$ to 1.7×10^{10} n/cm^2.s without affecting the specific doses.

Dose profiles calculated in an ellipsoidal head phantom for a unilateral irradiation using the fission converter beam (shown in Fig. 4) with reasonable assumptions for boron uptake (40 ppm in tumor with a 3.5:1 tumor to normal tissue concentration ratio) and RBE's (3.2 for neutrons, 1.0 for photons, 3.8 for ^{10}B in

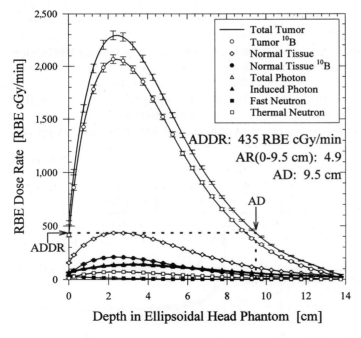

Fig. 4. RBE dose rate profiles calculated for unilateral irradiation of an ellipsoidal head phantom using the MIT fission converter beam with BPA. Boron uptake is 40 ppm in tumor with a 3.5:1 tumor to normal tissue concentration ratio. RBE's are 3.2 for neutrons, 1.0 for photons, 3.8 for ^{10}B in tumor and 1.35 for ^{10}B in normal tissue.

tumor and 1.35 for ^{10}B in normal tissue) are characterized by an advantage ratio (AR) of 4.9, an advantage depth (AD) of 9.5 cm, and an advantage depth dose rate (ADDR) of 435 RBE cGy/min. A healthy tissue dose of 1,000 RBE cGy (dose to tolerance) could be delivered in about 2 min. Dose profiles calculated for a bilateral irradiation with the fission converter beam using similar assumptions of boron uptake and RBEs yield an advantage ratio of 4.7; with zero boron in normal tissue, the advantage ratio is 8.0.

Conclusions

The high dose rate, high therapeutic ratio, and deep effective penetration make the fission converter-based epithermal neutron beam designed in this study suitable for routine clinical use in a high throughput patient treatment facility and equally well suited for advanced clinical trials as well as for a wide range of neutron capture research studies. The low, essentially negligible, inherent background components in this beam make it suitable for neutron capture therapy using improved tumor targeting compounds. The performance of this beam represents a major improvement over existing and most planned epithermal neutron beams.

Acknowledgements

This research was performed with support from the US Department of Energy under Contract No. DE-FG02-87ER6060.

References

1. Briesmeister JF (ed) MCNP — A general Monte Carlo N-Particle transport code version 4A. Los Alamos: Los Alamos National Laboratory, LA-12625, 1993.
2. Redmond EL II, Yanch JC, Harling OK. Monte Carlo simulation of the Massachusetts Institute of Technology Research Reactor. Nucl Tech 1994;106:1—14.
3. Kiger WS III. Neutronic design of a fission converter-based epithermal neutron beam for Neutron Capture Therapy. Nucl. E. Thesis, Massachusetts Institute of Technology, 1996.
4. Sakamoto S, Kiger WS III, Harling OK. Optimization of the neutronic design of the MIT fission converter beam. In: Larsson B, Crawford J, Weinreich R (eds) Advances in Neutron Capture Therapy, Volume 1, Medicine and Physics. Amsterdam: Elsevier Science, 1997;408—412 (these proceedings).
5. Moss RL, Aizawa O, Beynon D, Brugger R, Constantine G, Harling O, Liu HB, Watkins P. The requirements and development of neutron beams for Neutron Capture Therapy of brain cancer. J Neuro-Oncol 1997;33:27—40.
6. Yanch JC, Harling OK. Dosimetric effects of beam size and collimation of epithermal neutrons for boron neutron capture therapy. Radiat Res 1993;135:131—145.

© 1997 Elsevier Science B.V. All rights reserved.
Advances in Neutron Capture Therapy.
Volume I, Medicine and Physics.
B. Larsson, J. Crawford and R. Weinreich, editors.

Optimization of the neutronic design of the MIT fission converter beam

Shuichi Sakamoto, W. Steadman Kiger III and Otto K. Harling

Nuclear Reactor Laboratory, Massachusetts Institute of Technology, Cambridge, USA

Keywords: coolant thickness, coolant type, D_2O, epithermal neutron flux, epithermal neutron beam, fission converter, fuel configuration and loading, H_2O, heavy water, MITR-II fuel, Monte Carlo radiation transport code MCNP, sensitivity analysis, single plate, specific fast neutron doses.

Introduction

An extensive series of studies aimed at the design of an optimized fission converter-based epithermal neutron beam for NCT at the 5 MW MIT Research Reactor (MITR-II) have been performed [1,2]. A plan view of the current beam design is shown in [3]. This paper presents a portion of these studies related to the neutronic design of the fission converter: specifically, sensitivity analyses of coolant type and thickness, fuel configuration and loading. The general purpose Monte Carlo radiation transport code MCNP [2] was used to perform these analyses [4]. The studies of the neutronic design for other components of the fission converter-based beam are presented in [3].

Results

Using two different coolants, H_2O and D_2O, beam performance of fission converter designs using MITR-II reactor multiplate type fuel elements with fuel loadings ranging from 312 g ^{235}U per element (burned fuel) to 510 g ^{235}U per element (fresh fuel) were studied. A single-plate type fission converter was also studied with varying coolant thickness (ranging from 0.16 to 1.0 cm) on both sides of the flat fuel plate and different fuel enrichments (20 and 93%). These calculations are summarized in Table 1 and in the plot of epithermal neutron flux (ϕ_{epi}) vs. specific fast neutron dose (D_{fn}/ϕ_{epi}) shown in Fig. 1. With D_2O coolant, an epithermal neutron beam produces significantly higher intensity and lower fast neutron contamination than with H_2O coolant. For MITR-II fuel elements, D_2O coolant provides 30—50% more epithermal neutron flux relative to H_2O coolant and 60—70% greater epithermal neutron flux per unit power, while producing

Address for correspondence: Shuichi Sakamoto, Nuclear Reactor Laboratory, Massachusetts Institute of Technology, 138 Albany St. Bldg. NW13—252, Cambridge, MA 02139, USA. E-mail: ssakamo@-mit.edu

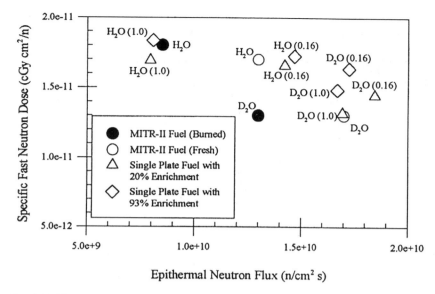

Fig. 1. Epithermal neutron flux vs. specific fast neutron dose at the patient position for different fuel configurations and coolants. Data labels denote coolant types and for single plate fuel, coolant thicknesses on the sides of the plate are in parentheses. Statistical uncertainties are less than the size of the data points.

30% lower specific fast neutron dose and also reducing the fission converter power by 10–20%. For all the cases presented in Table 1, the specific γ dose is very low ($<2 \times 10^{-11}$ cGy cm^2/n).

The differences in beam performance between these coolants can be explained by the neutron spectra presented in Fig. 2, which shows the partial neutron current spectra exiting from the fission converter in the direction of the patient position for both coolants. The shapes of the spectra are found to be independent of fuel loading. However, it is clearly seen that the use of D$_2$O coolant increases the spectrum above 100 eV significantly, relative to that of H$_2$O coolant. The neutrons which belong to this energy region are the slowing down source for the epithermal energy range produced by passing through the filter/moderator. Because of its higher scattering cross-section in the slowing down region and lighter mass relative to deuterium, hydrogen overmoderates the useful portion of the neutron spectrum without commensurate reduction of fast neutrons. The fission converter with D$_2$O coolant generates a harder spectrum that leads to higher epithermal neutron flux without a proportionate increase in the fast neutron dose.

It was expected that the reduced volume fraction of coolant in a single-plate fission converter relative to a converter using multiplate type fuel might offset the disadvantage of the overmoderation of H$_2$O coolant. The analyses of a single-plate type fission converter with about 7.5 kg of ^{235}U, which is consider-

Table 1. Converter power and in-air beam performance for different fuel types and coolants with varying fuel loading, enrichment and coolant thickness. In-air figures of merit were calculated at the patient position. The statistical error (one standard deviation) of each quantity is shown immediately below the value. The number shown below the coolant type for a single plate fission converter denotes the coolant thickness on both sides of the fuel plate. These calculations used a filter/moderator composed of 68 cm 70% AlF_3/30% Al + 2 cm Ti followed by an 8 cm thick Bi photon shield and a rectangular collimator with a 15 cm thick lead lining. The filter/moderator is surrounded by a 10 cm thick lead reflector.

Fuel type	Fuel loading kg ^{235}U-total	Coolant	Power kW	ϕ_{epi} n/cm²·s	D_{fn}/ϕ_{epi} cGy·cm²/n	ϕ_{epi}/P n/cm²·kJ
MITR-II fuel	3.4	D_2O	78.1	1.3E + 10	1.3E − 11	1.7E + 08
elements	Burned fuel		0.2%	1%	2%	1%
93% enriched		H_2O	83.1	8.5E + 09	1.8E − 11	1.0E + 08
			0.2%	2%	2%	2%
	5.6	D_2O	102.9	1.7E + 10	1.3E − 11	1.6E + 08
	Fresh fuel		0.2%	1%	2%	1%
		H_2O	124.9	1.3E + 10	1.7E − 11	1.0E + 08
			0.2%	1%	2%	1%
Single plate	7.5	D_2O	105.2	1.8E + 10	1.4E − 11	1.8E + 08
20% enriched		0.16 cm	0.6%	1%	2%	1%
		D_2O	102.4	1.7E + 10	1.3E − 11	1.7E + 08
		1 cm	0.6%	1%	2%	1%
		H_2O	95.1	1.4E + 10	1.7E − 11	1.5E + 08
		0.16 cm	0.6%	1%	2%	1%
		H_2O	67.7	7.9E + 09	1.7E − 11	1.2E + 08
		1 cm	0.7%	1%	2%	1%
Single plate	7.7	D_2O	92.7	1.7E + 10	1.6E − 11	1.9E + 08
93% enriched		0.16 cm	0.6%	1%	2%	1%
		D_2O	90.4	1.7E + 10	1.5E − 11	1.9E + 08
		1 cm	0.6%	1%	2%	1%
		H_2O	86.1	1.5E + 10	1.7E − 11	1.7E + 08
		0.16 cm	0.6%	1%	2%	1%
		H_2O	61.2	8.1E + 09	1.8E − 11	1.3E + 08
		1 cm	0.8%	2%	2%	2%

ably more than the 5.6 or 3.4 kg of ^{235}U in fresh and burned MITR-II fuel respectively, indicated that, except for the case with a thick H_2O coolant layer (1 cm), a single-plate fission converter with H_2O or D_2O coolant provides a significant advantage because it increases epithermal neutron flux by around 20—70% for H_2O and 30—40% for D_2O, relative to a fission converter using burned MITR-II fuel and the same coolant, without substantial increases in specific fast neutron dose. However, it was also shown that, compared with a D_2O cooled MITR-II fuel fission converter, a single-plate fission converter with the minimum thickness of H_2O coolant (0.16 cm) increases fast neutron contamination without a commensurate improvement of beam intensity. From engineering considerations, a coolant thickness of about 0.16 cm is estimated to be a practical minimum. The performance data for the various fuel configurations presented in

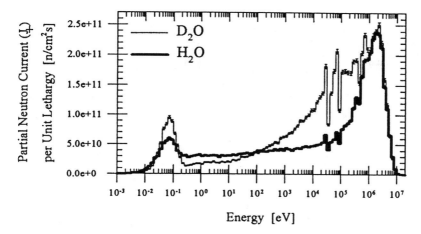

Fig. 2. Partial neutron current spectrum at the interface between the converter coolant and the inner tank in the direction of the patient position. For burned MITR-II fuel with the filter/moderator composed of 68 cm 70% AlF_3/30% Al + 2 cm Ti, the partial current is 34% higher with D_2O cooling than with H_2O cooling. Both spectra are normalized to 5.0 MW reactor power.

Table 1 indicate the clear superiority of D_2O coolant for the production of epithermal neutron beams. Heavy water cooling also provides lower specific fast neutron doses, however, acceptably low fast neutron contamination is also achieved with H_2O coolant as shown in Table 1 and Fig. 1.

The effect of varying the thickness of coolant surrounding the MITR-II fuel elements was also examined. The studies indicated that the epithermal neutron flux is maximized when the coolant thickness in front of and behind the fuel elements is minimized. Also, it was shown that, for coolant thicknesses of 0.16–0.79 cm, fuel element spacing does not affect the beam performance.

Acknowledgements

The research reported here was supported by the US Department of Energy under Contract DE–FG02–87ER 60600. One of the authors, S. Sakamoto, gratefully acknowledges the support of the Science and Technology Agency in Japan.

References

1. Harling OK, Kiger WS III. High-Intensity Fission-Converter-Based Epithermal Neutron Beam for Neutron Capture Therapy. In: Mishima Y (ed) Proc. 6th Int Symp on Neutron Capture Therapy for Cancer, held in Kobe, Japan, Oct. 31–Nov. 4, 1994. New York: Plenum Press, 1994;407–412.
2. Kiger WS III. Neutronic Design of a Fission Converter-Based Epithermal Beam for Neutron Capture Therapy, Nucl E Thesis, Massachusetts Institute of Technology, 1996.
3. Kiger WS III, Harling OK. Design studies for the MIT fission converter beam. In: Larsson B,

Crawford J, Weinreich R (eds) Advances in Neutron Capture Therapy, Volume 1, Medicine and Physics. Amsterdam: Elsevier Science, 1997;403—407 (these proceedings).

4. Briesmeister JF (ed) MCNP — A General Monte Carlo N-Particle Transport Code (Version 4A), Los Alamos National Laboratory, LA—12625 (1993).

© 1997 Elsevier Science B.V. All rights reserved.
Advances in Neutron Capture Therapy.
Volume I, Medicine and Physics.
B. Larsson, J. Crawford and R. Weinreich, editors.

Fission converter based epithermal beam-heat removal and safety under accident conditions

Balendra Sutharshan, Neil E. Todreas and Otto K. Harling

Nuclear Reactor Laboratory and Department of Nuclear Engineering, Massachusetts Institute of Technology, Cambridge, Massachusetts, USA

Introduction

A fission converter is used as the source of fast neutrons for the epithermal neutron beam. Eleven MIT reactor plate type fuel elements in the fission converter tank will be centered in the MIT reactor's thermal column area. Thermal neutrons from the MITR-II core incident on the fission converter fuel produce fast flux. These fast neutrons from the fission converter will be moderated down to epithermal energies and filtered to remove residual fast neutrons. The fission converter beam design provides epithermal neutron fluxes at the patient position in excess of 10^{10} n/cm^2.s with very low contamination of fast neutrons and γ rays. A cadmium shutter will be placed on the core side of the fission converter. The cadmium shutter is capable of reducing the incident flux on the fission converter fuel by a factor of 100 within 15 s. The schematic drawing of the design of the fission converter is shown in Fig. 1.

Thermal hydraulics design limits

Enhanced corrosion is possible on the MITR-II fuel elements if boiling occurs on the fuel plates for a long period of time. Therefore, the temperature of the coolant should be below its saturation temperature to prevent boiling during the steady-state operating condition. The coolant saturation temperature at the elevation of the fuel elements is 106°C. Therefore the fuel clad surface temperature should be below 106°C during the steady-state operating condition.

Since credible accidents occur very rarely and for short periods of time, brief periods of boiling are acceptable during such events. However, the temperature must be prevented from reaching the softening point of the fuel or the clad during all accidents. The MITR-II fuel element clad is made of Al-6061. The Al melting point (649°C) is much lower than the fuel (UAl$_x$) melting point (1,200°C). However, the Al softening temperature is 490°C. Therefore, the design limit for the credible accidents is set for less than 490°C.

Address for correspondence: B. Sutharshan, Nuclear Laboratory, Massachusetts Institute of Technology, 138 Albany St., Cambridge, MA 02139, USA.

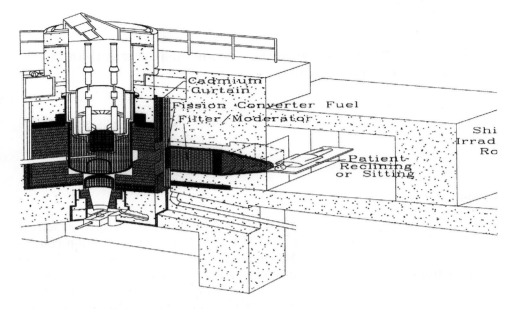

Fig. 1. Design of fission-converter beam.

Description of fission converter heat removal system

A schematic drawing of the fission converter heat removal system and the isometric view of the fission converter tank is depicted in Fig. 2. The power generated in the 11 MITR-II fuel elements is transported to the primary coolant by natural convection. The coolant path generated by the natural convection is shown by the arrows in the fission converter. The coolant in the upper plenum is removed from the converter by a suction pump through an outlet pipe. It is then returned to the downcomer region in the fission converter tank through an inlet pipe, after it has been cooled to the temperature of 40°C. The primary coolant can be either light water or heavy water.

The fission converter's secondary coolant is also the MITRs secondary coolant and it is light water. The primary coolant transfers the heat to the secondary coolant through a heat exchanger. The secondary coolant is then sent to the existing MITR-II cooling tower where it is cooled by the air circulation in the cooling tower. All of the primary piping, some of the secondary piping and the heat exchanger will be located above the level of the fission converter tank. This obviates the r d for antisiphon valves which would be required to prevent coolant loss in the event of a pipe break if the coolant system were below the level of the water in the fuel tank.

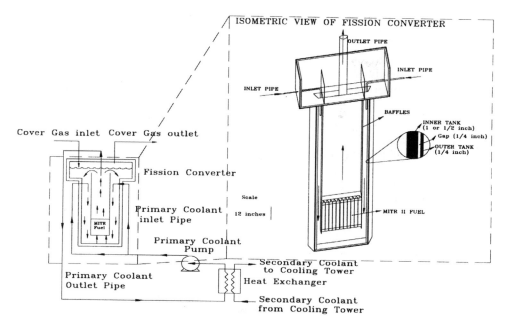

Fig. 2. Schematic drawing of fission-converter heat removal system.

Thermal-hydraulic analysis of natural convection

Steady-state operation

For all of the following thermal hydraulic analysis, the fission converter power is assumed to be 300 kW, which is well in excess of the maximum design power of 250 kW [1]. The maximum design power of 250 kW is calculated using a Monte Carlo code, MCNP, for the highest possible power, fresh fuel, reactor 10 MW (double its current power) and primary coolant of light water.

As a first step, a simple hand calculation was performed with the aid of MathCad software to calculate the total flow rate through the 11 fuel elements and the average temperature difference across a fuel element. The calculated average temperature difference across the fuel elements is 26°C, and the total flow rate through the 11 fuel elements is 2.8 kg/s. However, a simple hand calculation can provide only the total flow rate and the average temperature difference. The complete temperature and velocity fields within the fission converter tank are valuable information to identify hot spots, irregular flow patterns, mixing effects, and flow paths. Therefore the thermal hydraulic code TEMPEST [2] (transient energy momentum and pressure equation solution in three dimensions) was used to perform detailed calculations and to provide the temperature and the velocity fields. The fission converter is modeled in the Cartesian coordinate system. The modeled region must be divided into finite-difference cells arranged in three dimensions. Power profile, geometry and inlet temperatures are used by TEMPEST as the independent variables to analyze the fission converter. TEMPEST provides the velocity fields, the temperature fields and the pressure fields. During steady-state operating conditions, the maximum temperature in the fission converter is 80°C, which is much lower than the limiting condition of the boiling temperature at the fuel outlet. The average bulk temperature in the upper plenum is 72°C during steady-state operating conditions. The total flow rate through the 11 MITR-II fuel elements is 3.4 kg/s and the flow through the primary heat exchanger loop is 2.24 kg/s. A summary of steady-state operation results is given in Table 1.

Accidents

We have analyzed the following credible accidents:
— loss of flow, which includes failure of pump, simultaneous failure of pump and cadmium shutter, inlet pipe break and outlet pipe break; and
— loss of coolant.
Apart from these credible accidents scenarios, two bounding analyses were also studied. These are:
— simultaneous failure of the pump, the cadmium shutter and the MITR-II reactor scram; and
— instantaneous loss of all coolant in the fission converter tank.
Due to the limited space availability, the detailed analysis of all credible accidents scenarios cannot be presented in this publication. However, the analysis of credible accidents showed that none of them will create conditions which reach the design limits. In the following subsections, the two bounding analyses are discussed. Even these do not lead to very serious consequences.

Bounding analysis

Simultaneous failure of pump, the cadmium shutter and the MITR reactor scram
During this bounding case, there is no inflow or outflow to or from the fission converter, and also assumed that there is no heat loss from the fission converter

Table 1. Steady-state operation results.

	Hand calculations	Three-dimensional numerical calculation	Steady state design limits
Average temperature difference across a fuel	26°C	25°C	
Total flow rate through 11 fuel elements	2.8 kg/s	3.4 kg/s	
Maximum coolant temperature		80°C	
Maximum clad temperature		88°C	106°C

tank to the surrounding outside structures. The coolant temperature rises with time due to heating by the 300 kW converter power. When the temperatures of the coolant and the fuel clad reach boiling condition (temperature of 106°C), there will be boiling on the fuel plates. If it is assumed that the bubbles escape the system without any condensation, and after some time the liquid level will drop below the downcomer wall edge. Before the coolant level drops below the downcomer wall edge, there will be buoyancy-driven bulk flow in the fission converter tank. When the coolant level drops below the downcomer edge, there is no bulk flow. When there is a bulk flow the critical heat flux is 484 ± 160 kW/m² [3] and when there is no bulk flow, the critical heat flux is 25 ± 8.25 kW/m² [3]. The operating heat flux is 18.4 kW/m². Therefore the system will never experience any dry-out condition when the coolant level is above the downcomer wall edge. However, there is a possibility of a dry-out condition when the coolant level is below the downcomer wall edge. For this bounding analysis, the maximum clad temperature as a function of time is given in Fig. 3. Actually, there is essentially no possibility of failure of the MITR reactor scram. Therefore, there are 51 min available before possible fuel disruption to terminate this accident by scramming MITR-II.

Instantaneous loss of coolant

The structures around the fission converter are made of heavy concrete and graphite. No sharp protruding object is located near the fission converter tanks. It is impossible to identify a hole size for the fission converter that could be caused by a sharp object. However, the loss of coolant analysis is performed

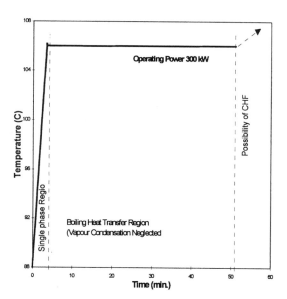

Fig. 3. The maximum clad temperature during pump, cadmium and MTR scram failure.

418

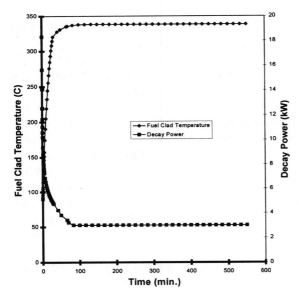

Fig. 4. Rapid loss of all coolant (Cd shutter closed and MITR at 10 MW).

assuming that the inner and the outer tanks bottom plates fail simultaneously. Therefore the coolant in the fission converter will be drained within a few seconds. It is assumed that the cadmium shutter will be closed when the liquid in the fission converter drops below the fuel elements' top. Decay heat drives the clad temperature transient behavior which exhibits an initial rise and is then limited after tens of minutes by radiation to the outside structures. The fuel clad temperature and the total power as a function of time is shown in Fig. 4. As it is obvious from Fig. 4 that the fuel clad temperature never exceeds the limit of the Al-6061 softening temperature of 490°C, no serious fuel disruption is expected even for this bounding analysis.

Conclusion

The authors have shown that no credible accidents will disrupt the fuel. Even incredible accident scenarios do not lead to fuel disruption.

Acknowledgements

The research reported here was performed with support from the US Department of Energy under Contract No. DE-FG02-87ER6060.

References

1. Kiger WS III. Neutronic Design of a Fission Converter-Based Epithermal Beam for Neutron

Capture Therapy. Nucl E Thesis, Massachusetts Institute of Technology, 1996.
2. Trent DS, Eyler LL. TEMPEST — A computer program for three-dimensional time-dependent hydrothermal analysis. Pacific Northwest Laboratory 1991;(Version N, Mod 33):PNL-4348.
3. Sudo Y, Kaminaga M. A New CHF Correlation Scheme Proposed for Vertical Rectangular Channels Heated From Both Sides in Nuclear Research Reactors. Transaction of ASME Vol 115, May 1993.

Epithermal beam in the RA-6 reactor

Daniel Bustos[1], Osvaldo Calzetta Larrieu[2] and Herman Blaumann[2]

[1]Instituto Balseiro; and [2]Departamento de Ingeniería Nuclear, Centro Atómico Bariloche, Comisión Nacional de Energía Atómica, Bariloche, Argentina

Introduction

At the beginning of 1992 a thermal neutron beam, whose main characteristics were adequate for boron neutron capture therapy (BNCT), was designed and built in the RA-6 reactor (open pool-type reactor with highly enrichment core and 500 kW of nominal power). This first experiment had two main purposes; to validate our calculation systems and to develop several measurement techniques used in the beam characterization as well as in "phantoms" dosimetry. This paper shows the design of an epithermal neutron beam (0.5 eV − 10 keV) which is under construction at the moment in the RA-6 reactor. It should be completed by next July (1997) and the first results of the measurements should be available by August. Due to the low reactor power, the design covers not only the neutron spectral filter and γ shields, but also the modifications that are being performed in the space which was filled by the internal and external thermal columns. The optimization process is discussed, fundamentally to determine the relative widths and the sequential positioning of each of the materials used, such as Al, Al_2O_3, Bi, Cd and LiF. This was carried out to leave the design level and begin the construction itself. The assembly of the different parts of the beam have been thought out in such a way that it is possible to perform modifications, if necessary, to improve the experimental results. The main parameters of the beam obtained in the design are:

$\Phi_{epithermal}$	$\approx$	1.5×10^9 n/cm^2 s
D_{fast}/n_{epi}	$\approx$	4.7×10^{-11} cGy.cm^2/n_{epi}
D_γ/n_{epi}	$\approx$	3×10^{-12} cGy.cm^2/n_{epi}
Beam aperture		up to 30 cm in diameter

The RA-6 Reactor

The RA-6 is a pool-type, 500 kW reactor, with U 90% enrichment fuel. It was designed for teaching, training and design studies. This installation has five irradiation channels, a pneumatic sample changer and a thermal column. The

Address for correspondence: Daniel Bustos, Instituto Balseiro, Centro Atómico Bariloche, Av.E. Bustillo 9.500, S.C. De Bariloche (8400), Río Negro, Argentina. E-mail: bustosd@cabib4.cnea.edu.ar

research facilities include radioprotection, reactor control, activation techniques and chemistry laboratories where professionals and students have been working since its inauguration in 1982. The BNCT studies in the RA-6 started in 1992, when a thermal neutron beam was designed and characterized. The experience acquired with this work allowed starting in 1995, and the epithermal neutron beam design is presented here.

Beam design

For the beam design, Al_2O_3 was chosen as moderator, and Al and Bi as γ shielding. To reduce the thermal neutron flux from the pool the filter was surrounded with Cd. Three sheets of this material were also put in two different places in the Al_2O_3 to minimize the γ thermal neutron capture radiation produced by moderation. Due to the low reactor power, it was necessary to choose the irradiation point as close as possible. For this reason the moderator was put only inside the pool. To choose the relative width of Al and Al_2O_3, a one-dimensional calculation was done using the HERMET transport code. Close to the core, the fast flux decreases more quickly than the epithermal flux. At larger distances from the core, on the other hand, the flux is lower and all neutrons tend to be thermalised. Again, Al_2O_3 moderates more quickly than Al. This combination of effects leads to optimum thicknesses of Al and of Al_2O_3.

For the final design the neutron and γ fluxes and doses were calculated with the transport code MCNP. Figure 1 shows the model with the cells used in MNCP. The code was run on a PC, with a very long calculation time. For this reason the core was homogenized for design calculation. To verify the results a simple spectrum calculation was done near the core, obtaining the same spectrum shape

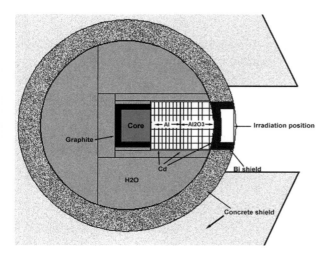

Fig. 1. A horizontal section of the RA-6 beam, showing the cells used in the MCNP calculation.

for both homogeneous and heterogeneous cases, with a greater absolute flux value for the latter. The irradiation point was chosen 20 cm to the Bi wall, to increase the ϕ_{epi}/ϕ_{fast} ratio. At this point the radial distribution of the flux up to 15 cm from the center was calculated. The variation obtained is much lower than statistical errors, so it is not possible to determine the variation in the flux value.

Results

Table 1 lists the flux calculated for the RA-6 epithermal beam, in comparison with other designs. The epithermal flux at the irradiation position is 1.5×10^9 n.cm^{-2} s^{-1}. Neutron and γ doses were estimated with the ICRP-21 neutron and photon flux-to-dose rate conversion factors. The total dose from fast neutron and γ radiation is low (1.5×10^{-11} cGy.n.cm^{-2}.s^{-1}). The statistical errors were 5% for neutron flux calculations and 10% for dose calculations. Figure 2 shows the flux spectrum at the irradiation position. The epithermal flux is considerably greater than the fast flux, leading to a low fast neutron dose.

Conclusions

A neutron moderator, thermal neutron and γ shield have been designed taking as neutron source the core of the RA-6. The short distance between the core and irradiation position allows an adequate epithermal neutron flux. Due to the satisfactory results obtained, the epithermal neutron beam designed is now being constructed in the RA-6. This installation will make it possible to continue the research necessary to implement NCT in Argentina.

Acknowledgements

The authors thank the financial support given by the organizers of the Symposium to D. Bustos to make possible his participation in this event.

Table 1. Comparison of epithermal beams (built or designed) for NCT.

Reactor	Power (MW)	Epithermal neutron flux (10^9 n. cm^{-2}. s^{-1})	Fast neutron dose per neutron (10^{-11} cGy. n^{-1}. cm^2)	γ dose per neutron (10^{-11} cGy. n^{-1}. cm^2)	Current/flux
RA-6	0.5	1.5	4.7	0.3	0.65
MURR [1]	10.0	9.5	2.9	0.4	0.82
BMRR [2]	3.0	1.8	4.3	1.3	0.67
MITR [3]	5.0	0.2	13.0	1.4	0.55
PETTEN [4]	45.0	0.33	10.4	8.4	0.8
GTRR [5]	5.0	10.0	3.4	0.1	0.9

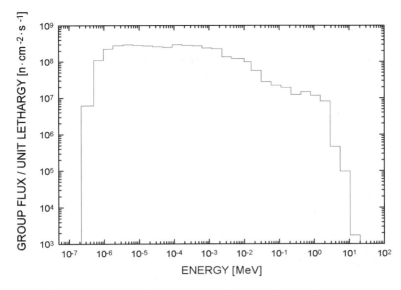

Fig. 2. Calculated neutron flux spectrum at the irradiation position.

References

1. Brugger RM, Shih JA, Liu HB. An epithermal neutron beam for capture therapy at the Missouri University research reactor. Nucl Tech 1992;98:322.
2. Liu HB, Brugger RM, Greenberg DD, Rorer DC, Hu JP, Hauptman HM. Enhancement of the epithermal neutron beam used for Boron Neutron Capture Therapy. Int J Radiat Oncol Biol Phys 1994;28:5.
3. Choi JR, Zamenhof RG, Yanch JC, Rogus R, Harling OK. Performance of the currently available epithermal neutron beam used at the Massachusetts Institute of technology reactor (MITR-II). In: Alen BJ et al. (eds) Progress in Neutron Capture Therapy for Cancer. New York: Plenum Press, 1992;53.
4. Watkins P, Constantine G, Stecher-Rasmussen F, Freudenreich W, Moss RL, Ricchena R. MNCP calculations for the design and characterization of the Petten BNCT epithermal neutron beam. In: Alen BJ et al. (eds) Progress in Neutron Capture Therapy for Cancer. New York: Plenum Press, 1992;71.
5. Less TJ, Brugger RM. Reactor moderated intermediate energy neutron beams for NCT. Strahlentherapie und Onkologie 1989;165:87.

Design optimization of thermal and epithermal neutron beams and depth-dose evaluation at the proposed Musashi reactor

Tetsuo Matsumoto

Atomic Energy Research Laboratory, Musashi Institute of Technology, Ozenji, Asao-ku, Kawasaki-shi, Japan

Introduction

The reactor at the Musashi Institute of Technology (Musashi reactor) is a TRIGA-II type reactor with a thermal power of only 100 kW. A thermal neutron beam with satisfactory characteristics was produced for use in boron neutron capture therapy (BNCT). Brain tumors of 99 patients and malignant melanoma of nine patients were treated at the Musashi reactor [1]. Unfortunately, the Musashi reactor was shut down in 1990 because of water leak trouble in the reactor tank. To justify installing a new tank and restarting the reactor, an expanded multipurpose utilization of the reactor is inevitable. In addition to extensive experience in thermal neutron capture therapy at the Musashi reactor, we now have a chance to design an epithermal neutron beam with wider applicability. There is also the need for thermal neutron beam for small animal studies and for the treatment of superficial neoplasms such as skin melanoma. If neutron beams in the above two energy ranges (suited to different applications of BNCT) should conveniently both become available from a single TRIGA-II reactor, such a development should further widen globally the prospects of successful BNCT practice. The present paper covers a comparative evaluation of alternative arrangements to generate both epithermal and thermal neutron beams suited to BNCT with the Musashi reactor.

Proposed design

The MCNP transport code [2] has been used for evaluating the intensities and extent of adulteration with extraneous radiations presented by the epithermal and thermal neutron beams expected to be generated by the various combinations of reflector and moderator arrangements. With a view to intensifying the neutron beam flux, various arrangements of reflector materials were first examined to ensure the core criticality. The reflector arrangements were then combined with various arrangements of moderator in order to optimize the neutron beam in terms of intensity and freedom from adulteration with neutrons of extraneous energy ranges and with γ rays.

The calculation proved the reference core (the core used in operation with 73 fuel elements with the graphite reflector) to present a K_{eff} value of 1.03. The calculation did not take into account the presence of the three control rods. The material forming the half zone in the reflector has been replaced by Al, in the search for more effective epithermal neutron flux generation. The replacement of graphite with Al is seen to have brought a sacrifice of K_{eff} which is due to increased neutron leakage from the core. To ensure criticality 5-cm-thick high-density graphite was replaced circularly instead of Al in the reflector zone near the core. The MCNP calculations also proved that graphite was the preferred material in both reflector and moderator for producing thermal neutrons while for epithermal neutrons a mixture of Al and aluminum oxide was the most suitable.

The optimized design facility with the above core is illustrated in Fig. 1, from the core to the irradiation ports in both thermal and thermalizing columns. To allow a patient to be installed at an irradiation port without the necessity of changing the existing biological shield, the patient irradiation point must be located at a distance of 175 cm from the core center. This distance is a very important factor on account of the sensitive dependence on distance that characterizes neutron flux intensity. For tempering the steep decline of flux intensity, so as to prevent excessive attenuation of the useful neutron flux, a void space was introduced in both columns. Collimation of both epithermal and thermal neutrons is brought about with blocks of lead and graphite. Shielding of γs is pro-

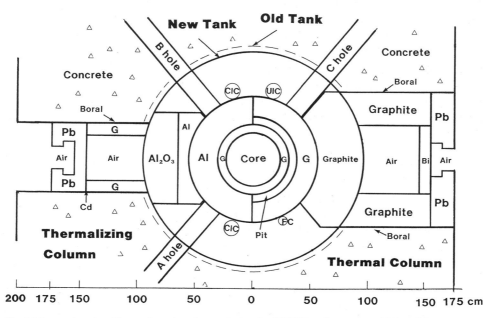

Fig. 1. Thermal and epithermal neutron beam design for BNCT at the proposed Musashi reactor.

vided by means of the bismuth (Bi) and lead (Pb) filters installed at the column exits.

Neutron beam characteristics at irradiation ports

The characteristics expected of the epithermal and thermal neutron beams at the patient irradiation ports of the thermalizing and thermal columns are summarized in Table 1, where they are compared with the corresponding values of currently available epithermal and thermal neutron beams [3]. The neutron flux intensity is 4.1×10^8 n/cm^{-2}.s^{-1} with 3% estimated statistical error for the epithermal, and 1.1×10^9 n/cm^{-2}.s^{-1} with 2% estimated statistical error for the thermal neutron beams, with the reactor operated at 100 kW. For equal reactor power, these performance values are significantly higher than available today at any of the other facilities cited in Table 1. Adulteration with fast neutrons and with γ rays would be 3.5×10^{-11} and 1.1×10^{-11} cGy/cm^2.n^{-1} for the epithermal and 0.9×10^{-11} and 1.4×10^{-11} cGy/cm^2.n^{-1} for the thermal neutron beam, respectively. The foregoing expected values fully meet the present target specifications. In terms of beam directionality, the neutron current-to-flux ratio (J) would be around 0.67, which indicates a degree of forward-direction anisotropy that should ensure good penetration into the tissue.

Table 1. Characteristics of proposed epithermal and thermal neutron beams at patient port at Musashi reactor and currently available epithermal and thermal neutron beams for BNCT.

Proposed thermal neutron beam

Reactor	Reactor power (MW)	Thermal neutron flux $\times 10^9$ (n/cm^2.s)	$D_{fast}/n_{th} \times 10^{-11}$ (cGycm^2/n)	$D_r/n_{th} \times 10^{-11}$ (cGycm^2/n)	J/ϕ
KUR [4]	5	3.0	—	0.6	—
JRR2 [5]	10	1.1	—	1.2	—
Musashi [1]	0.1	0.8	—	2.1	—
Proposed Musashi	0.1	1.1	0.9	1.4	0.67

Proposed epithermal neutron beam

Reactor	Reactor power (MW)	Epithermal neutron flux $\times 10^9$ (n/cm^2.s)	$D_{fast}/n_{epi} \times 10^{-11}$ (cGycm^2/n)	$D_r/n_{epi} \times 10^{-11}$ (cGycm^2/n)	J/ϕ
BMRR [3]	3	1.8	4.3	1.3	0.67
MITR [3]	5	0.2	13	13	0.55
PETTEN [3]	45	0.33	10.4	8.4	0.80
Proposed Musashi	0.1	0.41	3.3	1.3	0.67

Values given, except for the reactor power, are those in air at column exits.

Depth-dose evaluation in a phantom

The depth-dose distributions in a tissue phantom were calculated by using the proposed thermal and epithermal neutron beams in the optimized design facilities. The head model was represented by three concentric spheres, separating areas of scalp, skull and brain with their respective equivalent materials. The produced thermal neutron beams were confined by a 20-cm-thick collimator, having a conical aperture 20 cm in diameter tapering to 10 cm facing the head phantom while the epithermal neutron beam was not collimated. In the calculations, the ^{10}B concentrations were assumed to be 30 ppm in tumor, 10 ppm in blood and 3 ppm in tissue in normal brain. Figure 2A and B show total doses and different components of the physical radiation dose along the central axis of the tissue phantom for the proposed thermal and epithermal neutron beams, respectively. The epithermal neutron beam is superior to the thermal neutron beam in the treatment of deeper tumors due to peaking of thermal neutron flux by moderating of epithermal neutrons, while the thermal neutron beam is good for superficial tumors. The maximum usable depths to treat tumor are determined to be 4 cm and 6.5 cm for the thermal and epithermal neutron beams, respectively. The

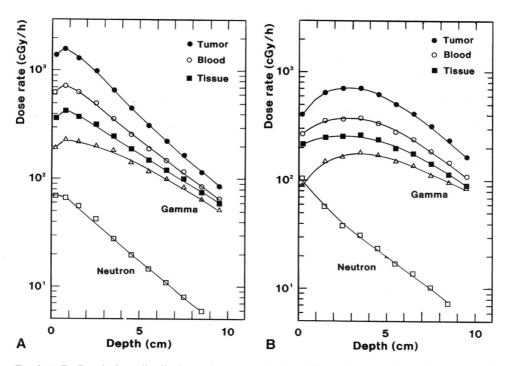

Fig. 2. **A,B**: Depth-dose distributions along central axis of tissue phantom for **A** thermal and **B** epithermal neutron beams: tumor, blood and normal tissue contain 30 ppm, 10 ppm and 3 ppm, respectively.

full-dose treatment time to obtain 3×10^{12} n/cm^{-2} of thermal neutron fluence needed in BNCT would be in about 2.5 h.

Conclusion

Design studies were carried out for the Musashi reactor (TRIGA-II, 100 kW) to generate epithermal and thermal neutron beams for application to BNCT. Monte Carlo calculations indicated that fairly pure epithermal and thermal neutron beams, attaining 4.1×10^8 n/cm^{-2}.s^{-1} and 1.1×10^9 n/cm^{-2}.s^{-1}, presenting good beam directionality, could be obtainable from the thermalizing and thermal columns, respectively. These beams are associated with a low fast neutron dose ($< 5 \times 10^{-11}$ cGy/cm^2.n^{-1}) and a low γ dose ($< 3 \times 10^{-11}$ cGy/cm^2.n^{-1}). Depth-dose calculations in a tissue phantom using both neutron beams showed that the proposed thermal and epithermal neutron beams would be useful to treat superficial (4 cm) and deeper (6.5 cm) tumors, respectively. The full-dose treatment would take about 2.5 h. The present study should serve to indicate how a TRIGA reactor could be modified for generating neutron beams suited to BNCT.

References

1. Matsumoto T, Aizawa O, Nozaki T, Sato T. Present status of the medical irradiation facility at the Musashi reactor. Pigment Cell Res 1989;2(4):240.
2. Briesmeister JF (ed) MCNP — A general Monte Carlo Code for Neutron and Photon Transport. Los Alamos National Laboratory: LA-7396-M, Rev.2, 1986.
3. Brugger RM. Summing up: The physics of NCT. In: Soloway AH et al. (eds) Advances in Neutron Capture Therapy. New York: Plenum Press, 1993.
4. Kanda K, Kobayashi T, Aizawa O, Wakabayashi H, Oka Y. Physics studies on neutron field and dosimetry for neutron capture therapy in Japan. In: Fairchild RF, Brownell FL (eds) Proceedings of the 1st International Symposium on Neutron Capture Therapy, Cambridge, MA, October, 1983. Upton, NY: Brookhaven National Laboratory, BNL51730 1984.
5. Shirai E, Takahashi H, Issiki M, Arigane K, Iwaya M, Hatanaka H, Hayakawa Y, Nakagawa Y. Clinical experience of BNCT for brain tumors at JAERI. In: Allen BJ et al. (eds) Progress in Neutron Capture Therapy for Cancer. New York: Plenum Press, 1992.

© 1997 Elsevier Science B.V. All rights reserved.
Advances in Neutron Capture Therapy.
Volume I, Medicine and Physics.
B. Larsson, J. Crawford and R. Weinreich, editors.

Neutron beams from beam tube oriented BNCT facilities in 10 MW MTR research reactors

Fabián Jatuff[1] and Valeria Gessaghi[2]

[1]INVAP S. E., Bariloche; and [2]Instituto Balseiro, Universidad Nacional de Cuyo, Bariloche, Argentina

Keywords: alumina, beam tube oriented, bismuth collimator, MCNP-4.2 code, MTR research reactors, refurbishment, research and university reactors, thermal columns.

Introduction

A neutron beam for boron neutron capture therapy (BNCT) requires the appropriate spectrum tuning with minimum damage due to undesired particles (fast neutrons and photons), appropriate epithermal (or thermal) flux intensity, minimum angular divergence and radial flatness over the beam port [1—3]. This includes the proper design of filters, γ shields and collimator geometry and materials, as well as exit beam aperture size and beam shutters [4].

For reactors with existing beam tubes, it is difficult to install a large facility because of the necessary changes to reactor internals and grid, thus a complete refurbishment of the reactor is necessary, which constitutes a very discouraging factor. Unfortunately, a large number of reactors are in this class including almost all operating research and university reactors which have, in principle, enough flux intensity to make BNCT feasible.

The case of reactors designed with a high-priority BNCT facility not relying on a fixed beam tube is different due to:
1) a very important source of particles (the facilities cover an entire face of the reactor); and
2) a minimum core-patient distance, generally lower than 2 m.

In this work, we present the neutron and photon fields' characterization obtained with the MCNP-4.2 code [5], at the beam port of two 10 MW plate-type research reactors showing the beam tube constraint. One reactor is the MPTRR [6], showing a BNCT facility producing a beam of thermal neutrons. The other reactor, the MXRR-1 [7], is a design with an epithermal BNCT facility.

The MPTRR and the MXRR-1 reactors

The MPTRR core is a rectangular array of $\sim 20\%$ ^{235}U enriched plate-type fuel elements of 65 cm height, surrounded by beryllium boxes. Over one of the core

---

Address for correspondence: Fabián Jatuff, INVAP SE, FP Moreno 1089, (8400) Bariloche, Río Negro, Argentina.

430

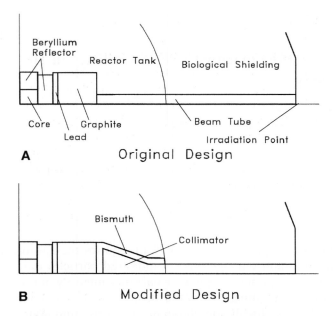

A   Original Design

B   Modified Design

Fig. 1. **MPTRR** thermal BNCT devices.

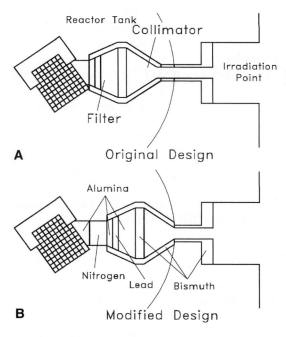

A   Original Design

B   Modified Design

Fig. 2. **MXRR-1** epithermal BNCT devices.

faces there is a graphite thermal column separated from the beryllium boxes by a 10-cm-thick lead shielding head (Fig. 1A). For the MPTRR, an optimization was studied: the inclusion of a bismuth collimator for the attenuation of photons in the tank and the maximization of the neutron flux intensity (Fig. 1B).

The MXRR-1 core is an irregular array surrounded partly by beryllium boxes, by three beryllium blocks and by water. The filter is placed in the grid (two rows of bismuth boxes, ~ 16 cm, and one row of alumina boxes), but the remaining filter and the small collimator are placed into a special block in the reactor tank, after which a beam tube with a diameter of about 20 cm reaches the outside in a cavity of the biological shielding (Fig. 2A). In this case, and due to the difficulties in making the filter block so close to the core, a small beam tube of ~ 40 cm diameter and 30 cm thickness, filled with nitrogen, is interposed between the grid and the filter block (Fig. 2B), and studied as a typical refurbishment update.

Results

The code MCNP-4.2 was used with volume tallies over the axes of the beams. In the direction of the beam, cells with thicknesses in the range 10—20 cm were defined. Statistics of about 2 million histories were counted, providing accurate results for only some of the fluxes up to the irradiation point. However, the results

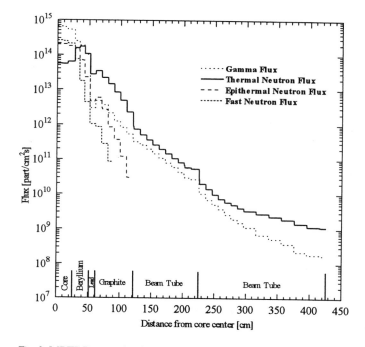

Fig. 3. MPTRR n- and γ-flux, standard device.

432

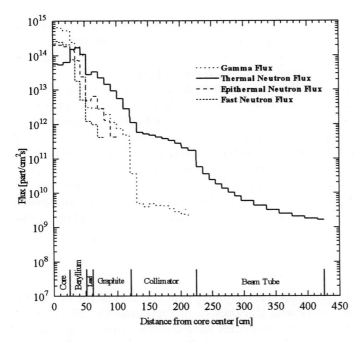

Fig. 4. MPTRR, n- and γ-flux, modified device.

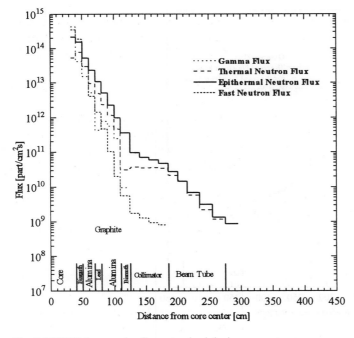

Fig. 5. MXRR-1, n- and γ-flux, standard device.

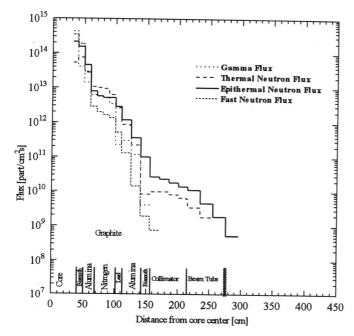

Fig. 6. MXRR-1, n- and γ-flux, modified device.

are shown only for the range of applicability defined (relative errors [5] lower than 10%). The particles were tallied in terms of the fast neutron flux ($E_n > 100$ keV), the epithermal neutron flux (0.4 eV $< E_n < 100$ KeV), the thermal neutron flux ($E_n < 0.4$ eV), and the total γ flux ($E\gamma < 10$ MeV).

Figures 3 and 4 show the penetration of neutrons and photons for the standard and modified BNCT devices of the MPTRR, respectively.

The attenuation of the γ flux due to the bismuth shielding can be observed together with the increment of the thermal neutron flux intensity in the collimator region ($\sim$ one order of magnitude). However, this increment in thermal flux intensity is not exhibited at the irradiation point (improvement of a factor of two only).

Figures 5 and 6 show the penetration of particles for the standard and modified BNCT devices of the MXRR-1, respectively.

The modification introduced alters the intensity of the epithermal neutron flux by only 30% at the irradiation point.

Conclusions

In the MPTRR BNCT facility, although the intensity of the (scalar) thermal flux is increased at the end of the collimator by one order of magnitude, fundamentally due to the increment of the cross flux, it leads only to a factor of two (or

434

less) increment at the irradiation point because of the extra collimation provided by the beam tube in the biological shielding.

For the MXRR-1, the results show that the discrimination (separation of a grid part and a block part) of the filter provides an unwanted collimation (in the intermediate tube region) because a further redispersion is expected. However, the separation of the two parts of the filter does not compromise the epithermal flux intensity at the irradiation point.

Acknowledgements

The authors wish to express their indebtedness to J.H. Boado Magan for his encouragement, financial support and criticisms during this research.

References

1. Aizawa O, Kanda K, Nozaki T, Matsumoto T. Remodeling and dosimetry on the neutron irradiation facility of the Musashi Institute of Technology reactor for boron neutron capture therapy. Nucl Tech 1980;48:150.
2. An S, Furuhashi A, Oka Y, Akiyama M, Kuga H. Development studies regarding the construction of epithermal-enriched neutron field for medical purposes at the University of Tokyo Yayoi fast reactor. Nucl Tech 1980;48:204.
3. Oka Y, Yanagisawa I, An S. A design study of the neutron irradiation facility for boron neutron capture therapy. Nucl Tech 1981;55:642.
4. Brugger RM, Shih J-LA, Liu HB. An epithermal neutron beam for neutron capture therapy. Nucl Tech 1992;98:322.
5. Briesmeister JF. MCNP — A General Monte Carlo Code for Neutron and Photon Transport, LA7396-M, Rev.2, Los Alamos National Laboratory, 1986.
6. Jatuff FE, Villarino EA. Hafnium as a neutron absorber in research reactors. Trans Am Nucl Soc 1995;73:414—416.
7. Lolich J, Abbate P, Otteguy O. 10-MW Multi-Purpose Research Reactor, INVAP S. E. (eds) Bidder Offer presented to the OAEP, Thailand, 1995.

The University of California at Davis/McClellan Nuclear Radiation Center (UC Davis/MNRC) Neutron Capture Therapy Program: description and mission

Susan A. Autry[1], James E. Boggan[1], Benjamin F. Edwards[2], Regina Gandour-Edwards[3], Hungyuan B. Liu[4], Wade J. Richards[4], Robert M. Brugger[5] and John P. Barton[6]

[1]Department of Neurological Surgery, [2]Center for Companion Animal Health, [3]Department of Pathology, [4]MNRC, University of California at Davis, California; and [5]Nuclear Engineering Department and [6]NRE Inc., University of Missouri-Columbia, Missouri, USA

Keywords: TRIGA reactor.

The Northern California Neutron Capture Therapy Study Group (NCNCTSG), composed of university, government, military, private sector resources, and personnel has been formed; spear-headed by the University of California at Davis, Department of Neurological Surgery, to establish a neutron capture therapy center at the McClellan Air Force Base Nuclear Radiation Center (MNRC). The program's ultimate goal is the treatment of pediatric and adult oncology patients. A scientific program involving research at the basic science, preclinical, and clinical levels has been designed to develop, and systematically evaluate new drugs for neutron capture therapy (NCT), in addition to design and implementation of an optimal neutron beam source and delivery system for use in NCT. The initial focus of the program is to establish the efficacy of NCT for the treatment of incurable brain tumors such as glioblastoma multiforme, but will expand to treat malignancies such as melanoma, skull base tumors, inherently radioresistant tumors (e.g., renal cell carcinoma), long bone sarcoma in children, and pediatric brain tumors.

For the past 4 years, the NCNCTSG has been performing feasibility and pilot studies using innovative and state-of-the-art technology in the areas of neutron capture agent (NCA) synthesis, pharmacokinetics and tissue biodistribution, ultrastructural localization of NCAs, and drug toxicity in small animals. The TRIGA reactor at the MNRC has now been upgraded from steady-state 1 MW to 2 MW operation. During the upgrade shutdown period, a cavity was bored through concrete biological shielding to the reactor tank wall. After installation of the shield/shutter system and completion of the treatment room, both thermal and epithermal neutron beams will be available for basic research in NCT of can-

Address for correspondence: Susan Autry, Department of Neurological Surgery, UC Davis, 2516 Stockton Blvd., Suite 254, Sacramento, CA 95817, USA.

cer. After the appropriate beam characterization and medical approval, clinical NCT may begin.

With renewed worldwide interest and encouraging results from ongoing NCT programs, a number of issues still requires adequate resolution before this form of therapy can be accepted as a primary treatment in the management of malignant brain tumors and other local neoplasms. The program developed by the NCNCTSG seeks to address these issues in a comprehensive and progressively focused research program that culminates in the use of neutron capture therapy for the treatment of localized malignancies, such as brain tumors in humans.

Acknowledgements

Special thanks to the DOD and DOE for funding the modifications/upgrades at the MNRC in order to provide a world class NCT facility.

The feasibility of a clinical thermal neutron facility for boron neutron capture therapy at the Argonaut Reactor in Petten

F. Stecher-Rasmussen[1], W.E. Freudenreich[1], W.P. Voorbraak[1] and C. Vroegindeweij[2]

[1]*Netherlands Energy Research Foundation, ECN; and* [2]*Commission of the European Communities, JRC, Petten, The Netherlands*

Introduction

There is strong confidence in a positive demonstration of the unique features of boron neutron capture therapy (BNCT) through the various clinical trials worldwide on BNCT with epithermal neutrons applied to brain tumours. Therefore, a search has started for further application of BNCT to other tumours rather than brain tumours. As the therapy reaction ^{10}B (n,α) ^{7}Li almost exclusively results from capture of thermal neutrons it is evident that a beam of thermal neutrons can be applied with an advantage to the treatment of superficial tumours.

In anticipation of increasing demand for additional neutron sources for extended future clinical application of BNCT, a feasibility study on a thermal neutron facility at the Argonaut Reactor of ECN, the low flux reactor (LFR) operating at a power of 30 kW, has been conducted.

The ECN Argonaut Reactor (LFR)

The LFR consists of a ring-shaped core surrounded by an inner and outer graphite reflector (Fig. 1). The core contains five fuel elements in an asymmetric configuration, and cooled by light water. An epithermal test facility has been developed at a tangential horizontal beam channel on the north side of the reactor. On the irradiation trolley on the east side of the reactor, a thermal neutron facility for radiobiological studies have been installed. At this irradiation position, a thermal neutron fluence rate for the free beam of $1.2 \times 10^{9} \mathrm{cm}^{-2}.\mathrm{s}^{-1}$ is obtained with a dose rate of γ rays and higher energy neutrons lower than 1 Gy h^{-1} [1].

A thermal column is located at the west side of the reactor. In the present computational study, a part of the thermal column was replaced by a moderator consisting of 0.5 mol% H_2O and 99.5 mol% D_2O. The thickness of this material was 23 cm. The moderator was enclosed by a 0.5-cm-thick Al tank. A bismuth slab of 12 cm thickness was placed between the Al tank and the irradiation position to shield the γ rays. Except for a window of 20 cm^2, the outward surface of

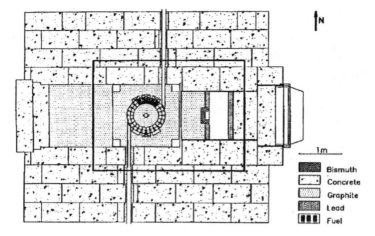

	Bismuth
	Concrete
	Graphite
	Lead
	Fuel

Fig. 1. Horizontal cross-section of the LFR (at midheight of the fuel). The thermal column is located on the west side of the reactor, the irradiation trolley on the east side.

this slab was covered by a 0.2-cm-thick 100% enriched ^{6}LiF sheet in order to reduce the unwanted thermal neutrons outside the irradiation window.

Design study of thermal-neutron clinical facility

Through numerous Monte Carlo calculations (MCNP4A) [2], an optimized configuration of a thermal neutron module, replacing a part of the thermal column, has been designed (Fig. 2).

This module consists of a heavy water slab followed by a bismuth shield. At the irradiation position, a thermal neutron fluence rate for the free beam of $1.4 \times 10^9 \mathrm{cm}^{-2}\mathrm{s}^{-1}$ is obtained with a dose rate of γ rays and higher-energy neutrons lower than 1 Gy h^{-1}.

Thermal neutron fluence distribution in tumour model

In a second step MCNP-calculations [2] have been performed for a tumour-bearing phantom at two distances from the irradiation window, respectively, 5 and 10 cm (Fig. 3). The tumour model contains 30 ppm ^{10}B and the healthy tissue model 0 ppm. The surface of the healthy tissue part of the phantom facing the irradiation window is covered by a 0.2-cm-thick 100% enriched ^{6}Li-tile. In Fig. 4 the thermal neutron fluence rate at depth in the phantom is shown. Due to backscattering of the neutrons the fluence rate in the phantom is increased from the free in-air value to $2.5 \times 10^9 \mathrm{cm}^{-2}.\mathrm{s}^{-1}$ (at 5 cm distance between irradiation window and tumour) and $1.6 \times 10^9 \mathrm{cm}^{-2}.\mathrm{s}^{-1}$ (at 10 cm distance), respectively.

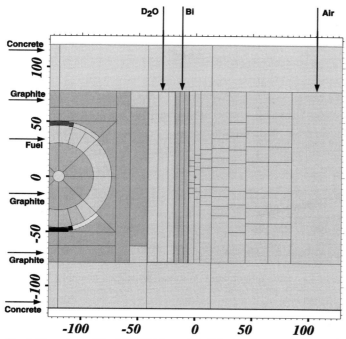

Fig. 2. Overview of the MCNP4A model of the free beam, the bismuth slab, the D$_2$O moderator and the reactor.

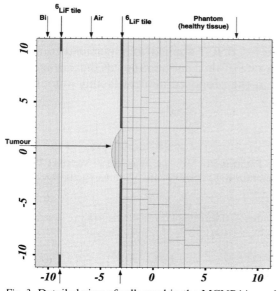

Fig. 3. Detailed view of cells used in the MCNP4A model of the tumour, bearing phantom at 5 cm from the Bi-shield.

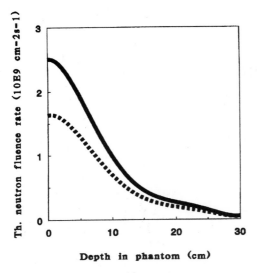

Fig. 4. Thermal neutron fluence rate as a function of depth in a tumour-bearing phantom. The solid curve shows the fluence rate for a 5 cm distance between the irradiation window and the phantom; the dotted curve for a 10 cm distance.

Conclusions

Due to thermalization and back-scattering, the thermal neutron fluence rate in the superficial tumour at 5 and 10 cm distances from the bismuth shield is approximately twice as high as the thermal neutron fluence rate in the free beam at the corresponding positions. The present study demonstrates the potential of the LFR as a neutron source for BNCT applied to superficial tumours, e.g., the melanoma type. The fluence rate of thermal neutrons at the surface of a tumour-bearing phantom irradiated in the proposed clinical facility amounts to $2.5 \times 10^9 \mathrm{cm}^{-2} . \mathrm{s}^{-1}$.

References

1. Stecher-Rasmussen F, Vroegindeweij C, Freudenreich WE, de Haas JBM, Verbakel WFAR. Development of the ECN Argonaut Reactor for BNCT Studies. In: Mishima Y (ed) Proceedings of the Sixth International Symposium on Neutron Capture Therapy for Cancer. Kobe November 1994. New York: Plenum Press, 1996;319.
2. Peeters TTJM, Freudenreich WE. Calculation of fluence rate distributions in a pre design clinical facility for BNCT at the LFR. Petten: ECN-report, ECN-I-95-046, December 1995.

Towards the final design of an accelerator-based facility for clinical boron cancer therapy (BCT)

T.D. Beynon[1], D.A. Allen[1], A. Beddoe[2], G. Constantine[1], L.G. Earwaker[1], N. James[3], S. Green[2], W.N. Morgan[2] and D.R. Weaver[1]

[1]*School of Physics and Space Research, University of Birmingham, Birmingham;* [2]*Department of Medical Physics, Queen Elizabeth Hospital, Birmingham; and* [3]*CRC Institute for Cancer Studies, University of Birmingham, UK*

Introduction

The Birmingham boron cancer therapy programme is centred around the Dynamitron accelerator in the School of Physics and Space Research. Using a lithium metal target and the $^7Li(p,n)^7Be$ reaction with a suitable moderator, the clinical requirements for a suitable neutron beam can be achieved with a proton current of 5—10 mA at an energy of 2.5—3.0 MeV. This presentation sets out the aims of the programme in a series of stages, indicating the level of achievement in each stage in the approach to a clinical facility.

Aims of programme

Stage I

Using the moderator design proposed by Allen and Beynon [1], a prototype clinical assembly has been built to allow physical measurements to be made to validate the design parameters. This moderator is a graphite-reflected heavy water (D_2O) system driven by a vertically downwards entering proton beam and a vertically downwards extracted neutron beam. This design indicated that a 2.8—3.0 MeV proton beam at 5—10 mA would produce an epithermal neutron beam with a fluence rate in excess of 10^9 $cm^{-2} \cdot s^{-1}$ and a neutron and photon dose per unit neutron fluence of less than 9×10^{-13} Gy cm^2 and 2×10^{-13} Gy cm^2, respectively. A series of bare beam measurements and measurements of flux and dose, for neutrons and photons, in a head phantom are reported in [2,3]. The results are compared with predictions using the Monte Carlo code MCNP which models the nucleonics of the complete assembly including the energy-angle yield of the lithium target. The measurements are typically within 2—3% of the predictions, therefore satisfactorily validating this particular accelerator-based design concept.

Stage II

This is the current stage of the Birmingham programme and, in summary, is as follows.

Accelerator upgrade
The Dynamitron in its present form could, with 1 mA proton capability, produce about 20% of the epithermal neutron fluence designated for a clinical facility. Work has already begun on upgrading the ion source and beam transport system to produce, initially, a 5 mA proton beam delivered to a thick metallic lithium target, with a later capability for delivering up to 10 mA should this be necessary. It is anticipated that the 5 mA beam will be available by the middle of 1997.

Target design
Concomitant with the accelerator upgrade is the design for a lithium metal target which can dissipate the $15-30$ kW of thermal power in the proton beam whilst maintaining the lithium metal below its melting point of 180°C. A design study which has yet to be validated is based on a multilayered Li-Au-Al system, with the gold layer serving to reduce the proton energy sufficiently to minimise γ production produced by the $^{7}Li(p,\gamma)$ reaction. The design incorporates a primary coolant of D_2O and a heat exchanger using H_2O in the secondary circuit.

Optimization of moderator performance
The moderator design described in [1], in which the proton and extracted neutron beams are both vertical, would lead to a number of problems in patient treatment. Consequently, a second series of design studies were investigated, extracting the neutron beam horizontally, though still with a vertical proton beam. Whilst full details of these studies will be published, it is evident that a compact graphite/heavy water configuration is capable of delivering 10.5 Gy(eq) to healthy brain tissue in $20-25$ min. A proton beam of energy 2.8 MeV at 5 mA is sufficient for this purpose. Fine tuning of these designs will be completed shortly, prior to a second series of measurements to validate this modified design. In this study particular attention has been paid to the effectiveness of neutron beam collimation on dose-depth characteristics and on a final design which would allow rapid geometric reconfiguration for a wider range of treatment applications.

Dose measurements and boron assaying
Whilst the programme will be embracing all the conventional methods for boron assay essential for treatment planning, a novel approach is being developed in which a three-dimensional map of the dose delivered to the tumour site and healthy brain can be obtained during the early stages of a treatment. This technique is based on the ability to do three-dimensional holography from incoherent sources using a Gabor zone plate, the incoherent source in this case being the

478 keV γ ray emitted during the $^{10}B(n,\alpha)^7Li$ reaction. More details of this work are given in [4].

Stage III

This stage of the Birmingham programme has already commenced and has as its aim the commencement of phase I patient trials in approximately 2 years time. It may be defined as follows:
1) to define and implement our programme in radiobiology;
2) to validate the three-dimensional dosimetry imaging technique;
3) to define and implement our treatment planning methodology; and
4) to design and build the clinical facility in the environs of the upgraded Dynamitron accelerator.

Further details of this stage, particularly on the proposed protocol and boron delivery drugs, are given by James et al. [5].

References

1. Allen DA, Beynon TD. A design study for an accelerator-based epithermal neutron beam for BNCT. Phys Med Biol 1995;40:807−821.
2. Tattam DA, Allen DA, Beynon TD, Constantine G, Green S, Scott MC, Weaver DR. Developmental and preliminary neutron fluence measurements in the Birmingham BCT beam. In: Larsson B, Crawford J, Weinreich R (eds) Advances in Neutron Capture Therapy, Volume 1, Medicine and Physics. Amsterdam: Elsevier Science, 1997;472−476 (these proceedings).
3. Green S, Kota C, James N, Maughan RL, Tattam DA, Beddoe A, Beynon TD, Weaver DR. Dosimetric characteristics of an accelerator-based beam for boron cancer therapy — experimental results. In: Larsson B, Crawford J, Weinreich R (eds) Advances in Neutron Capture Therapy, Volume 1, Medicine and Physics. Amsterdam: Elsevier Science, 1997;217−221 (these proceedings).
4. Allen DA, Beynon TD, Perks J, Rew G. In vivo on-line $^{10}B(n,\alpha)$ three-dimensional dosimetry using binary Gabor zone plate encoded γ-ray holography. In: Larsson B, Crawford J, Weinreich R (eds) Advances in Neutron Capture Therapy, Volume 1, Medicine and Physics. Amsterdam: Elsevier Science, 1997;229−236 (these proceedings).
5. James N, Green S, Morgan WN, Beddoe A, Beynon TD. Moving towards hospital-based boron cancer therapy. In: Larsson B, Crawford J, Weinreich R (eds) Advances in Neutron Capture Therapy, Volume 1, Medicine and Physics. Amsterdam: Elsevier Science, 1997;467−471 (these proceedings).

The TERA programme: status and prospects

Sandro Rossi[1,2] and Ugo Amaldi[1,2]

[1] TERA Foundation, Novara, Italy; and [2] CERN, Geneva, Switzerland

Introduction

Electron linacs are the most widely used X-ray sources in cancer radiotherapy (RT). The rate of installation of new 3 GHz linacs has been very high, so that today about 4,000 accelerators are used in the world [1]. They are considered to be better RT sources than cobalt bombs, because of the deeper penetration (Fig. 1) of the higher energy X-rays and their easier handling and availability. The potential market is large, in particular, if developing countries are taken into account. A single figure should suffice; as many as 50 linacs are at present installed in Indian hospitals alone.

High-energy photons have an unfavourable dose distribution in matter. Thus, in a typical treatment two opposite beams of X-rays are used so that, for a given dose to the tumour, the dose absorbed by the upstream and downstream healthy tissues is reduced. Four crossfire beams are also employed, yet the contour of a regularly shaped tumour can be followed with a precision which is at best centimetric. For irregular shapes, the situation is even worse.

Only recently, many (up to 12) crossing beams have been used in the so-called conformal radiation therapy (CRT) which, based on very accurate three-dimensional imaging and treatment planning, can follow contours with millimetric precision. In CRT the energy absorbed by the healthy tissues is globally the same, but is more uniformly distributed over the surrounding healthy tissues than in normal RT.

This is very important when the tumour is very close to one (or more) critical organ(s) that cannot be irradiated. Since the dose to the tumour is limited by the dose that can be absorbed by the critical organ(s), in CRT larger doses can be given to the tumour. Note that a 10% increase of the dose corresponds to a 15–20% increase in the probability of local control of the tumour, so that even a small increase in the dose is therapeutically worthwhile.

Address for correspondence: Sandro Rossi, CERN, 1211 Geneva 23, Switzerland.

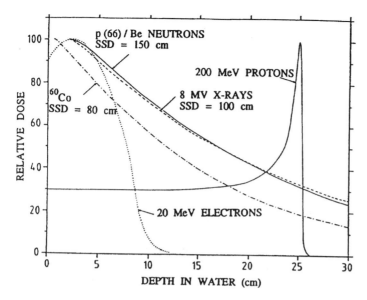

Fig. 1. Dose-depth curves in water of various beams of radiation.

Rationale for hadrontherapy and existing facilities

Deep hadrontherapy

Bob Wilson remarked (50 years ago) that the Bragg peak of monoenergetic protons (shown in Fig. 1) and of other charged hadrons easily allowed what is now called "conformal" treatment of deep-seated tumours [2]. To reach 25 cm in soft tissues, the kinetic energy of the protons has to be 200 MeV. For carbon ions, the most suitable light ions for tumour treatments, one needs 4,500 MeV, i.e., 375 MeV/u. Since the width of the Bragg peak of monoenergetic particles is very narrow, to irradiate thick targets, the energy of the charged particles has to be modulated in time either by an absorber of variable thickness or by changing the energy of the accelerator. With a spread-out Bragg peak (SOBP) of 8—10 cm, the distal fall-off of the dose takes place in 2—3 mm and the surface dose for protons (carbon ions) is typically 70% (50%) of the peak dose at a 20—25 cm depth. These conditions are much more favourable than those of X-rays (Fig. 1). Due to the convenient macroscopic energy distribution, a truly conformal radiotherapy can be performed with only one or two directions of incidence of the charged hadron beam. Moreover, the total energy delivered to the surrounding healthy tissues is definitely lower than in X-ray conformal radiotherapy (CRT). This allows an even larger tumour dose than in CRT for sites which are surrounded by critical tissues, as in the brain.

What about neutral hadrons? Neutron beams have been used in Berkeley since 1938 for oncological treatments [3]. Indeed about 50 MeV protons are sufficient to produce fast neutrons which, however, have a depth dose distribution not very different from megavoltage X-rays (Fig. 1). The advantage is that the deposition of energy is due to very low energy protons, which have a much larger stopping power (or LET = linear energy transfer) than the electrons set in motion by high-energy photons; more than 100 MeV/cm instead of a few MeV/cm. As a consequence of the different quality of the radiation field, neutrontherapy is suited to treat radio resistant tumours, i.e., the slowly growing hypoxic tumours which are insensitive to both X-rays and protons and represent about 10% of all the tumours treated with X-rays. Neutrontherapy, after the treatment of about 18,000 patients, is at present being given up because this most useful microscopic feature is more than counterbalanced by the unfavourable macroscopic dose distribution. Light ions, and in particular carbon ions, have instead combined the properties of a favourable dose distribution (crucial for conformal radiotherapy) and a large LET (necessary for curing radioresistant tumours).

At the end of 1996 about 18,000 patients had been treated with proton beams all over the world [4] and about 200 with carbon ions at HIMAC (Heavy Ion Medical Accelerator Centre) in Japan [5]. The pioneering work done in LBL with helium ions (about 2,000 patients) and neon ions (about 500 patients) was discontinued in 1992 [6]. As mentioned above, nowadays carbon ions ($Z = 6$) are considered to be better suited than helium ($Z = 2$) and neon ($Z = 10$) ions for the treatment of radioresistant tumours, because the LET (which for a given velocity is proportional to Z^2) is less than 100 MeV/cm at the entry point (so that in the first layers traversed they behave roughly as X-rays and protons), but is definitely larger than 100 MeV/cm in the SOBP which covers the tumour.

Proton therapy of eye melanomas, requiring 60—70 MeV protons, is performed in many European centres. Deep-seated tumours are treated in one dedicated hospital-based centre (at the Loma Linda Medical University Center) in California [7] and in 10 centres which originally were, or still are, nuclear research centres:

CPO	Orsay,	GWI	Uppsala,
HCL	Boston,	ITEP	Moscow,
IUCF	Indiana,	JINR	Dubna,
LINPh	St. Petersburg,	NAC	Faure,
PMRC	Tsukuba,	PSI	Villigen.

It can be seen that only two of them are in the European Union (CPO and GWI). The HIMAC facility in Chiba (Japan) is fully dedicated to ion therapy [5]. Together with Loma Linda, this is the only hospital-based hadrontherapy dedicated centre. As discussed in Section 3, in the next years the situation will change, in particular outside Europe.

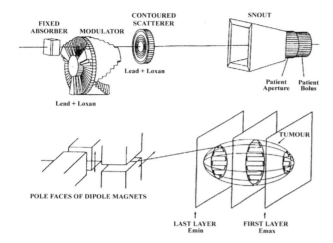

Fig. 2. "Passive" and "active" beam spreading systems. An active system can be based either on raster scanning (as in TV and shown here) or on voxel scanning.

Beam spreading systems

Figure 2 represents the two methods adopted for conformally irradiating a tumour target:
1) by widening the beam with an absorber, which acts as a scattering medium, a funnel of charged particles is produced, just as for the neutral photons used in RT: collimators and absorbers are used to shape the field; and
2) with two dipole magnets a pencil beam is directed in the chosen direction and the target is irradiated by moving the pencil beam and varying its energy.

For the about 20,000 patients treated until now with charged hadrons, only passive beam spreading systems have been used. They are installed at the end of the beam transport system. In all the centres these lines are fixed, while in Loma Linda they are the last part of three 10-m-high rotating isocentric gantries which allow irradiation from any angle. The alignment procedure is long; typically 20–30 min. Active systems have recently been tested in PSI and GSI (Darmstadt, Germany) and will be used on patients towards the end of 1996. At PSI a compact gantry and a voxel scanning system for protons has been constructed [8], while the carbon beam of the GSI synchrotron will be used to irradiate patients with a raster scanned pencil beam [9]. In the future, all the facilities will have active spreading systems, but medical doctors still prefer the passive method which is proven and guarantees a uniform irradiation in the transverse plane. Active systems will have to be very reliable to be accepted.

Number of potential patients and future hospital-based facilities

In Europe (3.2×10^8 inhabitants) about 50% of all the tumours are irradiated with high energy photons. This corresponds to more than 600,000 new X-ray treatments per year, which implies about 60,000 new patients with radioresistant tumours, who could profit from iontherapy. To substantiate this large figure, many clinical trials are needed at HIMAC, GSI and possibly other iontherapy centres. For protontherapy, solid clinical results exist for brain, eye, spinal cord tumours and a few other sites. Salivary glands, prostate and cervices have also been treated. A conservative analysis made in the framework of the TERA programme [10] concluded that about 5% of X-ray patients would profit, (i.e., about 30,000 in Europe). In a study for Europe, G. Gademann obtained much higher figures; 280,000 patients, of which about 25,000 are first priority cases [11]. Similar results are contained in a recent unpublished report prepared for the National Cancer Institute by H.D. Suit and collaborators of the Massachusetts General Hospital (MGH, Boston). Since a multigantry centre can treat about 1,000 patients/year (each one for 20 sessions lasting 20–30 min), one conservatively concludes that in Europe there is space for at least 20 protontherapy centres aiming at improving the local control of tumours close to critical organs.

In the world, by the year 2000, there will be at least four new dedicated facilities for hadrontherapy, besides Loma Linda and HIMAC. Two of them, one in the USA and the other one in Japan, are based on the cyclotron designed by IBA (Belgium) [12] and will be ready in 1998. The American Centre (NPTC) will have two rotating gantries; it is being built in Boston by the Massachusetts General Hospital (MGH) and utilises all the knowledge collected at the Harvard cyclotron. For the Japanese centre of Kashiwa (near Chiba), which is very similar to Boston, IBA has teamed up with Sumitomo. While these two centres will have only proton beams, in the Prefecture of Hyogo (Japan), a proton and ion centre is under construction and will be ready in 2001. The investment of US$275 million includes a 50-bed hospital. Mitsubishi Electric is building the accelerator and the high-tech facilities. The purpose is similar to the Italian CNAO Project (see below). The fourth funded hadron accelerator, to be presented below, is a novel 3 GHz linac, which has been designed in the framework of the Italian Hadrontherapy Programme, initiated in 1992 by the TERA Foundation.

Cost of protontherapy vs. other oncological treatments

In Chapter 16 of the "Green Book" [13], P. Chauvel and collaborators (Centre Antoine Lacassagne, Cyclotron Biomédical, Nice) show that a proton therapy centre based on three gantries would be economically competitive with a centre of X-ray conformal radiotherapy (CRT), which uses more than six crossfired X-ray beams, if the accelerator and the gantries require investments not greater than the costs chosen in the definition of a "compact" accelerator; about US$11 million for the accelerator and the first gantry, and about US$2 million dollars for each added gantry [14]. This would allow, taking into account both the lifetime of the facility and the staff costs, charges of about 1,000–1,100 DM for each 30 min session of protontherapy, so that a complete average treatment of

20 sessions would cost not more than 22,000 DM. This is a crucial point for the future developments of affordable hospital-based protontherapy facilities.

To understand the meaning of these figures it is worth recalling that X-ray radiotherapy is the cheapest of all oncological therapies. In fact, precise evaluations by G. Gademann [11] and by E. Borgonovi et al. of the Bocconi University [15] indicate that while a conventional radiotherapy costs between 6,000 and 7,000 DM, an average oncological surgery costs 15,000 DM and a heavy chemotherapy for a systemic tumour (as leukaemia) goes up to 60,000 DM. Recent calculations indicate that an average CRT with many X-ray fields may cost 17,000−19,000 DM.

Comparing these figures to those calculated for a "compact" proton accelerator and gantry system, (see Section 7 for a definition of "compact" accelerator) of which the cost is indicated above [13], and taking into account the costs of the failures, Chauvel et al. conclude that protontherapy is economically competitive with CRT. This argument represents a strong incentive to develop cheap proton accelerators and gantries, which do not require very special buildings for the installation and consume little electrical power. In a few years we shall know whether this interesting challenge has been met.

The TERA Foundation and the Hadrontherapy Programme

The TERA Foundation was created to raise funds and employ a staff fully devoted to the Hadrontherapy Programme. In 1996 more than 20 people worked full-time on the projects of the Foundation. Its 1995 budget was about 1,300,000 kLit (1 kLit = 1 DM). Already in autumn 1991, the INFN (Italian Institute for Research in Fundamental Nuclear and Subnuclear Physics) decided to finance the research part of this activity. Since then the support to the 12 Sections and Laboratories of INFN now working on the Programme, has increased; in 1996 it is about 80,000 kLit. ENEA (Ente Nazionale per le Nuove Tecnologie, l'Energia e l'Ambiente) joined the Programme in spring 1993 to contribute to the design of "compact" accelerators for protontherapy, a project led since then by Luigi Picardi of ENEA-INFN, Frascati. Also in 1993 the physicists of the Istituto Superiore di Sanità (the Italian National Health Institute sited in Rome) decided to join the Hadrontherapy Programme and requested and obtained funds for the construction of a proton accelerator.

Three Committees coordinate the R and D activities carried out in the framework of the Hadrontherapy Programme:
— the Pathologies and Treatments Committee,
— the Radiobiology Committee, and
— the Dosimetry and Microdosimetry Committee.
Their activities, not presented here, are common to all the projects of the Programme. As far as the direct intervention of the TERA Foundation is concerned, the design and construction activities of the Hadrontherapy Programme are organised in three projects:

1. The planning and the construction of a National Centre for Oncological Hadrontherapy (CNAO), a health care and research structure of excellence which will be the focal point of all the hadrontherapy activities and (being equipped with proton and ion beams to be used in parallel) will be able to treat (with protons) about 100 patients a year, and at a later stage, an equal number with carbon ion beams.
2. The design and the construction of a certain number of Protontherapy Centres equipped with proton accelerators of small dimensions and relatively cheap, possibly built by Italian industry; each of these will treat at least 200–300 patients a year with a proton beam and about double that number with an added treatment room. This is the "Compact" Accelerator Project, PACO.
3. The creation of an informatics and organisational network, called RITA (Italian Network for Hadrontherapy Treatment), which will connect the associated centres — distributed throughout Italy and abroad and situated in the public oncological institutions and in private clinics — with the centres where proton and ion beams will be made available. The specialised medical and physics staff in these associated centres will be able to discuss remotely, through multimedia connections, clinical cases with the experts of the Hadrontherapy Centre and those of the protontherapy centres by using the most modern informatic means. They will exchange diagnostics images and some of the physicians at these associated centres (sometimes after using conventional radiotherapies) will even be in a position to plan a successive treatment for their patients, who will then be irradiated in one of the centres where hadron beams are available.

The first two projects are described in the following Sections. Due to lack of space the RITA network and other Italian hadrontherapy projects not under the direct TERA responsibility will not be further discussed.

The CNAO Project

From the beginning of 1992 onwards, the TERA Foundation has been engaged in the design and realisation of the hadrontherapy centre CNAO based on a synchrotron which can accelerate protons to at least 250 MeV and carbon ions to at least 4,500 MeV, (i.e., at least 375 MeV/u). This will be a centre of excellence devoted to tumour hadrontherapy of more than 1,000 patients/year, to clinical research in cancer therapy and to R and D in the fields of radiobiology and dosimetry. The first study was completed in Spring 1994 and published in the form of a "Blue Book", which describes versions A and B of the Centro Nazionale di Adroterapia Oncologica (CNAO). Since the volume was much requested, a second edition of the Blue Book was distributed in 1995 [10]. Version C is described in the Addendum. G. Brianti is the Chairman of the CNAO Project Advisory Committee. In 1995, CERN funded a small research activity (the TERA Group) formed of part-time physicists and engineers who, since then, have contributed to the design of the medical synchrotron for protons and ions, which is at the heart of the CNAO project. At the beginning of 1996 a new optimised study of such a synchrotron was started at CERN under the leadership of Dr Philip Bryant. Five TERA staff members and two doctoral students from the AUSTRON Project (Vienna) participate in PIMMS (the Proton Ion Medical Machine Study), which aims at finding new optimised solutions for the synchrotron and the isocentric proton gantries. GSI (Darmstadt) — where Gerhard Kraft and collaborators will start patient treatment with carbon ions at the end of 1996 — is responsible for the design of the ion injector and of a gantry for carbon ions.

For a medical synchrotron the intensity of the extracted beams poses no special problem, since 10^{11} p/s and 3×10^{9} ions/s are sufficient. The issue is the time uniformity of the spill, because due to magnetic ripple, synchrotron pulses have time structures at many frequencies; this makes the active spreading of the beams particularly difficult. At HIMAC [5], this problem has been partially solved with an accurate (to a few 10^{-7}) but costly stabilisation of the magnet power supplies. The new study of the medical synchrotron is thus taking time uniformity of the extracted beam, which lasts about 1 s, as the highest priority, as already done at LEAR (CERN) for much longer time scales.

The work is not completed yet, but the main ideas behind a solution, possibly to be combined with other methods, can be explained with reference to Fig. 3, where the transverse beam size is represented. Due to the unavoidable ripple in the dipoles and quadrupoles, the resonance extraction lines (drawn at 45°) can be thought of as oscillating continuously in the directions indicated by the arrows. When the beam is uniformly pushed into resonance, for instance with a betatron core which has a very low ripple, the movement of the resonance lines produces a time nonuniformity. To reduce this effect, that part of the beam which

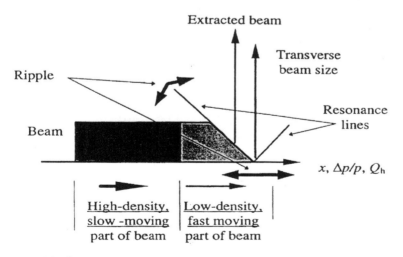

Fig. 3. The figure represents the extraction process. The arrows indicate the effect of the magnet ripple and the dashed areas the different densities of the beam.

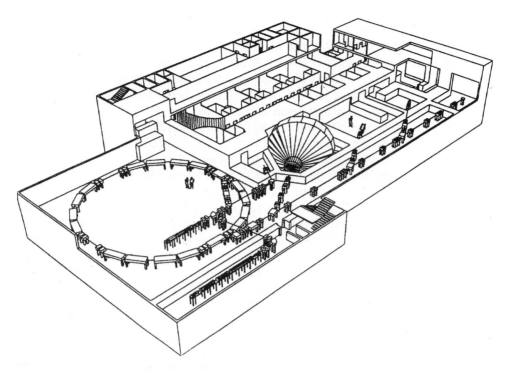

Fig. 4. The layout of CNAO (version D). The proton/carbon synchrotron has an average diameter of 22 m. The centre will have three rooms for proton treatment and one with a horizontal beam of ions. The building is extendable for the construction of other therapy rooms.

is closer to the resonance can be made to move much faster, so that the extracted beam is less sensitive to the ripple. While the design of the machine goes on, TERA physicists and engineers have defined a new layout of CNAO (version D). An image is given in Fig. 4.

The CNAO is intended as a centre of excellence and its multitask capability is demonstrated by the possibility of producing thermal neutrons for boron neutron capture therapy (BNCT). This facility has always been envisaged in the centre planning and it is seen as an upgrading of the present basic structure. A research group in Pavia (directed by Prof A. Zonta, Polyclinic of Pavia) is investigating the possibility of carrying out BNCT on explanted liver by employing thermal neutrons [16].

In the framework of the CNAO Project, Monte Carlo simulations [17] have been employed to study the possibility of producing thermal neutrons making use of part of the beam from one of the injectors of the accelerator complex. Neutrons are produced via (p,n) and (d,n) reactions using 11 MeV protons and 7 MeV deuterons impinging on a beryllium target. The moderating structure represented in Fig. 5 (taken from [17]) yields a thermal fluence of 5×10^{12}n cm^{-2} uniformly distributed in the irradiation cavity together with fast neutron

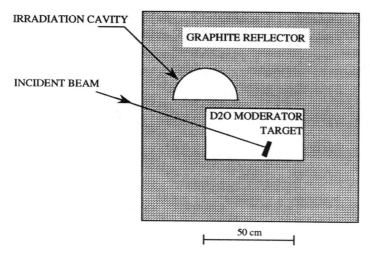

IRRADIATION CAVITY

GRAPHITE REFLECTOR

INCIDENT BEAM

D2O MODERATOR TARGET

50 cm

Fig. 5. A sectional view of the adopted moderating structure [17].

and prompt γ-ray doses lower than 0.5 Gy.

The proton and the deuteron currents appear to be within the limits of what is foreseen for the injector linacs of the CNAO synchrotron. An experimental verification has recently been carried out at the Laboratori Nazionali di Legnaro (Padova, Italy) using a 7 MeV deuteron beam to confirm the predictions of the simulations (the results are represented in the report by S. Agosteo et al. in these Proceedings).

In December 1995 the TERA Foundation offered to six hospital and oncological Institutes of Milan and Pavia, to the Polytechnical School of Milan, and to the Universities of Pavia and Milan, to set up a Consortium and realise the National Centre for Oncological Hadrontherapy near Milan. The Policlinico Ospedale Maggiore offered a site and on June 17th, 1996, a memorandum of understanding among these institutions and TERA was signed. Since summer 1996 a second report, called the "Red Book", on the status of CNAO, has been under preparation; it describes the layout of version D and will be ready by December 1996.

The "Compact" Accelerator Project PACO

The second project of the Hadrontherapy Programme, PACO, was started at the beginning of 1993. For about 3 years the four working groups designed four different types of 200 MeV proton accelerators with the aim of eventually comparing their characteristics and costs. The work done is described in the recently printed "Green Book" [13].

As a starting point, the apparently vague notion of "compact accelerator and gantry" is quantified with the purpose of reducing the cost of protontherapy.

The national centre CNAO is designed as a centre of excellence where the best performances will be achieved both for protons and carbon ions. To reduce the costs, ions (and thus the treatment of radioresistant tumours) should be left aside and "compact" accelerators should have somewhat more modest goals, of course without compromising the health care possibilities. It is obvious that striking such a balance is difficult, and the conclusions are somewhat arbitrary. It is worthwhile reproducing the definition here because the adjective "compact" has been, and is still misunderstood. In the framework of the Hadrontherapy Programme, a proton facility for therapy deserved the adjective "compact" if:

1. It accelerates a minimum of 2×10^{10} p/s to an energy of at least 200 MeV, reliably and reproducibly, so as to have a running efficiency close to that of present conventional electron linacs (98%).
2. It is possible to install the accelerator, the control room and the power supplies in a shielded bunker and a service area covering a total of less than 300 m^2.
3. It has a power consumption (during irradiation) of less than 250 kW.
4. It costs, without the buildings, not more than 17 million kLit (about US$11 million); this cost should include a rotating gantry with all the control and dose distribution systems, and should be able to run with both passive and active spreading systems.
5. The addition of a second gantry should cost less than 3 million kLit (about US$2 million).
6. A 70 MeV beam for eye therapy should also be foreseen and provided at low cost, if desired.

The required beam characteristics and field dimensions, not discussed here, are such that a "compact" accelerator can treat 85% of the about 5,000 Italian patients/year who, according to the analysis of the medical dictum of the Italian Association for Oncological Radiotherapy, could benefit from protontherapy. The different solutions studied by the Hadrontherapy Collaboration for the "compact" proton accelerators are: a conventional synchrotron, a high-field synchrotron, a high-frequency linac and a superconducting cyclotron. A room-temperature cyclotron was not considered since IBA is producing it. Instead, a chapter was written by P. Cohilis and Y. Jongen (Belgium) on a simplified and cheaper version of the IBA facility.

These five types of accelerators are described in five chapters of the "Green Book". The remaining chapters are devoted to the status and future plans of the RITA network and of the three activities coordinated by the three Committees mentioned above. There is no space here to discuss these subjects. The "Green Book" was prepared in connection with the entering of the Istituto Superiore di Sanità (ISS) into the field of hadrontherapy.

The TOP linac of ISS

In Autumn 1993 the Physics Laboratory — directed by Prof Martino Grandolfo of the Istituto Superiore di Sanità — which has been (since long ago) in the field of proton radiobiology and dosimetry, decided to request special funds for the construction of a prototype of a "compact" accelerator (and its rotating gantry) and to finance R and D programmes in the fields of radiobiology, dosimetry, networking, pathology and treatment planning. This programme is now known as the TOP Project of ISS, where TOP stands for "Terapia Oncologica con Protoni". The initial funds (6,000,000 kLit) were allocated in 1994 and appropriated in 1995 with the understanding that about 80% of this sum had to be spent for the construction of a prototype of a "compact" accelerator, of a type yet to be decided. A contribution of 2,330,000 kLit was granted at the end of 1995. Requests for about the same total amount are pending.

In September 1995 draft copies of the "Green Book" were distributed to the members of the Scientific Committee of the TOP project. After auditing the persons responsible for the various designs and considering the still limited funds available (8,330,000 kLit), in December 1995 the Committee advised ISS to concentrate on the construction of the first part of the high-frequency linac [18] whose injector should also be capable of producing PET isotopes. The Istituto Superiore di Sanità accepted this advice and in Spring 1996 found a convenient site located in between the ISS buildings and the Oncological Institute Regina Elena. Following the decision of ISS, the PACO project was terminated since its mission was accomplished.

The 3 GHz proton linac, designed in the framework of the Hadrontherapy Pro-

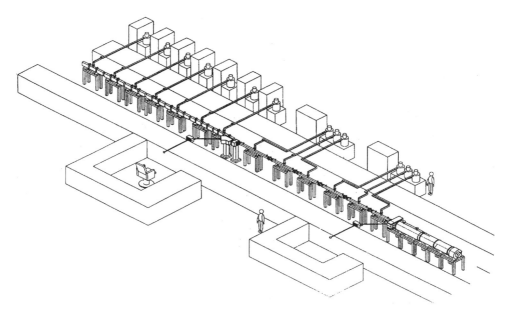

Fig. 6. The low-current 3 GHz protontherapy linac to be constructed in Rome by ISS, ENEA and TERA under the direction of Luigi Picardi (ENEA).

456

gramme, meets the challenge of accelerating low-energy protons with a high-frequency linac, in itself a scientifically interesting problem. As shown in Fig. 6, the high-frequency linac is made up of three sections; a 10 MeV injector of lower frequency (which can also produce PET isotopes), a new accelerating structure called a side-coupled drift tube linac (SCDTL), which has been patented by ENEA, and a conventional side-coupled linac (SCL). Each SCDTL tank contains five or six drift tubes about 1 cm long with a diameter of 3—4 mm. Permanent quadrupole magnets, located between adjacent tanks, focus the accelerated beam. The SCDTL section accelerates protons to 70 MeV, and is the one financed at present. The SCL part will be built at a later stage and will take the beam to 200 MeV.

The overall TOP linac project is coordinated by Dr Salvatore Frullani (ISS) and Dr Luigi Picardi (ENEA) has been nominated responsible for the construction of the high-frequency linac. The new project was presented to the authorities and to the public on June 24th, 1996, during the Second National Day on Hadrontherapy, held in Rome in the auditorium of the Istituto Regina Elena. The advantages of the high-frequency proton linac, compared, for instance, to a cyclotron are:

1) the beam emittance is 10 times smaller, so that the gantry can be lighter and less expensive;
2) the beam energy can be varied continuously between 140 and 200 MeV, as required by the tumour depth;
3) the accelerator has no injection or extraction problems;
4) a linac is modular and can be constructed in pieces; and

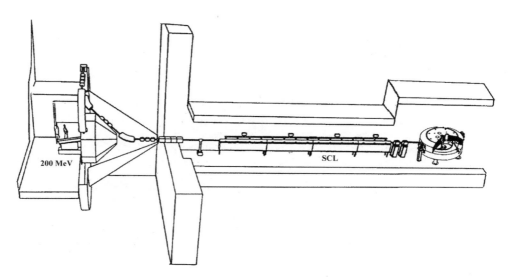

Fig. 7. The SCL part of the protontherapy linac can be used as a booster for a 60—70 MeV cyclotron. The parameters are given in [13].

5) when closely inspected, the surface occupied by the centre is not much larger than that needed by a cyclotron.

A 3 GHz linac booster for proton cyclotrons

With small modifications, the SCL part of the linac in Fig. 7 can also be used as a booster of a 60–70 MeV proton cyclotron. A section of the "Green Book" is devoted to this option, which is very interesting because there are at least 20 (50–70 MeV) cyclotrons in the world, which could be transformed into facilities for protontherapy of deep-seated tumours. In the "Green Book", the study was carried out with reference to the 62 MeV cyclotron of the cyclotron unit, Clatterbridge Hospital, UK [19]. In a total length of 13 m, nine modules made up of four tanks and powered by nine klystrons, take the proton beam from 62 to 200 MeV. The repetition rate is 400 Hz, which is good for a voxel active spreading of the beam. The overall linac capture efficiency, taking into account the fact that the linac acceptance is about 3 times the cyclotron omittance, is 1.5×10^{-4}, so that the average proton current at 200 MeV is 10 nA. The power is about 100 kW. By switching off klystrons, it is possible to vary the proton energy between 140 and 200 MeV.

The nonprofit TERA Foundation is at present looking for partners interested in transforming their cyclotrons into a 200 MeV variable energy facility for protontherapy.

References

1. Scharf WH, Chomicki OA. Medical accelerators in radiotherapy. Past, present and future. Physics Medica 1996;(In press).
2. Wilson RR. Radiological use of fast protons. Radiology 1946;47:487.
3. Stone RS. Neutron therapy and specific ionization. Am J Roentgenol 1948;59:771.
4. The statistics are published in Particles, the Journal of the Particle Therapy Co-ordination Group (PTCOG).
5. Sato H et al. EPAC94. In: Suller V, Petit-Jean-Genaz Ch (eds) Status Report on HIMAC. Singapore: World Scientific, 1996;417.
6. Castro JR. Heavy ion therapy: BEVALAC epoch. In: Amaldi U, Larsson B (eds) Hadrontherapy in Oncology. Amsterdam: Elsevier Science, 1994;208–216.
7. Coutrakon G et al. A performance study of the Loma Linda proton medical accelerator. In: Amaldi U, Larsson B (eds) Hadrontherapy in Oncology. Amsterdam: Elsevier Science, 1994;6: 282–306.
8. Pedroni E. Ref. 5, Status of proton therapy: results and future trends. In: Suller V, Petit-Jean-Genaz Ch (eds) Singapore: World Scientific 1996;:407.
9. Kraft G et al. The Darmstadt Programme HITAG: heavy ion therapy at GSI. In: Amaldi U, Larsson B (eds) Hadrontherapy in Oncology. Amsterdam: Elsevier Science, 1994;217–228.
10. Amaldi U, Silari M. The TERA project and the centre for Oncological Hadrontherapy. In: Campi D, Silari M (eds) Addendum (The whole collection is called the "Blue Book"). Frascati: INFN 1995.
11. Gademann G. Socioeconomic aspects of hadrontherapy. In: Amaldi U, Larsson B (eds) Hadrontherapy in Oncology. Amsterdam: Elsevier Science, 1994;59–66.

458

12. Jongen Y. Ref. 5, The case of ion beam applications s.a.: a technology spin-off from a University Accelerator Laboratory. In: Suller V, Petit-Jean-Genaz Ch (eds) Singapore: World Scientific, 1996;355.
13. Amaldi U, Grandolfo M, Picardi L (eds) The RITA Network and the Design of Compact Accelerators. (The so-called "Green Book"). Frascati: INFN 1996
14. Chauvel P et al. Cost comparison between protontherapy and conformal X-ray therapy. In: Amaldi U, Grandolfo M, Picardi L (eds) The RITA Network and the Design of Compact Accelerators. Frascati: INFN, 1996;433—439 (The so-called "Green Book").
15. Borgonovi E et al. Financial analysis of the activities of the Hadrontherapy Centre. In: Campi D, Silari M (eds) Addendum (The whole collection is called the "Blue Book"). Frascati: INFN 1995;535—545.
16. Pinelli et al. Development of a method to enlarge by Boron Neutron Capture process the therapeutical possibility of delivering autograft techniques to the case of diffused metastases (Taormina project), presented at the Vth International Conference on Applications of Nuclear Techniques "Neutrons in Research and Industry". Crete, Greece: 9—15 June 1996.
17. Agosteo S et al. Monte Carlo study of neutron production for BNCT. In: Amaldi U, Larsson B (eds) Hadrontherapy in Oncology. Amsterdam: Elsevier Science, 1994;525—532.
18. Weiss M et al. High-frequency proton linac. In: Amaldi U, Grandolfo M, Picardi L (eds) The RITA Network and the Design of Compact Accelerators (The so-called "Green Book"). Frascati: INFN 1996;215—256.
19. Weiss M et al. High-frequency Proton Linac. In: Amaldi U, Grandolfo M, Picardi L (eds) The RITA Network and the Design of Compact Accelerators (The so-called "Green Book"). Frascati: INFN 1996;215—256.

Neutron beam design for boron neutron capture synovectomy

E. Binello[1], R.E. Shefer[2] and J.C. Yanch[1]

[1]*Department of Nuclear Engineering and Whitaker College of Health Sciences and Technology, Massachusetts Institute of Technology; and* [2]*Newton Scientific Incorporated, Cambridge, Massachusetts, USA*

Introduction

Boron neutron capture synovectomy (BNCS) is a potential therapeutic modality for the treatment of rheumatoid arthritis [1]. There are two major differences between BNCS and boron neutron capture therapy (BNCT) which play an important role in the design of a therapeutically useful neutron beam. The first is the depth of the target tissue. The synovium lies 1.5–2.0 cm below the surface of the skin, implying that a softer beam will be required. Previous investigations have shown that neutrons in the energy range from thermal to about 1 keV maximize therapeutic ratios for BNCS [2]. Secondly, the concentrations available in the target tissue are much higher than in BNCT [2,3], implying a rapid treatment time for BNCS and low healthy tissue doses. In light of these differences, it is necessary to develop neutron beams specifically for BNCS.

BNCS can be performed using either reactor- or accelerator-based neutron sources. However, a compact accelerator-based source would be advantageous for clinical treatment. In this paper, Monte Carlo simulations were performed to examine several accelerator-based, neutron-producing reactions and their respective therapeutic parameters.

Methods

The neutron-producing reactions considered in this study are shown in Table 1. These nuclear reactions can be accessed using low-energy linear accelerators, commercial neutron generators or biomedical cyclotrons.

Simulations using MCNP [4] were performed to determine dose-depth distributions in a tissue-equivalent phantom resulting from an accelerator source of neutrons. The MCNP geometry used is shown in Fig. 1. The knee was chosen as the joint to be modeled because it is the joint on which surgical or radiation synovectomy is most commonly performed. Dimensions for the knee joint phantom were obtained from magnetic resonance images of a human arthritic knee. Ther-

Address for correspondence: Jacquelyn C. Yanch, Department of Nuclear Engineering and Whitaker College of Health Sciences and Technology, Massachusetts Institute of Technology, 45 Carleton Street, E25-330, Cambridge, MA 02139, USA.

Table 1. Light ion nuclear reactions investigated for BNCS.

Reaction	Ion energy (MeV)	Max. neutron energy (MeV)
$^7Li(p,n)^7Be$	2.50	0.8
$^9Be(p,n)^9B$	4.00	2.1
$^9Be(d,n)^{10}B$	2.60–7.00	7.0–11.0
$t(d,n)^4He$	0.25	14.0
$d(d,n)^3He$	0.25	2.5

mal neutron ($E_n < 0.36$ eV), nonthermal neutron and photon fluxes were converted to dose using fluence to kerma conversion factors [5,6]. A 1,000 ppm ^{10}B concentration was assumed in the synovium. Due to the magnitude of this concentration, the boron compound used for in vitro experiments, $K_2B_{12}H_{12}$ [2,3], was explicitly modeled in the calculations. All healthy tissues were assumed to contain 1 ppm of ^{10}B.

Based on previous findings [7], heavy water was chosen as the optimal moderator material and graphite as the optimal reflector material. The diameter of the moderator was chosen with consideration to the size of the joint, while the thickness of the reflector was fixed at 18 cm based on previous simulations which showed that the reflectivity of graphite saturates at this thickness for neutrons from Li(p,n) at 2.5 MeV proton energy [8].

The potential efficacy of the neutron-producing reactions listed in Table 1 was determined by examining two therapeutic ratios. The first was the ratio of synovium dose to skin dose. It has been empirically determined that a dose of about 10,000 cGy is required for destruction of the synovium [9]. This, combined with the fact that at 800 cGy mild skin erythema is observed [10], leads to a minimum therapeutic ratio of 12. The second was the ratio of synovium dose to bone

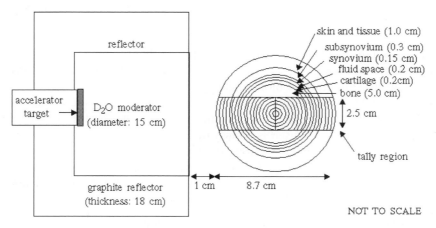

Fig. 1. Schematic of knee phantom and moderator/reflector assembly geometry used in MCNP simulations.

dose. This therapeutic ratio needs to be as large as possible due to the radiosensitivity of the bone surface [11]. For each neutron beam, therapy time was calculated using RBE values of 4.0 for the ^{10}B reaction products, 3.8 for all neutrons, and 1.0 for photons.

Results

A sample of a dose-depth profile through the tissue-equivalent phantom is shown in Fig. 2. This profile was obtained using a ^{9}Be(p,n) neutron source and a 20-cm-long D_2O moderator.

The two sharp peaks in the boron dose-depth profile of Fig. 1 represent the dose peaks due to ^{10}B in the synovium at both the front and back of the joint model (the model is cylindrical).

The therapeutic ratios and total time to deliver 10,000 RBE-cGy to the synovium for five neutron-producing reactions and varying moderator lengths are shown in Table 2.

The first three reactions listed in Table 2 produce favorable therapeutic parameters over the range of moderator lengths investigated. For the 20 cm moderator length, synovium-to-skin ratios exceed the minimum value of 12 by a factor of 2 or more and therapy times range from 8 to 15 min/mA of ion current. Proton and deuteron accelerators that operate at the required energies and currents, between 0.2–1.0 mA, have been developed and the development of multi-milliampere systems is under way [13,14].

While the ^{7}Li(p,n) reaction gives the highest therapeutic ratios, the ^{9}Be(p,n) and ^{9}Be(d,n) reactions have the advantage that beryllium has more favorable thermal, mechanical and chemical properties than lithium for use as an accelerator target. Use of the ^{9}Be(d,n) reaction has the further advantage that short therapy times can be achieved at relatively low accelerator beam energy. The d(d,n) and t(d,n) reactions do not appear to be suitable for therapy due to excessively long therapy times and poor therapeutic ratios.

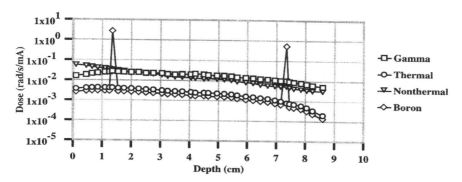

Fig. 2. Sample of individual dose-rate profile through the knee joint phantom.

Table 2. Therapy parameters.

Reaction	Ion energy (MeV)	Moderator length (cm)	Synovium/skin ratio[a]	Synovium/bone ratio[a]	Therapy time (min/mA)[b]
$^7Li(p,n)^7Be$	2.50	20	71	120	8
		35	171	213	27
		50	277	301	51
$^9Be(p,n)^9B$	4.00	20	43	73	15
		35	162	188	47
		50	236	281	69
$^9Be(d,n)^{10}B$	2.60	20	24	33	8
		30	50	57	17
		50	61	74	100
	7.00	50	32	41	7
$d(d,n)^3He$	0.23	30	13	19	2316[c]
		50	36	46	4540[c]
$t(d,n)^4He$	0.23	30	4	5	59[c]
		50	8	1	259[c]

[a]Dose ratios were calculated using physical doses; [b]therapy times were calculated using RBE doses; and [c]therapy times are for neutron fluxes obtainable from commercial generators [12]: 4×10^9 n/s for the d(d,n) and 4×10^{11} n/s for t(d,n).

Conclusions and future work

Therapeutically useful neutron beams for BNCS can be produced using an accelerator-source of neutrons via the $^7Li(p,n)$, the $^9Be(p,n)$ or the $^9Be(d,n)$ reactions. Monte Carlo simulations of a coaxial D_2O moderator and graphite reflector configurations predict high synovium-to-skin and synovium-to-bone dose ratios and acceptable therapy times for these reactions. Neutron beams based on the d(d,n) or t(d,n) reactions are not suitable for BNCS due to either very low dose rates (the d-d reaction) or to very poor therapeutic ratios (the d-t reaction). A tandem electrostatic accelerator capable of generating the proton beam currents required is operational at the Massachusetts Institute of Technology Laboratory for Accelerator Beam Applications [14]. Beam parameters will undergo final optimization once ^{10}B uptake has been confirmed in vivo. Animal experiments, using an antigen-induced arthritis rabbit model, are currently underway. Also in progress is a quantitative evaluation of the possible improvement in treatment time and therapeutic ratios with a multidirectional irradiation of the joint.

Acknowledgements

Portions of this work were supported by the INEL University Research Consortium and by the US National Institutes of Health under Grant No. R43AR43680.

References

1. Johnson LS, Yanch JC, Shortkroff S, Sledge CB. Temporal and spatial distribution of boron uptake in excised synovium. Proceedings of the Sixth International Symposium 011 Neutron Capture Therapy for Cancer, Kobe, Japan October/November 1994.
2. Binello E, Shortkroff S, Jones AG, Viveiros C, Young G, Davison A, Sledge CB, Yanch JC. In vitro analysis of ^{10}B uptake for boron neutron capture synovectomy. In: Larsson B, Crawford J, Weinreich R (eds) Advances in Neutron Capture Therapy. Volume 2, Chemistry and Biology. Amsterdam: Elsevier Science, 1997;609—613 (these proceedings).
3. Binello E, Shortkroff S, Jones AG, Viveiros C, Ly A, Sledge CB, Davison A, Shefer RE, Yanch JC. Research in boron neutron capture synovectomy. Proceedings of the 5th International Conference on Applications of Nuclear Techniques: Neutrons in Research and Industry, Crete, June 1996.
4. Breismeister JF. MCNP-A General Monte Carlo Code for Neutron and Photon Transport. LA 7396-M, Rev. 2, Los Alamos National Laboratory, 1986.
5. Caswell RS, Coyne JJ, Randolph ML. Kerma factors of elements and compounds for neutron energies below 30 MeV. Int J Appl Radiat Iso 1982:33:1227—1262.
6. Zamenhof RG, Murray BE, Brownell GL, Wellum GR, Tolpin EI. Boron neutron capture therapy for the treatment of cerebral gliomas. I. Theoretical evaluation of the efficacy of various neutron beams. Med Phys 1975;2:47—60.
7. Yanch JC, Shefer RE, Binello E. Design of low-energy neutron beams for boron neutron capture synovectomy. Proceedings of the 5th International Conference on Applications of Nuclear Techniques: Neutrons in Research and Industry, Crete, June 1996.
8. Yanch JC, Zhou X-L, Shefer RE, Klinkowstein RE. Accelerator-based epithermal neutron beam design for neutron capture therapy. Med Phys 1992;19:3:709—721.
9. Deutsch E, Brodack KR, Deutsch KR. Radiation synovectomy revisited. Eur J Nucl Med 1993; 20:1113—1127.
10. Nias AH. An Introduction to Radiobiology. New York: John Wiley & Sons, 1980.
11. ICRP-30: Reference Manual, International Commission on Radiation Protection, Elmsford, New York, 1975.
12. Fluxes are based on the Genie 46 neutron generator, SODERN, 20 avenue Descartes, 94451 Lineil-Brevannes, Cedex, France.
13. Shefer RE, Klinkowstein RE, Yanch JC. A high current electrostatic accelerator for boron neutron capture therapy. Proceedings of the 5th International Conference on Applications of Nuclear Techniques: Neutrons in Research and Industry, Crete, June, 1996.
14. Klinkowstein RE, Shefer RE, Yanch JC, Howard WH, Song H, Binello E, Blackburn BW, Daigle JL, Sears SM, Goldie CH, Ledoux RJ. Operation of a high current tandem electrostatic accelerator for boron neutron capture therapy. In: Larsson B, Crawford J, Weinreich R (eds) Advances in Neutron Capture Therapy. Volume 1, Medicine and Physics. Amsterdam: Elsevier Science, 1997;522—527 (these proceedings).

Towards hospital-based NCT

© 1997 Elsevier Science B.V. All rights reserved.
Advances in Neutron Capture Therapy.
Volume I, Medicine and Physics.
B. Larsson, J. Crawford and R. Weinreich, editors.

Moving towards hospital-based boron cancer therapy

N. James[1], S. Green[2], W. Morgan[2], A. Beddoe[2], D.A. Allen[3] and T.D. Beynon[3]

[1]CRC Institute for Cancer Studies, University of Birmingham, Birmingham; [2]Department of Medical Physics, Queen Elizabeth Hospital, Birmingham; and [3]School of Physics and Space Research, University of Birmingham, Birmingham, UK

Introduction

There are around 4,000 cases of high-grade astrocytoma per year in the UK, occurring at all ages with a peak incidence in later life, accounting for around 30% of all tumours of the central nervous system and around 1% of cancer deaths. Prognosis is poor with a median survival of 36 months in younger patients, dropping to less than 1 year for the older patients. Conventional treatment is with surgery followed by radiotherapy (RT) which has been shown, in randomised trials, to improve disease-free and overall survival [1]. There are also data suggesting increased benefit from increased dose [2]. However, few, if any patients are cured with currently available therapies. Prognostic factors include age, performance status and histological grade, and can be used to select the patients most likely to benefit from adjuvant RT, in terms of having the longest projected survival times with good neurological function. Patients die principally from uncontrolled local disease, making the glioblastoma a particularly good model for a new RT modality.

Trial design

The individual patient prognosis is affected both by the disease stage and its treatment, and this poses a problem for trial design. The traditional phase I trial [3] design is focused on patients with no viable conventional treatment options. Initial patients are treated at doses well below the predicted maximum tolerated dose (MTD). The dose is elevated after three patients have completed treatment and adequate follow-up to exclude dose-limiting toxicity. The subsequent three patients are treated at the next dose level until grade three or four toxicity is seen in two out of six patients at a dose level. This design is acceptable when there is no alternative therapy. However, RT has been shown to prolong disease-free and overall survival following surgery. Conventional RT and boron cancer therapy (BCT) cannot be given to the same patient as the dose limiting toxicities

Address for correspondence: Dr N. James, CRC Institute for Cancer Studies, University of Birmingham, Birmingham, B15 2TT, UK.

are permanent, cumulative and common to both modalities. Thus a patient has to forego conventional RT (and thus a proven, if short, improvement in survival and disease-free survival) in order to receive BCT, initially at subtherapeutic doses in any new facility such as that planned in Birmingham and as seen already underway elsewhere. It is hoped that in the Birmingham trials, the data accumulated in Brookhaven and Massachusetts General will be able to inform the starting doses chosen, enabling doses nearer to therapeutic levels to be used.

Patient selection

Most RT series show a correlation between patient parameters such as low age, good performance status, superficial site of tumour, degree of surgery (biopsy vs. debulking) and favourable outcome. Thus the factors that predict good outcome also favour participation in trials at relatively remote, research reactor establishments. Care must therefore be exercised in interpreting the results of such series. Also, recruitment to such trials must be carefully carried out as, particularly for phase I studies, results are not likely to be any better than conventional RT and may even be worse for the reasons outlined above. Patients are reluctant to take part in phase I trials, with little evidence of possible benefit, and thus treating relatively good prognosis patients in the early stages of a dose escalation poses ethical and consent problems [4].

On the other hand, a concern with any RT modality is late damage, which will take at least 6 months to appear in most cases, thus patients with a very poor prognosis are not suitable for phase I studies as many will not survive long enough to exhibit late effects.

Birmingham BCT programme

Patient selection and boron capture agent

We propose to address the patient selection dilemma outlined above by initially treating patients 55—70 years old who have a good performance status, are suitable for debulking and whose tumours show good uptake of boron, using BPA as the capture agent. This group has a median survival of around 9 months with conventional therapy, which should allow the assessment of any late effects induced.

Beam delivery in a clinical setting

The accelerator beam under construction is sited in the School of Physics of the University of Birmingham campus, adjacent to the Queen Elizabeth Hospital which houses the regional departments of Oncology and Neurosciences as well as the Cancer Research Campaign Institute for Cancer Studies. All relevant clinical facilities are thus available within easy reach of the accelerator. Figure 1

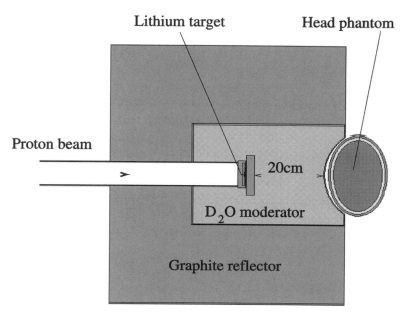

Fig. 1. Schematic diagram of the moderator assembly with a head phantom.

shows diagrammatically the structure of the target and moderator assembly. Figure 2 shows the tumour and normal tissue corrected doses achievable with the accelerator beam using a head phantom and boron loadings achievable with BPA.

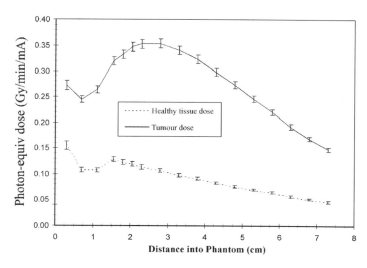

Fig. 2. Biologically adjusted in-phantom doses in tumour and normal tissue using the Birmingham BNCT beam. The doses are calculated using RBE and CBE factors derived from the Brookhaven animal modelling studies, using a boron-10 loading of 30 and 10 mg/g for tumour and normal tissue.

Dosimetry

This will follow the system used at Brookhaven. BPA uptake studies will be carried out at the time of debulking neurosurgery and used to model the boron concentrations in tumour, blood and normal brain. In addition, we are developing a holographic boron imaging system based on capture of the induced 478 kV γ from the $^{10}B(n,\alpha)^6Li$ reaction. Phantom studies with this system give good three-dimensional resolution to around ± 5 mm. As this system effectively images in real-time the physical dose distribution arising from the $^{10}B(n,\alpha)^6Li$ reaction, we believe it should give very useful information about the efficacy of BCT, in particular in relation to doses delivered at sites of subsequent relapse. Figure 3 shows an image obtained with the system, using a ^{99}Tc source to represent a tumour within a head phantom.

Radiobiology of accelerator beam

We do not propose to carry out an extensive radiobiology programme prior to clinical study inception. Our justification for this is that the beam components

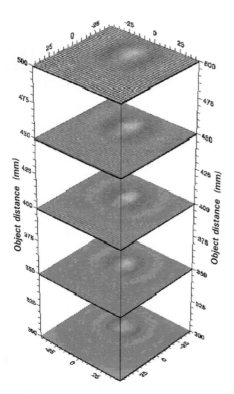

Fig. 3. 3D image of an ellisoid 'tumour' in a head phantom using the holographic imaging system.

are well characterised and the radiobiology of these components is well studied both in animals and increasingly in human patients. We believe that further studies will not greatly improve the accuracy of the estimated safe dose for starting clinical trials. Replication of the prudent phase I design used at Brookhaven should allow an adequate clinical safety margin and hasten the inception of phase II trials at doses likely to be in the therapeutic range.

Conclusions

Glioblastoma is the most studied and most suitable malignant disease for BCT trials. We propose to start clinical trials with our hospital-based accelerator system using BPA as the capture agent. A standard dose escalation phase I approach will be used, informed by the results of the ongoing BPA glioblastoma trials at Brookhaven and Massachusetts General. Patient selection criteria will be modified to focus on older patients with an intermediate prognosis rather than young patients with a relatively good prognosis, who will be included when a more optimum dose schedule has been developed for phase II studies. The γ holography system we are developing should give valuable additional information about physical dosimetry during therapy, which is not at present available with existing systems.

References

1. Walker MD et al. Evaluation of BCNU and/or radiotherapy in the treatment of anaplastic astrocytomas. J Neurosurg 1978;49:333.
2. Walker MD, Strike TA, Sheline GE. An analysis of the dose response relationship in the radiotherapy of malignant gliomas. Int J Radiat Oncol Biol Phys 1979;5:1725.
3. Winograd B. New drug development. In: Peckham M, Pinedo H, Veronesi U (eds) Oxford Textbook of Oncology. Oxford, UK: Oxford University Press, 1995; Chapter 4.5.
4. Emanuel EJ. A phase I trial on the ethics of phase I trials. J Clin Oncol 1995;13:1049–1051.

Advances in Neutron Capture Therapy.
Volume I, Medicine and Physics.
B. Larsson, J. Crawford and R. Weinreich, editors.

Developmental and preliminary neutron fluence measurements in the Birmingham BCT beam

D.A. Tattam[1], D.A. Allen[1], T.D. Beynon[1], G. Constantine[1], S. Green[2], M.C. Scott[1] and D.R. Weaver[1]

[1]*School of Physics and Space Research, University of Birmingham; and* [2]*Department of Medical Physics, Queen Elizabeth Hospital, University Hospital Birmingham, NHS Trust, Edgbaston, Birmingham, UK*

Introduction

The dynamitron accelerator at the University of Birmingham is a 3-MV machine, currently capable of producing a continuous 1 mA proton beam. A design by Allen et al. [1] details a boron cancer therapy (BCT) facility using an accelerator-based neutron source. The design uses the lithium (p,n) reaction with 2.8 MeV protons as the neutron source. At this energy the total neutron yield is 1.37×10^9 n μC^{-1} [2] with a maximum neutron energy of 1.1 MeV. The neutrons are then partially moderated by heavy water (D_2O) contained in an Al tank. The heavy water is poisoned with natural lithium nitrate; the ^6Li content absorbs thermal neutrons without emitting a γ ray. Surrounding the Al tank is a 20-cm-thick reactor-grade graphite reflector to maximise the therapeutic flux. A concave exit surface was originally chosen, as it was thought to lead to a greater flux than a flat or convex surface if the head is the tumour containing organ. Between the lithium target and the heavy water vessel is a lead γ shield which attenuates the 478 keV γ rays from the Li (p,n) reaction. A schematic of the experimental assembly is shown in Fig. 1.

The design of the assembly was performed using the general purpose Monte Carlo code MCNP [3]. An experimental program was set up in conjunction with further MCNP simulations as a method of validating the defining calculations. Codes based on Monte Carlo techniques may be used in the future for treatment planning; hence validation of this sort is vital.

The work described here includes foil activation experiments and boron trifloride (BF_3) proportional counter work performed in a water head phantom placed at the exit surface of the moderator assembly. A parallelepiped light water head phantom was chosen for consistency with other work [4]. The phantom used has perspex walls only 0.8 cm thick, and has overall dimensions of $14 \times 15 \times 18$ cm. BF_3 measurements have been made in-phantom before and after

---

Address for correspondence: David Tattam, School of Physics and Space Research, University of Birmingham, Edgbaston, Birmingham B15 2TT, UK. E-mail: d.a.tattam@bham.ac.uk

the addition of lithium nitrate to the D_2O. The gold foil activation experiments were performed in-phantom after the addition of the lithium nitrate. All work presented here has been performed on the axis defined by the proton beam.

MCNP was used to model the complete system all the way from the source to the reaction in the particular detector used. The neutron spectrum from the lithium target has been calculated using knowledge of slowing down and the neutron production cross-sections [5] for protons on lithium. The angular distribution of this source term has been verified experimentally [6] using a shadow cone technique with a DePangher long counter [7]. The source term determined in this way is then used as the initial point in the Monte Carlo simulation which employs a complete description of the geometry, including the water phantom.

Experimental method

Boron trifloride measurements

BF_3 measurements have been performed in the water head phantom. Two sets of experiments and simulations have been performed, the first before the lithium nitrate was dissolved in the heavy water and the second afterwards. A 0.5 inch BF_3 tube was used in proportional counter mode to allow discrimination against γ events, the γ's originating almost entirely from hydrogen neutron capture in the water phantom. MCNP simulates the number of $^{10}B(n,\alpha)^7Li$ reactions in the sensitive region of the BF_3 tube taking into account the gas-filling pressure and isotopic composition of the boron. The assumption is made that every event in this region is counted. The MCNP simulation is then compared directly to the experimental result without further normalisation.

Gold foil activation experiments

Thin gold foils (0.1 mm) were placed separately on axis at the depths of interest.

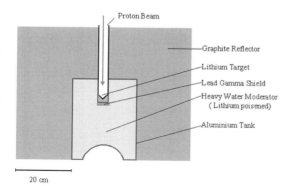

20 cm

Fig. 1. A Schematic of the experimental assembly.

A proton beam current of 30 μA was incident on the lithium target for a period of around 10 min. A hyperpure germanium detector is used to measure the 411 keV γ activity of the irradiated foils coming from the ^{197}Au(n,γ)^{198}Au reaction. Taking into account the time of irradiation, transfer time and counting time the number of ^{197}Au(n,abs)^{198}Au reactions per unit beam charge per unit foil volume (ξ) can be calculated, as shown by Eqn. 1.

The MCNP simulation uses full ENDFB/V [8] cross-section files and hence allows for any flux depression in the foil. MCNP then tallies the number of ^{197}Au(n,abs)^{198}Au reactions per micro Coulomb per unit volume of the foil, which is then compared to the value measured experimentally.

$$\xi = \frac{Ct_1\lambda}{\varepsilon IVQ(1 - e^{-\lambda t_1})e^{-\lambda t_2}(1 - e^{-\lambda t_3})} \tag{1}$$

ξ = Activations per micro Coulomb per unit volume of foil
C = Counts in photopeak measured in time t_3
λ = Decay constant of ^{198}Au
ε = Photoefficiency of detector at photopeak for geometry used
I = Intensity of decay mode leading to photopeak (0.995)
V = Volume of foil
Q = Total charge landed on target during irradiation
t_1 = Irradiation time
t_2 = Time between end of irradiation and start of counting
t_3 = Time of counting

Results

BF_3 measurements in water phantom — before addition of lithium nitrate to D_2O

A comparison of the MCNP results with the experimental results is shown in Fig. 2. It is important to note that these comparisons are absolute; there is no scaling

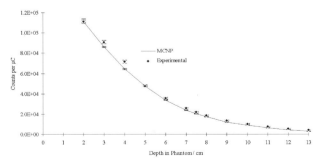

Fig. 2. BF$_3$ counts per μC in a water phantom; experimental and MCNP results, before addition of lithium to moderator.

on either the measurement or the calculation. The agreement is generally good at all depths although experimentally there are more thermal neutrons towards the rear of the phantom than are predicted. This is probably due to room return neutrons not being taken into account in the MCNP model.

BF₃ measurements in phantom — after addition of lithium nitrate to D₂O

The BF_3 measurements in phantom were repeated after the addition of the lithium nitrate to the heavy water (1 kg lithium nitrate into 17.5 l of heavy water). The comparison of the experimental work to the calculation is shown in Fig. 3. The agreement is again good at all depths except towards the rear giving confidence in the experimental work and the calculation. The room return component can again be seen at the rear of the phantom.

Gold foil in water phantom — after addition of lithium nitrate to D₂O

As stated earlier gold foils were placed individually in the water phantom along the central axis. The results and the comparison with the calculation are shown in Fig. 4.

Once again the comparison is with absolute values and the agreement between measurement and calculation give further confidence that the computational model is correctly simulating the experiment.

Conclusions and Discussion

The results presented here give confidence in the MCNP model used for the prototype assembly, from the definition of the source right through to the simulation of the experiment and make it clear that it may be used with confidence for further optimisation studies. Equally importantly, this initial work gives confidence in using Monte Carlo techniques as a basis for a treatment planning code. This work is concerned with verification of the thermal neutron component in

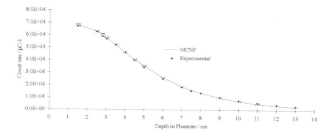

Fig. 3. BF_3 counts per μC in a water phantom; experimental and MCNP results, after addition of lithium to moderator.

476

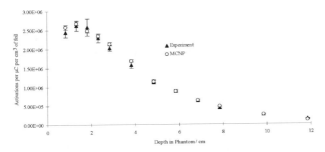

Fig. 4. Gold foil activations per μC/cm^3 of foil in a water phantom; experimental and MCNP results.

the head phantom. Work also presented at this symposium [9] further validates the code for faster neutrons and photon transport.

Acknowledgements

I would like to thank other members of the Birmingham BCT group not listed and the Engineering and Physical Sciences Research Council for my funding during my study.

References

1. Allen DA, Beynon TD. A design study for an accelerator-based epithermal neutron beam for BNCT. Phys Med Biol 1995;40:807–821.
2. Campbell J, Scott MC. Scientific and industrial applications of small accelerators, 4th Conf. (Denton, TX, 1976) New York: IEEE, 1976.
3. Briesmeister JF (ed) MCNP, A General Monte Carlo Code for Neutron and Photon Transport. Los Alamos, NM: Los Alamos Laboratory, 1986;Report LA-7396-M revision 2.
4. Gupta N et al. Effect of head phantom size on ^{10}B and ^{1}H(n,γ)^{2}H dose distributions. Med Phys 1993;20(2):1.
5. Liskien H, Paulsen A. Neutron production cross sections and energies for the reactions ^{7}Li(p,n)^{7}Be and ^{7}Li(p,n)^{7*}Be. Atomic Data Nucl Tables 1975;15:No. 1.
6. Tattam DA. BNCT Neutron Yields From Lithium Oxide and Lithium Metal. MSc. Thesis, School of Physics and Space Research, University of Birmingham, 1994.
7. Hunt JB. Calibration of the Birmingham De Pangher Long Counter for (a) SbBe (γ,n) Photo neutrons and (b) AmBe (α,n) Neutrons. National Physical Laboratory Report.
8. Garber D (ed) ENDF/B-V. National Nuclear Data Center, Brookhaven National Laboratory, Upton, NY: Oct 1975;Report BNL − 17541 (ENDF − 201).
9. Green S et al. Dosimetric Characteristics of an Accelerator Based Beam for Boron Cancer Therapy (BCT). Conference proceedings, Seventh International Symposium on Neutron Capture Therapy for Cancer, Zurich, Sept 1996.

1997 Elsevier Science B.V.
Advances in Neutron Capture Therapy.
Volume I, Medicine and Physics.
B. Larsson, J. Crawford and R. Weinreich, editors.

Experimental investigation of filtered epithermal photoneutron beams for BNCT

David W. Nigg[1], Hannah E. Mitchell[1], Yale D. Harker[1] and J. Frank Harmon[2]

[1]*Idaho National Engineering Laboratory, Idaho Falls; and* [2]*Idaho State University, Pocatello, Idaho, USA*

The Idaho National Engineering Laboratory (INEL) has been investigating the feasibility of a concept for an accelerator-based source of epithermal neutrons for boron neutron capture therapy (BNCT) that is based on the use of a two-stage photoneutron production process driven by an electron accelerator. In this concept [1,2], relativistic electron beams impinge upon heavily shielded tungsten targets located at the outer radius of a small cylindrical tank of circulating heavy water (D_2O). A fraction of the energy of the electrons is converted in the tungsten targets into radially inward-directed bremsstrahlung radiation. Neutrons subsequently generated by photodisintegration of deuterons in the D_2O within the tank are directed to the patient through a suitable beam tailoring system. Initial proof-of-principal tests using a low-current benchtop prototype of this concept have been conducted. Testing has included extensive measurements of the unfiltered photoneutron source [2] as well as initial measurements of unfiltered epithermal-neutron spectra produced using two different advanced neutron filtering assemblies, as described here.

A tunable electron linear accelerator manufactured by the Varian Corporation was used to drive the experimental apparatus shown in Fig. 1. The electron beam energy was established at a nominal average value of 6 MeV with an approximately Gaussian distribution in energy with an estimated spread of ± 2 MeV (2 σ). The forward-peaked bremsstrahlung radiation from the tungsten accelerator target was collimated by a cylindrical tungsten shield and was subsequently directed into a sealed cylindrical lucite container of D_2O where a well characterized source of photoneutrons [2] is produced. Neutron filtering and moderating structures were placed downstream of the heavy water photoneutron source region. This arrangement would not be typical of an actual clinical device, where the axis of the neutron beam would be at right angles to that of the electron beam to reduce photon contamination at the patient irradiation point. For these experiments, however, it was desired to have a simple geometry that could be easily modeled in theoretical calculations.

The first neutron filtering and moderating assembly of interest was constructed

Address for correspondence: David W. Nigg, Idaho National Engineering Laboratory, P.O. Box 1625, Idaho Falls, ID 83415, USA.

478

Fig. 1. Experimental apparatus for the filtered epithermal photoneutron experiments, showing the $AlF_3/AL/LiF$ filter.

of a composite material (69% Al_3F, 30% Al, and 1% natural LiF), developed [3] by the Technical Research Center of Finland (VTT — Finland) and provided (for this work) to the INEL by VTT under a research agreement. The dimensions of the filter region were $30 \times 30 \times 40$ cm. The filter thickness along the beam axis was 30 cm. The measured density of the VTT filtering material was 3.01 g/ cm^3. The entire filter was surrounded by 2.54 cm of borated polyethylene to provide a degree of isolation from room return of neutrons.

The second filtering and moderating assembly was composed of laminated 0.635 cm Teflon^{TM} (CF_2) and Al sheets. Teflon^{TM} is an inexpensive, readily available, chemically stable material with good radiation resistance which, in combination with Al, was postulated to be an effective neutron filtering material, provided that there is not an unacceptable level of spectral degradation by elastic scattering from carbon. The Teflon^{TM}/Al filtering region had a cubic configuration, 30.5 cm on a side and the entire filter region was again surrounded by borated polyethylene.

Neutron intensity and spectral measurements using standard resonance and threshold activation foil techniques, were made at two locations in the experimental apparatus:

1) on the electron beam axis, between the D_2O photoneutron source region and the filter region (the "upstream" side of the filter); and

2) on the opposite, "downstream", side of the filter, again on the beam axis.

In the experiments involving the VTT filtering material, indium, gold and copper foils were placed at azimuthally symmetric locations about the beam axis on the downstream side of the filter. Only indium foils were used on the upstream side of the filter. This provided three linearly independent foil response functions on the upstream side of the filter; neutron capture in indium with and without cadmium, and inelastic scatter in indium, which was experimentally corrected for photon activation by the 336 keV γ-line of ^{115m}In by repeating all measurements using light water rather than heavy water in the photoneutron production region. Five response functions were available on the downstream side (the same three indium response functions along with neutron capture in the gold and copper foils).

Effective coarse-group-average response functions for each foil, required for the direct spectral unfolding process that was employed, were computed using a 27-group DORT [4] model of the entire apparatus, with input cross-section data generated by the COMBINE [5] code. The coarse-group data (one coarse group per foil response function) were prepared by averaging the 27-group detailed foil cross sections over the calculated a priori 27-group neutron fluxes within each coarse group at each foil location.

In the Teflon^{TM}/Al filter experiments, a single cadmium-covered indium foil was placed on the upstream side of the filter for normalization and five indium foils, followed by one copper foil, were stacked in a single cadmium-covered package that was placed on the beam axis on the downstream side of the filter. The center indium foil in the downstream package was thus shielded from resonance neutrons, forcing it to have a linearly independent spectral response, relative to that of the first indium foil in the stack. Also, the copper foil was heavily shielded from neutrons below about 100 eV by the intervening indium foils, forcing its spectral response toward the energy range of the primary resonance for this particular foil material. Four spectral response functions having a useful degree of linear independence were thus available from the downstream foil package. Effective coarse-group-average response functions used in the spectral unfolding process were computed in this case using an MCNP [6] model of the filter and foil package, since the COMBINE resonance model is not appropriate for stacked foils.

The results of the on-axis filtered photoneutron experiments are shown in Figs. 2 and 3. A priori calculated neutron spectra, for the upstream and downstream measurement locations, are shown along with the measured neutron flux data unfolded from the foil activation rates using a direct inversion of the matrix equation, describing the relationship between the foil activation rates and the corresponding neutron fluxes in each coarse energy group, over the range of interest. In these figures, the spectral data are plotted at the lethargy (logarithmic) mid-

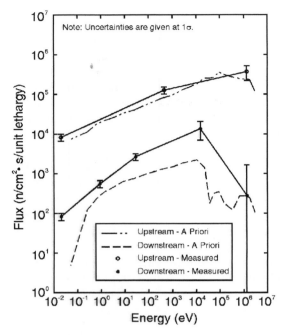

Fig. 2. A priori and measured photoneutron spectra for the 30 cm aluminum-aluminum fluoride-lithium fluoride filtering assembly (electron current = 3.7 μA).

point of each coarse energy group defined in the direct unfolding process. The calculated spectra are normalized to the actual measured electron beam current in each case using the measured activation rates of the upstream indium foils which, as demonstrated by the unfiltered neutron source experiments [2], have a well-characterized relationship to the electron beam current and the photoneutron production rate.

Both the VTT filtering material and the Teflon^{TM}/Al filter, produced neutron spectra that, within the unavoidably large experimental uncertainty characteristic of the apparatus used, were generally as expected, with the VTT material being somewhat more effective in reducing the fast neutron component of the spectrum for a given filter thickness. It thus appears that on the basis of neutronic performance, the proposed photoneutron device could offer a promising alternate approach to the production of epithermal neutrons for BNCT. Future work on this concept will be focused on construction of a new experimental prototype using a much higher power L-band electron accelerator, with a system geometry having the irradiation point on an axis at right angles to the electron beam axis. This will reduce the uncertainties and will permit a more realistic measurement of the photon content of the neutron source at the irradiation point. Control of photon contamination to acceptable levels at the irradiation point is crucial to the success of the overall concept. In addition, experimental optimization studies

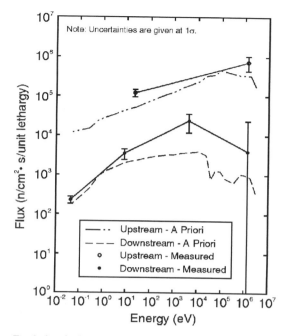

Fig. 3. A priori and measured photoneutron spectra for the 30 cm aluminum-Teflon filtering assembly (electron current = 6.2 µA).

leading to the design of a full-scale device will also be greatly facilitated by the next prototype.

Acknowledgements

This study was performed under the auspices of the US Department of Energy, Office of Energy Research, DOE Idaho Operations Office, Under Contract Number DE-AC07-94ID13223.

References

1. Nigg DW, Yoon WY, Jones JL, Harker YD. A compact accelerator-based photoneutron source for BNCT. Trans Am Nucl Soc 1994;70:7–8.
2. Nigg DW, Mitchell HE, Yoon WY, Harker YD, Jones JL. An accelerator-based epithermal photoneutron source for BNCT. In: Mishima Y (ed) Proc 6th Int Symp on NCT, Kobe, Japan. New York: Plenum Press, 1994.
3. Auterinen I, Hiismaki P. Epithermal BNCT neutron beam design for a TRIGA II reactor. In: Barth R, Soloway A (eds) Advances in Neutron Capture Therapy. Columbus, OH: Plenum Press, NY, 1993;81–84.
4. Rhoades WA, Childs RL. An updated version of the DOT-4 one- and two-dimensional neutron/photon transport code. 1982;ORNL-5851.

5. Grimesey RA, Nigg DW, Curtis RL. COMBINE/PC - A portable ENDF/B version 5 neutron spectrum and cross-section generation program. 1991;EGG-2589.
6. Briesmeister JF. MCNP - A general Monte Carlo Code for neutron and photon transport. Los Alamos, NM: Los Alamos National Laboratory, 1986;LA-7396 (Rev 2).

Advances in Neutron Capture Therapy.
Volume I, Medicine and Physics.
B. Larsson, J. Crawford and R. Weinreich, editors.

An accelerator-based thermal neutron source for BNCT

S. Agosteo[1,2], G. Bodei[1], P. Colautti[5], M.G. Corrado[3], F. d'Errico[6], S. Monti[7], M. Silari[4]* and R. Tinti[7]

[1]*Dipartimento di Ingegneria Nucleare, Politecnico di Milano, Milano; [2]Istituto Nazionale di Fisica Nucleare (INFN), Sezione di Milano, Milano; [3]Università degli Studi di Milano, Dipartimento di Fisica, Milano; [4]Consiglio Nazionale delle Ricerche, Istituto Tecnologie Biomediche Avanzate, Milano; [5]INFN, Laboratori Nazionali di Legnaro, Padova; [6]Dipartimento di Costruzioni Meccaniche e Nucleari, Università degli Studi di Pisa, Pisa; and [7]ENEA-ERG-FISS-FIRE, Bologna, Italy*

Introduction

This work is in the framework of the Hadrontherapy project [1−3], which proposes a hospital-based facility for proton and light-ion therapy in Italy. In this context, the beam current delivered by the 11 MeV proton linac and by the 3 MeV u^{-1} ion linac (the two injectors of the main accelerator, with maximum average current 150 μA) can be exploited to produce neutrons via (p, n) and (d, n) reactions for boron neutron capture therapy (BNCT) of the explanted liver. The surgical technique, consisting of liver explantation, tumour removal and reimplantation of the organ, was developed at the Policlinico S. Matteo in Pavia (Italy) [4] and has been performed on a few patients. BNCT of explanted livers is intended to be performed only in the case of multiple tumours, when surgery is impossible. Some irradiations on animal livers have been performed at a research reactor in Pavia [5]. The neutron source should guarantee a thermal neutron fluence of $5 \cdot 10^{12}$ cm^{-2} in 3 h at maximum, thus requiring a minimum thermal neutron fluence rate of $5 \cdot 10^{8}$ cm^{-2}.s^{-1}. The spatial distribution of the neutron fluence at the irradiated organ should be uniform to minimise its attenuation with depth. In the source design, the cumulative absorbed dose due to fast neutrons and prompt γ rays was limited to 1 Gy for a treatment dose of 20 Gy (from the ^{10}B (n,α) ^{7}Li reaction). However, this limit can be slightly increased, keeping in mind that the normal liver tolerance for a single fraction treatment is 10 Gy. The accelerator-based source was designed with Monte Carlo simulations [6,7], using the MCNP-4.2 [8] code. A beryllium target bombarded either by 11 MeV protons or 7 MeV deuterons was considered for neutron production.

In addition to liver treatment, the possibility of using the same accelerator-

---

Address for correspondence: Stefano Agosteo, Dipartimento di Ingegneria Nucleare, Politecnico di Milano, via Ponzio 34/3, I-20133 Milano, Italy. E-mail: agosteo@ipmce7.cesnef.polimi.it
*Present address: CERN, CH-1211 Geneve 23, Switzerland.

based source for BNCT of malignant melanoma is under study [9]. The thermal neutron fluence required is 10^{13} cm^{-2} in 3 h. The cumulative fast neutron and prompt γ-ray dose was limited to 2 Gy, considering that the irradiation can be fractionated. A prototype of the accelerator-based source is being tested at the CN Van De Graaff accelerator of the Laboratori Nazionali di Legnaro (Italy), using 7 MeV deuterons impinging on a beryllium target. In the following, the experimental data and the calculation results will be discussed, referring separately to liver and skin irradiations.

Liver treatment

Figure 1 shows a sectional view of the irradiator prototype, designed with MCNP. A nuclear graphite (density 1.7 g/cm^{-3}) reflector contains a heavy water moderator, in turn enclosing the beryllium target. An irradiation cavity is placed inside the graphite reflector above the heavy water tank, backward with respect to the deuteron beam direction, in order to minimise the fast neutron fluence. The heavy water tank was made of stainless steel, later substituted by Al 1050, to reduce the thermal neutron absorption and prompt γ rays. The results of neutron fluence rate (thermal, epithermal and fast) and prompt γ-ray measurements inside the irradiation cavity with the stainless steel tank configuration are discussed in [10]. The agreement with Monte Carlo calculations was satisfactory, but the prompt γ-ray dose inside the irradiation cavity was unacceptably high (see Table 1).

The thermal and epithermal (0.4 eV $-$ 10 keV) neutron fluence rates were measured with bare and cadmium-covered indium foils and the prompt γ dose was estimated with ^{7}Li TLDs, whose response was assessed up to 7 MeV photons. The γ activity of the irradiated In foils was measured with a 2×2 inch NaI scin-

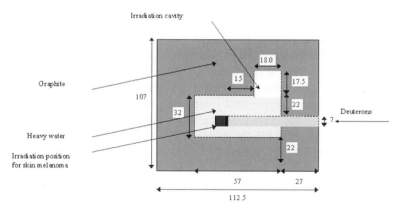

Fig. 1. A sectional view of the prototype of the accelerator-based neutron source (not to scale) with the irradiation cavity to house the liver. The position for irradiation of skin melanoma (lying on the lateral surface) is also indicated. Dimensions are in cm.

Table 1. Calculated (MCNP) and measured (^{7}Li TLDs) prompt γ-ray doses at the irradiation positions, referred to a whole treatment (dose to the tumour 20 Gy).

	Calculated dose (Gy)	Measured dose (Gy)
Liver irradiation cavity		
Stainless steel tank	13.28 ± 0.06	21.84 ± 0.21
Aluminium tank	3.00 ± 0.02	4.79 ± 0.02
Skin melanoma irradiation position		
Aluminium tank	17.19 ± 0.95	18.26 ± 0.20

tillator. BF$_3$ proportional counters were also employed to measure thermal neutrons for comparison. The nominal deuteron current impinging on the beryllium target was 100 nA while irradiating In foils. A lower nominal current (1 nA) was employed with BF$_3$ detectors to eliminate pile-up effects. The deuteron current was measured with a Faraday cup and electron suppressor, connected to a charge integrator. A BF$_3$ proportional counter was placed at a fixed position during the whole set of measurements in order to check the charge integrator stability. The results of a single measurement were discarded when the ratio of the neutron fluence detected by the BF$_3$ counter at the fixed position to the measured current was not consistent with those of the whole set of measurements. The following sources of normalisation uncertainties were taken into account for the In activation technique: NaI scintillator peak efficiency, thermal and epithermal flux depression factors, average current striking the beryllium target, foil weight, epithermal effective cross-section, and cadmium correction factor. The probability distribution and the average value of the normalisation uncertainties were assessed with the Monte Carlo method, by considering a uniform probability distribution for each source of bias. The same method was applied to the measurements with BF$_3$ counters, considering the following sources of bias, detector sensitivity, counting time, average deuteron current and detector positioning. A more detailed description of the measurements and of the uncertainty analysis can be found in [10].

The thermal and epithermal fluences were calculated at several positions in the irradiation cavity with MCNP4A [11]. The thermal and epithermal fluence rates per unit deuteron current calculated and measured (In foils) at 45 different positions inside the irradiation cavity with the Al tank configuration are shown in Fig. 2. A systematic discrepancy between the calculated and measured data can be observed. The calculated thermal neutron fluence rate is 50% higher than the measured one, whereas for the epithermal fluence rates and the MCNP results are only 25% higher. A similar effect was observed in the BF$_3$ counters. These discrepancies were initially attributed to the contamination of the heavy water, mainly because the moderator was also substituted when the Al tank configuration was set up; the effect was investigated with MCNP simulations. Figure 3 shows the average thermal and epithermal fluence rate per unit deuteron current in the irradiation cavity vs. light water contamination in the heavy water. The

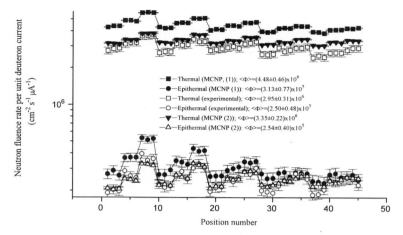

Fig. 2. Calculated and measured neutron fluence rates per unit deuteron current at 45 positions inside the liver irradiation cavity. **1:** calculation with 100% D_2O and full tank (level 32 cm). **2:** calculation with 12.75% light water content and D_2O level 27.5 cm. The fluence rates ‹φ› averaged over all positions are indicated.

prompt γ-ray dose was also calculated in a spherical phantom with the same weight and composition as the liver [12] vs. light water content, resulting in an increase of a factor 2 with a 30% light water content, a factor 3 with a 50%, up to a factor 8.5 with pure light water. The fluence rate decrease was fitted with an exponential function;

$$\phi = C exp(-x/t)$$

where φ is the fluence rate per unit deuteron current, x is the light water content

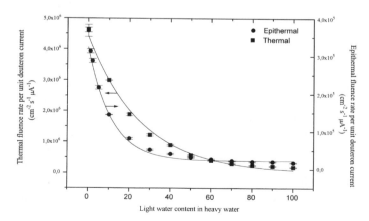

Fig. 3. Thermal and epithermal fluence rates per unit deuteron current vs. light water content. The exponential fit (see text) is indicated with solid curves.

in heavy water (weight percent), C is a constant and t is the light water weight percentage giving a fluence rate decrease of a factor $1/e$. A steeper decrease can be observed in the epithermal fluence rate (t = 11.2 ± 0.2 and 25.7 ± 0.2 for the epithermal and thermal components, respectively), contradicting the behaviour shown in Fig. 2. Therefore, the effect of a noncomplete filling of the tank was investigated by considering different levels of pure heavy water in a set of simulations. The results showed a linear epithermal fluence rate increase and a quasi-constant behaviour of the thermal component in the irradiation cavity by decreasing the heavy water level. Finally, the two effects were combined, considering the light water content (12.75%) responsible for the thermal fluence rate decrease and the level (-4.5 cm) causing an epithermal fluence increase contrasting the steeper decrease mentioned above. The results of the simulation of the combined effects are shown in Fig. 2 (see open and solid triangles), pointing out a better consistency with the experimental data. A set of simulations considering impurities in the nuclear graphite moderator and in other structural materials was performed, but the combined effect mentioned above seems to explain the observed discrepancy completely. The hydrogen content of the employed heavy water is currently under experimental verification. The heavy water content in the stainless steel tank configuration was ($98.4 \pm 0.8\%$) by volume.

Repeated measurements were performed to assess the uncertainty of the prompt γ-ray dose in the irradiation cavity and the results (measured and calculated) are listed in Table 1. The higher values of the measured data are attributed to the fluorescence X-rays produced by deuterons striking the collimators in the Faraday cup, not considered in the simulations. A lead shield covering the Faraday cup will be added in the future. The average thermal neutron fluence rates per unit deuteron current in the irradiation cavity are $(1.71 \pm 0.15) \times 10^6$ cm^{-2}.s^{-1} μA^{-1} (measured) and $(4.48 \pm 0.46) \times 10^6$ cm^{-2}.s^{-1} μA^{-1} (calculated with pure heavy water) for the configurations with stainless steel and Al tank, respectively. Consequently the deuteron current required for 3 h treatment are 271 μA (stainless steel tank) and 103 μA (Al tank), the latter being within the maximum value (150 μA) that will be delivered by the ion injector foreseen for the Hadrontherapy project.

Skin melanoma treatment

The irradiation field necessary for the treatment of skin melanoma was optimised [9] with Monte Carlo simulations using the MCNP-4A code. The chosen irradiation position is on a lateral surface of the assembly and is shown in Fig. 1. The thermal and epithermal fluences were measured with In foils and BF$_3$ counters at nine different positions inside the 10 cm^2 irradiation field, showing a satisfactory uniformity. A discrepancy with the calculated data similar to that described in the previous section was observed and removed in the same way. The prompt γ-ray dose rate was calculated and measured with ^{7}Li TLDs (see Table 1). The average thermal fluence rate per unit deuteron current in the irradiation field with pure heavy water is $(6.00 \pm 0.19) \times 10^5$ cm^{-2}.s^{-1} μA^{-1}. It is a 3-h treatment and would therefore require 1.5 mA more than can be delivered by the ion injector foreseen for the Hadrontherapy project. A high-current accelerator designed for this purpose is needed.

Discussion and Conclusions

Simulations with phantoms placed at the irradiation positions described in the previous sections and referring to the Al tank configuration were performed to draw some clinical remarks. In particular, a wedge phantom with the composition, average dimensions and weight [12] of an adult liver was placed inside the irradiation cavity. Two spherical regions (diameter 1 cm) were considered to simulate tumours at the centre and in proximity of the surface of the phantom. The boron content was 10 μg/g^{-1} and 50 μg/g^{-1} in the normal liver and in the tumours, respectively. The physical doses referred to a whole treatment are listed in Table 2. It should be noted that the ^{10}B (n,α) ^{7}Li dose is higher in the central tumour region because of the thermalisation of the epithermal component. Moreover, the prompt γ-ray dose accounts for photons produced both in the liver phantom and in the moderating structure, while the measurements refer only to those produced in the structural materials.

Thus the dose to normal liver exceeds the tolerance value of 10 Gy, mainly because of prompt γ rays, almost half of which are produced in the structural materials (see Table 1) and can be attenuated with filters. A higher value of prompt γ-ray dose resulted for a whole skin melanoma treatment, mainly because a more intense deuteron current is required in this case. A cubic soft tissue phantom (side 10 cm) was placed in contact with the melanoma irradiation position. A superficial region 3-mm-thick was considered according to the average depth of skin melanomas. The fast (> 10 keV) neutron and prompt γ-ray doses at the phantom surface for a whole treatment were 17.6 ± 3.0 Gy and 17.2 ± 0.1 Gy, respectively, while in the whole phantom they were 6.4 ± 1.2 Gy and 8.5 ± 1.5 Gy.

In conclusion, the accelerator-based thermal neutron source described in the present work requires a photon filter near the irradiation cavity before it can be

Table 2. Neutron and prompt γ-ray doses (Gy) to a deep and a superficial tumour and to normal tissue in a liver phantom inside the irradiation cavity (see text).

	Deep tumour	Superficial tumour	Normal liver
^{10}B content (μg/g^{-1})	50	50	10
^{10}B (n,α) ^{7}Li	19.10 ± 0.80	14.58 ± 0.76	4.98 ± 0.01
^{14}N (n,p) ^{14}C	0.61 ± 0.02	0.47 ± 0.02	0.79 ± 0.01
Fast neutrons	1.06 ± 0.19	0.85 ± 0.20	0.98 ± 0.01
Prompt γ rays	7.86 ± 0.55	4.59 ± 0.44	6.84 ± 0.03
Total	28.63 ± 0.99	20.49 ± 0.90	13.59 ± 0.03

used for liver treatment. Future studies on skin melanoma irradiation will concentrate on the design of photon filters, together with the use of lithium targets and proton beams.

References

1. Amaldi U, Rossi S. The TERA facility: status and prospects. In: Larsson B, Crawford J, Weinreich R (eds) Advances in Neutron Capture Therapy, Volume 1, Medicine and Physics. Amsterdam: Elsevier Science, 1997;#—# (this volume).
2. Amaldi U, Silari M (eds) The TERA Project and the Centre for Oncological Hadrontherapy. Frascati: INFN Publisher, 1994.
3. Campi D, Silari M (eds) The National Centre for Oncological Hadrontherapy — Updates and Revisions. Frascati: INFN Publisher, 1995.
4. Vischi S, Spada M, Alessiani M, Fossati GS, Maestri M, Guagliano A, Dionigi P, Zonta A. Proceedings XXI Congresso Società Italiana di Chirurgia d'Urgenza, Pisa, Italy, October 1992 (in Italian).
5. Pinelli T, Altieri S, Fossati F, Zonta A, Prati U, Roveda L, Nano R. Development of a method to enlarge by BNCT process the therapeutical possibilities of the liver autograft technique to the case of diffused metastases. In: Vourvopoulos F (ed) Proceedings of the Fifth International Conference on Applications of Nuclear Techniques, Neutrons in Research and Industry. Crete, Greece: June 1996;(In press).
6. Agosteo S, Bodei G, Leone R, Silari M. Monte Carlo study of a thermal neutron source generated by 11 MeV protons and 7 MeV deuterons. In: Nigg DW (Chair) Proceedings of the First International Workshop on Accelerator-Based Sources for BNCT, Jackson, Wyoming, September 1994. Jackson, Wyoming: Idaho National Engineering Laboratory CONF-940976, 1994;255—268.
7. Agosteo S, Bodei G, Leone R, Silari M. Monte Carlo study of neutron production for BNCT. In: Amaldi U, Larsson B (eds) Hadrontherapy in Oncology, Excerpta Medica, International Congress Series 1077. Amsterdam: Elsevier Science BV, 1994;525—532.
8. Briesmeister JF, Hendricks J. MCNP4 Newsletter, X-6: JFB—91—177, Los Alamos National Laboratory, Los Alamos, New Mexico, April 1991.
9. Agosteo S, Colautti P, Corrado MG, d'Errico F, Monti S, Silari M, Tinti R, Tornielli G. Feasibility study for BNCT of skin melanoma with an accelerator-based neutron source. In: Proceedings of the Fifth International Conference on Applications of Nuclear Techniques, Neutrons in Research and Industry. Crete, Greece: June 1996;(In press).
10. Agosteo S, Colautti P, Corrado MG, d'Errico F, Matzke M, Monti S, Silari M, Tinti R. Characterisation of an accelerator-based neutron source for BNCT of explanted livers. Radiat Protect Dosimet 1996;(In press).
11. Briesmeister JF (ed) MCNP — A general Monte Carlo N-Particle Transport Code — Version 4A. Los Alamos, New Mexico: Los Alamos National Laboratory LA-12625-M, 1993.
12. Smyder WS (Chair) International Commission on Radiological Protection, Report of the Task Group on Reference Man. ICRP report no 23. Oxford, UK: Pergamon Press, 1975.

© 1997 Elsevier Science B.V. All rights reserved.
Advances in Neutron Capture Therapy.
Volume I, Medicine and Physics.
B. Larsson, J. Crawford and R. Weinreich, editors.

Feasibility of boron neutron capture enhancement of fast neutron therapy utilizing a superconducting cyclotron

Richard L. Maughan, Chandrasekhar Kota and Jeffrey D. Forman

Gershenson Radiation Oncology Center, Barbara Ann Karmanos Cancer Institute, Harper Hospital and Wayne State University, Detroit, Michigan, USA

Introduction

The enhancement of fast neutron therapy by using the boron neutron capture reaction was first proposed by Waterman et al. [1] in 1978. The fast neutron therapy facility at Harper Hospital uses a state-of-the-art compact superconducting cyclotron to accelerate deuterons to an energy of 48.5 MeV [2,3]. The deuteron beam is incident on an internal beryllium target. Irregularly shaped beams are produced using a unique multirod collimator [4]. The cyclotron is mounted on a gantry and can be rotated through a full 360° about the patient treatment couch.

Measurements have been made in the d(48.5) + Be fast neutron beam at Harper Hospital using a paired Rossi-counter microdosimetry technique which allows the neutron, γ ray and ^{10}B dose (for 50 ppm of ^{10}B in tissue) to be determined. The ^{10}B dose enhancements measured in a water phantom at 10 cm depth for a 10 × 10 cm field are approximately 2% [5], insufficient to be clinically significant. However, it may be possible to modify the fast neutron beam, using suitable filtering and moderating materials, thus increasing the thermal and epithermal components of the beam to such an extent that clinically useful ^{10}B enhancement can be achieved. In an accompanying paper [6] the effect of filtering the d(48.5) + Be fast neutron beam with various materials (Fe, Al, Pb and W) in order to increase the relative thermal neutron component has been investigated. In this work the degree of enhancement that must be achieved for the treatment of glioblastoma multiforme with boron neutron capture enhanced fast neutron therapy (BNCEFNT) is discussed, together with the possibility of modifying the Harper Hospital fast neutron beam to permit such treatments.

Clinical application

The treatment of glioblastoma multiforme with boron neutron capture therapy (BNCT) is currently under clinical investigation in phase I/II clinical trials, uti-

---

Address for correspondence: Richard L. Maughan, Gershenson Radiation Oncology Center, Harper Hospital, 3990 John R, Detroit, MI 48201, USA.

lizing reactor produced epithermal neutron beams at Brookhaven National Laboratory (BNL) [7] and Massachusetts Institute of Technology (MIT) in the USA. In the late 1970's a fast neutron clinical trial for the treatment of gliomas was undertaken by the Radiation Therapy Oncology Group (RTOG) which coordinates National Cancer Institute (NCI) sponsored clinical trials in the USA. In this phase III trial patients who had undergone surgical resection of their tumors were treated with a mixed beam regimen of 50 Gy photons delivered to the whole brain, followed by a 15-Gy equivalent neutron boost to the tumor bed. Alternatively, patients received 50 Gy of photons to the whole brain followed by a 15-Gy photon boost [8]. Although the survival of patients in the two groups was not statistically different some interesting observations were made in autopsied patients. In the neutron treatment group a majority of autopsied patients (nine of 12) showed no histological evidence of persistent disease although normal brain damage was unacceptably high and death was ascribed to this cause. In the photon treated patients there was evidence of persistent disease in all autopsied cases (12 of 12) but normal brain damage was acceptable and death was ascribed to persistent progressive disease.

Stelzer et al. [9] have reviewed these data together with data from the University of Washington in Seattle and the Medical Research Council (MRC) in Britain, and have constructed a dose response curve for local control. The MRC data suggest that a total fast neutron dose of 12 Gy may be tolerable for normal brain irradiation [10], while Stelzer's dose response curve requires an effective high LET tumor dose of 15.8 Gy to give a tumor local control rate of 77%.

The modified fast neutron beam

Figure 1 shows the details of the cyclotron treatment "head". Beam currents of up

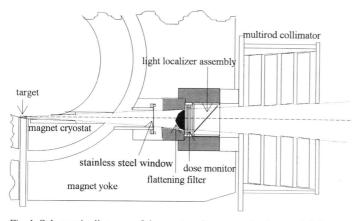

Fig. 1. Schematic diagram of the neutron beam production and delivery system at the Harper Hospital neutron therapy facility. For the measurements presented here the light localizer system was removed and the filter materials (Al, Fe and Pb) were inserted in its place.

to 15 μA are accelerated, although this beam current limit is set by the power dissipation in the beryllium target (750 W). The beam strikes the target at a glancing angle giving a power density of approximately 750 W·cm^{-2}. The neutron beam passes through an aperture in the median plane of the cryostat containing the magnet coil and exits the acceleration vacuum chamber through a stainless steel window before passing through a flattening filter, light localizing system and on to the multirod collimator. In a series of experiments, described in an accompanying paper [6], the light localizing device was removed and various beam filtering materials (Al, Fe and Pb) were installed in the void space thus created. In order to measure the effects of tungsten filtration, the light local-izer was left in place and the multirod collimator was closed. Microdosimetric measurements were made using the paired Rossi type A-150 tissue equivalent plastic (TEP) proportional counters; the counters were identical except that one counter was constructed from A-150 TEP which had been uniformly loaded with 50 μg·g^{-1} of ^{10}B. The dose enhancement resulting from the α particles and ^{7}Li particles produced by the neutron capture reactions can be measured by comparing the event size spectra, where an enhanced α/^{7}Li particle peak is observed. From an analysis of these spectra it is possible to separately determine the neutron, γ ray and ^{10}B dose produced by the various filtering materials. The microdosimetric measurements also allow an assessment of the relative biological effectiveness (RBE) of the various beam components and their variation with depth in a phantom. The magnitude of these RBEs relative to the RBE of the unmodified fast neutron beam can also be estimated.

Measurements with steel (25 cm) and tungsten filters (18.7 cm) show the largest dose enhancements. In Table 1 the results of the measurements made with these materials by Kota et al. [6] are given. The individual dose rate components have been weighted with an RBE factor to obtain a biologically weighted total dose rate normalized to the RBE of the unmodified fast neutron beam (3.0). A deuter-on beam current of 100 μA has been assumed and the times needed to deliver a fractionated therapeutic dose (~ 150 cGy) have been estimated for a range of depths in a water phantom. The dose enhancement resulting from the addition of ^{10}B relative to the fast neutron and γ-ray doses in the modified beam based on the biological dose rates is also tabulated.

Discussion

The mean energy of the d(48.5) + Be neutron beam is approximately 20 MeV and the mean energy of the heavily attenuated beam will be considerably lower. From the data of Kota et al. [6], the depths in a water phantom at which the neu-tron dose components are reduced to 50% of their maximum value are 7.4 and 9.0 cm, for the steel and tungsten attenuated beams, respectively. With the filter material positioned immediately after the monitor ionization chamber (Fig. 1) it is still possible to use the multirod collimator for shaping the fast neutron and γ-ray components of the modified beam, although some deterioration of the penumbral characteristics of these dose components is to be expected as a result of the increased scatter. For the tungsten-filtered beam this depth-dose characteristic is comparable to that of the beam used in the MRC trial cited earlier [10]. In this trial patients were treated with two parallel opposed lateral fields and a single frontal or occipital field, or a pair of opposing frontal-occipital fields and a single lateral; with wedges as appropriate. For a tumor at 7.5 cm depth (i.e., approximately on the mid-line of the brain), from the data in Table 1, with a tungsten-filtered beam, this beam arrangement would give an average ^{10}B enhancement of $\sim 40\%$ throughout the brain for 50 ppm of ^{10}B in tissue. In practice the boron concentration in normal brain tissue is about one third of that in the tumor with boronophenylalanine (i.e., a normal tissue dose enhancement of 13%). Hence if the normal tissue dose is limited to 12 Gy a physical fast neutron dose of 10.6 Gy (12 ÷ 1.13) should be delivered. This results in an enhanced dose to the tumor of 14.9 Gy (10.6 × 1.40). With the steel filtered beam the average dose enhancement is higher ($\sim 50\%$) resulting in a tumor dose of 15.4 Gy. Thus, according to the tumor-dose response curve constructed by Stelzer et al., [9] doses of 14.9 and 15.4 Gy result in local tumor control rates of $\sim 50\%$ and $\sim 60\%$, respectively. The situation may be even better for tumors situated at depths less than 7.5 cm. Hence, a considerable improvement in the local control rate seems possible with the modified fast neutron beam using existing drugs. An improved drug capable of delivering larger concentrations of ^{10}B to tumors and/or with better partition between the tumor and normal tissue would result in even greater local tumor control rates.

A remaining technical problem which needs to be solved concerns the feasibility of operating the superconducting cyclotron with 100 μA of deuteron beam. The ion source is capable of producing these beam currents and it seems feasible to construct a beryllium target capable of handling the power (4.85 kW at a power density of about 2.5 kW cm^{-2}); Blackburn et al. are designing a target capable of handling ion beams with power densities of ~ 10 kW cm^{-2} [11]. The

Table 1. Details of RBE-weighted dose rates and fractional ^{10}B dose enhancement obtained with modified fast neutron beams.

Filter material	Depth of measurement in cm	RBE weighted dose rate cGy min^{-1} 100 μA^{-1}			RBE weighted total dose rate cGy min^{-1} 100μA^{-1}	Fractional ^{10}B dose enhancement $D_{\alpha + Li}/D_{N + \gamma}$	Time to deliver dose (150 cGy) with 100 μA of beam in min.
		N	γ	α + Li			
Fe	3	6.8	0.9	3.9	11.6	0.51	13
	5	4.8	0.9	3.7	9.4	0.65	16
	10	3.0	1.0	1.7	5.7	0.43	27
	20	1.1	0.8	0.8	2.7	0.42	56
W	3	17.1	1.1	7.7	25.9	0.42	6
	5	13.4	1.2	7.3	21.9	0.50	7
	10	8.1	1.1	2.8	12.0	0.30	13
	20	3.6	0.9	1.6	6.1	0.36	25

problem arises because the neutron flux produces a significant heat load on the superconducting magnet cryostat. This heat load is such that the helium boil-off rate increases from approximately 2.3 l·h^{-1} with no beam to 5—7 l·h^{-1} with 12.5 μA of deuteron beam. It is possible to introduce additional shielding between the target and the cryostat, but tests will be necessary to assess its effectiveness in reducing the heat load. In the present mode of operation the cryostat is "batch-filled" with approximately 70—80 l of liquid helium each morning. An alternative mode of operation is to continuously supply the cryostat with cryogen maintaining a constant level of liquid in the cryostat. In this mode of operation it may be possible to accommodate the high boil off rates expected with 100 μA of beam, for the short periods of time associated with a BNCEFNT treatment (i.e., 10—20 min), since liquid is supplied from a 500 l storage dewar and the liquefier system is capable of supplying up to 24 l·h^{-1}. With a treatment time of 10 min predicted for treating a tumor at 7.5 cm depth it would also be possible to reduce the beam current requirement to 50 μA. All dose rate measurements have been made at a source-to-surface distance (SSD) of 183 cm; the SSD can be reduced to 150 cm allowing a further 50% reduction in the beam current. With a combination of these strategies (coil shielding, continuous flow operation and reduced beam current) it seems likely that the coil heating problem can be overcome.

Conclusions

Microdosimetry measurements of fast neutron, γ-ray and ^{10}B dose components in a suitably filtered fast neutron beam demonstrate that such beams may provide a useful modality for treating glioblastoma multiforme. Previous trials with fast neutrons only suggest that BNCEFNT may provide a therapeutic window which will allow improved tumor control to be achieved without untoward normal brain complications. It appears feasible to produce a modified fast neutron beam that will be suitable for such treatments. Future work will include a thorough characterization of the modified beam profile for each of the dose components and Monte Carlo calculations to optimize the beam filtration for ^{10}B enhancement and dose rate.

References

1. Waterman FM, Kuchnir FT, Skaggs LS, Bewley DK, Page BC, Attix FH. The use of ^{10}B to enhance the tumor dose in fast-neutron therapy. Phys Med Biol 1978;23:592—602.
2. Maughan, RL, Powers WE, Blosser HG. A superconducting cyclotron for neutron radiation therapy. Med Phys 1994;21:779—785.
3. Maughan RL, Yudelev M. Physical characteristics of a clinical d(48.5) + Be neutron therapy beam produced by a superconducting cyclotron. Med Phys 1995;22:1459—1465.
4. Maughan RL, Blosser GF, Blosser EB, Yudelev M, Forman JD, Blosser HG, Powers WE. A multirod collimator for neutron therapy. Int J Radiat Oncol Biol Phys 1996;34:411—420.
5. Maughan RL, Kota C, Yudelev M. A microdosimetric study of the dose enhancement in a fast

neutron beam due to boron neutron capture. Phys Med Biol 1993;37:1957—1961.

6. Kota C, Maughan RL, Burmeister J, Forman JD. A modified fast neutron therapy beam for boron neutron capture enhanced fast neutron therapy (BNCEFNT). In: Larsson B, Crawford J, Weinreich R (eds) Advances in Neutron Capture Therapy, Volume 1, Medicine and Physics. Amsterdam: Elsevier Science, 1997;496—500 (these proceedings).

7. Elowitz EH, Chadha M, Coderre JA, Iwai J, Joel D, Slatkin DN, Chanana AD. A phase I/II trial of BNCT for glioblastoma multiforme using intravenous boronophenylalanine-fructose complex and epithermal neutrons: early clinical results. In: Larsson B, Crawford J, Weinreich R (eds) Advances in Neutron Capture Therapy, Volume 1, Medicine and Physics. Amsterdam: Elsevier Science, 1997;56—59 (these proceedings).

8. Griffin TW, Davis R, Laramore G, Hendrickson F, Rodrigues-Antunez A, Hussey D, Nelson J. Fast neutron radiation therapy for glioblastoma multiforme. Results of an RTOG study. Am J Clin Oncol 1983;6:661—667.

9. Stelzer KJ, Lindsley KL, Cho PS, Laramore GE, Griffin TW. Fast neutron radiotherapy: the University of Washington experience and potential use of concomitant boost with boron neutron capture. Radiat Prot Dosim (In press).

10. Catterall M, Bloom HJ, Ash DV, Walsh L, Richardson A, Uttley D, Gowing NFC, Lewis P, Chaucer B. Fast neutrons compared with megavoltage X-rays in the treatment of patients with supratentorial glioblastoma: a controlled pilot study. Int J Radiat Oncol Biol Phys 1980;6: 261—266.

11. Blackburn B, Howard W, Song H. Development of a water-cooled beryllium target for producing neutrons in a high current tandem accelerator. Med Phys 1996;23:1497 (Abstract).

Advances in Neutron Capture Therapy.
Volume I, Medicine and Physics.
B. Larsson, J. Crawford and R. Weinreich, editors.

A modified fast neutron therapy beam for boron neutron capture enhanced fast neutron therapy (BNCEFNT)

Chandrasekhar Kota, Richard L. Maughan, J. Burmeister and J.D. Forman

Gershenson Radiation Oncology Center, Harper Hospital and Wayne State University, Detroit, Michigan, USA

Introduction

In recent years, a small but concerted effort has been made by researchers in fast neutron therapy to use the boron-10 neutron capture reaction to provide tumor boosts in fast neutron therapy [1]. This modality can be termed boron neutron capture enhanced fast neutron therapy (BNCEFNT) [2].

In this paper, we present the first results on efforts to modify the d(48.5) + Be fast neutron therapy beam at Harper Hospital in Detroit for BNCEFNT. The emphasis is on efforts to produce a BNCEFNT beam for the treatment of gliomas, thereby presenting an extension of fast neutron therapy as an alternative to BNCT. An accompanying paper by Maughan et al. [3] discusses the rationale behind BNCEFNT for gliomas and the feasibility of using the Harper Hospital superconducting cyclotron for this purpose.

Methods and Materials

The fast neutron therapy facility at Harper Hospital is based on a d(48.5) + Be fast neutron beam produced by a superconducting cyclotron and collimated by a multirod collimator. This neutron beam is isocentric, with a depth dose comparable to a 4 MeV photon beam and is comparable to conventional LINACs in its daily operations [4]. All proposed modifications to this beam were subject to the constraint of retaining the currently available use of the fast neutron beam. Figure 1 shows the schematic representation of the cyclotron and the beam delivery and collimation system. The conventional neutron beam has a light localizer assembly between the target and the collimator which is the only dispensable component that can be replaced by the beam modifier. The dimensions of the modifier that would fit in this space without interfering with any other components are 21 × 21 × 25 cm.

An empirical experimental approach was employed to evaluate different modi-

---

Address for correspondence: Chandrasekhar Kota, Gershenson Radiation Oncology Center, Harper Hospital and Wayne State University, 3990 John R., Detroit, MI 48201, USA.

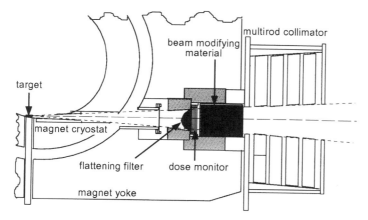

Fig. 1. Schematic representation of the d(48.5) + Be fast neutron beam delivery system.

fying materials because of the lack of reliable neutron cross-section data above 20 MeV necessary for computations. Four different materials were evaluated for modifying the fast neutron beam; these were iron, lead, aluminum and tungsten. Commercially available iron, lead and aluminum of nominal purity were cut into ~5 × 10 × 25 cm bricks and stacked in the available space as shown in Fig. 1. The collimator was used to define a 15 × 15 cm square field at the iso-center (183 cm). To evaluate tungsten as a modifying material, the multirod collimator was completely closed, providing an effective thickness of ~18.7 cm of tungsten for modifying the beam. In this case, there was no collimation of the beam.

The modified neutron beams were characterized in terms of γ, neutron and boron dose components in a lucite walled 30 × 30 × 30 cm water phantom placed at a source to surface distance (SSD) of 183 cm. These dose components were measured as functions of depth along the central axis of the beams. A 0.1 cm^3 A150 tissue-equivalent plastic (TEP) ion chamber (FWT, Goleta, CA; type IC 18) was used to measure the γ-plus-neutron dose. A miniature GM tube (FWT; type GM1-S), shielded against thermal neutrons by a 480 mg cm^2 ^{6}LiF cap, was used to measure the γ dose, which was used to separately calculate the neutron dose.

The dual proportional counter technique was used to independently measure the γ, neutron and boron dose and their single-event spectra. This technique involves the use of a Rossi type 0.5 inch LET counter with an A-150 TEP wall (TE counter) and a second, identical counter with 50 µg/g of ^{10}B incorporated in the A-150 TEP (^{10}B counter), and has been described in detail elsewhere [2]. Values of the saturation-corrected, dose-mean lineal energy y*, were calculated from the measured microdosimetric spectra using a saturation parameter of 124 keV/µm. Ratios of y* values of these modified high LET neutron beams were assumed to be proportional to ratios of their relative biological effectiveness

(RBE) in the dose ranges of ~150 cGy pertinent to fractionated BNCEFNT, based on a similar assumption in fast neutron therapy [5]. The biological effectiveness of the neutron and boron dose components relative to the unmodified fast neutron beam, RBE_n were calculated as the ratios of the corresponding y^* values.

Results and Discussions

The four different modifying materials were evaluated in terms of the effect they produced on the three different dose components, relative to the original fast neutron beam. These materials, in decreasing order of transmission for the neutron plus γ dose were Al, Pb, W and steel. Table 1 shows the absolute dose rates for the γ, neutron and boron dose components for 100 μA of beam current with the different materials. The γ and neutron dose components measured using the ion chamber and the proportional counter techniques agreed to within 10% except for tungsten where it was within 20%. The discrepancy in all cases is attributed to the error in the γ dose estimation with the proportional counters due to the lower lineal energy cutoff. From this table, it is seen that the γ dose rate remains relatively constant for the different materials. For the neutron dose component, the ratio of the dose rate at 3 cm to that at 10 cm depth changes significantly in going from Al to steel, indicating a decrease in the depth for 50% dose D_{50}.

To study the change in the effectiveness of the beams with spatial locations, the spectra measured by the TE counter were separated into neutron and γ spectra. The RBE_n of the neutron component at different depths for the different materials, was calculated using the methods described earlier. The biological effectiveness of the unmodified neutron beam relative to γ dose was taken to be 3.0 for normal tissues based on radiobiological and clinical estimates. With Al as the beam modifying material, RBE_n of the neutron component was found to be very close to one, with no significant variations with depth. With steel, tungsten and lead as the beam modifying materials, RBE_n of the neutron component decreased with depth from 1.23 to 0.95, 1.53 to 1.22 and 1.18 to 1.05, respec-

Table 1. Dose rates (cGy/min) for the γ, neutron and boron dose components obtained with the different beam-modifying materials for 100 μA of beam current.

Depth	Steel			Tungsten			Lead			Aluminum		
	G	N	B	G	N	B	G	N	B	G	N	B
3 cm	2.60	5.52	2.02	3.40	11.1	4.0	3.08	14.7	3.10	3.58	31.6	4.01
5 cm	2.70	4.11	1.89	3.54	9.57	3.76	3.05	13.0	2.77	3.64	29.6	3.77
10 cm	2.93	2.90	0.88	3.33	6.43	1.45	2.82	9.40	1.38	3.21	22.9	2.07
20 cm	2.25	1.14	0.41	2.69	2.89	0.85	2.38	4.77	0.64	2.52	12.1	1.04

Abreviations: G = gamma; N = neutron; B = boron.

tively. The biological effectiveness of the γ and the boron component is expected to remain constant which was verified by calculations; the RBE_n of the boron dose was calculated to be 1.92.

The effective dose rates were calculated as a linear summation of the fractional dose-rate contributions multiplied by RBE_n for each dose component. This procedure is based on the fact that at the doses involved in fractionated neutron therapy (~ 150 cGy), the number of secondary charged particles traversing the "sensitive volumes" in each cell is small, which precludes a synergistic interaction between these components. Table 2 shows the effective dose rates for 100 µA of beam current in hypothetical tissue and tumor obtained with the different beam-modifying materials. The effective dose rates in normal tissue were obtained by assuming a boron concentration of 17 µg/g of ^{10}B, representing a 3:1 partition between tumor and tissue.

Table 2 shows the advantage factor (AF = effective tumor dose rate/effective normal tissue dose rate) as a function of depth for the different materials. From this data, it is evident that all beam-modifying materials produce beams that provide a therapeutic advantage for currently achievable boron concentrations in brain tumors. However, for beams produced by steel and tungsten modifiers, AF is greater than 1.2 for all depths. In an accompanying paper, Maughan et al. [3] have reviewed the literature on fractionated fast-neutron therapy for gliomas. From this review, it is evident that a 20% gain in the tumor dose can be clinically significant for the treatment of gliomas with fast neutrons. Depending on constraints associated with treatment times, the beams produced by the steel or tungsten modifier can be used to treat gliomas with a significant therapeutic gain. The maximum beam current produced by the cyclotron at present is 15 µA. The feasibility of producing a beam current of 100 µA, to which the data in Table 2 is normalized, is discussed by Maughan et al. [3].

Conclusions

Four different materials: steel, tungsten, lead and aluminum, have been investigated for modifying the d(48.5) + Be fast neutron beam to obtain clinically significant dose enhancements with 50 µg/g of ^{10}B in the tumor and a tumor to tis-

Table 2. Effective dose rates (cGy/min) in tissue (17 µg/g of ^{10}B) and tumor (50 µg/g of ^{10}B) obtained with the different beam-modifying materials for 100 µA of beam current.

Depth	Steel			Tungsten			Lead			Aluminum		
	1	2	3	1	2	3	1	2	3	1	2	3
3 cm	8.9	11.6	1.30	20.6	25.9	1.26	20.3	24.3	1.20	37.5	42.7	1.14
5 cm	6.8	9.4	1.38	17.1	21.9	1.28	17.4	20.9	1.20	33.6	38.5	1.15
10 cm	4.6	5.7	1.24	10.1	12.0	1.19	11.9	13.7	1.15	26.3	29.0	1.10
20 cm	2.1	2.7	1.28	4.9	6.1	1.24	6.2	7.0	1.13	14.0	15.4	1.10

Abbreviations: 1 = tissue; 2 = tumor; 3 = advantage factor.

sue ratio of 3:1. Of these materials, tungsten and steel produced advantage factors greater than 1.2 for thicknesses of 25 and 18.7 cm, respectively. For these thicknesses of steel and tungsten, clinically acceptable dose rates of 5.7 and 12 cGy/min are produced at a tumor located at 10 cm depth for a deuteron beam current of 100 $\mu\alpha$ These dose rates can be increased by a factor of 1.5 by positioning the patient/phantom at a shorter SSD of 150 cm. Studies to obtain these higher beam currents are under way. Present study indicates that BNCEFNT for gliomas is feasible with the modified beams described earlier.

Acknowledgements

We would like to thank Dr A.T. Porter for his encouragement and support for this work.

References

1. Laramore GE, Wootton P, Livesey JC, Wilbur DS, Risler R, Phillips M, Jacky J, Buchholz TA, Griffin T, Brossard S. Boron neutron capture therapy: A mechanism for achieving a concomitant tumor boost in fast neutron radiotherapy. Int J Radiat Onc Biol Phys 1994;28:1125—1142.
2. Kota C. Microdosimetric considerations in the use of the boron neutron capture reaction in radiation therapy. PhD thesis, Wayne State University, Detroit, USA, 1996.
3. Maughan RL, Kota C, Forman JD. Feasibility of boron neutron capture enhancement of fast neutron therapy utilizing a superconducting cyclotron. In: Larsson B, Crawford J, Weinreich R (eds) Advances in Neutron Capture Therapy. Volume 1, Medicine and Physics. Amsterdam: Elsevier Science, 1997;490—495 (these proceedings).
4. Maughan RL, Powers WE, Blosser HG. A superconducting cyclotron for neutron radiation therapy. Med Phys 1994;21:779—785.
5. Binns PJ, Hough JH. Lineal energy measurements in two fast neutron beams: d(16) + Be and p(66) + Be. Radiat Prot Dos 1988;23:385—388.

© 1997 Elsevier Science B.V. All rights reserved.
Advances in Neutron Capture Therapy.
Volume I, Medicine and Physics.
B. Larsson, J. Crawford and R. Weinreich, editors.

Feasibility of the utilization of BNCT in the fast neutron therapy beam at Fermilab

Katja Langen[1,2], Arlene J. Lennox[2,3], Thomas K. Kroc[2] and Paul M. DeLuca, Jr.[1]

[1]University of Wisconsin, Department of Medical Physics, Madison, Wisconsin; [2]Neutron Therapy Facility at Fermilab, Batavia, Illinois; and [3]Saint Joseph Hospital, Elgin, Illinois, USA

Keywords: BNCT, dose boost, neutron therapy.

Introduction

The Neutron Therapy Facility at Fermilab has treated cancer patients since 1976. Since then more than 2,300 patients have been treated and a wealth of clinical information accumulated. The therapeutic neutron beam at Fermilab is produced by bombarding a beryllium target with 66 MeV protons. The resulting continuous neutron spectrum ranges from thermal to 66 MeV in neutron energy. It is clear that this spectrum is not well suited for the treatment of tumors with boron neutron capture therapy (BNCT) only. However, since this spectrum contains thermal and epithermal components we are investigating whether BNCT can be used in this beam to boost the tumor dose. There are clinical scenarios in which a selective tumor dose boost of 10−15% could be clinically significant. For these cases the principal treatment would still be fast neutron therapy but a tumor boost could be used either to deliver a higher dose to the tumor tissue or to reduce the dose to the normal healthy tissue while maintaining the absorbed dose level in the tumor tissue.

Clinical rationale

The clinical rationale for this study is based on the poor prognosis of certain brain tumor patients. Following diagnosis the expected survival time for patients diagnosed with glioblastoma multiforme is around 8 months and can be extended by another 4 months with radiation therapy. There is no difference in survival between fast neutron and photon therapy patients, but the cause of death does depend on the treatment modality. A regrowth of the tumor is the primary cause of death in photon patients whereas with fast neutron therapy one achieves tumor control but patients sustain a high degree of normal tissue damage that causes death [1]. These clinical results indicate a small therapeutic ratio of glioma

Address for correspondence: Katja Langen, University of Wisconsin-Madison, Department of Medical Physics, 1530 MSC, 1300 University Avenue, Madison, WI 53703, USA.

to normal brain tissue. In order to increase the survival the therapeutic ratio must be increased. BNCT has the potential to achieve just that in fast neutron beams.

A selective dose enhancement in the tumor tissue will allow a corresponding reduction in the overall absorbed dose level, therefore reducing the normal tissue complications.

Materials and Methods

We are investigating modification of the existing neutron energy spectrum by filtration in order to increase the low energy component of the beam thus enhancing the boron neutron capture dose boost. Monte Carlo calculations are used to simulate the effects of various filter materials. Microdosimetric techniques are used to measure the boron dose enhancement in a given beam. The ultimate choice of the filter assembly will depend on the irradiation technique used, e.g., will BNCT be administered simultaneously with fast neutron therapy or in a separate session? Demands on the filter assembly change with irradiation technique. The choice of technique will on the other hand be dictated by the effects that can be achieved with different filter materials.

Monte Carlo calculations were performed using MCNP [2]. For some selected materials, data files were available that extended to 100 MeV [3]. These files were used for the following calculations. The neutron energy spectrum for the Fermilab facility was calculated by Ross et al. [4]. We used this neutron fluence spectrum as a source for our calculations. Neutrons were emitted into a cone to simulate a collimated neutron field. At the isocenter distance we modeled a cylindrical water phantom that is surrounded by 5 mm of bone surface, to simulate a head. Slabs of filter materials were placed adjoining to the head phantom. Figure 1 shows a schematic of the beam and phantom model. Monte Carlo scor-

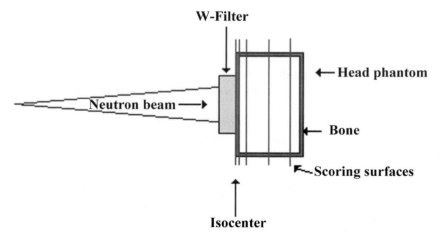

Fig. 1. Schematic of the geometry used for the Monte Carlo calculations.

ing surfaces were set at the bone and brain surface as well as at various depths in the head phantom. Several filter materials were investigated; tungsten having the most favorable effects on the neutron energy spectrum. Figure 2 shows Monte Carlo results obtained at 50 mm depth in the head phantom for several tungsten filter thicknesses. Spectra are normalized to the highest energy bin. These results indicate that the thermal and epithermal neutron rates increase with the tungsten filter thickness, however, the dose rate reduction due to the tungsten filters will limit the acceptable tungsten filter thickness. A dose rate reduction by a factor of 10 is expected for a 100-mm tungsten filter.

Microdosimetry can be employed to directly measure the dose boost in the neutron beam using the following technique: in order to simulate a boronated tumor, a proportional counter was constructed with an A-150 tissue-equivalent plastic wall that is loaded with 200 ppm ^{10}B. This counter is simultaneously irradiated with a regular A-150 tissue-equivalent plastic counter that is identical to the boronated counter in every aspect except the boron additive to the wall. A difference in counter responses is then due to the boron additive in the one counter wall.

Preliminary results

Initial measurements and calculations were completed. Monte Carlo calculations indicate a potential for tungsten filtration of the beam. Therefore, a 90-mm thick tungsten filter was used to modify the neutron beam. Figure 3 shows the microdosimetric spectra measured in the filtered beam at 50-mm water depth. An equal area under a microdosimetric spectra is equal to an equal absorbed dose

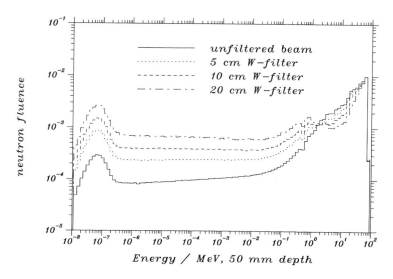

Fig. 2. Monte Carlo results calculated for 50 mm depth in the head phantom.

504

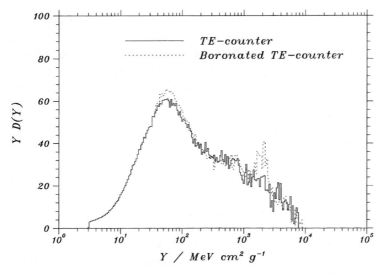

Fig. 3. Microdosimetric spectra measured in the neutron therapy beam at Fermilab. The beam was filtered by 90 mm of tungsten.

in the wall material. Analysis of the data indicates a 5—7% boron dose enhancement as measured with the 200 ppm loaded counter.

The measurement confirms the usefulness of tungsten as a beam filtration material. However, future measurements will focus on further increasing the boron dose enhancement. Besides beam filtration we will investigate the effects of beam reflectors as well as the use of different materials for beam collimation.

References

1. Saroja KR, Mansell J, Hendrickson FR, Cohen L, Lennox AJ. Failure of accelerated neutron therapy to control high grade astrocytomas. Int J Radiat Oncol Biol Phys 1989;17:1295—1297.
2. Briesmeister FJ (ed) MCNP 4 A general Monte Carlo code for neutron transport and photon transport. Los Alamos National Laboratory 1993; LA-012625-M.
3. Young PG, Arthur ED, Bozoain M, England TR, Hall GM, LaBauve RJ, Little RC, MacFarlane RE, Madland DG, Perry RT, Wilson WB. Transport data libraries for incident proton and neutron energies to 100 MeV. Los Alamos National Laboratory 1990;LA-11753-MS.
4. Ross MA, DeLuca PM, Jr., Jones DTL, Lennox AJ, Maughan RL. Calculated fluence spectra at neutron therapy facilities. Radiat Prot Dosim (In press).

Measurements of neutron energy spectra from a thick beryllium target with incident proton energies from 3 to 4 MeV

Gang Yue, Jinxiang Chen, Ruixia Song and Shanglian Bao

Institute of Heavy Ion Physics, Peking University, Beijing, P.R. China

Introduction

At the present time, many designs have been proposed to generate epithermal neutrons (neutrons in the energy range from 0.4 eV – 10 keV), which is considered to be optimal for BNCT, with different accelerators and the associated moderating systems. Most attention was focused on using low-energy protons (2.5 MeV) bombarding thick ^{7}Li metal targets. This reaction is considered to have a proper neutron spectrum with neutron energies < 1 MeV. For practical treatments the proton beam current was estimated to be 4 – 50 mA [1,2]. Such currents will cause a significant challenge to the target cooling system, because lithium has a low melting point (181°C) and low thermal conductivity (85 W/m°C) [3]. To avoid these difficulties, targets of ^{9}Be metal, which has a high melting point and a high thermal conductivity, could be considered to be another choice for generating BNCT useful neutrons. With a 4 MeV incident proton energy, the neutron spectrum is composed of the neutrons from ^{9}Be (p,n), ^{9}Be (p,pn) and ^{9}Be (p,p) (n) reactions [4] and the neutron yield is predicted to be comparable to that of a 2.5-MeV proton-caused ^{7}Li (p,n) reaction. The latter two reaction channels would release "soft" neutrons and make the spectrum comparable to that of a ^{7}Li (p,n) reaction [5]. If the ratio of a high energy neutron yield (> 1 MeV) to a low-energy neutron yield (< 1 MeV) is reasonably low, ^{9}Be metal could be a promising target for BNCT. Experimental measurements are needed to verify if this is the real case. In this work, neutron spectra using 4, 3.5 and 3 MeV protons striking thick ^{9}Be targets with a thickness of 1.5 and 3 mm were measured via the time-of-flight (TOF) technique at 0° with respect to the incident proton beam. The results are compared to those using 2.5 MeV protons striking a 2-mm-thick ^{7}Li target, which was also obtained in this work.

Experiment

Two 32-mm-diameter disk-shaped ^{9}Be targets with thicknesses of 1.5 and 3 mm,

---

Address for correspondence: Gang Yue, Institute of Heavy Ion Physics, Peking University, Beijing 100871, P.R. China.

respectively, were purchased from China National Nonferrous Metals Industry Corp. The purity of ^{9}Be in the targets is higher than 98%. A pulsed proton beam with a 3 MHz repetition rate was produced using the Peking University 4.5-MV electrostatic accelerator. The pulse width is about 1.8 ns. The detector used for neutron spectrum measurements consisted of a 104 mm (diameter) × 50 mm (thickness) ST-451 liquid scintillator coupled to a XP2040 photomultiplier. The efficiency curve of this detecting system (with a threshold of 400 keV) has been measured and calculated by J. Chen [6]. An ORTEC 439 charge integration unit was used in the experiment to monitor the target current. Time-of-flight spectra for two ^{9}Be targets with different thicknesses were measured. The proton beam current was about 5 μA. The flight path was set at 2.663 m. For comparison a ^{7}Li (p,n) ^{7}Be time-of-flight spectrum was measured with an incident energy of 2.5 MeV. A thick ^{7}Li metal target (about 2 mm thick) was used in this measurement.

Results and Discussion

Two typical TOF spectra with a 1.5-mm-thick ^{9}Be target and incident energies of 4 and 3 MeV are shown in Figs. 1−2, respectively. The 3.5 MeV proton-induced neutron spectra have similar shapes to those of 4 MeV spectra. In each spectrum the narrow and symmetric peak on the right end presents the γ-ray peak and the continuum shows the neutrons with different energies. The interesting part of the spectra for incident energies of 3.5 and 4 MeV are the two broad peaks (peaks B and C) appearing on the left-hand side of the main neutron peak (peak A). For the 3 MeV spectrum only one peak on the left-hand side of the main neutron peak was observed. Peak B has a neutron energy of about 1.2 MeV for 4-MeV incident energy spectrum and about 1.1 MeV for 3.5-MeV incident energy spectrum. Peak C is in the same channel (about channel 169) for all the time spectra, corresponding to a neutron energy around 638 keV independent of the incident proton energy. Because the threshold for producing another group

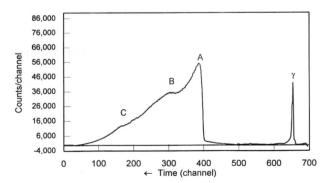

Fig. 1. The neutron TOF spectrum using 4 MeV protons striking a 1.5-mm-thick ^{9}Be target (with background subtracted). The flight path was 2.663 m.

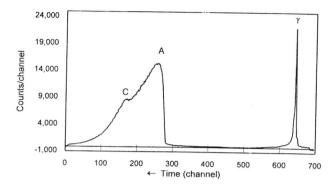

Fig. 2. The neutron TOF spectrum using 3 MeV protons striking a 1.5-mm-thick ^{9}Be target (with background subtracted). The flight path was 2.663 m.

of neutrons by decaying to the 2.3 MeV excited state of ^{9}B is 4.64 MeV, neither of these two broad neutron peaks could be the second group neutrons from ^{9}Be (p,n) ^{9}B reaction.

Marion and Levin [4] presented an excitation curve for the ground state neutrons from the ^{9}Be (p,n) ^{9}B reaction. Two resonance peaks at proton energies of 2.56 and 4.6 MeV were shown in the curve. With an incident energy of 2.56 MeV, the outgoing neutron energy at 0° would be 639 keV, matching the neutron peak at the far left of each spectrum obtained in this work. Therefore, we believe that the neutron peak on the far left of each spectrum with incident energy of 4 or 3.5 MeV is formed by the 2.56-MeV proton-induced neutrons. For the spectrum with incident energy of 3 MeV, the only peak (peak C) on the left-hand side of the main neutron peak is in about channel 169. It means that this peak

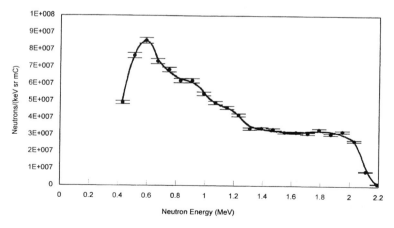

Fig. 3. The neutron energy spectrum using 4 MeV protons striking a thick ^{9}Be target. The data in the curve are the average data of 1.5-mm-thick target runs and 3-mm-thick target runs. The threshold of the measurement is 400 keV.

508

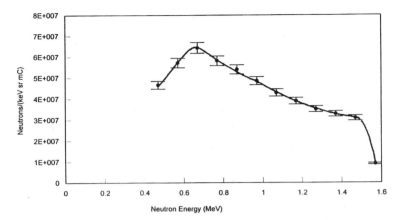

Fig. 4. The neutron energy spectrum using 3.5 MeV protons striking a 1.5-mm-thick ^{9}Be target. The threshold of the measurement is 400 keV.

is at least partly caused by the 2.5 MeV resonance. The first broad neutron peak (peak B) on the left-hand side of the main neutron peak in the spectra with incident energies of 4 and 3.5 MeV, which also probably appears in the spectrum with incident energy of 3 MeV and is overlapped with the 2.56 MeV resonance peak, could be caused by the reactions ^{9}Be (p,pn), ^{9}Be (p,p) ^{9}Be*(n) and other reactions mentioned in [4] and [5].

The TOF spectra are converted to energy spectra by dividing each spectrum into some certain energy bins to obtain the number of counts in each bin. The measured counts in each of the energy bins were divided by the average efficiency value for the bin to obtain the neutron number in the bin. Figures 3—5 show the converted energy spectra for the ^{9}Be target. In all these energy spectra, the sig-

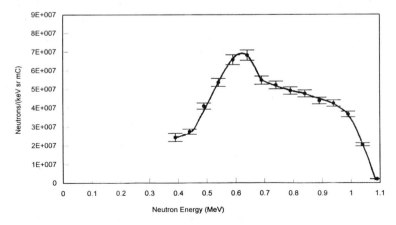

Fig. 5. The neutron energy spectrum using 3 MeV protons striking a 1.5-mm-thick ^{9}Be target. The threshold of the measurement is 400 keV.

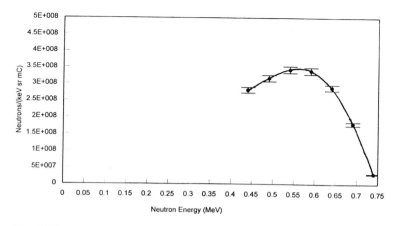

Fig. 6. The neutron energy spectrum using 2.5 MeV protons striking a 2-mm-thick ^{7}Li target. The threshold of the measurement is 400 keV.

nificant increase of the neutron counts was shown in the energy range from about 600 keV to about 1.2 MeV, corresponding to the contributions of peak B and C in the TOF spectra. Figure 6 shows the neutron energy spectrum using 2.5 MeV neutrons striking a 2-mm-thick ^{7}Li target. A comparison of the measurement results for ^{9}Be and ^{7}Li targets is shown in Table 1.

From Table 1, one can see that the neutron yield from reactions of 4 MeV proton bombarding a thick ^{9}Be target is comparable to that of a ^{7}Li (p,n) ^{7}Be reaction (thick lithium target). But only about half of the neutrons from ^{9}Be source fall in the energy range 400 keV to 1 MeV. With incident energy of 3.5 MeV, the neutron yield of the ^{9}Be source is lower by about a factor of 1.75 than that of ^{7}Li (p,n) ^{7}Be reaction and only about 63% of the neutrons fall in the energy range of 400 keV to 1 MeV. At these two energy points, moderating neutrons with energy higher than 1 MeV to the epithermal region may cause a significant sacrifice of neutron flux. The neutron yield of ^{9}Be source with incident energy of 3 MeV is about a third of that from the ^{7}Li (p,n) ^{7}Be reaction, but more than 96% of the neutrons have energies less than 1 MeV.

Table 1. The neutron yields of using protons striking thick beryllium and lithium targets at 0°. The threshold of the measurements is 400 keV.

Target	Proton energy (MeV)	Neutron yield $1/(sr\ mC)$	Fraction of neutrons with energy $400 \leqslant E_n < 1$ MeV for Be target and $E_n < 1$ MeV for Li target (%)
^{7}Li	2.5	9.123×10^{10}	100
^{9}Be	3.0	3.152×10^{10}	96.4
	3.5	5.199×10^{10}	63.4
	4.0	8.016×10^{10}	53.4

510

Acknowledgements

This work is supported in part by the OUR International Science and Technology Development Co., Ltd. The authors would like to thank Jianyong Wang and Shengwen Quan for their assistance in the accelerator operation.

References

1. Yanch JC, Zhao X-L, Klinkowstein RE. Accelerator-based epithermal neutron beam design for neutron capture therapy. Med Phys 1992;19(3):709−721.
2. Wang C-KC, Eggers PE, Crawford HL. Accelerator neutron irradiation facility for hospital-based neutron capture therapy. In: Soloway AH et al. (eds) Advances in Neutron Capture Therapy. NY: Plenum Press, 1993;119−123.
3. Laramore GE. Nonreactor sources of epithermal neutron beams for boron neutron capture therapy (BNCT): A user's perspective. Proceedings of the First International Workshop on Accelerator-based Neutron Sources for Boron Neutron Capture Therapy. Jackson, Wyoming, September 11−14, 1994;25.
4. Jerry B, Levin M, Levin JS. Investigation of the ^{9}Be (p,n) ^{9}B and ^{9}Be (p,$\alpha\gamma$) ^{6}Li reactions. Phys Rev 1959;115(1):144.
5. Wang CK. Thick beryllium target as an accelerator-based neutron source for neutron capture therapy. Proceedings of the First International Workshop on Accelerator-based Neutron Sources for Boron Neutron Capture Therapy. Jackson, Wyoming, September 11−14, 1994;161.
6. Chen J, Shi Z, Tang G. Experimental determination of the relative fast-neutron efficiency of a ST 451 liquid scintillation detector. Nucl Electron Detect Tech 1993;13(6):323.

©1997 Elsevier Science B.V. All rights reserved.
Advances in Neutron Capture Therapy.
Volume I, Medicine and Physics.
B. Larsson, J. Crawford and R. Weinreich, editors.

Measurement of the ^{9}Be(p,n) thick target spectra for use in accelerator-based boron neutron capture therapy

W.B. Howard[1], S.M. Grimes[2], T.N. Massey[2], S.I. Al-Quaraishi[2], D.K. Jacobs[2], C.E. Brient[2] and J.C. Yanch[3]

[1]*Massachusetts Institute of Technology, Department of Physics, Cambridge, Massachusetts;* [2]*Ohio University, Department of Physics and Astronomy, Athens, Ohio; and* [3]*Massachusetts Institute of Technology, Department of Nuclear Engineering and Whitaker College of Health Sciences and Technology, Cambridge, Massachusetts, USA*

Keywords: beryllium, BNCT, boron neutron capture synovectomy, MNCP, neutron.

Introduction

Thick target neutron energy spectra of the reaction ^{9}Be(p,n) have recently been measured using standard time-of-flight (TOF) techniques at the Ohio University Accelerator Laboratory (OUAL). Previous measurements of this reaction have been reported [1], however, the data set has been expanded to include back angles (110–148.5°), and a new estimation of the total yield has been calculated. Because the neutron production threshold of this reaction is low, and the thermal properties of beryllium are favorable for heat removal, the reaction is an important high-intensity source of low-energy neutrons. The data are of particular importance in accelerator-based boron neutron capture therapy and boron neutron capture synovectomy [2] (AB-BNCT and AB-BNCS, respectively). In AB-BNCT and AB-BNCS, a particle reaction is used to produce energetic neutrons, which are then moderated to form an epithermal therapy beam for BNCT or BNCS.

BNCT- and BNCS-related research is being conducted at MIT's Laboratory for Accelerator Beam Applications using a tandem electrostatic accelerator with a maximum proton energy of 4.1 MeV. To investigate the use of beryllium and other target materials, accurate thick target neutron spectra are needed. These data are needed as input into Monte Carlo simulation codes, such as MCNP [3], for the development of suitable moderator and filter assemblies for epithermal beam design. The data are also needed for the investigation of target cooling schemes and facility shielding requirements. Because these data did not exist for the reaction ^{9}Be(p,n) using proton energies below 4.1 MeV, it was necessary to use neutron TOF to obtain them experimentally. The measurements of the ^{9}Be(p,n) spectra were completed at OUAL using 4.0, 3.7, 3.4 and 3.0 MeV protons. By selecting a low proton pulse rate frequency, neutrons with energies as low as 70 keV were detected.

Address for correspondence: Prof J.C. Yanch, Massachusetts Institute of Technology, Room E25–330, 45 Carleton Street, Cambridge, MA 02139, USA.

This paper describes the experimental methods used to determine the neutron energy spectra, including the calibration of the neutron detectors. Samples of the data are presented, with an explanation of the sources of error. Initial MCNP simulations of the dose rates in phantom, using ^{9}Be(p,n) as the neutron source, are also presented.

Experimental methods

Standard TOF techniques were used at the OUAL tandem Van de Graaff accelerator to determine the neutron energy spectra. H$^-$ ions produced in a sputter ion source are formed into a pulsed beam by a klystron buncher. The H$^-$ pulse is then accelerated to the high-voltage terminal, where two electrons are stripped from the ions. The resultant protons are then accelerated in the high-energy stage of the accelerator. The axis of the accelerator is perpendicular to the axis of the flight tunnel, so the protons must be redirected by using a beam swinger [4]. The target chamber is mounted at the end of the beam swinger gantry, which rotates so that spectra can be measured at laboratory angles up to 160°. The beryllium target was thick enough to stop 4 MeV protons, and the beryllium purity was 99%. The neutron spectra were measured at the various combinations of energy and angle shown in Table 1.

Neutrons produced at the target pass through a 30 cm collimator before reaching the flight tunnel which is buried beneath 3 m of earth. This shielding results in excellent background reduction. For these measurements, a 10 m flight path was used. The evaluation of neutron spectra at energies below approximately 500 keV requires the use of detectors which are sensitive to low-energy neutrons. To yield accurate energy information, the detectors must also have the capability of generating fast timing information. Four lithium-loaded glass scintillators were used for these experiments based on their fast response time and sensitivity to low-energy neutrons. In addition, one NE213 liquid scintillation detector was used as a check for the neutron spectra at energies greater than 1 MeV. The detectors were calibrated using the neutron spectrum of ^{27}Al(d,n) at 120°, using 7.44 MeV deuterons. This reaction was first accurately characterized using a fission chamber [5]. Below 250-keV neutron energy, the efficiency curves for the lithium glass detectors were based on previously published results [6].

Results and Discussion

Neutron energy spectra are shown in Fig. 1. Representative error bars reflecting

Table 1. Spectra measurement parameters.

Proton energy	Angles at which neutron spectra were measured
4.0, 3.7 MeV	0, 20, 40, 60, 80, 110, 115, 120, 125, 130, 135, 145, 148.5
3.4, 3.0 MeV	0, 40

the total statistical error of the measurements are shown at 0.25, 0.5, 1.0 and 1.5 MeV on Fig. 1B. The magnitude of the statistical error is less than 5% over most of the data set. An additional source of uncertainty is the error associated with the determination of the intrinsic efficiencies of the detectors. The magnitude of this error is approximately 10%. As a secondary check on the absolute accuracy of the data, several spectra of the reaction $^9Be(d,n)$ were measured at 0°, using the same detectors and equipment, immediately preceding the $^9Be(p,n)$ measurements, so that the spectra could be compared with previously published data [7]. Deuteron energies from 2.6 to 7.0 MeV in 400 keV increments were used. Agreement between the two sets of data is very good.

The explanation of the shape of the various neutron yield spectra is the topic of

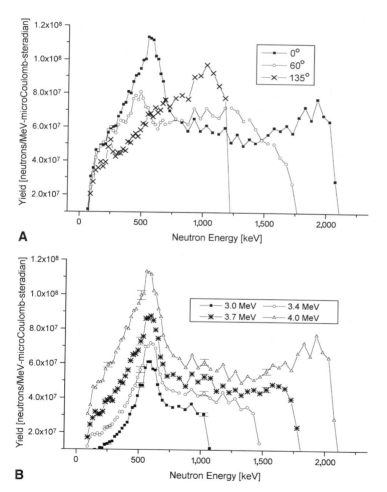

Fig. 1. **A:** Shows neutron energy spectra of the reaction $^9Be(p,n)$ using 4.0 MeV protons at three angles. **B:** Neutron energy spectra of the reaction $^9Be(p,n)$ at 0° using various energy protons.

ongoing research both at MIT and OUAL. Several contributing reactions have been previously reported, and are included in Table 2 [8]. The neutrons produced with energies above 1 MeV are believed to be due primarily to the production of the compound nucleus ^{10}B, followed by decay to one of the states of ^{9}B and the emission of a neutron. The peak in the spectra near 600 keV is believed to be produced in the decay of the second (2.443 MeV) excited state of ^{9}Be. The ^{9}Be nucleus is excited via the reaction ^{9}Be(p,pn). A peak near this energy has been seen before in experiments using a stilbene crystal for neutron detection [8].

The total neutron yield of the reaction can be estimated by integrating the various neutron spectra over the measured energy range and solid angle. Initially, only the forward angles (1—110°) were measured, and the estimated total yield was significantly less than the value predicted (1.36×10^{12} neutrons/mC) on the basis of published cross-sections obtained using a 4π detector [9], and stopping powers of beryllium [10]. Subsequent experiments were therefore recently carried out to measure the backward angles. Using a proton bombarding energy of 4.0 MeV, the absolute total yield (i.e., no normalization was used) is now estimated to be 1.05×10^{12} neutrons/mC, based on the complete data set (0—148.5°). The two estimates of neutron yield now agree within 23%. Unfortunately, the magnitude of the experimental error in the published cross-sections is not clearly stated in [9]. However, it is reasonable to assume an error of at least 10—15% based on other experiments of this type. Considering the 5% statistical error, and 10% detector error associated with the measurements reported here, the agreement between the two values is quite good.

The measured ^{9}Be(p,n) spectral data are currently being used to design therapy neutron beams for AB-BNCT and AB-BNCS. The design process has been previously described [11]. Figure 2 shows a sample of the data from the optimization studies assuming a BNCT treatment of brain cancer. In Fig. 2, the various BNCT components are plotted as a function of depth in a cylindrical volume of brain tissue, along the axial center line. When compared to similar studies using the neutron source reaction ^{7}Li(p,n), E_p = 2.5 MeV, a larger moderator must be used due to the higher neutron energies in the ^{9}Be(p,n) source spectra. A complete phantom optimization study is now underway using the source reaction ^{9}Be(p,n), and proton bombarding energies 4.0 and 3.7 MeV.

Table 2. Neutron producing reactions from protons bombarding beryllium.

Reaction	Q (MeV)
^{9}Be (p,n) ^{9}B	− 1.9
^{9}Be (p, ^{5}He) ^{5}Li	− 4.4
^{9}Be (p, nα) ^{5}Li	− 3.5
^{9}Be (p, p′) ^{9}Be* → ^{8}Be + n	− 1.7
^{9}Be (p, p′) ^{9}Be* → α + ^{5}He	− 2.5
^{9}Be (p, p′) ^{9}Be* → n + α + α	− 1.6

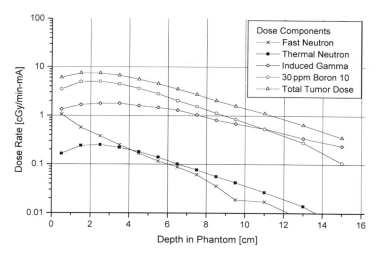

Fig. 2. Dose rate vs. depth in a phantom as predicted by MCNP. The various BNCT dose components are shown along the axial centerline of the brain phantom.

Acknowledgements

This work was supported in part by the US Department of Energy, Grant No. DE-FG02-89ER60874, and the John and Fannie Hertz Foundation.

References

1. Howard WB et al. Measurement of the ^{9}Be(p,n) thick target spectra for use in accelerator-based Boron Neutron Capture Therapy. Med Phys 1996;23(7):1233−1235.
2. Johnson LS et al. Temporal and spatial distribution of boron uptake in excised human synovium. Sixth international symposium on neutron capture therapy for cancer. In: Mishima Y (ed) Cancer Neutron Capture Therapy. Kobe, Japan: Plenum Press, 1996;183−188.
3. Briesmeister JF. MCNP − A general Monte Carlo N-particle transport code, Version 4A. Los Alamos National Laboratory: Report LA−12625, Los Alamos, NM. 1988.
4. Finlay RW et al. The Ohio University beam swinger facility. Nucl Instrum Meth 1982;198: 197−206.
5. Meadows JW. Characteristics of the samples in the FNG fission deposit collection. Argonne National Laboratory: Report ANL/NDM-118, Argonne, IL. 1990.
6. Neill JM et al. Calibration and use of a 5-inch lithium glass detector. Nucl Instrum Meth 1970; 82:162−172.
7. Meadows JW. The thick target ^{9}Be(d,n) neutron spectra for deuteron energies between 2.6 and 7.0 MeV. Argonne National Laboratory: Report ANL/NDM-124, Argonne, IL. 1991.
8. Lone MA, Robertson BC. Characteristics of neutrons from beryllium targets bombarded with protons, deuterons, and alpha particles. Nucl Instrum Meth 1981;189:515−523.
9. Gibbons JH, Macklin RL. Total neutron yields from light elements under proton and alpha bombardment. Phys Rev 1959;114(2):571−580.
10. Ziegler JF. TRIM-95, IBM Yorktown, NY 10598.
11. Yanch JC et al. Accelerator-based epithermal neutron beam design for neutron capture therapy. Med Phys 1992;19(3):709−722.

Advances in Neutron Capture Therapy.
Volume I, Medicine and Physics.
B. Larsson, J. Crawford and R. Weinreich, editors.

Balancing neutron yield and moderator dimensions in accelerator neutron sources

Rajat J. Kudchadker[1], Jay F. Kunze and J.F. Harmon
[1]*Idaho State University, Pocatello, Idaho, USA (Formerly at University of Missouri, College of Engineering, Columbia, Missouri, USA)*

Introduction

In the early 1990s, a number of investigators [1,2,3] had proposed designs based on the $^7Li(p,n)^7Be$ reaction using 2.5 MeV protons, where the neutron yield curve (Fig. 1) flattens out near the maximum. The threshold for this reaction is 1.881 MeV in the laboratory system. The Q value is -1.645 MeV. A proton energy of 2.5 MeV was chosen so as not be too far above the 2.378 MeV threshold energy for the Be product nucleus to reach an excited state, producing some 430 keV γs. Most of the designs were aimed at optimizing the epithermal flux at the patient for the purpose of treating tumors at a nominal depth of 5—7 cm in the brain. The net results of much of this work were designs that had moderator thickness in the order of 20 cm of heavy-water or beryllium oxide. Useful (epithermal, 1 eV—10 keV) beam currents at the patient were such that proton beam currents of 20 mA would be needed to produce neutron beam intensities at the patient, nominally the same as that available at the Brookhaven Medical Research Reactor (BMRR). Beam currents of 20 mA would result in target heating rates of 50 kW, and removing this heat from solid lithium targets of acceptable area was virtually impossible. As a result, much attention has been focused in recent years on clever target designs that could accommodate these high heating rates. To date no feasible target design has been found to satisfy these high heat load requirements.

Benchmark experiments

Having all used Monte Carlo codes, most investigators [1—3] nominally agreed on the order of magnitude of the neutronic results, even although they also used different codes (i.e., MCNP and MORSE). We decided that confirmation of the validity of the use of such codes would be needed to assure that designs were credible. Consequently, in 1992 measurements commenced using the Van de Graaff accelerator at Idaho State University, with maximum proton energy of

Address for correspondence: Rajat J. Kudchadker, Idaho State University, Pocatello, ID 83209, USA.

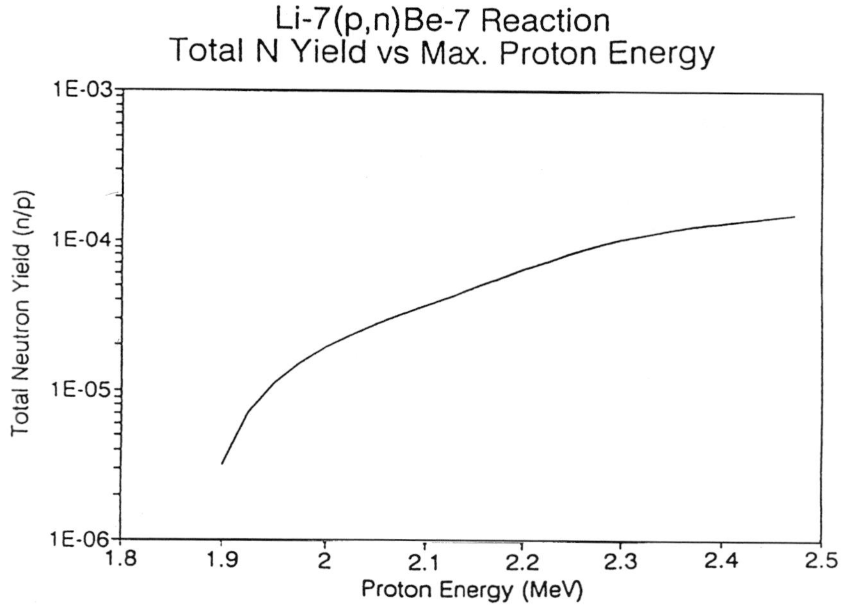

Li-7(p,n)Be-7 Reaction
Total N Yield vs Max. Proton Energy

Fig. 1. Neutron yield as a function of proton energy.

2.3 MeV. However, instability of the high voltage and the beam current caused us to transfer the benchmark to the 2.0 MeV radiofrequency quadrupole (RFQ) proton linear accelerator. The beam energy was very stable, making the neutron spectrum entering the moderator-reflector system rather accurately known using the (p,n) cross-section data and assuming a thick metallic lithium target. For the benchmark, absolute neutron yields could be measured by counting the decay of the ^{7}Be target, with its 53 day half-life. To get a useful benchmark, the moderator thickness was substantially reduced. A much lower neutron yield from the target would be the sacrifice for obtaining a useful benchmark for the evaluation of computer design models of the moderator-reflector systems. With much reduced moderator thickness, neutron beam intensities were considerably larger than in the earlier designs, a result of the increase in solid angle from the target to the end of the moderator (the patient location, see Fig. 2), plus the reduced scattering loss in the moderator. These enhancements more than compensated for the lower target neutron yield. For instance, when the moderator was reduced to only a few centimetres, plus the cooling water behind the target, the yield at the exit of the moderator was actually several times higher than that from the earlier designs. Subsequently, serious design calculations with energy and moderator variations were begun in attempt to find optimum neutron yields with appropriate levels for the unwanted fast neutron and γ doses.

518

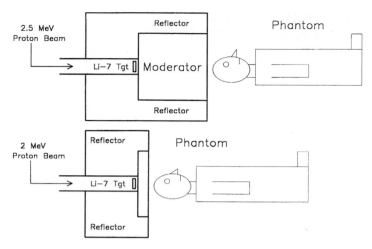

Fig. 2. Comparison of the patient location for the 2.5 and 2 MeV proton beams.

Current design

The design results in Tables 1 and 2, for the configuration nominally shown in Fig. 2, are not necessarily optimal. The results reported herein are at 2.0 MeV proton energy on target, just 120 keV above threshold. The authors have also begun studies with other investigators [4], including some benchmark experiments, at lower energies virtually within 30 keV of threshold, at proton energies of 1.91 MeV where virtually all neutrons are produced in the forward direction in the laboratory system (though isotropic in the center of mass).

Results

Table 1 shows the benchmark results for the 2.0-MeV proton beam on lithium, where the activity per foil at the end of each run, obtained experimentally, is compared with that obtained by the MCNP computer code. A close comparison is seen between the MCNP and experimental results in the gold foils. Table 2 gives a comparison between the existing Brookhaven Medical Research Reactor

Table 1. Comparison of benchmark experiments and MCNP calculations for 2.0 MeV protons. (Gold foil data in phantom.)

Moderator — 2 cm D_2O Target cooling — 2 cm H_2O	Thermal neutrons		Epithermal neutrons	
	MCNP	Experimental	MCNP	Experimental
Activity at surface (Bq/foil)	162	194	283	204
Activity at 1 cm (Bq/foil)	225	225	227	153
Activity at 5 cm (Bq/foil)	128	131	45	32
Activity at 9 cm (Bq/foil)	30	34	5	7

Table 2. Comparison of accelerator-based neutron sources with existing reactor-based neutron sources.

Neutron source	Accelerator [2] (2.5 MeV)	Accelerator [a] (2.0 MeV)	Accelerator [a] (1.92 MeV)	Reactor [b] BMRR (3MW)
Moderator	BeO (20 cm)	BeO (5 cm)	—	—
Target cooling	—	2 cm H_2O	2 cm H_2O	—
Reflector	Al_2O_3	Al_2O_3	Al_2O_3	—
Total useful neutron flux at irradiation position > 1 eV (n/cm^2/s) @ 1 mA	1.02E + 08	4.45E + 08	6.85E + 08	8.4E + 08
γ dose/useful neutron (cGycm^2/n)	2.49E − 11	3.70E − 11	3.96E − 11	2.00E − 11
Fast neutron dose/useful neutron (cGycm^2/n)	2.99E − 11	1.10E − 10	1.63E − 10	4.8E − 11
Current/flux ratio (J/ϕ)	0.66	0.70	0.77	0.80

[a]γ and neutron doses were measured in the phantom (not in air). [b]Reference: H.B. Liu et al. Seventh International Symposium on BNCT abstracts, Zurich, Switzerland, 1996.

beam and the proposed accelerator beams at the conventional (previous) proton energy of 2.5 MeV, that at 2.0 MeV (the main subject of this paper), and results

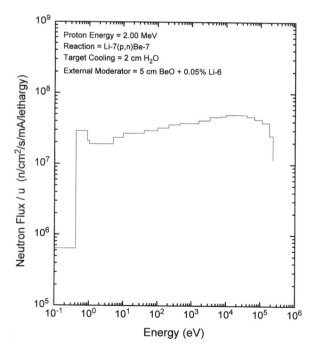

Fig. 3. Neutron flux per unit lethargy.

just above threshold at 1.92 MeV. The plot of neutron flux per unit lethargy, for the case of 2.0 MeV protons and 5 cm BeO moderator with 0.05% ^{6}Li added to both the moderator and aluminum oxide reflector, is shown in Fig. 3. The ^{6}Li "contaminant" is to help remove thermalized neutrons. The angular dependence of neutron yield for the 2.5, 2.0 and 1.92 MeV cases are shown in Fig. 4. This figure clearly shows the predominance of neutron emission in the forward direction for the 2.0 MeV case. In the case of proton energies within 40 keV of the threshold, all of the neutron emission is in the forward hemisphere in the laboratory system.

Summary and Conclusions

The results herein reported yield neutron beams (at the patient) of intensity and forward peaking (J/ϕ) essentially equivalent to that presently available at the BMRR, with target proton beam intensity of only 3 mA. This can be achieved with very little moderator and coolant thickness, nominally 2–7 cm. Both light and heavy-water have been tried, and combinations of both. In this case, it appears that light water has the advantage over heavy water of more effectively reducing the noncapture neutron dose. The use of heavy water, however, results in the highest useful neutron fluxes at the patient. The resulting 6 kW on target can be removed with standard cooling methods.

It is suspected that an optimum energy might lie somewhere between these results at 2.0 MeV and the near threshold results at 1.91 MeV [4]. Furthermore, the variations possible would seem to indicate that designs should be performed

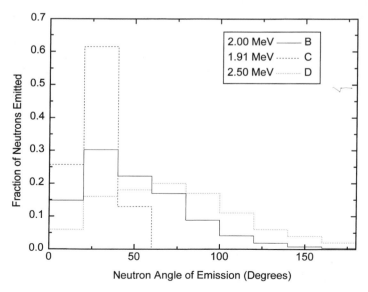

Fig. 4. Fractional neutron yield vs. angular intervals for the ^{7}Li (p,n) ^{7}Be reaction.

on moderator (type and thickness) for each patient situation, varying both the type of moderator and thickness to obtain optimum effect for a particular tumor at a particular depth. The noncapture neutron kerma is higher than for the 2.5 MeV earlier designs, and higher than for the BMRR. It appears that the effective RBE factors are nominally the same for the three accelerator spectra (RBE $\sim$ 2.3), using the factors of Blue et al. [5]. However, it is recommended that there must be further examination of the seriousness of the fast neutron dose, in light of the interest of using combination fast neutron therapy with BNCT boost.

The net effect is that ^{7}Li (p,n) accelerator targets, at only 3 mA proton currents at 2.0 MeV or less, easily state-of-the-art for current accelerator designs (either electrostatic or RFQ accelerators), can produce BNCT beams for treatment of glioblastomas with the intensity and nominal overall effectiveness of that available at the BMRR and other research reactors at present. This result makes it feasible for establishment of brain cancer treatment centers at virtually any hospital or clinic, using accelerators with a capital cost less than two million dollars. These accelerators have essentially none of the safety and licensing issues and have much reduced capital costs compared to the citing and installation of reactors at hospital locations.

References

1. Wang CK, Blue TE, Gahbauer R. A neutronic study of an accelerator based neutron irradiation facility for boron neutron capture therapy. Nucl Tech 1989;84:93.
2. Wu TH, Brugger RM, Kunze JF. Low energy accelerator based neutron sources for Neutron Capture Therapy. In: Soloway AH, Barth RF, Carpenter DE (eds) Advances in Neutron Capture Therapy. New York: Plenum Press, 1993.
3. Dolan TJ. Idaho National Engineering Laboratory: Internal laboratory report, private communication, 1989.
4. Harmon JF, Kudchadker RJ, Kunze JF, Serrano SW, Zhou XL, Harker TD, Hamm RW. Accelerator neutron sources for neutron capture therapy using near threshold charged particles reactions. Fourteenth International Conference on the Applications of Accelerators in Research and Industry, Denton, Texas, 1996.
5. Wollard JE, Blue TE, Gupta N, Gahbauer RA. Development and application of neutron field optimization parameters for an accelerator based neutron source for boron neutron capture therapy. Nucl Tech 1996;115:100.

522

© 1997 Elsevier Science B.V. All rights reserved.
Advances in Neutron Capture Therapy.
Volume I, Medicine and Physics.
B. Larsson, J. Crawford and R. Weinreich, editors.

Operation of a high current tandem electrostatic accelerator for boron neutron capture therapy

R.E. Klinkowstein[1], R.E. Shefer[1], J.C. Yanch[2], W.B. Howard[3], H. Song[3], E. Binello[2], B.W. Blackburn[2], J.L. Daigle[2], S.M. Sears[3], C.H. Goldie[4] and R.J. Ledoux[5]

[1]Newton Scientific, Inc., Winchester, Massachusetts; [2]Department of Nuclear Engineering and Whitaker College of Health Sciences and Technology, Massachusetts Institute of Technology, Cambridge, Massachusetts; [3]Department of Physics, Massachusetts Institute of Technology, Cambridge, Massachusetts; [4]Vivirad High Voltage Corporation, Billerica, Massachusetts; and [5]Pyramid Technical Consultants, Inc., Waltham, Massachusetts, USA

Keywords: accelerator, neutron capture therapy.

Introduction

A high current tandem accelerator for boron neutron capture therapy (BNCT) research has been installed in a shielded facility at the Massachusetts Institute of Technology (MIT) Laboratory for Accelerator Beam Applications (LABA). This accelerator, which can deliver multi-milliampere proton or deuteron beams at energies of up to 4.1 MeV, is being used to validate simulations of optimum neutron beams for BNCT and to assess the suitability of accelerator neutron sources for use in hospital-based treatment facilities. To these ends, several proton- and deuteron-induced nuclear reactions are being investigated, including $^7Li(p,n)$, $^9Be(p,n)$, and $^9Be(d,n)$, and heat removal strategies for the cooling of neutron-producing targets at high accelerator beam power are being tested. Neutron beam designs for the treatment of deep-seated tumors [1] and for the treatment of rheumatoid arthritis [2] are being experimentally evaluated. In addition, shielding requirements for installation of this device in a clinical setting are being determined. In the following sections, we describe the design principles and operation of the accelerator, and progress towards the development of accelerator-based beams suitable for therapy.

The high current tandem accelerator

Figure 1 shows the high current tandem accelerator designed by Newton Scientific, Inc. (NSI) and installed at the MIT LABA. In a tandem accelerator, a negative ion beam is injected into a uniform-gradient accelerating tube and

Address for correspondence: Ruth E. Shefer, Newton Scientific, Inc., 245 Bent Street, Cambridge, MA 02141, USA.

Fig. 1. The 4.1 MeV tandem accelerator installed at the LABA at MIT.

accelerated to a high voltage terminal maintained at a constant, positive potential. There, the ions are stripped of two electrons and the resulting positively charged ions are accelerated in a second uniform-gradient tube to a target at ground potential. When they reach the target, the accelerated ions have attained an energy equal to twice the product of their charge and the terminal voltage. Several features of the accelerator shown in Fig. 1 allow it to operate at currents which surpass those of conventional tandem designs [3]. Firstly, the negative hydrogen or deuterium beam is produced in a multicusp negative ion source designed to deliver up to 5 mA of negative ion current. Stable and reliable operation of this type of source at H^- currents of over 10 mA has been achieved. This is in contrast to other commonly used H- and D-sources, such as duo-plasmatrons or sputter sources, which are typically limited to currents of less than 100 µA. Secondly, the NSI tandem incorporates a high-frequency (20–50 kHz), switch-mode-type, high-voltage generator which can deliver about 8.5 mA of charging current to the high voltage terminal at 1.25 MV, and reduced currents at voltages of up to 2.05 MV. With an overall power efficiency of greater than 90%, the high voltage generator allows the acceleration of 10 kW beams of protons or deuterons to energies of up to 4.1 MeV. Finally, the accelerator utilizes magnetically suppressed accelerating tubes which allow the acceleration of high ion currents with minimal X-ray generation from secondary particles produced in the vacuum beamline.

In addition to the technical requirements for BNCT, considerable attention has been given to the development of an easy-to-use PC-based accelerator control system. The mouse-driven control interface, which was designed and implemented by Pyramid Technical Consultants, allows system functions to be controlled and monitored from a remote computer. While providing full freedom to set all operating parameters, the user interface also provides the option for automatic feedback stabilization of ion source and accelerated current.

As of late summer 1996, the negative ion source and injector have been operated at continuous proton beam currents of 5 mA, and 0.8 mA of current has been accelerated to a water-cooled beam collector at the target position. During operation, no X-radiation was measured at the accelerator tank wall using a survey meter with a sensitivity of 0.1 mr/h. Extension of the accelerator operating regime to 4 mA at 2.5 MeV final beam energy and over 1 mA at 4 MeV is currently underway.

The accelerator system shown in Fig. 1 is 4.3 m in length and weighs approximately 1,000 kg. It's relatively small size and low weight, combined with the very low radiation fields in the vicinity of the accelerator itself during operation, make this device very well suited for hospital installation.

Target and moderator design for BNCT

Towards the development of a practical hospital-based neutron source for BNCT, two aspects of neutron beam design are under investigation: high power accelerator target design, and the characterization of neutron beams produced via the ^{7}Li(p,n), ^{9}Be(p,n), and ^{9}Be(d,n) nuclear reactions. A high-power target using submerged water-jet impingement cooling has been designed and fabricated, and is currently being tested [4]. Heat transfer calculations combined with literature data predict that it should be possible to remove up to 6 kW/cm^2 of beam power using this cooling configuration. A photograph of the prototype target is shown in Fig. 2. The target comprises a target disk 4.4 cm in diameter brazed to a stainless steel housing and cooled directly on its back side by water flow from a submerged nozzle centered behind the surface. The distance from the nozzle to the back surface of the target is variable from 0.25 to 2.5 cm. The predicted maximum power handling capability of the prototype target is 57 kW (3.7 kW/cm^2 critical heat flux) at a coolant flow rate of 9 l/s. Initial heat removal experiments, carried out using an aluminum target disk, have verified theoretical predictions at low power. Aluminum is a useful substitute for beryllium in the evaluation of target performance because of its similar thermal conductivity. These experiments are now being extended to the irradiation of beryllium target disks at high beam power. This target geometry could also be used for the irradiation of lithium by applying a coating of lithium metal (or a less reactive lithium compound) to a suitable substrate disk.

Fig. 2. Prototype high power accelerator target for bombardment of beryllium or lithium.

Experimental verification of neutron dosimetry in a brain phantom has commenced. Monte Carlo simulations have shown that the ^{7}Li(p,n) and ^{9}Be(p,n) reactions can be expected to produce therapeutic neutron beams when combined with suitable moderator and reflector assemblies [1,5]. The latter reaction has the advantage of excellent target thermal and mechanical properties, but requires a higher accelerator energy (~ 4 MeV) to produce neutron yields comparable to ^{7}Li(p,n) at 2.5 MeV. The ^{9}Be(d,n) reaction [6] has a comparable yield to ^{7}Li(p,n) at ~ 2.5 MeV, but requires additional moderation because of its relatively high maximum neutron energy. A dedicated accelerator beamline has been constructed in order to test computational predictions for various moderator/reflector designs. The beamline is contained within a radiation vault having 3–4 ft thick concrete walls and separated from the accelerator control room by a 2 ft thick concrete door. As shown in Fig. 3, the accelerator beam is focused, using a magnetic quadrupole lens, onto a neutron-producing target positioned at the inner wall of a cylindrical lead reflector. For these experiments, a low-power water-cooled target was used. The D_2O moderator material is contained in a cylindrical cavity within the reflector. The neutron irradiation port is 24 cm in diameter and the depth of the moderator can be adjusted from 17 to 27 cm by inserting lead spacers into the reflector cavity. In preliminary experiments, a brain equivalent phantom [7] was placed at the irradiation port and neutron dose vs. depth profiles were measured using calibrated dual ionization chambers. Results obtained for a ^{9}Be(d,n) beam, reported in [8], were in very good agreement with simulation predictions.

Other ongoing research

In addition to the research described, the high current tandem accelerator at MIT LABA is also being used to investigate other aspects of neutron capture

Fig. 3. Accelerator beamline used in neutron dosimetry measurements showing (left to right), quadrupole focusing magnet, lead reflector surrounding D_2O moderator, and brain phantom.

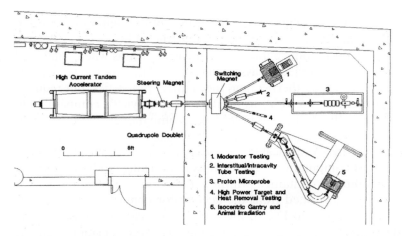

Fig. 4. Layout of the accelerator room and radiation vault, showing switching magnet and five experimental beamlines.

therapy. These include boron neutron capture synovectomy (BNCS) [2,9], a potential new treatment for rheumatoid arthritis, and accelerator-based neutron brachytherapy [10] using an interstitial or intracavity probe. All of this work is presently being conducted using a single accelerator beamline. In late fall of 1996, the accelerator output beamline will be connected to a switching magnet having five independent beamlines, thereby reducing experimental setup time. The installation of an isocentric gantry on one beamline is currently being evaluated. This gantry would allow the potential advantages of multidirectional irradiations for BNCT and BNCS to be experimentally investigated. Figure 4 shows the layout of the accelerator facility, including the five experimental beamlines. A scanning proton microprobe endstation is also planned. The microprobe, which is being constructed by Pyramid Technical Consultants, will be capable of mapping the distribution of trace elements in tissue using proton-induced X-ray emission and nuclear reaction analysis.

Acknowledgements

This work was supported by the US Department of Energy under Grant No. DE-FG02-89ER60874, the US National Institutes of Health under Grant No. R43 AR43680, and the Idaho National Engineering Laboratory University Research Consortium.

References

1. Yanch JC, Zhou X-L, Shefer RE, Klinkowstein RE. Accelerator-based epithermal neutron beam design for neutron capture therapy. Med Phys 1992;19:709–721.

2. Binello E, Shefer RE, Yanch JC. Neutron beam design for boron neutron capture synovectomy. In: Larsson B, Crawford J, Weinreich R (eds) Advances in Neutron Capture Therapy, Volume 1, Medicine and Physics. Amsterdam: Elsevier Science, 1997;459—463 (these proceedings).

3. Shefer RE, Klinkowstein RE, Yanch JC. A high current electrostatic accelerator for boron neutron capture therapy: Proc International Conference on Neutrons in Research and Industry, Crete 1996, SPIE 2867 1997;41—47.

4. Blackburn BW, Klinkowstein RE, Yanch JC, Song H, Howard WB. Development of a high-power, water-cooled beryllium target for the production of neutrons in a high-current tandem accelerator. Proc 14th International Conference on the Applications of Accelerators in Research and Industry, Denton TX 1996;(In press).

5. Howard WB, Yanch JC, Grimes SM, Massey TN, Al-Quaraishi SI, Jacobs DK, Brient CE. Measurement of the ^{9}Be(p,n) thick target spectrum for use in accelerator-based BNCT. Med Phys 1996;23:1233—1235.

6. Meadows JW. The thick target ^{9}Be(d,n) neutron spectra for deuteron energies between 2.6 and 7.0 MeV. Argonne National Laboratory Report ANL/NDM-124. Nov 1991.

7. Harling OK, Roberts KA, Moulin DJ, Rogus RD. Head phantoms for neutron capture therapy. Med Phys 1995;22:579—583.

8. Yanch JC, Shefer RE, Klinkowstein RE, Song H, Blackburn B, Howard WB. Use of the ^{9}Be(d,n) nuclear reaction for BNCT: simulation and experimental measurement. In: Larsson B, Crawford J, Weinreich R (eds) Advances in Neutron Capture Therapy, Volume 1, Medicine and Physics. Amsterdam: Elsevier Science, 1997;564—569 (these proceedings).

9. Binello E, Yanch JC, Shortkroff S, Vivieros C, Young G, Jones AG, Sledge CB, Davison A. In vitro analysis of ^{10}B uptake for boron neutron capture synovectomy. In: Larsson B, Crawford J, Weinreich R (eds) Advances in Neutron Capture Therapy, Volume 2, Chemistry and Biology. Amsterdam: Elsevier Science, 1997;609—613 (these proceedings).

10. Song H, Yanch JC, Klinkowstein RE. An interstitial/intracavity accelerator-based neutron source for fast neutron brachytherapy. In: Larsson B, Crawford J, Weinreich R (eds) Advances in Neutron Capture Therapy, Volume 1, Medicine and Physics. Amsterdam: Elsevier Science, 1997; 543—548 (these proceedings).

528

Accelerator-based intense and directed neutron source for BNCT

V.N. Kononov, V.I. Regushevskiy, N.A. Soloviev and A.I. Leipunskiy

Institute of Physics and Power Engineering, Obninsk, Russia

Introduction

The development of a neutron source with a proper intense neutron energy spectrum and acceptable for hospital application, is a major goal that would greatly expand the use of boron neutron capture therapy (BNCT). The absolute nuclear safety of accelerator-based neutron sources for BNCT makes them very attractive for wide use in medical clinical practice, in comparison with reactor-based ones. The most modern accelerator-based approaches are based on getting extremely intense fast neutron fluxes followed by neutron spectrum softening and space forming in a moderator [1]. This leads to a significant increase in accelerator beam and target power (up to some 10s and even 100 kW). As an alternate approach we present a conceptual design of a neutron source on the basis of the reaction ^{7}Li (p,n) ^{7}Be near the threshold, primarily proposed in [2—4].

Neutron yield and spectra from ^{7}Li (p,n) ^{7}Be reaction near threshold

The ^{7}Li (p,n) ^{7}Be reaction, having a threshold at $E_p = 1881$ keV, is widely used by nuclear physicists as an intense source of monoenergetic neutrons. This reaction has a moderate intensity of accompanying γ radiation from proton reactions with lithium and other target materials. The neutron production cross-section in this reaction is well known [5] and has the feature of a sharp threshold owing to a very wide resonance with J = 2 [6]. Produced neutrons have an isotropic angular distribution in the center of mass (CM) system, and near threshold are emitted in the laboratory system within a narrow cone along the proton beam direction. Thus the neutrons have naturally "kinematic collimation". From a consideration of the ^{7}Li (p,n) ^{7}Be reaction kinematics and using experimental data of reaction cross-section and stopping power protons in lithium, we have derived the following expression for neutron production near threshold up to $E_p = 2,000$ keV in thick lithium targets [3]:

Address for correspondence: V.N. Kononov, Institute of Physics and Power Engineering, 1 Bondarenko Sq., Obninsk, Kaluga Region, 249020, Russia.

$$Y_{\pm} = 3 \cdot 10^3 \sqrt{E_p - 1881} \left(1 + 6\sqrt{\frac{E_p - 1881}{E_p}}\right)^{-2}$$

$$\frac{\alpha(z \pm cos\psi)}{Zcos\psi \pm (49 - sin^2\psi)} \frac{neutron}{eV \cdot sr \cdot \mu C} \tag{1}$$

where $Y_{\pm} = d^2n/dE_n d\omega$ is the double differential neutron yield per neutron energy interval and 1 μC proton charge in neutrons/sr μC eV; E_p is the proton energy in keV; ψ is the angle of neutron emission in the laboratory system relative to the proton beam direction; Z and α are dimensionless parameters; $Z^2 = \alpha^{-2} - sin^2\psi$, $\alpha^2 = M_p M_n E_p (M_{Be} M_{Li}(E_p - 1881))^{-1}$, which involve the masses of the particles taking part in the reaction. In this notation the neutron energy E_n in the laboratory system is [6]:

$$E_{n\pm} = \frac{M_n M_p}{(M_{Be} + M_n)^2} E_p(Z \pm cos\psi)^2 \tag{2}$$

In Eqns. 1 and 2 indexes "+" and "$-$" are evidence of double-valued neutron energy and yield at $\alpha > 1$, corresponding to emission in front or back hemisphere in the CM system. The angular and neutron energy, dependent on the doubly differential neutron yield per μC proton beam for thick metallic lithium target and proton energy $E_p = 1885$ keV, calculated by using Eqns. 1 and 2, is illustrated in Fig. 1A. Neutron yields, calculated and measured by time of flight, are in good agreement [3]. Figure 1B is the total neutron yield per μC in conical layers with a laboratory angle ι and an angular width of 1°. Figure 1 shows the following important features for BNCT of the near-threshold ^{7}Li (p,n) ^{7}Be reaction neutron source:

— the neutron source has a particular space direction and therefore may be used for irradiation in open geometry without a moderator-collimator assembly; and

— the neutron spectrum has a maximum of about 50 keV.

The total neutron yields from a metallic lithium target at proton energy of 1,885 keV and 1,891 keV at proton current 10 mA, are $2.18 \cdot 10^{10}$ and $7.14 \cdot 10^{10}$ n/s. The useful neutron fluxes at the irradiation point, which is 3 cm in front of the target, are $1.7 \cdot 10^9$ and $5.6 \cdot 10^9$ n/cm^{2}s for a target diameter of 5 cm. These are 3.5 and 11 times more useful neutron flux than discussed in [1]. The near-threshold ^{7}Li (p,n) ^{7}Be reaction neutron source allows us to change the irradiation conditions such as a diameter of the irradiation spot, direction of tumor irradiation, etc.

A

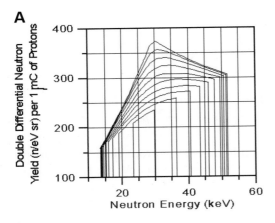

B

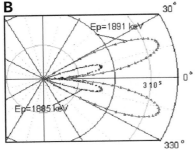

Fig. 1. **A:** Double differential neutron yield $Y = d^2n/dE_n d\omega$ (neutron/eV sr) per µC protons from a thick metallic lithium target at a proton energy of 1885 keV for different angles from 0.5° up to 18.5° with a step of 2° in laboratory system. **B:** Total neutron yield from thick metallic lithium target per µC protons at proton energies of 1885 keV and 1891 keV in cone layers at laboratory angle $\psi \pm$ 0.5° in polar coordinates.

Depth and radial distributions of absorbed dose components

A computer study of absorbed radiation dose distribution for near threshold $^7Li(p,n)$ ^7Be neutrons was carried out to determinate its features. The calculation was performed with the Los Alamos National Laboratory Monte Carlo neutron photon computer code MCNP 4A [7]. As a first step we are testing the computing scheme by comparison with the detailed calculations of Ivanov and Ryabukhin [8]. For the plane parallel to the 20-keV neutron beam we obtained satisfactory agreement with their results. The depth-dose distribution components in a phantom for near-threshold ^7Li (p,n) ^7Be neutrons at $E_p = 1885$ keV, and a target diameter of 5 cm are presented in Fig. 2. The phantom was 3 cm from the target and represents as in [8] a 30-cm-thick block. Its composition is: H-10.1%, C-12.1%, N-3.1% and O-73.6% by weight.

As can be seen in Fig. 2, the maximum absorbed dose to the tumour is $1.5 \cdot 10^{-11}$ to $5 \cdot 10^{-12}$ cGy/source neutron for a ^{10}B concentration of 30 µg/g in

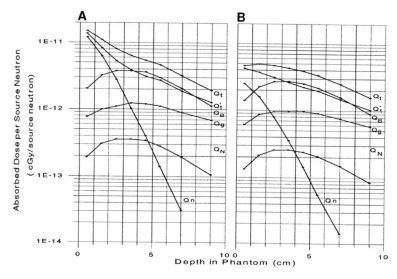

Fig. 2. The absorbed depth-dose distribution in 30-cm-thick phantom near neutron beam axis (**A**) and 3.5 cm from beam axis (**B**). Here, Q_t — total absorbed dose to tumour with 30 μg of ^{10}B/g tissue; Q'_c — total absorbed dose to normal tissue with 10 μg of ^{10}B/g tissue; Q_B — absorbed dose due to ^{10}B (n,α) ^{7}Be reaction with 30 μg of ^{10}B/g tissue; Q_g — absorbed dose due to γ-rays generated in phantom, Q_N — absorbed dose due to ^{14}N (n,p) ^{14}C reaction; and Q_n — absorbed dose due to recoiling nuclei.

the tumour. Therefore, the maximum absorbed dose rate is 0.3—0.1 cGy/s at 10 mA proton beam current and a target diameter of 5 cm. Then for a maximum irradiation dose of 20 Gy to the tumour, the treatment time is about 100 min and at E_p = 1891 keV is only 10 min. The directionality of our neutron source is retained in the radial absorbed dose distribution. It is expected that a more realistic phantom and a higher proton energy would reveal more advantages of accelerator-based near-threshold ^{7}Li (p,n) ^{7}Be sources for BNCT.

Conclusion

The major characteristics of accelerator-based near-threshold ^{7}Li (p,n) ^{7}Be neutron sources for BNCT have been discussed. For a 10 mA proton beam with an energy of 1.885 MeV, the useful neutron yield concentrates in a narrow cone with an angle of 18.6° and is $2.18 \cdot 10^{10}$ neutron/s. The neutron flux, evaluated at the irradiation point, for a target diameter of 5 cm is $1.7 \cdot 10^9$ neutrons/cm^{2}s. With this source it is possible to irradiate in open geometry without a moderator-collimator assembly. The ratio of the total absorbed dose rate to the neutron flux at the irradiation point is $2 \cdot 10^{-10}$ cGy/ncm^{-2}, which is higher than the value of this ratio which has been estimated for a proposed reactor- and accelerator-based BNCT facilities. The maximum absorbed dose rate is 0.3—0.1 cGy/s

532

at a proton beam current of 10 mA, target diameter of 5 cm and phantom-target distance of 3 cm. For a dose of 20 Gy to the tumour, the treatment time is about 100 min and at a proton energy of 1,891 keV it is only 10 min. The therapeutic gain for tumour and normal tissue with ^{10}B concentrations of 30 and 10 μg/g is found to be 1.7.

The proton beam current of 10 mA could be produced today at low energy electrostatic accelerators, e.g., the cascade generator KG-2.5 in IPPE or a compact multimilliampere tandem accelerator [9]. The water cooling will be used to remove 18 kW of beam heating of target at a heat density of 1 kW/cm^2. It follows that the technical possibility exists today to design accelerator-based near-threshold ^{7}Li (p,n) ^{7}Be neutron sources with enough intensity for clinical BNCT applications. Because of the high surface dose, this method is best suited for skin tumours. It could also be used for BNC synovectomy, where the ^{10}B load can be two orders of magnitude higher than in BNCT [10,11]; or in an interstitial scheme [12].

References

1. Wang C-K et al. A Neutronic study of an accelerator-based neutron irradiation facility for boron neutron capture therapy. Nucl Technol 1989;84:93.
2. Kononov VN et al. Accelerator-based neutron sources application for neutron capture therapy. In: Proc 2nd All-Union Symp on the Use of Charged-Particle Accelerators in the National Economy, Leningrad, SU, October 1—3, 1975, vol 2. Leningrad: Efremov Inst. of Electrophysical Apparatus, 1976;60—68 (in Russian).
3. Kononov VN et al. Absolute yield and spectrum of neutrons from ^{7}Li (p,n) ^{7}Be reaction. Atomnaya Energia 1977;43:303—305. (In English: Sov At Energy 1977;43:947.)
4. Kononov VN et al. ^{7}Li (p,n) ^{7}Be reaction near threshold: the prospective neutron source for BNCT. In: Proc 1st Int Workshop on Accelerator-Based Neutron Sources for BNCT, Jackson, USA, September 11—14, 1994, vol 2. 1994;CONF-94096:447—483.
5. Liskien H, Paulsen A. Neutron production cross section and energies for ^{7}Li (p,n) ^{7}Be and ^{7}Li (p,n) ^{7}Be*. Atomic and Nucl Data Tables 1975;15:57—84.
6. Marion TB, Fowler JL (eds). Fast Neutron Physics. New York: Interscience, 1960.
7. Breismeister JF (ed). MCNP-A General Monte Carlo N-Particle Transport Code, Version 4A. LASL-Report:LA-12625-M, 1993.
8. Ivanov VN et al. Tissue doses due to irradiation with neutron beams. Atomnaya Energia 1975;39:360 (in Russian).
9. Shefer RE et al. Tandem electrostatic accelerators for BNCT. In: Proc 1st Int Workshop on Accelerator-Based Neutron Sources for BNCT, Jackson, USA, September 11-14, 1994, vol 1. 1994;89:CONF-94096.
10. Binello E et al. Neutron beam design for boron neutron capture synovectomy. In: Larsson B, Crawford J, Weinreich R (eds) Advances in Neutron Capture Therapy. Volume 1, Medicine and Physics. Amsterdam: Elsevier Science, 1997;459—463 (these proceedings).
11. Binello E et al. In vitro analysis of ^{10}B uptake for boron neutron capture synovectomy. In: Larsson B, Crawford J, Weinreich R (eds) Advances in Neutron Capture Therapy. Volume 2, Chemistry and Biology. Amsterdam: Elsevier Science, 1997;609—613 (these proceedings).
12. Song H et al. An interstitial/intracavity accelerator-based neutron source for fast neutron brachytherapy. In: Larsson B, Crawford J, Weinreich R (eds) Advances in Neutron Capture Therapy. Volume 1, Medicine and Physics. Amsterdam: Elsevier Science, 1997;543—548 (these proceedings).

1997 Elsevier Science B.V.
Advances in Neutron Capture Therapy.
Volume I, Medicine and Physics.
B. Larsson, J. Crawford and R. Weinreich, editors.

Design of a new BNCT facility based on an ESQ accelerator

W.T. Chu[1], D.L. Bleuel[1], R.J. Donahue[1], R.A. Gough[1], M.D. Hoff[1], J. Kwan[1], K.-N. Leung[1], B.A. Ludewigt[1], C. Peters[1], T.L. Phillips[1,2], L.L. Reginato[1], J.W. Staples[1], R.P. Wells[1] and S.S. Yu[1]

[1]*Ernest Orlando Lawrence Berkeley National Laboratory, University of California, Berkeley; and* [2]*University of California, San Francisco, California, USA*

Introduction

We plan to build a boron neutron capture therapy (BNCT) facility based on electrostatic quadrupole (ESQ) accelerator technology. It is an experimentally proven technology capable of delivering a high proton current for producing a neutron intensity greater than what is required for BNCT clinical trials. We also present a design of a lithium neutron production target with adequate cooling of the heat generated by the high-current proton beam.

Clinical requirements for an accelerator-based BNCT facility

Studies have identified a ^{7}Li target as an excellent choice for producing neutrons for BNCT via the ^{7}Li (p,n) ^{7}Be reaction. This reaction has a 1.88 MeV proton energy threshold, and a prominent resonance at 2.3 MeV which drops sharply at 2.5 MeV. Therefore, use of 2.5 MeV protons is generally thought to produce the highest neutron yield for BNCT. Bleuel et al. [1] have studied the dose rate and quality of the epithermal neutron beam as function of moderator thickness and incident proton energy for three moderator materials, namely, BeO, D_2O, and Al/AlF$_3$. The useful (1 eV$-$10 keV) neutron flux peaks at an incident proton energy around 2.3 MeV, where the epithermal neutron flux is roughly 35% higher than that at a proton energy of 2.5 MeV. The neutron energy spectrum can be varied by changing the proton beam energy and moderator thickness with the potential of optimization for different tumor depths. Therefore, the accelerated proton energy should be tunable from 2.0 to 2.5 MeV. Bleuel et al. have also shown that 2.3$-$2.5 MeV protons at a current of 20 mA impinging onto a Li target produce enough neutrons to achieve the same dose rate available at the Brookhaven Biomedical Research Reactor operating at 3 MW, and with appropriate moderation and filtering, provide a clinically superior neutron energy spectrum. Therefore, the accelerated proton current should exceed 20 mA d.c.

Address for correspondence: William T. Chu, 71$-$259, Lawrence Berkeley National Laboratory, University of California, Berkeley, CA 94720, USA.

ESQ accelerator development

At LBNL, Kwan et al. [2] have been developing high-current d.c. accelerators using ESQ columns for neutral particle beam injectors for tokamak fusion reactors, and injectors for heavy ion induction linear accelerators (for inertial fusion reactors). An ESQ accelerating 100 mA of He^+ to 200 keV and another delivering 800 mA of K^+ at 2.0 MeV (1 μs long pulses) have been successfully tested. Unlike straight-line electrostatic accelerators, in ESQ accelerators the transverse focusing is independent of the longitudinal accelerating electric field, and can be very strong (important for a high-current beam) without incurring a longitudinal field near or exceeding the breakdown limit. Another advantage in applying a strong transverse electric field is that the secondary electrons (or ions) generated within the accelerator column are quickly removed, instead of being allowed to multiply and eventually develop into a column arc-down. High energy stray electrons produce unwanted X-rays.

High-voltage power supply development

In order to meet the requirement for future high current application, e.g., up to 100 mA, we decided to investigate the coupled-transformer technique previously considered in the neutral beam program at LBNL to generate high voltages at high currents. Both ferrite-coupled and air-core transformers were considered and small-scale prototypes were constructed and tested. Results indicated that either technique could deliver the desired 100 mA at 2.5 MV but the air-core device is more compatible with the existing steel vacuum tank of the ADAM injector. ADAM is a gas-insulated 2.5 MV d.c. accelerator powered by a dynamitron-type power supply, which was previously used for the SuperHILAC heavy ion linac. Low-voltage tests were performed on the impedance and voltage distribution along the air-core transformer, indicating that the coupled transformer technology offers an order of magnitude lower impedance than the shunt-fed capacitively coupled dynamitron type of drive. It means that 100 mA should be achievable [3].

Ion source

An ion source has been developed to provide high brightness hydrogen ion beams with high atomic species (i.e., mostly H_1^+ and little H_2^+ or H_3^+) and long lifetime between servicing [4]. We have demonstrated that the rf-driven multicusp source is capable of delivering a high current density beam (> 1 A/cm^2) with an atomic hydrogen fraction as high as 94%. Thus the use of a bulky magnetic mass separation magnet can be avoided. The exit aperture diameter is 6 mm and the required rf input power to the source plasma generator is approximately 2.5 kW.

Beam transport system

The extracted proton beam (~ 2.5 MeV) will be transported to the target area through a beam line consisting of a magnetic focusing lens (which is also useful in separating the heavier molecular ions from the protons to prevent wasting heating of the target surface) and a wobbler to spread out the beam spot size.

A conceptual ESQ accelerator design for BNCT application

The main acceleration is done in 13 ESQ modules. One extra nonaccelerating ESQ is placed at the end for beam matching into the transport line. The ESQ has a bore diameter of 6 cm. The column is 3.8 m long and is made of 70 alumina rings that are 45 cm in diameter. The design is modular; each ESQ module has several alumina rings brazed together and the full assembly is held under compression by tie rods. El·ctrode alignment tolerance is less than 0.1 mm. All electrodes are made of co(·r which has good thermal, electrical and vacuum properties. We will reuse , surplus ADAM injector high-pressure vessel, the insulator supporting structure, and the high-voltage dome. The accelerator assembly is enclosed inside a 6.1-m-long, 2.4-m-diameter steel tank. The accelerator column will be pressurized (125 psi) with insulating gas such as sulfur hexafluoride gas (SF_6).

Neutron-production target

A beam of 2.5 MeV protons at 20 mA presents a heat-load of 50 kW to the target. The heat generated by the proton beam must be efficiently removed in order to prevent the lithium from melting (melting point $179°C$). Assuming a diameter of the proton beam of 10 cm and a target area of 100 cm^2, uniform energy deposition would result in a heat-load of 500 W/cm^2. For a Gaussian beam profile, the peak heat-load (in the center) is 1,280 W/cm^2, or by tilting the target to at a $30°$ incident angle the maximum heat-load can be halved to 640 W/cm^2.

Our design is based on a convectively cooled aluminum substrate coated by a 45 μm (effective thickness is 90 μm for $30°$ incident protons) thick Li layer which is protected by a $1-2$ μm thick aluminum coating. Heat is dissipated by water flowing through closely spaced, narrow coolant passages (microchannels) cut into the back side of the heat absorbing surface. This concept relies on enhancing the surface area for heat transfer and utilizing relatively modest heat transfer coefficients. The size and spacing of these channels and the required coolant flow and pressure drop are subject to optimization. The cooling strategy proposed for this application is an adaptation of past experience at LBNL of a high heat-load beam dump and an extension of the microchannel concept to a copper alloy substrate for the design of a photon absorber at the advanced light source. The thermal response was calculated using the finite-element code ANSYS for the target subjected to a Gaussian heat load and cooled by $20°C$ water with a flow velocity of 9 m/s. The result show a maximum temperature at the cooling chan-nels of 103°C which is about 15°C less than the boiling point of water at the ele-vated pressure in the channel. The maximum temperature on the heat-absorbing surface does not exceed 140°C which is well below the melting point of lithium. A structural analysis based on a full three-dimensional finite-element model showed that the maximum thermally induced stress encountered in the cooling substrate is about 130 MPa, which is less than the yield strength of pure alumi-num.

The LBNL BNCT facility

The new BNCT treatment room will be developed in an existing shielded patient irradiation enclosure at the Bevatron, previously used as a treatment room by the heavy ion biomedical program. This room has a useful interior floor area of approximately 6.4 × 8.5 m (55 m^2) and is surrounded by concrete shielding that varies from 1.2−3 m in thickness (see Fig. 1). The accelerator itself will be located immediately outside the irradiation room, in a high-bay experimental hall which has a heavy-duty reinforced floor, and is serviced by a 30 ton crane. An area approximately 18 × 18 m (324 m^2) will accommodate the accelerator, proton beam line and supporting equipment. This site is located in close proxim-ity to the Laboratory's Nuclear Medicine Facilities, the Imaging Facilities and the Isotope Production Cyclotron.

Conclusions

The ESQ technology opens up the possibility of building a high-current d.c. elec-trostatic accelerator that can meet the requirements of BNCT. The ESQ configu-ration has a clear advantage towards suppressing electrical arc-downs and is therefore capable of operating at high current. At present, the critical path is the development of a compact, high current, multimegavolt d.c. power supply and a lithium target that can withstand the high beam power.

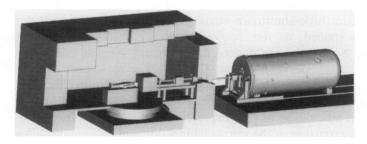

Fig. 1. A schematic drawing showing the ESQ accelerator, the external beam line through the shield-ing wall, the moderator assembly, and a patient on the patient positioner inside the shielded treatment room.

Acknowledgements

This work is supported by the Director, Office of Energy Research of the US Department of Energy under Contract No. DE-AC03-76SF00098.

References

1. Bleuel DL, Donahue RJ, Ludewigt BA. On optimizing the ^{7}Li (p,n) proton beam energy and moderator material for BNCT. Presented at the Fourteenth International Conference on the Application of Accelerators in Research and Industry, Denton, Texas, November 6—9, 1996; to be published in the Proc. of the Conference (1997).
2. Kwan JW, Anderson OA, Reginato LL, Vella MC, Yu SS. Electrostatic quadrupole DC accelerators for BNCT applications. Proc of the First Int Workshop on Accelerator-Based Neutron Sources for Boron Neutron Capture Therapy. Jackson, WY, Sept. 11—14, 1994. Idaho National Engineering Laboratory: 1995;CONF-940976:111—120 also LBL #35540.
3. Reginato LL, Ayers J, Johnson R, Peters C, Stevenson R. Designing power supplies for 2.5 MV, 100 mA d.c. for BNCT. Presented at the Fourteenth International Conference on the Application of Accelerators in Research and Industry. Denton, Texas, November 6—9, 1996; to be published in the Proc of the Conference (1997).
4. Leung K-N. Ion Sources for High Purity Ions. 1996;LBNL-39051.

538

Increase of the neutron fluence with a ^{238}U reflector for a spallation target based epithermal beam

Jean-Philippe Pignol[1], Pascal Cuendet[3], Pierre Chauvel[1], Cheikh Diop[3], Nicole Brassart[1], Georges Fares[2], Joël Herault[1], Alain Ballagny[3] and Ahmed Hachem[2]

[1]*Cyclotron Biomédical, Nice;* [2]*Laboratoire de Radiochimie, Parc Valrose, Nice; and* [3]*CEA, CEN de Saclay, Gif sur Yvette cedex, France*

Introduction

Neutron capture therapy (NCT) requires a very high flux of moderated and filtered neutrons to permit patient irradiations with a total fluence between 10^{12} and 10^{13} neutron.cm^{-2}, delivered in a reasonable time (i.e., less than 1 h/fraction) [1]. On the other hand to ensure the economic viability of such installations, which means efficient patient handling, the epithermal beam must be available in a hospital or at least in a nearby facility. Among accelerator-based facilities designed to produce such beams are the spallation sources, in which high energy proton beam hits a target composed of heavy elements [2,3]. There are many cyclotrons dedicated to fast neutron therapy all around the world. The most recent ones produce fast neutrons through the reaction of high-energy protons on a thick beryllium target. In these facilities the initial proton beams are designed for fast neutron therapy (i.e., 50–70 MeV with a current of 20–40 μA), and therefore are well below the minimum requirements for NCT based on spallation targets [3].

We have tried in this work to study the feasibility of an epithermal beam based on the characteristics of the Nice or Louvain-la-Neuve biomedical cyclotrons (60–65 MeV and 25 μA protons) which are very similar to the Louvain la Neuve cyclotron. In order to increase the primary neutron flux we have used a ^{238}U target, together with a reflector made of the same material. The reflector plus a moderator/filter assembly have been evaluated with the FLUKA [4] and MCNP-4A codes [5].

Material and Methods

The calculation was done in three steps:
1. The primary neutron yield was simulated for various proton energies (34, 65, 100 and 256 MeV) with the FLUKA code [4]. A spherical, thick target made of ^{238}U, larger than the proton range, was simulated, surrounded by low

pressure gas, in order to obtain the double-differential neutron yield for 12 logarithmic energy bins and for seven different angles (0—15°, 15—45°, 45—75°, 75—105°, 105—135°, 135—165° and 165—180°). The yield was expressed in neutrons/bin.proton source, i.e., integrated over the energy range and the solid angle. The overall neutron yield was also calculated.

2. The transport of these neutrons was simulated with MCNP-4A Monte Carlo code [5], using ENDF/B-6, or when available (for hydrogen, oxygen and carbon) ZZ-LA100 [6] cross-sections, which are ENDF/B-6 evaluations for neutrons of energy up to 100 MeV Various configurations of the reflector, made of lead, tungsten, iron or uranium were tested in order to augment the neutron flux at the irradiation port. Finally, a 10-cm radius reflector embedded in a protector made of PbF_2 [7] and boronated polyethylene was used for further calculations. A moderator/filter assembly was tested, made of 324 mm of heavy water, followed by a cadmium foil of 1-mm thickness and 100 mm of lead (Fig. 1). The external dimensions of the final assembly were $80 \times 80 \times 82.5$ cm.

3. At the irradiation port, the energy deposition was linked to the different components of the beam, i.e., γ and fast neutrons, and neutron capture reactions on hydrogen, nitrogen and an assumed 30 ppm ^{10}B concentration in a tumor.

Results

The total initial neutron yields over 4π, evaluated with FLUKA in neutrons per source proton, were 0.034, 0.172, 0.499, 2.829 for 34, 65, 100 and 256 MeV protons, respectively. The yields at various angles and at different energies for 256 MeV protons have been compared with the HIEAS experimental benchmark distributed through the NEA data bank [8]. The agreement between experimental and calculated data was found to be very good at this high energy.

Table 1 shows that the use of a ^{238}U reflector allows an increase of nearly 30% in the total neutron yield at 90°, essentially due to fission reactions rather than the (n,xn) reaction.

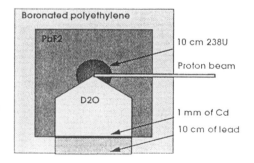

Fig. 1. Target and moderator assembly used for simulation.

Table 1: Increase of the primary neutron yield using various reflector materials. The fast fissions produced in ^{238}U explain its superiority.

Material	(n,xn)	Fission	Total/neutron source
^{238}U	0.05	0.27	1.32
Fe	0.02	0	1.02
W	0.06	0	1.06
Pb	0.07	0	1.07

The spectrum at the epithermal port as calculated with MCNP-4A is shown in Fig. 2.

The thermal component of this spectrum is removed efficiently by the Cd foil, and while the primary neutrons are mainly emitted at 1 MeV, the heavy water moderator assembly shifted this energy to the epithermal range. On the other hand, a strong 1 MeV component persists in the final spectrum, which is responsible for an undesirable background dose deposition in the phantom. Figure 3 shows the dose calculated in a phantom made of human tissue equivalent material. The different components have been modified following previously published RBE values [9,10].

Discussion

For the target design presented here, it can be calculated that an irradiation with a total fluence of $5 \cdot 10^{12}$ n/cm^2 at 5-cm depth will require an irradiation time of 2 h, which is a meaningful value for clinical use. The main interest is that the calculations are based on the characteristics of existing biomedical cyclotron proton

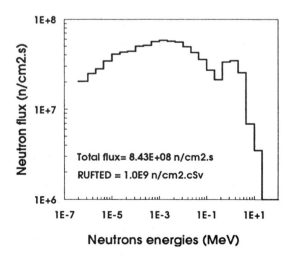

Fig. 2. Neutron spectrum at the irradiation port of the spallation target.

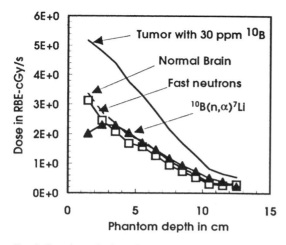

Fig. 3. Depth equivalent dose curve in a spherical phantom using previously published RBE values [9,10].

beams, i.e., a 65 MeV proton beam with a current of 20 μA, values which were initially designed for fast neutron therapy. We can conclude that a suitable epithermal beam is possible at this kind of facility, and that the use of a target and a reflector made of ^{238}U can improve the neutron yield. The other alternatives which have been published rely on fission plates [11], but these will transform the facility into a nuclear installation, subject to considerably more stringent rules.

Acknowledgements

The Monte Carlo code MCNP-4A and the cross-section files ENDF/B5, B6 and ZZ-LA100 were kindly provided to our institution by the NEA data bank, Paris.

References

1. Fairchild RG, Bond VP. Current status of 10B-neutron capture therapy: Enhancement of tumor dose via beam filtration and dose rate, and the effects of these parameters on minimum boron content: a theoretical evaluation. Int J Rad Onc Biol Phys 1985;11:831–840.
2. Conde H, Crawford JF, Dahl B, Grusell E, Larsson B, Petterson CB, Reist H, Sjostrand NG, Sornsuntisook O, Thuresson L. The production by 72 MeV protons of keV neutrons for ^{10}B neutron capture therapy. Strahlenther Oncol 1989;165:340–342.
3. Arkuszewski J, Crawford JF, Stepanek J, Teichmann S. Neutron production for BNCT by protons of different energies. Proceedings of the International Workshop on Accelerator-Based Neutron Sources for BNCT, Jackson, Wyoming, USA, 11–14 September 1994.
4. Fasso A, Ferrari A, Ranft J, Sala PR. FLUKA: Performances and Applications in the Intermediate Energy Range. Proceedings of the Specialists' Meeting on Shielding Aspects of Accelerators, Target and Irradiation Facilities. Arlington, Texas, April 28–29 1994.
5. Briesmeister JF (ed) MCNP — A General Monte Carlo Code for Neutron and Photon Trans-

port, version 4-A. Los Alamos National Laboratory, LA-7396-M, 1986.

6. Young PG (ed) Transport Data Libraries for Incident Proton and Neutron Energies to 100 MeV. Los Alamos National Laboratory, LA-11753 MS, July 1990.

7. Liu HB. PbF_2 compared to Al_2O_3 and AlF_3 to produce an epithermal neutron beam for radiotherapy. Med Phys 1996;23:279—280.

8. Nakashima H, Sakamoto Y, Tanaka SI, Hasegawa A, Fukahori T, Nishida T, Sasamoto N, Tanaka S, Nakamura T, Shin K, Hirayama H, Ban S, Uwamino Y, Ishibashi K, Kawashi K, Hayashi K, Iwai S, Sato O, Yamano N. Benchmark problems for intermediate and high energy accelerator shielding. JAERI Data Code 94—012.

9. Coderre J, Makar M, Micca P, Nawrocky M, Liu HB, Joel D, Slatkin D, Amols H. Derivations of relative biological effectiveness for the high-LET radiations produced during boron neutron capture irradiations of the 9L rat gliosarcoma in vitro and in vivo. Int J Radiat Oncol Biol Phys 1993;27:1121—1129.

10. Morris G, Coderre J, Hopewell J, Micca P, Nawrocky M, Liu HB, Bywaters T. Response of the central nervous system to boron neutron capture therapy using a rat spinal cord model. Radiother Oncol 1994;32:249—255.

11. Liu HB, Brugger RM, Rorer DC, Tichler PR, Hu JP. Design of a high-flux epithermal neutron beam using ^{235}U fission plates at the Brookhaven Medical Research Reactor. Med Phys 1994;21:1627—1631.

An interstitial/intracavity accelerator-based neutron source for fast neutron brachytherapy

H. Song[1], J.C. Yanch[2] and R.E. Klinkowstein[3]

[1]Department of Physics, Massachusetts Institute of Technology; [2]Department of Nuclear Engineering, Massachusetts Institute of Technology; and [3]Newton Scientific, Inc., Cambridge, Massachusetts, USA

Introduction

The potential of accelerator-based fast neutron brachytherapy, with or without dose augmentation by boron neutron capture therapy (BNCT), is under investigation at MIT's laboratory for accelerator beam applications (LABA). The proposed therapy modality involves the interstitial or intracavity insertion of a narrow, evacuated accelerator beam tube such that its tip (containing the neutron producing target) is placed within, or in close proximity to, the tumor [1—3]. Like fast-neutron brachytherapy using ^{252}Cf needles [4], this approach is likely to be most effective in the treatment of large, bulky tumors due to the long mean free path of energetic neutrons. In addition, for spatially extended tumors or disseminated disease, the effectiveness of fast neutron brachytherapy may be further improved by dose augmentation via boron neutron capture therapy due to boron atoms located in distant tumor cells. The magnitude of this additional dose will depend not only on the concentration of ^{10}B in the tumor cells, but also on the distance from the neutron source and on the energy spectrum of the neutrons leaving the source. In this last respect, accelerator-based fast neutron brachytherapy offers a distinct advantage over the neutron-emitting radioisotope, ^{252}Cf, in that the neutron energy spectrum can be somewhat tailored to the presumed target volume simply by adjusting the energy of the accelerated charged particle.

A number of aspects of accelerator-based fast neutron brachytherapy are under investigation, including dose distribution, treatment time, heat dissipation, candidate charged particle reactions and dose augmentation by BNCT. Encouraging results of dosimetric and heat removal calculations [2,3] (briefly described below) led to the design and construction of a prototype device for use in experimental studies. Reported here are preliminary measurements of heat removal following proton bombardment of the prototype device using the tandem electrostatic accelerator [5] at LABA.

Dosimetry and heat transfer calculations

Dosimetric simulations of a neutron source in the center of a brain-equivalent

544

phantom have demonstrated that a fast neutron dose of 20 Gy could be delivered to the boundary of a 5-cm-diameter tumor in less than 2 min/mA of particle current for 2.5 MeV protons on lithium, 4.0 MeV protons on beryllium, or 2.6 MeV deuterons on beryllium [2,3]. Treatment time either decreases or increases as the particle bombarding energy is raised or lowered, and neutron yield is correspondingly enhanced or reduced. The magnitude of dose augmentation by BNCT is highest for low particle bombarding energies but can be as much as 60% 2 cm beyond the edge of a 6-cm diameter tumor using 2.5 MeV protons on lithium [2]. This dose enhancement is considerably larger than that seen with ^{252}Cf sources [6]. Thus, from a dosimetric point of view, accelerator-based fast neutron brachytherapy appears to be extremely promising both with and without dose augmentation by BNCT.

An investigation of the ability of brain tissue to dissipate heat (by conduction and by convection by circulating blood) quickly demonstrates, however, that the temperature rise near the neutron-producing tip will be clinically unacceptable and active cooling of the device must be carried out [2,3]. The initial prototype of the brachytherapy device was therefore designed as a tube-in-tube, as illustrated in Fig. 1. The inner evacuated accelerator tube has an inner diameter of 3 mm and is placed inside a 6-mm outer-diameter tube; cooling water running between the tubes carries away much of the heat generated at the tip and along the sides of the inner accelerator tube. Heat transfer calculations predict that a maximum heat load of 567 W can be carried away with this configuration assuming a maximum tissue temperature rise of 3°C and a water flow rate through the device (driven by tap water pressure) of 45 cm^3/s. Knowledge of the maximum tolerable heat load permits the determination of maximum accelerator beam currents for various neutron producing reactions and various bombarding energies. Then, using dose vs. distance curves, generated by computer simulation, it is possible to determine treatment time for the various reactions, as a function of tumor size. Examples are provided in Table 1 which shows maximum allowable beam current, and total time (assuming a power level of 567 W) to deliver 20

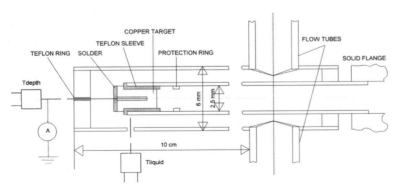

Fig. 1. Schematic illustration of the prototype accelerator-based brachytherapy device.

Table 1. Beam currents and treatment time for various reactions.

Reactions	Beam current (μA)	Treat time (min)
$^7Li(p,n)$ $E_p =2.5$	227	7.3
$^7Li(p,n)$ $E_p =3.0$	189	3.4
$^7Li(p,n)$ $E_p =4.1$	138	1.5
$^9Be(p,n)$ $E_p =4.0$	142	5.2
$^9Be(d,n)$ $E_d =2.6$	218	3.4

Gy to the edge of a 5-cm diameter tumor for a number of different charged parti-cle reactions. (Note that no neutron RBE values have been used in the calculation of treatment times.)

Heat transfer calculations were carried out with the assumption that local boil-ing along the outer surface of the inner tube does not occur. Such boiling could create a drop in water pressure in the cooling channel, resulting in failure of the cooling system. For this reason the prototype design illustrated in Fig. 1 was con-structed and experimental heat removal studies were initiated using the 4.1 MeV tandem electrostatic accelerator at MIT LABA. In the interest of radiation safety, a neutron-producing target material was not included on the target cap for these experiments. The copper target cap is electrically insulated from the remainder of the device with a Teflon sleeve so that accurate estimates of accelerator current, reaching the target location, can be made. One thermocouple inserted deep into the cap and soldered in place, measures the temperature inside the target cap, T_{depth} (the layer of soft solder is not uniform in thickness contributing some measure of uncertainty to calculations of heat transfer). A second thermocouple measures the local water temperature, T_{liquid}, in the target region to ensure that local boiling does not occur.

Experimental investigation of heat removal

Figure 2 shows the prototype device mounted on the accelerator beam line at LABA. Earlier attempts to deliver sufficient particle current to the tip of the inner tube with the device mounted immediately after the accelerator (Fig. 2A) were unsuccessful due to the large beam diameter relative to the solid angle subtended by the tip of the 10-cm-long inner tube. Recent experiments, however, have been carried out with a steering magnet and a quadrupole doublet added to the beam line so that the beam can be steered and focused. In addition, the tube alignment relative to the beam-axis can now be adjusted using two stepping motors along the two axes perpendicular to the beam. These additions are seen in Fig. 2B which shows the needle tube and stepping motors in the foreground and the quadrupole magnet in the background. The steering magnet and accel-erator are located in an adjacent room behind the 3-ft-thick concrete wall seen in Fig. 2B.

A water-cooled aperture used to limit the beam diameter to 2.54 mm was

546

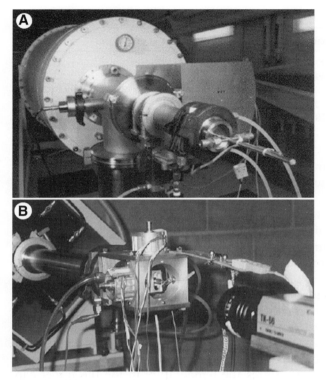

Fig. 2. **A**: The prototype brachytherapy device is shown mounted immediately following the accelerator on the beam line at LABA. **B**: The device is now shown mounted following a focusing magnet to direct the beam down the tube. The steering magnet and accelerator are located in an adjacent room. Two stepping motors are used to position the device so that maximum beam current reaches the tip.

placed immediately before the brachytherapy tube. In addition to the two temperature measurements (T_{depth} and T_{liquid}), measurements of accelerator beam current deposited on the aperture, on the target cap, and on the rest of the inner tube were made at various heat loads. Assuming a uniform heat flux from the vacuum surface to the liquid, the temperature profiles within the target were calculated from T_{depth} using the heat conduction equation:

$$H = Ak(\Delta T/\Delta X)$$

where $\Delta T/\Delta X$ is the temperature gradient along the target cap, H is the heat load, A is the cross-sectional area of the target, and k is the thermal conductivity. The cooling water was maintained at a flow rate of 0.8 l/min with a temperature between 16 and 18°C throughout the experiment. At a head load of 38 W, the largest heat load generated in this experiment, the temperature profile was determined to be: target surface 147°C, T_{depth} 120°C, copper-solder surface 71°C, and solder-liquid surface 29°C.

Discussion and Conclusions

Although the total heat load delivered to the target cap in these preliminary experiments is not large, a number of conclusions can already be reached. First, using appropriate steering and focusing elements it is possible to deliver a significant fraction of accelerator beam current down the narrow inner tube to reach the tip. Note, however, the dimensions of the prototype device were chosen to be as small as practicable for the case of interstitial insertion into the brain. Clinical precedent exists for both neutron brachytherapy of cranial tumors [4], and for accelerator-based (photon) brachytherapy in the brain [7]. For clinical situations involving intracavity insertion of the device, the requirement for small dimensions can be relaxed, considerably increasing both the fraction of accelerator beam on target, and the volume of coolant flow between the tubes. This in turn leads to an increase in the total allowable current on target and higher potential dose rates.

Second, although the preliminary experiments described here deposited a maximum heat load of only 38 W on the tube tip, this power level already corresponds to neutron dose rates (and therefore total therapy times) which is practical for clinical treatment. The time to deliver a total tumor dose of 20 Gy to the boundary of a 5-cm-diameter tumor (assuming no dose augmentation by BNCT) ranges from 30 to 120 min, for the reactions and particle energies listed in Table 1. If neutron RBE values of 3.8 are applied, these treatment times are reduced to between 8 and 30 min.

Third, with a target surface temperature of only 147°C, it may be possible to use the copper target cap as a backing for either a lithium or a beryllium target. An alternative possibility is to make the target cap of beryllium instead of copper. Beryllium has a thermal conductivity slightly more than half that of copper. The temperature gradient within the target cap will then be about twice that seen with copper. Calculation of heat conduction is straightforward and predicts a target surface temperature of approximately 215°C, considerably below that of beryllium's melting temperature of 1,290°C.

Future experimental work will involve testing heat removal as heat load is increased beyond the 38 W measured here. A neutron-producing target will then be inserted into the device, and dosimetric characterization using different particle bombarding energies, will be carried out in a water phantom. Should this device prove to be of sufficient clinical interest, a number of practical issues would need to be addressed. For instance, in the experiment described here, pressure exerted on the outside of the device tip assisted in aligning the axis of the tube with the accelerator beam. In a clinical setting, other means of positioning the tube will be required. For example, supports with adjustable lengths attached close to the opposite end of the tube may be useful. Also, current experiments are carried out with the brachytherapy fixed area horizontally aligned. In the clinic, accurate positioning of the tube within the patient would be carried out using an isocentric gantry system, such as the system proposed previously for multidirectional external delivery of epithermal neutron beams [8].

References

1. Crawford J. The potential of internal neutron sources in capture therapy. In: Allen B et al. (eds) Progress in Neutron Capture Therapy for Cancer. New York: Plenum Press, 1992;203—205.
2. Song HJ, Yanch JC. An interstitial accelerator-based neutron source for fast neutron brachytherapy. In: Proceedings of the 1996 Topical Meeting: Radiation Protection and Shielding, No. Falmouth, MA, April 21—25, 1996, Advances and Applications in Radiation Protection and Shielding. La Grange Park, IL: American Nuclear Society, 1996;2;665—672.
3. Song HJ, Yanch JC, Klinkowstein RE. An accelerator-based neutron source for fast neutron brachytherapy. In: Duggan JL, Morgan IL (eds) Proceedings of the 14th International Conference on the Application of Accelerators in Research & Industry, part two, Denton, Texas, November 1996. New York: American Institute of Physics Press, 1996;1273—1276.
4. Patchell RA, Murayama Y, Tibbs PA, Beach JL, Kryscio RJ, Young AB. Neutron interstitial brachytherapy for malignant gliomas: a pilot study. J Neurosurg 1988;68:67—72.
5. Klinkowstein RE et al. Operation of a high current tandem electrostatic accelerator for boron neutron capture therapy. In: Larsson B, Crawford J, Weinreich R (eds) Advances in Neutron Capture Therapy. Volume 1, Medicine and Physics. Amsterdam: Elsevier Science, 1997; 522—527 (these proceedings).
6. Yanch JC, Zamenhof R. Dosimetry of ^{252}Cf sources for neutron radiotherapy with and without augmentation by BNCT. Radiat Res 1992;131:249—256.
7. Dinsmore M, Harte KJ, Sliski AP, Smith DO, Nomikos PM, Dalterio MJ, Boom AJ, Leonard WF, Oettinger PE and Yanch JC. A new miniature X-ray source for interstitial 1992; radiosurgery: device description. Med Phys 1996;23(1):45—52.
8. Yanch JC, Shefer RE, Binello E. Design of low-energy neutron beams for boron neutron capture synovectomy. In: Vourvopoulos F (ed) Neutrons in Research and Industry. Bellingham, WA: SPIE, 1997;2867:31—40.

Intense cyclotron-based neutron sources for medical applications

Pascal Cohilis, Yves Jongen and Thierry Delvigne
Ion Beam Applications s.a. (IBA), Chemin du Cyclotron, Louvain-la-Neuve, Belgium

Introduction

Since their discovery in 1932, neutrons have played an important role in fundamental research. Nowadays, neutrons also have a wide range of applications in various other disciplines, such as energy applications, medicine, biology, materials science, and in industry [1–3]. In order to meet all the requirements for neutrons in these different fields, much effort has been devoted to the development of appropriate sources. Clearly, no single type of source can satisfy the various needs of the different applications. Besides the use of a source such as ^{252}Cf, which undergoes spontaneous nuclear fission accompanied by the emission of neutrons, three types of methods are presently used to produce neutrons: nuclear reactions produced by the radiation emitted from radioactive isotopes [2,4,5]; the fission process in nuclear reactors [2]; and nuclear reactions produced by energetic charged particles accelerated on suitable targets. The present paper will concentrate on the third method.

Accelerator-based neutron sources

Energetic charged particles accelerated onto suitable targets produce a wide variety of reactions involving the emission of neutrons. It is therefore obvious that accelerators, like electrostatic generators and cyclotrons for example, are adaptable as sources of neutrons [2,4–7]. In particular, the production of nearly monoenergetic neutrons over a wide range of energies is one of the most valuable functions of accelerators. The important characteristics for each of the source reactions used for this purpose are their kinematic quantities (Q-values, etc.,), their excitation functions, their angular distributions and the competing neutron-producing reactions.

The following source reactions are commonly used for the production of monoenergetic neutron beams in the energy range of 0.1–20 MeV: ^{7}Li(p,n)^{7}Be, ^{3}H(p,n)^{3}He, ^{2}H(d,n)^{3}He, and ^{3}H(d,n)^{4}He. In the range of a few keV to about 1

Address for correspondence: Pascal Cohilis, Ion Beam Applications s.a. (IBA), Chemin du Cyclotron, 3 B-1348 Louvain-la-Neuve, Belgium.

MeV, (p,n) reactions in a number of medium weight nuclei, like ^{45}Sc and ^{63}Cu for example, are also commonly used. Other reactions such as ^{7}Li(d,n)^{8}Be and ^{9}Be(d,n)^{10}B are used to produce high neutron yields, but with more complicated neutron spectra. For example, the ^{9}Be(d,n)^{10}B reaction produces a neutron spectrum consisting of a number of peaks, so the reaction is used as a source of neutrons which are then thermalised.

The yields of these commonly used neutron-producing reactions are generally well-known [7]. For example, the ^{9}Be(d,n)^{10}B reaction is a good candidate as a copious neutron source with low and medium energy cyclotrons when there are no particular requirements for monoenergetic neutrons. Other reactions for this purpose include ^{7}Li(p,n)^{7}Be and ^{9}Be(p,n)^{9}B, which produce high yields of neutrons of mixed energy when used in conjunction with accelerators in the 5—20 MeV range.

The accelerator-produced neutron fluxes will depend either on the maximum beam current available from the accelerator or the maximum amount of heat which can be dissipated in the target. The power dissipation at a well-cooled beryllium target can easily reach 1 kW, i.e., 100 μA at 10 MeV, thus giving a yield of 10^{12} neutron·s^{-1} for the ^{9}Be(d,n)^{10}B reaction [7]. Therefore, taking water as moderator and a slowing-down length of 5.7 cm, the thermal flux attainable from this reaction will be around $2.5 \cdot 10^{9}$ neutrons·cm^{-2}·s^{-1}.

Accelerators, and in particular low or medium energy cyclotrons, should therefore be taken into account when considering the installation of a neutron source facility. In the past, cyclotrons were, above all, confined to fundamental research. They were complicated machines needing a staff of qualified personnel for operation and maintenance. The recent evolution in cyclotron technology may open up new horizons. Nowadays, cyclotrons like those designed for medical radioisotope production are compact, entirely automated and reliable devices. Some of them are designed to give very high extracted beam intensities (a few mA) while keeping the power consumption very low.

Neutron sources based on IBA cyclotrons

Some of the IBA cyclotrons [8,9] presently used for automatic radioisotope production are well suited for economic copious neutron production through some of the indicated nuclear reactions.

For example, Cyclone 30 is a 30 MeV, fixed-field, fixed-frequency, H^{-} cyclotron for radioisotope production. Typical extracted currents are between 400 μA and 2000 μA, according to the versions. Cyclone 18/9 (18 MeV proton, 9 MeV deuteron) and Cyclone 10/5 (10 MeV proton, 5 MeV deuteron) are negative ion cyclotrons equipped with two permanently installed internal sources, one for H^{-}, the other for D^{-} ions. The extraction of ions is done by the stripping method. Extracted currents are around 35 μA for deuterons and in the 60—100 μA range for protons. The Cyclone 18+ cyclotron is a positive ion version of the 18/9 cyclotron, delivering 18 MeV proton beams with typical intensities of 2 mA. The

Cyclone 3D is an extremely compact cyclotron delivering deuterons of 3.8 MeV. The extraction is performed by means of an electrostatic deflector. Typical external beam intensity is around 50 µA, but upgraded versions at 100 µA and 2 mA are possible. All these cyclotrons are designed for easy operation and reliability. They are entirely controlled by a high-level programmable logic controller with a user-friendly, PC-based Windows® interface, making all aspects of cyclotron operation accessible to low-qualification personnel.

Table 1 presents neutron yields and fluxes calculated for typical beams accelerated by these compact cyclotrons onto thick beryllium targets. Neutron yields are based on [7]. Thermal neutron fluxes are calculated assuming a water or similar hydrogenous material as moderator and a slowing-down distance of 5.7 cm [2]. The purpose of these calculations is only to indicate the orders of magnitude of the thermal fluxes available; they neglect such factors as neutron capture in the moderator for example. The calculated values are several orders of magnitude higher than those obtained from radioisotope neutron sources, and typically only one order of magnitude smaller than the values obtained from nuclear reactors, which are the most intense neutron sources now available. They also compare well with D-T generators, like sealed-tube generators for example, which deliver neutrons in the range 10^8-10^{12} neutrons $\cdot s^{-1}$[4].

The ADONIS system: an intense, cyclotron-driven, subcritical neutron source

Technetium 99-m, the most widely used radioisotope in nuclear medicine, is normally supplied to hospitals as ^{99}Mo/^{99m}Tc generators. Most of the ^{99}Mo used in nuclear medicine is obtained as a fission product of ^{235}U and is produced in a very small number of aging research reactors which are due, in the next few years, for major refurbishment or decommissioning. An attractive, competitive alternative to these nuclear reactors also used for research, industrial applications, and medical applications, is ADONIS (Accelerator-Driven Optimised Nuclear Irradiation System) which is a cyclotron-based spallation neutron source with neutron multiplication by fission [10].

Table 1. Neutron yields and thermal neutron fluxes calculated for typical beams accelerated by IBA compact cyclotrons on thick beryllium targets.

IBA cyclotron	Incident particle	Incident energy (MeV)	Beam intensity (µA)	Yield (neutrons·s^{-1})	Flux (neutrons·cm^{-2}·s^{-1})
Cyclone 3D	d	3.8	50	1.4×10^{11}	3.4×10^8
Cyclone 3D	d	3.8	100	2.9×10^{11}	7.1×10^8
Cyclone 3D	d	3.8	2000	5.7×10^{12}	1.4×10^{10}
Cyclone 18/9	p	18	100	1.0×10^{13}	2.4×10^{10}
Cyclone 18+	p	18	2000	2.1×10^{14}	5.1×10^{11}
Cyclone 30	p	30	400	1.3×10^{14}	3.2×10^{11}
Cyclone 30	p	30	800	2.6×10^{14}	6.4×10^{11}
Cyclone 30	p	30	2000	6.5×10^{14}	1.6×10^{12}

The system includes a 150 MeV, high-intensity cyclotron and a molten Pb-Bi primary target surrounded by secondary targets in a water moderator. The secondary targets contain a subcritical amount of highly enriched ^{235}U, for neutron multiplication. Because the mass of ^{235}U is strictly subcritical, and arranged so as to produce the highest possible reactivity, any perturbation to the system will reduce the reactivity. The mechanical layout of the system is such that the introduction of additional targets is a mechanical impossibility. The noncritical nature of the system makes it more acceptable for the public than a nuclear reactor and should simplify the licensing process. Price, cost of operation, disposal of radiowaste and of decommissioning are also advantageous compared to nuclear reactors.

The primary target material is a flowing liquid lead-bismuth eutectic alloy. The flowing target allows the heat to be transported through convection of the target material itself. The proposed target is vertical with the liquid lead-bismuth flowing out of a ring-type nozzle into an open channel. Here the fluid interacts with the proton beam and is in direct contact with the vacuum. The flow exits the bottom of the target region, is pumped through a heat exchanger, and then returns to the target. A drain tank is used to hold the solid and liquid alloy during start-up or shut-down. Electromagnetic pumps were chosen to deliver the forced convection in the Pb-Bi circuit. The ^{235}U secondary targets are planar and placed around the spallation source in an annulus destined to cool them. They are supposed to be placed in two storeys with 10 targets per storey. The optimal configuration has been calculated with neutronic calculation codes. Typical thermal neutron fluxes at the location of the secondary targets are of the order of 6×10^{13} neutrons·cm^{-2}·s^{-1}, which is very similar to what is obtained in most research nuclear reactors also used for radioisotope production and other applications.

The innovative concept of autoextraction

The use of negative ion technology allows extraction by means of stripping of the H$^-$ ions in a thin carbon foil, leading to an extraction efficiency close to 100%. This technology is therefore, up to now, the technology of choice for applications where high-intensity beams must be extracted. However, the requirements of the vacuum quality are high and, to avoid electromagnetic dissociation, low magnetic fields must be used. The consequence is that cyclotron sizes quickly increase with energy when negative ions are accelerated, which is nevertheless necessary if high-intensity extracted beams are required. From this point of view, any technological innovation leading to the use of positive ion technology together with an extraction system allowing a nearly 100% extraction efficiency would represent an unquestionable improvement. It could lead, in the future, to the construction of even more compact high-intensity cyclotrons, suitable for in-hospital cyclotron-based neutron sources.

IBA is presently working on a totally new concept for the extraction of high currents of positive ions [11]. This new concept, called autoextraction, will provide close ιο 100% extraction efficiency without the need for extraction elements that could easily be damaged by high currents, like septa for electrostatic or magnetic extractors. The basic principles are the following: in an isochronous cyclotron, the average field increases with radius to compensate for the relativistic mass increase of the accelerated particles. Close to the pole edge, it becomes impossible to maintain an isochronous radial field profile. The actual field falls below the ideal field, reaches a maximum, and starts to decrease. When the actual field starts departing from the ideal isochronous field, the accelerated particles start to lag with respect to the accelerating voltage on the dee. When the phase lag reaches 90°, the acceleration stops: this point represents the limit of acceleration. At an other (generally larger) radius, the field index, defined as $N = R/B \, dB/dR$, reaches the value -1. This point is the limit of radial focusing. Past this point, the magnet is unable to hold the ions, and the ions escape the influence of the magnetic field. We call the radius where N reaches -1 the limit of self-extraction. If the gap is large, like in most existing cyclotrons, the radial fall of the field is quite gradual, and the limit of acceleration is found at a radius significantly smaller than the limit of self-extraction. Transporting the beam from the first limit to the second is the task of the extraction system, generally including an electrostatic deflector.

In a magnet with a smaller gap, the fall of the magnetic field close to the pole boundary is much sharper. As a result, the limit of acceleration falls much closer to the limit of self-extraction, and the extraction is much easier. When the magnet gap at extraction becomes very small (i.e., smaller than 20 times the radius gain per turn at extraction), the limit of self extraction is reached before the limit of acceleration, and the beam spontaneously escapes the magnetic field when the pole edge is reached. This corresponds to autoextraction. Provided that experience confirms our numerical simulations now in progress, this new extraction method for positive ions is likely to replace the use of negative ions in cyclotrons designed for high currents. This could lead, in the future, to the construction of even more compact high-intensity cyclotrons, suitable for in-hospital cyclotron-based neutron sources.

References

1. Walker J. Uses of neutrons in engineering and technology. Proceedings of the Conference on The Neutron and its Applications. Schofield P (ed) Conference Series Number 64, The Institute of Physics, Bristol and London 1982.
2. Hunt SE. Nuclear Physics for Engineers and Scientists. John Wiley & Sons 1987.
3. A turn-key neutron therapy system based on a gantry-mounted, superconducting, 50 MeV-deuteron cyclotron. IBA document 1993.
4. Neutron Sources For Basic Physics and Applications. OECD/NEA Report. Cierjacks S (ed), Pergamon Press, 1983.
5. Curtiss LF. Introduction to Neutron Physics. Van Nostrand Nuclear Science Series 1959.
6. Lone MA, Chidley BG. Accelerator neutron sources for radioscopy. Proceedings of the First International Topical Meeting on Neutron Radiography System Design and Characterisation, Ontario, Canada.

7. Hawkesworth MR, Walker J. Basic principles of thermal neutron radiography. Proceedings of the 1st World Conference on Neutron Radiography, San Diego, California, USA, 1981.
8. Connard E, Abs M, Dom C, Hardy L, Jongen Y, Ladeuze M, Laycock S, Vanderlinden T. Current status and future of cyclotron development at IBA. EPAC '90, Nice, 1990.
9. Jongen Y. The Cyclone 30, a 30 MeV, high intensity H⁻ cyclotron for radioisotope production. Proceedings of the 7th Conference on Applied Accelerators, St. Petersburg, 1992.
10. Cohilis P, Jongen Y, Lannoye G, Aït Abderrahim H, D'hondt P, Van Den Durpel L. Recent advances in the design of a cyclotron-driven, intense, subcritical neutron source. Proceedings of the EPAC 96 Conference, Sitges, June 1996.
11. Jongen Y, Vandeplassche D, Cohilis P. High intensity cyclotrons for radioisotope production or the comeback of the positive ions. Proceedings of the CYCLOTRONS '95 Conference, Cape Town, October 1995.

Advances in Neutron Capture Therapy.
Volume I, Medicine and Physics.
B. Larsson, J. Crawford and R. Weinreich, editors.

Theoretical study of a spallation neutron source for BNCT

S. Teichmann and J.F. Crawford

Institute for Medical Radiobiology, University of Zurich and Paul Scherrer Institute, Villigen, Switzerland

Keywords: LAHET, MCNP, spallation neutron source.

Introduction

To provide alternatives to reactor-based neutron sources for boron neutron capture therapy (BNCT), new concepts to deliver epithermal neutrons ($\sim$ keV) for therapy are being studied worldwide. With its two ring cyclotrons supplying 72 MeV and 600 MeV protons, the Paul Scherrer Institute (PSI) would be well suited for the construction of a spallation neutron source for BNCT [1–3]. The feasibility of such an alternative was examined, using MCNP [4] alone and in combination with the high-energy particle transport code LAHET [5].

Finding the "best" moderator layout

The neutrons emerging from the spallation target (e.g., tungsten) have MeV energies up to the full beam energy and need to be moderated by a suitable combination of materials to obtain an epithermal spectrum at the irradiation position. Most of the calculations were done with MCNP, using an evaporation neutron source with the energy distribution $p(E) = cEe^{-E/a}$, where a = 1.29 MeV. Cell heating tallies were used to find the depth-dose distributions in a phantom head, represented by a tissue-filled sphere of 10 cm radius; F6 tallies for the neutron and photon doses and F4 tallies combined with FM4 cards for the boron-related doses. Since MCNP can handle neutrons only up to 20 MeV, LAHET was used to check the importance of neutrons above that energy. LAHET simulates the spallation reaction and the transport of neutrons with energies above 20 MeV. The corresponding neutron dose was then estimated by assuming a constant Kerma factor of 7.1×10^{-11} Gy/cm^2. Due to lack of statistics, this fast-neutron dose represents an average over the surface of the phantom head. Neutrons below 20 MeV are written to a file which can subsequently be processed by HMCNP, a special version of MCNP.

Various moderator materials and geometries were tried. Rather than producing a well-defined epithermal neutron beam, the goal was to generate a neutron

Address for correspondence: J.F. Crawford, Institute for Medical Radiobiology of the University of Zurich and the Paul Scherrer Institute, CH-5232 Villigen PSI, Switzerland.

bath around the head by surrounding it as much as possible with moderator material, thereby obtaining a more homogenous dose distribution throughout the brain. During the design calculations, emphasis was laid on this homogeneity, i.e., on achieving more or less flat depth-dose distributions throughout the head, and on minimizing the incident neutron dose, i.e, the neutron dose to the skin, while maintaining a high therapeutic dose and a low background dose. Figure 1 shows the best layout found so far for a 72 MeV proton beam on a tungsten target. It is a hemispherical layout of radius 120 cm, with the patient sitting in the center. To reduce the dose from fast neutrons, the protons come in tangentially at some distance from the patient. An Ni cone surrounds the target area to slow down the most energetic neutrons. It is positioned at the end of a cylinder consisting of a mixture of 70 vol% AlF_3, 30 vol% Al and 1 vol% ^6Li. The use of this mixture was inspired by the Finland project [6]. The remaining moderator material is a composition of 50% at. Al and 50 at.% Fe.

Beam characteristics for the "best" layout with 72 MeV protons

The results shown were obtained from the combination LAHET/HMCNP. It was seen, however, that they agree very well with results from MCNP alone. Figure 2 shows the neutron energy spectrum at the irradiation position, averaged over the surface of an empty sphere representing the patient's head. There are no thermal neutrons and none above 20 MeV. The bulk of the neutrons have energies between a few eV and about 10 keV. To obtain the most homogeneous dose distribution inside a patient's head, it was found that halfway through the irradiation, the patient should be rotated once by 180° around his body axis (z-axis). This also reduces the neutron dose to the skin. Figure 3 shows the resulting depth-dose distributions along two axes; one going through the side of the head (x) and one through the top (z). Only physical doses are considered. The bottom

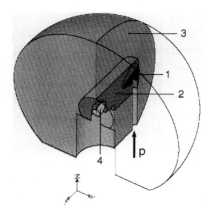

Fig. 1. "Best" moderator layout; 1 — Ni, 2 — $AlF_3/Al/^6Li$ (70:30:1 vol.%), 3 — Al/Fe (50:50 at.%), 4 — tissue.

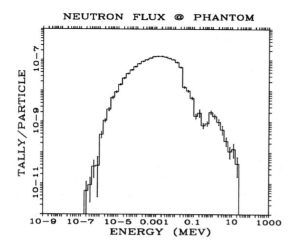

Fig. 2. Calculated neutron spectrum at the irradiation position.

curve represents the fast neutron dose, with an additional contribution from nitrogen capture; at zero depth, it shows the incident neutron dose (iNd). The middle curve includes in addition the photon dose and a background dose due to 3 ppm ^{10}B, thus representing the total background dose. The top curve represents the total therapeutic dose, including background from neutrons and photons, plus the dose due to 30 ppm ^{10}B. It reaches a maximum at about 3—4 cm depth, the peak total dose (pTd), and falls off only slightly with increasing depth. The background dose at the pTd depth is labeled total background dose (tBd), for the purpose of making comparisons. It can be seen that the two distributions, for the x- and the z-axis, are comparable.

Comparison with some reactor beams

To make comparisons with some of the existing or planned reactor beams, only the beam characteristics refering to the x-axis of the "best" layout were used. Table 1 shows epithermal neutron fluxes, fast neutrons per epithermal neutron,

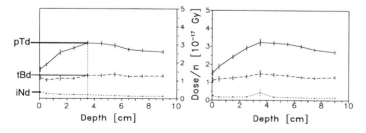

Fig. 3. Depth-dose distributions on two axes for the layout in Fig. 1; solid line: n + γ + 30 ppm ^{10}B, short dashes: n only.

Table 1. Comparison of beam parameters.

	Epithermal flux [10^9 n/cm^{2}s]	Fast n/epithermal n [10^{-13} Gy/n/cm^2]	γ/Epithermal n [10^{-13} Gy/n/cm^2]
Petten/NL	0.33	12.6	8.4
FiR/Finland	3.5	2.6	1.0
BMRR/USA	1.2	4.8	1.4
"best" layout x	1.4	5.3	4.6

and photons per epithermal neutron. Here, epithermal is defined as the energy range between 0.4 eV and 10 keV. The data for the reactor facilities in Petten/ Netherlands, Finland (FiR) and Brookhaven/USA (BMRR) were taken from [7]. Table 2 compares dose characteristics, using the terms defined above; incident neutron dose normalized to the peak total dose (iNd/pTd) and peak total dose divided by total background dose (pTd/tBd). The peak total dose in units of Gray/h for the "best" layout was calculated from the MCNP output, giving Gray per neutron, by assuming a 100 µA proton beam (a realistic assumption) and a spallation yield of 0.16 neutrons per proton (as calculated with LAHET for a thick target). The data for Petten and the BMRR were extracted from the figures in [8] which represent measured values. The data for the FiR were extracted from the figure in [9] which is based on calculations. With respect to the quantities in Tables 1 and 2, it can be seen that the described spallation neutron source would be comparable to the other selected reactor beams. In addition, it would be able to provide a very uniform dose distribution throughout the head with only one patient rotation.

Higher proton energies

The effect of using a 250 MeV or a 600 MeV proton beam on a thick tungsten target, (i.e., thick enough to stop the protons) was examined without changing the moderator layout. At these energies, the combination LAHET/HMCNP must be used. As can be seen in Table 3, the incident neutron dose increases by a factor of three and five, respectively, without a significant increase in the peak total dose. In particular, there now is a large amount of neutrons above 20 MeV at the irradiation position. Although one could afford to lose more neutrons in additional moderator material because of the much higher spallation neutron yield

Table 2. Comparison of dose characteristics; see text for explanation of abbreviations.

	iNd/pTd	pTd/tBd	pTd [Gy/h]
Petten/NL	0.2	2.5	7.5
FiR/Finland	0.03	3.5	18.0
BMRR/USA	0.7	3.0	13/MW
"best" layout x	0.1	2.4	11.2

Table 3. Comparison of different proton energies for the layout in Fig. 1.

	n/p	iNd ($\leq$ 20 MeV) $[10^{-17}$ Gy/n]	iNd ($\geq$ 20 MeV) $[10^{-17}$ Gy/n]	Total iNd $[10^{-17}$ Gy/n]	iNd/pTd
72 MeV	0.16	0.35	—	0.35	0.11
250 MeV	2.44	0.95	0.22	$\geq$ 1.17	0.34
600 MeV	11.49	0.99	0.79	$\geq$ 1.78	0.53

(a factor of 15 and 72, respectively, from Table 3), a practical solution seems unlikely.

References

1. Conde H, Grusell E, Larsson B, Pettersson C-B, Thuresson L, Crawford JF, Reist H, Dahl B, Sjöstrand NG. Time of flight measurements of the energy spectrum of neutrons emitted from a spallation source and moderated in water. Nucl Instrum Meth Phys Res 1987;A261:587–590.
2. Conde H, Crawford JF, Dahl B, Grusell E, Larsson B, Pettersson C-B, Reist H, Sjöstrand NG, Sornsuntisook O, Thuresson L. The production of 72 MeV protons of keV neutrons for ^{10}B neutron capture therapy. Strahlenther Onkol 1989;165:340–342.
3. Arkuszewski J, Crawford JF, Stepanek J, Teichmann S. Neutron production for BNCT by protons of different energies. In: Nigg DW (Chair) Proceedings of the International Workshop on Accelerator-Based Neutron Sources for BNCT, 11–14 September 1994. Jackson, WY: Idaho National Engineering Laboratory, report CONF-940976, 1994;215–224.
4. Briesmeister JF (ed) MCNP — A General Monte Carlo N-Particle Transport Code, ver 4A. Los Alamos National Laboratory, 1993;LA-12625-M.
5. Prael RE, Lichtenstein H. LAHET code system user guide. Los Alamos National Laboratory, 1989;LA-UR-89-3014.
6. Auterinen I, Hiismäki P. Aluminum-Aluminum Fluoride composite as neutron moderator for epithermal BNCT. In: Proc of the 6th Int Symp on Neutron Capture Therapy for Cancer, October 31–November 4, 1994, Kobe, Japan.New York: Plenum Press, 1996.
7. Moss RL. Review of reactor-based neutron beam development for BNCT applications. In: Soloway AH, Barth RF, Carpenter DE (eds) Advances in Neutron Capture Therapy. Proceedings of the 5th Int Symp on NCT, September 14–17, 1992, Columbus, Ohio. 1993;Table 2:1–7.
8. Gabel D, Moss R. BNCT — Towards Clinical Trials of Glioma Treatment. Proceedings of an Int Workshop, September 18–20, 1991, Petten, Netherlands. 1992;Figure 4:39 and Figure 1:16.
9. Auterinen I, Kallio M. Proceedings of the CLINCT BNCT workshop, September 11–14, 1993, Helsinki, Finland. 1994;Figure 8:21.

©1997 Elsevier Science B.V. All rights reserved.
Advances in Neutron Capture Therapy.
Volume I, Medicine and Physics.
B. Larsson, J. Crawford and R. Weinreich, editors.

Gantry for NCT with a neutron point source

M. Fülöp and P. Ragan

Institute of Preventive and Clinical Medicine, Bratislava, Slovakia

Introduction

A feasibility study is being made for a cyclotron facility for 72 MeV protons to be built in Slovakia. The main planned activities of the cyclotron are in the fields of nuclear medicine (production of radioisotopes for oncology and for positron emission tomography — PET) and in radiotherapy (neutron capture therapy — NCT and therapy by fast neutrons and protons). Neutrons for NCT will be produced by the spallation process, in which 72 MeV protons impact on a tungsten target. Therapeutically useful fluxes, (i.e., $10^9 \cdot cm^{-2} \cdot s^{-1}$ at a depth of 7 cm) based on 72 MeV protons with an intensity of 100 μA were shown to be feasible by Crawford et al. [2]. Because the proton beam of 100 μA is rather high for a hospital cyclotron, we have been trying to find a way to decrease requirements on the proton beam. The intensity of the proton beam is given by design and development of an epithermal neutron beam delivery system for NCT. In our work a gantry with high efficiency for the production of epithermal neutrons for NCT, which makes it possible to use a relatively small cyclotron for NCT, is presented.

Methods

The gantry utilises a new type of reflector system which concentrates neutrons onto the tumour position. The reflector system is based on the anisotropic scattering of fast neutrons in heavy materials. The design of the moderators and reflectors of intermediate neutrons in the gantry was calculated by the MCNP [1] code for a fission spectrum (Watt energy spectrum in the MCNP code with default coefficients).

Results and Discussion

The spallation process due to the 72 MeV protons impacting on the heavy target produces neutrons with an energy spectrum similar to a fission spectrum. The

Address for correspondence: Marko Fülöp, Institute of Preventive and Clinical Medicine, Limbova 14, SK-833 01 Bratislava, Slovakia. E-mail: fulop@upkm.sanet.sk

conversion coefficient — 10 µA proton beam to 10^{13} emitted neutrons — was derived by our MCNP calculation in which the experiments reported by Crawford et al. [2] at the cyclotron at PSI were simulated. The design of the gantry irradiation geometry for brain treatments is shown in Fig. 1. The gantry consists of a proton channel with a tungsten target which emits fission neutrons, lead reflectors, fast and intermediate neutron moderators (C and D_2O) with channels of Al_3F) leading intermediate neutrons closer to the patient head, absorbers of thermal neutrons and γ radiation (Bi and ^6Li) and shields of neutrons escaping from the gantry surface. The reflector system is rotationally symmetric about the horizontal axis which lies in the plane of the figure. The dose distribution in the brain was calculated in spherical volumes of 2 cm diameter which were located at various depths in the brain as shown in Fig. 1.

The RBE dose rates in an ellipsoidal phantom is composed of skull (and brain). Equivalent material was calculated for RBE values of 1, 4, and 4 for photons, neutrons and ^{10}B reaction products, respectively. Tallied γ and neutron doses as well as the dose from thermal neutron capture on nuclei of ^{10}B (taking the kerma coefficient to be 7.6×10^{-8} Gy/cm^2 and assuming a concentration of 40 mg $\cdot$ g^{-1} of ^{10}B in tumour and 10 mg $\cdot$ g^{-1} of ^{10}B in healthy tissue) were used for the determination of tissue doses from high and low LET particles. The γ radiation which originates from neutron production was not taken into account. Dose characteristics and thermal neutron fluence per emitted neutron are shown in Fig. 2. The dose characteristics of the therapeutic beam produced by 72 MeV protons expressed in units per 10 µA proton beam are given in Table 1. The depths in tissue at which the dose to tumour (with a concentration of 40 ppm of ^{10}B) will be equal to the maximal dose to the healthy tissue with 0 and 10 ppm

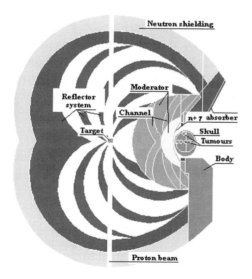

Fig. 1. Design of the gantry for NCT based on the 72 MeV proton-W spallation reaction.

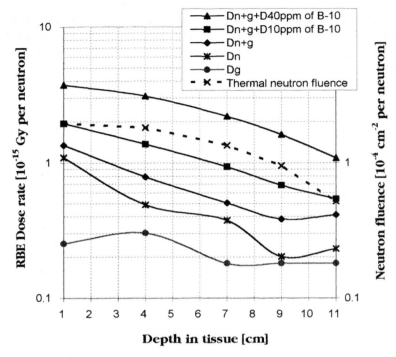

Fig. 2. Depth dose distribution in head phantom.

of ^{10}B are AD_{max} and AD_{min}, respectively.

The advantage ratio (AR) is equal to the integral of the total tumour dose, divided by the integral of the total background dose (assuming no ^{10}B in healthy tissue) over the entire effective treatment depth, (i.e., from 0 cm to AD_{max}). The values of AD_{max} and AD_{min} in Table 1 are greater than AD_{max} = 8.4 cm and AD_{min} = 7.0 cm, as published by Yanch et al. [3], which confirms the good quality of the therapeutic beam. Because of the isotropic irradiation geometry, resulting in homogeneous irradiation of the brain, our value of AR is lower than AR = 5.5, reported in that work [3].

Conclusion

A gantry based on a point neutron source for NCT has been proposed. Thera-

Table 1. Parameters of a therapy beam of an accelerator, based on 10 µA of a 72 MeV proton beam producing neutrons by a spallation reaction in a tungsten target.

Neutron source	AD_{min} [cm]	AD_{max} [cm]	RBE dose at 7 cm [Gy.min^{-1}]	AR	Dose composition [%] high LET/low LET/^{10}B
10 µA 72 MeV p-W	8	10	1.21	3	16/8/76

peutically useful fluxes based on 72 MeV protons can be obtained by the proposed gantry with a proton beam of 10 µA. The gantry is under technical projection and we assume that during the next year physical verification with a ^{252}Cf neutron source will be performed.

References

1. Briesmeister JF. MCNP — a general Monte Carlo code for neutron and photon transport. Los Alamos National Laboratory Report LA7396-M Rev 2.
2. Crawford JF, Larsson B, Reist H et al. Accelerator-based boron neutron-capture therapy. In: Amaldi U, Larsson B (eds) Proceedings of Int Symp on Hadrontherapy, Como, Italy, 1993. Hadrontherapy in Oncology. Amsterdam: Excerpta Medica, Intl. Conf. #1077, 1994;518—524.
3. Yanch JC, Kim JK, Wilson MJ. Design of a californium-based epithermal neutron beam for neutron capture therapy. Phys Med Biol 1993;38:1145—1155.

Use of the ^{9}Be(d,n) nuclear reaction for BNCT: simulation and experimental measurement

J.C. Yanch[1], R.E. Shefer[3], R.E. Klinkowstein[3], H. Song[2], B. Blackburn[1] and W.B. Howard[2]

Departments of [1]Nuclear Engineering and [2]Physics, Massachusetts Institute of Technology; and [3]Newton Scientific Inc., Cambridge, Massachusetts, USA

Introduction

The potential for deuteron-based charged particle reactions to be used as sources of epithermal neutron beams for neutron capture therapy is under investigation. Many (d,n) reactions, (e.g., using deuteron, tritium, or beryllium targets) are very prolific at relatively low deuteron energies. The advantage of high neutron yields, however, is offset by the fact that these reactions have positive Q-values, leading to the emission of high energy neutrons even at low particle bombarding energies. In this paper, the dosimetry of neutrons produced by 2.6 MeV deuterons on a beryllium target is evaluated in tissue-equivalent phantoms of the brain, first by computer simulation, and second by experimental dosimetry measurements using a high current 4.1 MeV tandem accelerator in conjunction with a moderator/reflector assembly and an elliptical brain phantom.

Simulation

The neutron energy spectrum resulting from 2.6 MeV deuteron bombardment of a thick beryllium target [1] is shown in Fig. 1. Although the majority of neutrons are emitted with energies less than 2.0 MeV, a significant fraction has energies between 2 and 8 MeV. At 2.6 MeV the total yield from this reaction is 1×10^{12} n/s/mA. The energy spectrum shown in Fig. 1 was assumed to be emitted isotopically from the beryllium target and, in combination with different moderator/reflector assemblies, was evaluated dosimetrically in a cylindrical phantom composed of brain-equivalent materials. Dosimetric evaluation was carried out with the MCNP simulation code using methods previously described [2]. Briefly, individual dose components were calculated along the central axis of the cylindrical phantom by convoluting particle flux with relevant fluence-kerma conversion factors. RBE factors of 4.0, 3.8 and 1.0 were applied to the ^{10}B reaction products, neutrons, and photons, respectively. A ^{10}B concentration of 30 ppm in the tumor was assumed.

Results indicate that a variety of moderator/reflector configurations will pro-

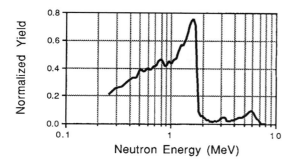

Fig. 1. The normalized spectrum of neutrons emitted at 0° with respect to 2.6 MeV deuterons incident on a thick Be-metal target [1].

duce epithermal neutron beams potentially suitable for clinical use. Examples are shown in Fig. 2A, B and C which plot dose vs. depth in a cylindrical brain phantom for three moderator/reflector configurations. In each example, a 24-cm-diameter, 35-cm-long cylindrical D_2O moderator is used. An 18-cm-thick reflector made of lead, graphite or lithium carbonate surrounds the moderator on three sides. Advantage depths and RBE dose rates (per milliampere of deuteron current) for each beam are given in Table 1. The data in Fig. 2 and Table 1 demonstrate that at a deuteron energy of 2.6 MeV, the ^{9}Be (d,n) reaction is a potential candidate for accelerator-based boron neutron capture therapy (BNCT). Esti-

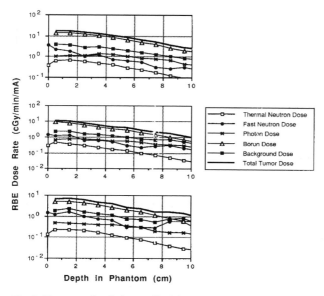

Fig. 2. Dose vs. depth in a cylindrical brain-equivalent phantom. Neutrons resulting from 2.6 MeV deuterons on a beryllium target are moderated by a 24-cm-diameter, 35-cm-long D_2O moderator with an 18-cm-thick reflector composed of **A:** lead, **B:** graphite, or **C:** Li_2CO_3.

Table 1. Advantage depths and RBE dose rates for the three beams.

Reflector material	Advantage depth (cm)	RBE dose rate at 1.5 cm (cGy/min/mA)	RBE dose rate at 7 cm (cGy/min/mA)
Lead	8.6	17.3	5.7
Graphite	6.8	10.2	2.5
Li_2CO_3	6.0	7.0	2.0

mates of total tumor dose rates are high relative to existing reactor-based clinical beams. For example, with a lead reflector, a tumor dose-rate at the midline of the brain of almost 23 RBE cGy/min could be achieved using the 4 mA tandem electrostatic accelerator [2] at MIT's Laboratory for Accelerator Beam Applications (LABA). The fast neutron dose component at the phantom surface, however, is a relatively large component of the total surface dose (roughly 50%) suggesting that a more extensive moderator may be desirable. This would, in turn, reduce the total dose rate to the phantom. Further work to optimize the dosimetric characteristics of this beam is under way.

Experimental measurement

In order to verify the accuracy of the simulation method to predict the various contributions to dose in a tissue-equivalent phantom, experimental measurements of fast neutron, thermal neutron and photon dose rates resulting from a moderated ^9Be (d,n) neutron beam were carried out. Rather than construct a new moderator/reflector assembly for these measurements, an existing assembly [3,4] (previously optimized for use with the ^7Li (p,n) nuclear reaction) was used. This assembly consists of a 24-cm-diameter, 27-cm-long D_2O moderator surrounded by an 18-cm-thick lead reflector and will produce a much harder neutron spectrum than those simulated for Fig. 2. In order to compare simulation and experimental results a new MCNP run was carried out (see below) in which the dimensions of the assembly used in the experiments were accurately modeled.

Dosimetric measurements of the moderated, 2.6 MeV $d^+ \rightarrow Be$ neutron beam were obtained in a 14 cm elliptical, water-filled brain phantom [5]. Dose components were assessed along the centerline of the phantom at depths of 1 and 7 cm using the protocol established by the MITR BNCT group [6]. The experimental setup is shown in Fig. 3, which shows the brain phantom with an ionization chamber detector positioned for measurement of dose along the midline. Figure 4 provides an end-view of the moderator/reflector assembly and phantom in position. The deuteron beam was generated by the 4.1 MeV tandem electrostatic accelerator located at LABA. A beam current of 30 μA was used for these experiments. This accelerator is located in an adjacent room behind the 3-foot-thick concrete wall seen in Fig. 4.

The fast neutron and photon dose rates were measured using the dual ionization chamber technique. Two small ionization chambers (Far West IC-18 and IC

Fig. 3. Experimental setup showing the elliptical brain phantom (on loan from MITR BNCT group [5]) at the irradiation port of the moderator/reflector assembly.

18G) were inserted one at a time into the water-filled head phantom. Tissue-equivalent gas or CO_2 flowed continually through the IC-18 and IC-18G, respectively. The integrated ionization current was measured using a sensitive electrometer (Keithley 617). Ionization currents were approximately $1-3 \times 10^{-13}$ coulomb/min-μA. From these values, the dark currents, which were approximately $1-10 \times 10^{-15}$ coulomb/min-μA, were subtracted (the dark current are collected with the HV applied, but with no radiation field present). The fast neutron and photon dose components were then calculated using the calibration factors provided by the MIT Reactor BNCT Group.

The thermal neutron fluence was measured using gold activation foils. Two gold foils were taped to a plastic rod and placed at depths of 1 and 7 cm in the phantom. These foils were irradiated for approximately 45 min. The activities of the

Fig. 4. End view of the experimental setup showing the elliptical phantom placed at the irradiation position in front of the D_2O moderator. The accelerator is located behind the concrete shielding wall in a separate room.

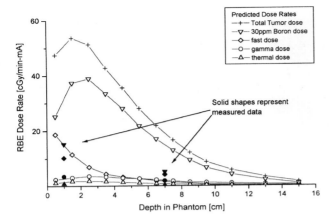

Fig. 5. Comparison of simulated and experimental measurements of dose-rates in the brain phantom. Deuteron beam energy is 2.6 MeV; the D_2O moderator is 27 cm long and surrounded by an 18-cm-lead reflector. Open symbols represent experimental measurements taken at 1.0 and 7.0 cm.

foils were measured using a high purity germanium detector. First the saturation activities of the foils were calculated. Then, the thermal neutron fluences were calculated assuming that the saturated activity of a cadmium covered foil to that of an uncovered foil was 0.408. These dose components were then determined using the fluence to kerma conversion method.

The experimentally determined dose components are shown on Fig. 5 and compared with dosimetric data predicted by MCNP simulation. Overall the agreement between experiment and simulation is good. At a depth of 7 cm, the measured dose components are within 30% of predictions. Nearing the surface, the measured fast neutron dose is almost a factor of two greater than predicted whereas the measured thermal dose is 30% lower than expected on the basis of simulation. Part of the discrepancy may be a result of the difference in phantom shape (i.e., elliptical vs. cylindrical). Photon doses are in very good agreement. Future experimental work will be carried out to both refine these measurement techniques as well as to obtain a full three-dimensional dose characterization in the phantom.

References

1. Meadows JW. The thick target ^{9}Be(d,n) neutron spectra for deuteron energies between 2.6 and 7.0 MeV. Argonne, IL: Argonne National Laboratory, ANL/NDM-124, 1991;49 pages.
2. Yanch JC, Zhou X-L, Shefer RE, Klinkowstein RE. Accelerator-based epithermal neutron beam design for neutron capture therapy. Med Phys 1992;19(3):709–721.
3. Klinkowstein RE et al. Operation of a high current tandem electrostatic accelerator for boron neutron capture therapy. In: Larsson B, Crawford J, Weinreich R (eds) Advances in Neutron Capture Therapy, Volume 1, Medicine and Physics. Amsterdam: Elsevier Science, 1997; 522–527 (these proceedings).

4. Yanch JC, Shefer RE, Hughey BJ, Klinkowstein RE. Accelerator-based epithermal neutron beams for neutron capture therapy. In: Soloway AH, Barth RF, Carpenter DE (eds) Advances in Neutron Capture Therapy. New York: Plenum Press, 1993.

5. Rogus R, Harling OK, Yanch JC. Mixed field dosimetry of epithermal neutron beams for BNCT at the MITR-II research reactor. Med Phys 1994;21(10):1611—1625.

6. Harling OK, Roberts KA, Moulin DJ, Rogus RD. Head phantoms for neutron capture therapy. Med Phys 1995;22(5):579—583.

© 1997 Elsevier Science B.V. All rights reserved.
Advances in Neutron Capture Therapy.
Volume I, Medicine and Physics.
B. Larsson, J. Crawford and R. Weinreich, editors.

Physical aspects of HDR ^{252}Cf remote afterloading neutron brachytherapy

V. Atkocius, A. Miller, E. Atkociene and M. Kersuliene

Lithuanian Oncology Center, Vilnius, Lithuania

Introduction

The relatively new form of radiation therapy — ^{252}Cf neutron brachytherapy is expected to be highly effective for treatment of different cancers, especially for radioresistant bulky malignant tumors [1]. In late 1988 the first patient was treated with ^{252}Cf neutron brachytherapy at the Lithuanian Oncology Center (LOC). Clinical techniques were developed after familiar methods of conventional γ brachytherapy. Over the past years of use of this new modality these techniques were altered according to the new findings. One of the most challenging problems was to develop adequate physical and radiobiological models for use of this isotope. The dosimetric and radiobiological methods used at LOC for treatment planning of HDR remote afterloading neutron brachytherapy will be discussed.

Material and Methods

Equipment

The Russian-made HDR remote afterloading ^{252}Cf brachytherapy apparatus ANET-V has been in use in the LOC since late 1988. Technical details and radiation safety consideration of this equipment can be found elsewhere [2]. The unit was designed to provide isodose distribution and treatment times somewhat comparable to those of conventional ^{192}Ir and ^{60}Co brachytherapy machines. Also, ANET-V was intended to be used predominantly for gynecological and rectum cancers. Therefore, the vendor was not significantly limited by the dimensions of the sources. The ^{252}Cf sources are encapsulated in stainless steel with a physical length of 16 mm and a diameter of 3 mm. The active length and diameter are 10 and 1.4 mm, respectively. The ANET-V is equipped with three ^{252}Cf high-activity sources. The device has a separate channel for each source. The source of 1,500 µg initial activity travels along the central channel with a 10 mm step size. It is designated as a uterine source for gynecological applications. Two sources for vaginal ovoids are 300 µg initial activity each and occupy one dwell position.

Patients

Since 1988, 386 patients have been treated with ^{252}Cf neutron HDR brachytherapy. Most treatments (259 patients) have been performed for advanced cancer of the cervix and corpus uteri. The central 1,500 µg initial activity source has been employed for treatment of rectal and anal carcinoma (94 patients), esophagus carcinoma (14 patients), prostate carcinoma (five patients), soft tissue sarcoma (four patients), nasal carcinoma (two patients) and malignant glioma (eight patients). Neutron brachytherapy was either combined with external beam radiotherapy or pre-/postoperative radiotherapy, or it was the sole treatment.

Treatment planning

PC-based "in house" computer software was written to calculate two-dimensional isodose distributions for an ANET-V insertion. The data of Zyb at al. [3] for neutron and γ-dose rates around these sources (Table 1) has been incorporated into the computer system. The software optimises dwell times to achieve prescribed isoeffective dose in Gy-eq. at the prescribed distance and at the same time to keep limited dose at the points which represent critical organs. The dose is calculated and reported in terms of isoeffective dose. The isoeffective dose is defined as:

$$D_{iso} = D_n \times RBE + D_\gamma,$$

where D_n and D_γ are physical neutron and γ doses, respectively.

The semiempirical equations plotted by Riabuchin [4] from different radiobiological data are employed to compute the RBE values:

$$RBE = (0.698)^{lg\,W} \times 8.95, \text{ for } 5 \text{ cGy/h} \leqslant W \leqslant 400 \text{ cGy/h, or}$$

Table 1. Neutron (top row) and γ (bottom row) dose rate (cGy/hr × µg) of the Cf-252 ANET-V source.

φ (degree)	Radius (cm)								
	0.2	0.4	0.8	1.2	1.6	2.0	4.0	8.0	10.0
0	—	—	6.22	2.00	0.989	0.588	0.116	0.0197	0.0100
	—	—	2.32	0.707	0.356	0.219	0.0583	0.0164	0.00679
10	182.2	77.8	6.00	1.97	0.986	0.587	0.117	0.0199	0.0101
	101.76	43.69	2.52	0.824	0.428	0.269	0.0722	0.0198	0.0125
30	60.0	23.3	4.93	1.85	0.957	0.578	0.117	0.0200	0.0101
	33.17	12.57	2.494	0.977	0.530	0.337	0.0897	0.0240	0.0151
45	41.8	15.9	4.24	1.73	0.923	0.565	0.116	0.0200	0.0101
	22.97	8.46	2.21	0.955	0.535	0.345	0.0930	0.0248	0.0157
90	27.8	11.1	3.39	1.55	0.864	0.540	0.115	0.0200	0.0101
	15.1	5.79	1.84	0.887	0.519	0.341	0.0949	0.0254	0.0160

$$RBE = 0.357 \times (0.262 \, Lg \, W + 0.117), \text{ for } 400 \, cGy/h < W,$$

where W is the sum of physical dose rate for neutron and γ components of ^{252}Cf source.

The RBE for fractionated treatment is calculated as:

$$RBE_N = RBE \times N^{0.2},$$

where N is the total number of fractions.

Results

Dose prescription

The Manchester system is employed for gynecological treatment planning. The plane of calculation passes through the middle of the ovoids and intersects the tandem. The dose is prescribed to the point A for the corpus uteri and to the points A and B for cervix. Nevertheless, we recognize the importance of the ICR-38 recommendations for dose specifications. The ICRU-38 report has been directed to the gynecological intracavitary radiation treatment with γ-emitting isotope. However, we decided to follow this protocol as closely as possible, because the standardised data are essential to compare treatments with different regimes and qualities of irradiation. After the insertion of the catheters and prior to the actual treatment, two orthogonal films are taken on the simulator. Using the orthogonal reconstruction technique the coordinates of the points related to the lymphatic trapezoid, pelvic wall, bladder and rectum are identified. The doses to these points are reported as well as the dimensions of the target and reference volume. The 1,500 µg of ^{252}Cf initial activity source is used for treatments of rectal, soft tissue, esophagus, prostate cancers and malignant gliomas. The most common prescribed distance from the center of treatment catheter for these sites is 1.5, 1.5, 1.0, and 2.5 cm, respectively. For malignant gliomas visible on CT the tumor margin was chosen as the prescribed distance, which is normally 1−3 cm.

Fractionation

The variation in prescribed dose per fraction as well as in the number of fractions has been quite large and is summarised in the Table 2.

Discussion

The most questionable aspect of the ^{252}Cf treatment planning is radiobiology of this quality of radiation. Riabuchin et al. have summarised their own quite extensive experience with ^{252}Cf in vivo and in vitro studies and previously published

Table 2. Fractionation regimes for Cf-252 HDR afterloading brachytherapy.

Location	Dose per fraction iGy	Fractions per week	Total number of fractions
Ca of cervix uteri	8—10	1	6—4
Ca of corpus uteri	9—10	1—2	6—4
Rectal carcinoma	3—5	1—2	8—6
Prostate carcinoma	6—6.5	1	3
Esophagus carcinoma	3.5—4	1—2	5—7
Malignant glioma	10—20	1	1

data. The isoeffective doses calculated according to their equations provide good guidance to the physicians as far as anticipation of treatment result is concerned. However, the wide range of dose prescription and irradiation schedule clearly indicates that conventional treatment prescription cannot be simply applied to the ^{252}Cf treatments using these RBE values. Additional clinical evaluation is needed to find the optimum dose prescription.

The physicians prefer to deal with the conception of the isoeffective dose even knowing that this dose does not exactly correspond to the γ dose. The knowledge of physical dose and dose rate of the components of ^{252}Cf irradiation makes very little sense to them. Furthermore, the isoeffective dose uniformly calculated is very convenient to compare treatment results of different modalities and to record the case report. The physical dose and dose rate of the γ and neutron components are also important to report for research purposes.

References

1. Maruyama Y, van Nagel JR, Yoneda J, Donaldson ES, Gallion HH, Kriscio RJ. Cf-252 neutron brachytherapy: treatment for cure of cervical cancer. Nucl Sci Appl 1991;4:181—192.
2. Elisiutin GP, Komar VY, Chekonadski VN, Drygin VN, Spasokukotskaya ON. ANET-V apparatus with Cf-252 sources for intracavitary radiotherapy of cancer patients. Medizinskaya Tekhnika 1987;3:23—28 (in Russian).
3. Zyb A. Effects of Cf-252 gamma-neutron irradiation. Energoatomizdat, Moscow, 1996.
4. Riabuchin YS. Relative biological effectiveness of Cf-252 neutrons. Med Radiol 1985;Vol XXX(No. 4):53—60 (in Russian).

Index of authors

578

Keyword index

580

582